THE TECHNICAL APPLICATIONS OF RADIOACTIVITY

VOLUME 1

THE TECHNICAL
APPLICATIONS OF RADIOACTIVITY

VOLUME 1

By

ENGELBERT BRODA

*Professor at the Institute of Physical Chemistry
of the University of Vienna*

and

THOMAS SCHÖNFELD

*Lecturer at the Institute of Inorganic Chemistry
of the University of Vienna*

PERGAMON PRESS
OXFORD · LONDON · EDINBURGH · NEW YORK
TORONTO · PARIS · BRAUNSCHWEIG

VEB DEUTSCHER VERLAG FÜR GRUNDSTOFFINDUSTRIE
LEIPZIG

Pergamon Press Ltd., Headington Hill Hall, Oxford
4 & 5 Fitzroy Square, London W.1

Pergamon Press (Scotland) Ltd., 2 & 3 Teviot Place, Edinburgh 1

Pergamon Press Inc., 44–01 21st Street, Long Island City, New York 11101

Pergamon of Canada, Ltd., 6 Adelaide Street East, Toronto, Ontario

Pergamon Press S.A.R.L., 24 rue des Écoles, Paris 5e

Vieweg & Sohn GmbH, Burgplatz 1, Braunschweig

Translated from the 3rd German edition of *Die technischen Anwendungen der Radioaktivität, Band 1*, published by VEB Deutscher Verlag für Grundstoffindustrie Leipzig, with amendments

First English edition 1966

2277/66

CONTENTS

FOREWORD TO THE FIRST EDITION

THE technical application of radioactivity has undergone very rapid development during recent years. The time is therefore ripe for a comprehensive introduction to this topic, though the task is not an easy one. In the present book numerous examples of the potentialities of nuclear physics and nuclear chemistry for the peaceful development of industrial productivity will be given. Relevant work presented at the international conferences held during 1955, and in particular at the Geneva Conferences on the Peaceful Uses of Atomic Energy, has been considered. It is hoped that this survey will lead to the development of further applications.

The book is written for scientific or technical workers who have received at least a secondary school education; a basic knowledge of chemistry and physics is assumed. Mathematical derivations involving differential and integral calculus have been avoided, and special care has been taken to make the subject matter clear qualitatively. Nevertheless, for the understanding of the behaviour of radioactive substances, and for practical work with them, an understanding of exponential functions is necessary.

The book first gives the fundamentals of modern atomic theory. This is followed by an introduction to the basic facts of radioactivity and the methods used for measuring it, as well as to chemical operations with radioactive substances. Then follows the discussion of the use of radioactivity in industry, which constitutes the main part of the book. Many of the applications described are at present only in an experimental stage.

In the early days of the study and application of radioactive materials many scientists, technicians, medical men and other workers fell victim to radioactive rays, either through carelessness or through ignorance of the dangers involved. Nowadays the biological effects of such rays have been thoroughly studied, and with a few simple precautions the danger in using radioactive materials can be eliminated. These precautions are dealt with in the last section of the book.

Vienna, June 1956   *The authors*

FOREWORD TO THE SECOND EDITION

THE considerable interest aroused by this book in the short time since it appeared has made it necessary to produce a second edition. This is evidence of the varied applications and the great significance of radioactivity in industry.

Vienna, March 1957   *The authors*

FOREWORD TO THE THIRD EDITION

SINCE the second edition appeared, further advances have been made in the industrial application of radioactivity. It was therefore necessary to re-write the book completely for the third edition. We have been able, in the main, to retain the plan followed in the previous editions but, in view of the greatly extended material, a few chapters have been split into two, and the book has been separated into two volumes. The second volume, which consists of the two specially long Chapters, 11 and 12, of the first and second editions ("Absorption and Scattering of Radioactive Radiations in Measurement and Control", and "Technical Applications of the Effects of Radioactive Radiations on Materials") will follow later. The former Chapter 13, which deals with protection against radiation, is included in the present volume so that the reader can take the appropriate precautions.

It may be pointed out here that stable isotopes, instead of radioactive isotopes, may be used for labelling elements. Because of the short life of the radioactive isotopes, stable isotopes offer sometimes the only practical possibility to carry out labelling. In important cases the present book therefore refers to information obtained with stable isotopes. However, since our own specialized experience lies outside this field, we have refrained from descriptions of measuring and working methods with stable isotopes.

In submitting this book to the scientific and industrial readers again, we express the hope that it will be of service to them.

Vienna, Summer 1962   *The authors*

NOTE ON BIBLIOGRAPHY

IT SHOULD be noted that Cyrillic (mainly Russian) names have been transcribed according to the usual procedure. On the other hand, the spelling of names is naturally left unaltered when the work appears in a language written in Latin characters. The author himself sometimes varies the spelling of his name according to whether he is writing for a German, English or French journal. Thus the names of some Russian authors have been spelled in more than one way. The titles of Russian books and journals have been translated. The appendage "Russ." in such cases means that the work has been published in Russian.

The reports of important international conferences on the application of isotopes [Geneva 1955 and 1958 (United Nations), Paris 1957 (Unesco) and Copenhagen 1960 (International Atomic Energy Agency)], have been indicated by numbers. The volume and page numbers for the collected reports published as books have also been added: e.g., Geneva Report 266 (1955), vol.9, p.273. The complete bibliographical references for the conferences mentioned are:

Proceedings of the International Conference on the Peaceful Uses of Atomic Energy (Geneva, 8–20 August 1955), New York 1956.

Proceedings of the Second United Nations International Conference on the Peaceful Uses of Atomic Energy (Geneva, 1–13 September 1958), Geneva 1958.

Radioisotopes in Scientific Research (Proceedings of the International Conference held in Paris, September 1957), Edited by R.C.Extermann, London 1958.

Radioisotopes in the Physical Sciences and Industry (Conference Proceedings; Copenhagen, 6–17 September 1960), Vienna 1962.

The reports of the Conference on the Peaceful Uses of Atomic Energy, convened by the Academy of Sciences of the U.S.S.R. in July 1955, have been indicated by "Moscow Atomic Energy Conference 1955". The page numbers given refer to the conference proceedings in Russian. An English translation also exists. The bibliographical reference is: Conference of the Academy of Sciences of the U.S.S.R. on the Peaceful Uses of Atomic Energy (1–5 July 1955), Moscow 1955; English translation, New York 1955.

ACKNOWLEDGEMENTS

WE WISH to express our thanks to: Cambridge University Press (Fig. 4), Pergamon Press (Figs. 17, 24 and 27), *Radiology* (Fig. 19), *Analytical Chemistry* (Fig. 26), Penguin Books Ltd. (Fig. 27), *Industrial and Engineering Chemistry* (Fig. 31), *Transactions of the Metallurgical Society of AIME* (Fig. 32), *Research* (Fig. 33), The Institute of Physics and The Physical Society (Fig. 34), Akademische Verlagsgesellschaft (Figs. 35 and 36), and *Atompraxis* (Fig. 38), as well as to the authors, for permission to reproduce the figures.

1. INTRODUCTION

1.1. The Importance of Radioactivity for Science and Industry

A new era in the progress of science began in the eighteen-nineties with the discovery of radioactivity by Henri Becquerel, and Pierre Curie with his wife Marie Curie-Sklodowska. The study of radioactivity has greatly enlarged and enriched our knowledge of the structure of the atom. It has removed any remaining doubts as to the correctness of the atomic theory, which had been supported and developed for more than two thousand years by such leading scientific thinkers as Democritus, Newton, Lomonosov, Dalton, Mendeleev and Boltzmann. It was the discovery of radioactivity which led to the concept that the atom consists of a nucleus and extranuclear electrons, an idea which was the starting point for the development of atomic and nuclear physics.

Apart from atomic and nuclear physics, radioactivity has also contributed to extremely important advances in the most diverse branches of science. Even a casual glance at current scientific journals shows that a considerable and ever-increasing part of the articles deals with some properties or applications of radioactive substances and their radiations. While this is primarily true of physics and chemistry, biologists and medical workers also make use of such substances, both for the elucidation of metabolic processes and for irradiating living tissue. Astronomers use the radioactivity of meteorites to determine their ages, while geologists employ similar methods for determining the age of formations of the different strata of the Earth. Meteorologists use radioactivity for the investigation of air currents, and hydrologists for water currents. Lastly, archaeologists and historians employ it to determine the ages of mummies and other objects of ancient times.

Sooner or later, all sciences must advance human wellbeing, and nuclear science is no exception. Industrial processes of ever-widening scope utilize radioactivity for the improvement of production methods. Radioactive substances are of great value in research laboratories devoted to mining, industry and agriculture, where they are employed to test and improve existing production methods, or to develop new methods to replace them. They are also being increasingly used in controlling the operation of machines or in bringing about particular types of reactions.

At the Second Geneva Conference on the Peaceful Uses of Atomic Energy (1958), the annual benefit obtained by the industrial application of radioactive substances was estimated at 1500 million (old) roubles for the Soviet Union, 500 million dollars for the United States, and a million pounds for Great Britain. In a more recent (1965) survey carried out by the International Atomic Energy Agency for 25 countries (not including the U.S.S.R.) and published under the title *Industrial Radioisotope Economics* the annual savings due to industrial applications of radioactive substances are given as 300 to 400 million dollars. Obviously, all these figures are only rough estimates.

1.2. The Development of Knowledge about the Atomic Nucleus

Before discussing the technical applications of radioactivity we shall briefly survey the historical development of our knowledge of the atomic nucleus. After the fundamental discoveries of the eighteen-nineties, the next twenty years or so were principally occupied with the investigation and the classification of the numerous natural radioactive substances and their radiations. During this period the foundations were laid for the most important practical working and measuring procedures with radioactive substances.

In 1919, Rutherford observed for the first time an artificial transformation of stable elements by bombardment with rays emitted by radioactive substances. Thirteen years later Cockcroft and Walton achieved the first transformation of elements without the use of radioactive substances, employing accelerators capable of producing similar rays. In these machines charged particles were accelerated by means of a large potential difference, and thus reached high kinetic energies.

In 1932, on the basis of earlier observations by Bothe and Joliot, Chadwick discovered a new elementary particle, the neutron, which soon proved capable of bringing about nuclear transformations with very high yields. In 1934, Frédéric and Irène Joliot-Curie showed that artificial transformations often lead to radioactive substances unknown in nature, and so discovered artificial radioactivity. It was soon recognized that all elements could exist in radioactive forms. Fermi was very successful in making artificial radioactive species with slow neutrons.

These fundamental discoveries solved the ancient problem of the transmutation of elements. For thousands of years man had dreamed of the possibility of converting cheap and abundant materials into rare and valuable ones; for centuries the alchemists of many royal courts had attempted to bring about such transmutations, especially that of mercury into gold. The scientists of the nineteenth century showed that these endeavours were futile, because the methods available to the alchemists were not effective. It now appeared, however, that radioactivity is due to spontaneous transmutation, and that the artificial conversion of elements is also possible.

A new stage began in 1939, when Otto Hahn and Fritz Strassmann published their discovery of the fission of uranium. Soon thereafter Lise Meitner predicted that this process should lead to the liberation of large amounts of energy, and this was confirmed experimentally by Otto Frisch. A little later Joliot, together with Halban and Kowarski, showed that neutrons were produced in the fission process. Joliot suggested that the fission of uranium might be carried out as a chain reaction, so that large amounts of uranium would be transformed in a short time. He pointed out that, if this were possible, both radioactive substances and energy could be produced on a scale previously unthought of. This idea was realized in practice a few years later. In 1942, the first uranium reactor was put into operation in Chicago. In the following years nuclear reactors have been developed in many countries, and their energy output has increased steadily. Such reactors today produce most of the radioactive substances used for scientific, technical and medical purposes. These substances are now cheap and abundant, and may be produced directly in various chemical forms, or subsequently converted into the desired chemical form (Chapter 4).

The importance of the nuclear reactor for the production of energy lies in the fact that it provides an entirely new source of energy in which fuel consumption is extremely low. The energy liberated in the nuclear fission of one kilogram of uranium corresponds to that produced by burning about 2500 tons of coal. In June 1954 the first atomic power station in the world was put into operation in the Soviet Union, and in the following years larger power stations were erected in Great Britain, the Soviet Union and the United States, giving a total electrical output of many thousand megawatts.

Uranium is not a particularly rare element in the crust of the Earth, being more abundant than such well-known elements as mercury, arsenic or iodine. It could thus easily supply a large proportion of the energy requirements of mankind for thousands of years. The known deposits of thorium are even greater, and this may also be used for the production of atomic energy. It is not, however, our purpose here to discuss further the large-scale production of heat and electrical energy from the atomic nucleus.

With the development in the knowledge of the atomic nucleus and with the improvement in the production methods for radioactive substances, there has been a corresponding development in instrumentation. For many years the measurement of radioactive phenomena was uncertain, troublesome and, because of unknown radiation effects, frequently dangerous. The skill of the observer and the subjective judgment often required in such measurements greatly influenced the results. Nowadays, very sensitive and reliable measuring equipment is available commercially in many types, and it is possible to learn its operation with much less specialist training and operating experience than formerly.

1.3. Survey of the Applications of Radioactive Substances

From a practical standpoint we may divide the applications of nuclear transformations (omitting the field of energy production) into two large groups.

The first group is the use of "radioactive indicators", as called by Paneth and Hevesy who originated the method in 1913. The terms "radioactive tracers" or "labelled atoms" are now more common than "radioactive indicators". Here the radiations are used to detect the radioactive substances, any radiation effect other than that on the detection instruments being unnecessary and undesirable. It is usually best to use very small quantities of the radioactive substance. The rays emitted permit one to study the behaviour of atoms in the most varied systems.

Detection of atoms by means of their radioactivity has a number of advantages. The limits of detection are often by several orders of magnitude lower than those of other methods. Since we can distinguish between labelled and unlabelled atoms or molecules, the course of the labelled atoms may be followed in a system containing chemically identical atoms or molecules. This is true of no other procedure. Moreover, the measurement often requires little effort and is rapid; it may also be non-destructive. In Chapters 6–12 we shall give numerous examples of the industrial applications of labelled atoms.

In the second group of applications, the radioelements are used as sources of radiations. The radiations from nuclear transformations have extremely high energies, and they may therefore bring about deep-seated changes in many materials. For example, gas molecules may acquire electrical charges on irradiation, and thus become ionized. These ions may then be used to neutralize electrical charges on dust particles or on drops of liquid during many industrial processes. One can also utilize the chemical effects of radiations, for instance, for producing or improving plastics. In the pharmaceutical and foodstuffs industry the rays can be used for sterilization, i.e., for the destruction of micro-organisms and other infestations. The radiation can also change the hereditary characteristics of plants and animals. This type of radiation effect has already been successfully employed for breeding new varieties of plants. The exploitation of radiation effects will be discussed in Volume 2.

During their passage through layers of material the rays undergo various changes, especially with respect to direction, intensity and energy. For a given radiation source, the extent of the changes depends upon the kind and the dimensions of the material through which they pass. By studying these changes, information about the nature of the interposed layer can be obtained. A widely used method of this type is the continuous measurement of the thickness of plastic and metal sheets, textiles, etc. Such measurements can serve the automatic control of production (see again Volume 2). Radioactive radiations are also used instead of X-rays for industrial radiography, i.e., for the non-destructive inspection of industrial products. These applications, which are primarily a matter for radiographers, will not be further discussed in this book.

In 1963, the International Atomic Energy Agency in Vienna issued a Survey *Radioisotope Applications in Industry*, consisting of a large number of selected references to the international literature, classified by industries. In the survey *Industrial Radioisotope Economics* (p. 1), the extent of the actual utilization of the various methods for the use of radioisotopes in industry has been analysed for each participating country and according to the types of application.

2. FUNDAMENTALS OF RADIOACTIVITY

2.1. The Atom as a Planetary System

The modern theory of the structure of the atom has been established by Rutherford and Bohr before the First World War. According to this theory (which has, of course, undergone important extensions and modifications in subsequent years) the atom consists of two principal parts. In the centre is an extremely small nucleus, of radius from 1.5×10^{-13} to 10×10^{-13} cm. Circling around the nucleus, in the same way as planets circle around the Sun, are the electrons. The most probable value of the diameter of a single electron is similar to that of the smaller atomic nuclei.

The distance between the nucleus and the electrons depends on the atom, but it is always very large in comparison with the diameter of either the nucleus or the electron. The overall atomic radius is of the order of magnitude of the Ångstrom unit (10^{-8} cm). The major part of the atomic volume may therefore be roughly regarded as "empty" space.

In contrast with the solar system, electrons surrounding the nucleus are not maintained in their orbits by the force of gravity, but by electrical attraction. These Coulomb forces arise because the electrons are negatively charged, and the nuclei positively charged. Under normal conditions the total negative charge of the extranuclear electrons is equal to the positive charge of the nucleus, so that the atom is electrically neutral.

The charge on a single electron is 4.8×10^{-10} absolute electrostatic units, or 1.6×10^{-19} coulombs (ampere-seconds). This is the smallest charge ever observed, and is therefore called the "elementary charge". Since the atom is electrically neutral, the positive charge on the nucleus must equal the negative charges of the electrons, and the positive charge must therefore be an integral multiple of the elementary charge.

It has also been found that each elementary electrical charge in the nucleus corresponds to that of a single particle, called the proton. Every nucleus therefore carries as many charges as it contains protons. The nucleus of the hydrogen atom, for example, contains one proton, that of helium two, that of iron twenty-six, and that of uranium ninety-two. The number of protons in the nucleus is the "charge number" or the "atomic number" of the chemical element in question. This number is fixed for each chemical element. All atoms of the same element show the same atomic number, while, on the other hand, atoms of different elements never possess the same atomic number.

From the numerical identity of the charges of electron and proton it follows that in the electrically neutral condition the number of electrons surrounding the nucleus of an atom must equal that of the protons within the nucleus. Hence the nuclei of hydrogen, helium, iron and uranium are surrounded by 1, 2, 26 and 92 electrons, respectively.

5

Although the electron has the same charge as the proton, its mass is very much smaller. The mass of the proton is 1.67×10^{-24} g, while that of the electron is only $\frac{1}{1837}$ of this, or 9.1×10^{-28} g. The electrons thus make only a very small contribution to the total mass of the atom, most of which is concentrated in the nucleus.

2.2. The Electrons in the Atoms

According to the quantum theory, each electron goes around the atomic nucleus in a definite orbit. The theory does not allow the electron (in contrast with the planets in the solar system) to follow all orbits conceivable from the usual mechanical laws; there is a limited number of "permitted" orbits for the electrons of every type of atom, each of which corresponds to a definite binding energy. Electrons which are close to the nucleus are subject to a stronger attractive force than those further away. To remove the inner electrons from the atom it is therefore necessary to do more work than would be required for the outer electrons. That is, the binding energy diminishes with increasing distance from the nucleus.

To put the situation more precisely, each orbit may be occupied by at most two electrons, distinguished from each other only by their spin. (Using an analogy to classical mechanics, the spin is considered to be a quantity describing rotation of the electrons about their own axis.) The two electrons in a single orbit have closely similar energies.

The orbits may be considered to form certain groups; all the orbits of such a group constitute a "shell". These shells are designated, in order of increasing distance from the nucleus, as the *K*-, *L*-, *M*-, *N*-, *O*-, *P*- and *Q*-shells.

The energy required for the total removal of an electron from the atom can be supplied in the form of radiation, i.e., according to the energy required (in the order of increasing energy) as visible, ultraviolet or X-radiation. Conversely, the atom may emit energy by radiation when an electron from outside is captured and enters one of the orbits. Removal of electrons from the atom may also be brought about by interaction with rapid particles, such as electrons which come close to the atom or collide with it.

Since the orbits correspond to different energies, energy will also be liberated or absorbed when an electron, while remaining within the atom, is transferred from one orbit to another. Since the lowest orbits (lying nearest to the nucleus) give the strongest binding, energy is liberated during the fall of an electron from a higher to a lower orbit, and this energy may also appear as radiation. On the other hand, when an electron is raised from a lower to a higher orbit it is necessary to overcome the attractive force of the nucleus, and the energy must therefore be supplied, e.g., by the absorption of radiation. When all electrons are in the lowest possible orbits, the atom is said to be in the "ground state". In contrast, an atom in which an electron moves in a more distant orbit is described as "excited".

When an electron from an outer orbit, or from outside the atom, falls into an inner shell, the energy liberated is relatively high, and is emitted in the form of X-rays. This can only occur, however, if a place in the inner shell is vacant, that is, if an electron has previously been removed from it.

It is possible to remove an electron completely from an atom by the impact of a rapidly moving electron. Thus, electrons can be accelerated in X-ray tubes, and when their kinetic energy is large enough to expel, for instance, an *L*- or *K*-electron from the "target" (the anti-cathode), the *L*- or *K*-lines of the element in question suddenly appear. The X-ray lines of the spectrum correspond to the energy differences between the *L*- or *K*-shells of the atom and shells further out.

In addition to this "characteristic radiation", X-rays are also produced at the anti-cathode by the retardation of the fast electrons. This radiation is called "bremsstrahlung" and shows a continuous energy spectrum which is superimposed upon the characteristic radiation.

X-radiation has always properties identical with γ-radiation of the same energy, and will therefore be discussed together with the latter.

When an electron is entirely removed from an atom, the rest of the atom carries a single positive charge. For the hydrogen atom, which possesses only one orbital electron, the rest corresponds to the atomic nucleus itself, while for instance in an atom of iron the rest consists of a nucleus together with 25 electrons. These electrically charged atomic rests are called positive "ions".

The liberated electron can easily attach itself to certain types of atoms, thus forming negative ions. By the removal or addition of more than one electron, ions with multiple charges arise.

2.3. Molecules

The chemical nature of an element is expressed in terms of the capacity of its atoms to interact with atoms of the same or other elements. This interaction may lead to the formation of chemical compounds, in which several atoms combine to give a molecule. For example two hydrogen atoms (H) form a hydrogen molecule (H_2), or a bivalent oxygen atom (O) combines with two hydrogen atoms to give a water molecule (H_2O), or a univalent chlorine atom unites with one hydrogen atom to form hydrogen chloride (hydrochloric acid, HCl).

Chemical processes, such as the formation of compounds just referred to, and also intermolecular forces are based on the interaction of the orbital electrons. The nature of compounds therefore depends on the electrons of the atoms, and in particular on their number. The nucleus does not take any direct part in chemical interaction, though its charge number (atomic number) indirectly influences the chemical properties by determining the number of extranuclear electrons of the electrically neutral atom. It has already been pointed out that all atoms characterized by the same atomic number behave as a single chemical element.

The fundamental connection existing between the number of the electrons (or atomic number) and the chemical properties is well expressed in the periodic system of the elements. On the basis of earlier work, Mendeleev clearly set out this system long before the development of the modern picture of the nuclear atom. Later it was given a firm theoretical foundation by the atom model which we have described. In the periodic system the chemical elements are arranged in a simple way into groups characterized by similarity in chemical properties. For example, the halogens (fluorine, chlorine, bromine and iodine together with the radioelement astatine, recently prepared artificially) form a single group within the periodic system, while the alkali metals (lithium, sodium, potassium, rubidium, caesium and francium) form another such group.

These regularities are due to the fact that the chemical properties are determined mainly by the outer electrons. The inner electrons occur in closed shells and do not take much part in chemical interactions. These closed shells contain definite numbers of electrons. Therefore, groups of elements exist which have the same number of outer electrons and, in consequence, have similar chemical properties: the atoms of all the alkali metals, for example, each have a single external, reactive electron.

In molecules, just as in free atoms, the electrons move in definite orbits, corresponding to definite energy values which depend on their distance from the nuclei. Also in molecules electrons are capable of being transferred from orbit to orbit, so that the molecules as well may exist in ground, excited or ionized states. Further discussion of the connection between the chemical properties of the elements and the underlying structure of their atoms lies outside the scope of this book. Instead we turn to a consideration of the structure of the atomic nucleus, which is the decisive factor in the phenomenon of radioactivity.

2.4. Isotopy

While the proton and the electron were already known as elementary particles at the time of the development of the planetary model of the atom, the neutron was not discovered until 1932. We now know that all atomic nuclei contain neutrons in addition to protons, except that of ordinary hydrogen, which consists merely of a single proton. Most atomic nuclei, in fact, contain more neutrons than protons. In this way, the Earth consists predominantly of neutrons, which are, however, bound in atomic nuclei, and thus "camouflaged". Neutrons and protons are bound to each other by specific nuclear forces which are not of an electrical character and act only at extremely short distances (of the order of 10^{-13} cm). These attractive forces operate between neutrons, between neutrons and protons, and also between protons, though in the last case the electrical repulsive forces are superimposed upon them.

The mass of the neutron is nearly equal to that of the proton (see Appendix 2). Since both kinds of elementary particles occur in the nucleus, they are also described collectively as "nucleons". The total number of nucleons in the nucleus or atom is its "mass number". Thus, atomic nuclei are characterized by two numbers, the charge or the atomic number previously referred to (number of protons), and the mass number (number of nucleons). Obviously, both of these must always be whole numbers. The atomic number is often designated by the letter Z, the mass number by A. The number of neutrons (N) is therefore given by the difference $A - Z$. Species of atoms, i.e., all atoms showing the same value of A and Z and also the same nuclear energy state (see p. 14), are called nuclides. As an illustration, Table 1 gives the characteristic numbers of a few natural nuclides.

While each chemical element is characterized by a definite charge number, there is no such limitation for the number of neutrons. The number of extranuclear electrons is in no way affected by the number of neutrons in the nucleus. As we can see from Table 1, atoms of one and the same chemical element can therefore show different neutron numbers and mass numbers.

TABLE 1. THE STABLE ISOTOPES OF SOME ELEMENTS

Element	Atomic number Z	Mass number A	Neutron number N
Hydrogen	1	1 or 2	0 or 1
Phosphorus	15	31	16
Chlorine	17	35 or 37	18 or 20
Iodine	53	127	74
Mercury	80	196, 198, 199, 200, 201, 202 or 204	116, 118, 119, 120, 121, 122 or 124

Nuclides which do not differ in their charge number, but only in the mass number and the number of neutrons, are called isotopes. For example, while the elements phosphorus and iodine naturally occur only in the form of single isotopes, i.e., with fixed values of N and A, other natural elements consist of mixtures of isotopes. Thus, natural chlorine consists of 75·4 per cent of an isotope of mass number 35, and of 24·6 per cent of an isotope of mass number 37. Natural hydrogen contains about one part in 7000 of a heavier isotope, heavy hydrogen or deuterium. In contrast to ordinary, light hydrogen (protium), this contains a neutron in addition to the proton in the nucleus. Experience shows that the isotopic composition of most elements is nearly (but not entirely) identical for all terrestrial samples, irrespective of their origin.

Nuclides may also be produced artificially as we shall show in more detail later. Thus a radioactive hydrogen isotope, the "super-heavy" hydrogen or tritium, has been made artificially. Its nucleus contains two neutrons in addition to the proton. Similarly, radioactive phosphorus isotopes have been prepared which show the same atomic number ($Z = 15$) as natural phosphorus but have $N = 15$ or 17 instead of 16.

The three hydrogen isotopes may be written briefly as $_1^1H$, $_1^2H$ and $_1^3H$, similarly the natural isotopes of chlorine as $_{17}^{35}Cl$ and $_{17}^{37}Cl$, and the three isotopes of phosphorus which we have mentioned as $_{15}^{30}P$, $_{15}^{31}P$ and $_{15}^{32}P$. The superscript is the mass number, and the subscript the charge or atomic number of the isotope. Alternatively, $_{15}^{30}P$ and $_{17}^{37}Cl$ may be written phosphorus-30 or chlorine-37.

Strictly speaking, the word "isotope" should only be used in connection with other isotopes of the same element, in the same way as a person can be spoken of as a brother only if other brothers or sisters exist. The use of the word "nuclide" is free from such a limitation.

The relationship between the mass number, the actual mass of a nuclide, and the atomic weight of the element, must be briefly discussed here. During the last decades, oxygen was generally used as the reference point for atomic and nuclide weights.

However, the international commissions dealing with this question have now decided that in future atomic weights of elements and weights of nuclides should be referred to carbon-12 taken as 12·0000. The weight of a nuclide, i.e., the weight of the neutral atom containing the nucleus of a certain species, differs in general from the mass number, which is an integer, by a small amount that never exceeds 10 per cent of an atomic weight unit. This difference is due to two factors: Firstly, there is a small difference between the mass of a neutron on the one hand and the sum of the masses of a proton and an electron on the other hand, i.e., between the components out of which the nuclide can be considered to be formed. Secondly, binding energy is liberated when nucleons come together to form a nucleus. According to the relationship given by Einstein, such a loss in energy is equivalent to a loss in mass (mass defect). The second factor is more important than the first.

From the weights of the individual isotopes and their abundances in the natural element, the atomic weight of an element can be calculated.

With weights based on oxygen separate scales were used for atomic weights and for nuclide weights. The nuclide weights were referred to oxygen-16 taken as 16·0000 (physical scale), the atomic weights to naturally occurring oxygen taken as 16·0000 (chemical scale). Since natural oxygen contains, in addition to oxygen-16 (mass 16·0000; abundance 99·76 per cent), small amounts of oxygen-17 (mass 17·0045; abundance 0·04 per cent) and of oxygen-18 (mass 18·0049; abundance 0·2 per cent), a factor of 1·00027 had to be applied in converting weights from one scale to the other.

With the ^{12}C-scale of atomic weights now coming into use the distinction between chemical and physical atomic weights is eliminated. The new scale has the important advantage against the old chemical scale that the atomic weights of elements are no longer referred to natural isotope mixtures, which do show some small variations. The values for the atomic weights on the new scale differ only very slightly from the former chemical values.

2.5. Isotope Effects

The concept that the isotopes of an element are chemically identical, which we have applied so far, holds only approximately. Theory and observation show that in spite of the identity of the composition of the electron shells noticeable chemical differences between isotopes may arise when the difference in the mass numbers is relatively great. These differences are, however, only quantitative and not qualitative, with the single exception of helium at very low temperatures.

For medium-heavy or heavy atoms, the relative differences in the mass numbers of the isotopes are small. In the case of chlorine it is 6 per cent. Only a very small difference in chemical behaviour is therefore to be expected. On the other hand, the two natural isotopes of hydrogen differ in mass by a factor of 2, which naturally leads to a considerable difference in their behaviour. The melting point of heavy water, the oxide of heavy hydrogen, is 3·82 °C compared with 0 °C for natural water; its boiling point is 101·42 °C, compared with 100 °C. Therefore, in the fractional distillation of water the deuterium content of the residue tends to increase.

In this extreme case, the relative concentrations of the two isotopes may be markedly altered in the course of chemical reactions as well. A well-known example is the electrolysis of water where under certain conditions light hydrogen is evolved seven times more rapidly than heavy hydrogen. The reaction is therefore used industrially for the concentration of heavy water. The chemical difference between tritium and protium is of course even greater than that between deuterium and protium. In the special case of hydrogen, separate chemical symbols are given to the heavier isotopes, deuterium (D) and tritium (T).

Enrichment and impoverishment due to isotopy are called isotope effects. In this book we shall have little occasion to discuss such effects, since only for hydrogen they are so marked as to play a significant role in relation to technical problems. From here on we shall therefore usually ignore isotope effects.

2.6. Radioactivity

Although isotopy is only rarely of consequence for chemical reactions, it is very important for nuclear reactions (nuclear transformations). These transformations constitute a new kind of reaction, fundamentally different from chemical reactions. As we have seen, chemical reactions are determined by the extranuclear electrons, and the nucleus itself remains unaffected; in nuclear reactions, on the other hand, we are concerned with transformations of the nucleus, which may then in consequence cause changes in the extranuclear region of the atoms involved.

We may distinguish between two main groups of nuclear transformation. On the one hand, there are spontaneous decompositions of unstable nuclei, which we call radioactive disintegrations. On the other hand, artificial transformations of stable or unstable atomic nuclei may be brought about through bombardment with elementary particles, with other nuclei, or with quanta of electromagnetic radiation of high energy.

The manner and the velocity of the decay, if any, of an atomic nucleus depends on its composition and energy state. Among the various isotopes of an element, one or more may be stable, while others may be radioactive. Thus, the phosphorus isotope $^{31}_{15}P$ is stable, $^{30}_{15}P$ is radioactive with short life, and $^{32}_{15}P$ is radioactive with long life. Of the three hydrogen isotopes, one, tritium, is radioactive.

As far as chemical behaviour is concerned, it is quite irrelevant whether an atom is radioactive or not. As long as a radioactive isotope has not in fact undergone disintegration, it behaves in the same way as a stable isotope. This is of fundamental importance for the use of radioisotopes as tracers (radioactive indicators).

Radioactivity is usually recognized by the fact that the nucleus in the course of its transformation emits one or several rays. The most important radioactive transformations are accompanied by the emission of α-, β- or γ-radiation, which will now be discussed.

2.7. α-radiation

α-rays consist of extremely rapid, doubly-ionized positive helium ions (helions), i.e., helium atoms which have lost both their electrons, and so consist only of the bare nuclei. Such nuclei (α-particles, $^4_2$He) contain two protons and two neutrons.

α-decay is a characteristic property of many nuclei with high charges, i.e., nuclei containing many protons. Charges which are confined together in a small space strongly repel each other. This may lead to the spontaneous expulsion of charged particles. Protons are never emitted singly in such radioactive reactions, but always in the form of α-particles. The reason for this striking fact is to be found in the high stability of the helium nucleus, which is consequently easily formed during the spontaneous decay of highly charged nuclei. α-decay occurs for example in the most abundant uranium isotope, $^{238}_{92}$U, in ordinary radium, $^{226}_{88}$Ra, and in radium emanation (radon), $^{222}_{86}$Em. Since α-decay causes the nucleus to lose two protons and two neutrons, this spontaneous transmutation may be represented, in the case of radium, by the equation:

$$^{226}_{88}\text{Ra} = {}^{222}_{86}\text{Em} + {}^4_2\text{He}.$$

The sums both of the superscripts and of the subscripts must be the same on the right- and the left-hand sides of the equation, since neither the total charge number (subscript) nor the number of nucleons (superscript) can alter in a nuclear reaction. For the reaction described, one of the reaction products is the nucleus of radon, which is itself radioactive and capable of α-decay.

2.8. β-radiation

β-decay, which is not restricted to highly charged nuclei, is much more frequently found. The fundamental characteristic of these reactions is the transformation of a nucleon within the nucleus into the other type of nucleon. A neutron is transformed into a proton, or a proton into a neutron.

The emission of fast negative electrons (β-particles) from the atomic nucleus is often observed. The physicists believe that the electron as such does not exist in the nucleus before disintegration, but is formed in the course of disintegration. Since the sum of the charges does not change in a nuclear reaction, it follows that during β^--decay the positive charge on the nucleus must increase by one unit. Since there is no change in the mass number, this is only possible if a neutral nucleon in the nucleus is converted into a positively charged one, that is, a neutron is changed into a proton.

In another type of β-decay, a positive electron or positron is emitted (β^+-decay). It follows that in this case a proton in the nucleus must be converted into a neutron. As far as known up to now, positron emission does not occur in nature, but it is by no means uncommon among artificial radioactive nuclei. Positrons vanish very quickly after formation through "annihilation", that is, through reaction with negative electrons. Two γ-rays of 0·51 MeV each, emitted in opposite directions, are the only product of this process. (This is the reverse of "pair formation", see p. 23.)

A third type of β-decay resembles positron emission in also leading to a reduction of nuclear charge by the conversion of a proton into a neutron. But though this process is considered a form of β-decay, no β-particle is emitted. Instead, the nuclear transformation occurs by the absorption of an electron from a shell into the nucleus, where it neutralizes a proton. This process is called "orbital electron capture". Since the electron usually comes from the shell next to the nucleus, the K-shell, the expression "K-capture" is also used. Electron capture occurs with natural and artificial radioactive nuclei. How electron capture may be observed will be explained below.

The three types of β-decay can be expressed in the following manner:

Emission of negative electrons $\quad \binom{A}{Z} = \binom{A}{Z+1} + {}_{-1}^{0}e$

Emission of positrons $\quad\quad\quad\quad \binom{A}{Z} = \binom{A}{Z-1} + {}_{+1}^{0}e$

Electron capture $\quad\quad\quad\quad\quad\quad \binom{A}{Z} + {}_{-1}^{0}e = \binom{A}{Z-1}$

where e denotes an electron. The mass number of the electron is zero since it contains no nucleon. Also in these equations the sums of the subscripts and of the superscripts must remain the same on the left- and the right-hand sides of the equations. Examples of the three types of β-decay are:

Emission of negative electrons $\quad {}_{15}^{32}P = {}_{16}^{32}S + {}_{-1}^{0}e$

Emission of positrons $\quad\quad\quad\quad {}_{15}^{30}P = {}_{14}^{30}Si + {}_{+1}^{0}e$

Electron capture $\quad\quad\quad\quad\quad\quad {}_{4}^{7}Be + {}_{-1}^{0}e = {}_{3}^{7}Li$

2.9. γ-radiation

In contrast with α- and β-radiation, γ-radiation does not consist of rapidly moving corpuscles, but of electromagnetic radiation similar to visible light, and moving with the same velocity. Like visible radiation, it exists in definite quantities of energy known as quanta or photons. But the energy of each of these quanta is very much greater, often a million times greater, than that of a quantum of visible light. Since γ-radiation contains neither nucleons nor electrical charges, its emission or absorption has no influence on the mass number or charge number of a nucleus.

When an excited nucleus changes into the ground state, the energy lost may be emitted as γ-radiation. The loss of energy may occur stepwise, so that several γ-quanta are emitted in sequence (called a "cascade" of γ-quanta).

Often γ-radiation is emitted as a consequence of α- or β-disintegrations that leave the resultant nucleus in an excited state. The emission of radiation takes place when the excited nucleus falls spontaneously to the ground state. In most cases, γ-ray emission follows so soon after that of the α- or β-particles that it seems to take place simultaneously, although strictly speaking this is not true.

In other cases, however, a delay is observed. A time interval of hours, days or even longer may occur. By analogy with chemical isomerism, the two forms of the nucleus which occur in such cases (ground state and excited state) are known as nuclear isomers. This is because they differ not with respect to composition, but only in their energy content, and therefore presumably in the configuration of the nucleons. The spontaneous transition from the excited to the ground state can then be called γ-decay.

γ-radiation is a kind of energetic electromagnetic radiation and it is therefore in physical nature identical with X-radiation. Its quanta have often even higher energy. The criterion for distinguishing the two types of radiation is based, however, not on the energy, but on the origin of the radiation. Radiation emitted by nuclei, and also radiation emitted in electron–positron annihilation, is called γ-radiation; energetic electromagnetic radiation of other origin, in particular from electronic shells, is called X-radiation. The effects of γ- and X-radiation are, however, identical, and the two types of rays cannot be distinguished once they have been emitted.

2.10. Radiation from the Extranuclear Region Due to Radioactivity

Although the radiation arising in radioactive processes usually comes directly from the nucleus (nuclear radiation), these processes can also lead to the emission of radiation from the extranuclear region of the disintegrating atom. Such radiation may consist either of fast electrons or of X-rays. The effects of these electrons correspond to those of β-radiation, while X-radiation acts like γ-radiation of the same energy.

For a rather simplified and not quite correct picture of the origin of fast electrons one can assume that a photon, originating in the nucleus, expels an electron from the same atom. The energy of the photon is partly used up in removing the electron from the atom, and the rest appears as the kinetic energy of the electron. Such a process is called "internal conversion". It may proceed with a yield of 100 per cent so that the γ-rays as such do not appear at all. In internal conversion a "hole" is produced in the shell which must sooner or later be filled up by another electron from a shell further from the nucleus. As this electron "approaches" the nucleus, energy is liberated and is emitted as an X-ray.

X-rays also arise in the course of electron capture (the third form of β-decay), since this also leaves a "hole" in an inner shell. When electron capture leads directly to the ground state of the nucleus, γ-radiation is not emitted, the only evidence of electron-capture then being the emission of X-rays. In this connection it should be noted that the interaction of radioactive rays with other atoms in the samples, or in the surrounding materials, e.g., in the mounting, may also change the type or the energy of the radiation. For example, the absorption of β-rays in a sample may result in the emission of the characteristic X-rays of elements present in it.

2.11. Energy of Radiations

The types of disintegration we have described and the associated radiations are summarized in Table 2. Those given in parentheses need not always be present. X denotes the emission of X-rays, *e* the emission of electrons from the extranuclear region by internal conversion. The radiation emitted must be characterized not only by its type, but also by its energy.

TABLE 2. TYPES OF RADIOACTIVE DISINTEGRATION AND RADIATIONS EMITTED

Type of disintegration	Radiations
1. α-disintegration	$\alpha\ (\gamma)$
2. β-disintegration	
(a) Electron emission	$\beta^-\ (\gamma)\ (e,\ \mathrm{X})$
(b) Positron emission*	$\beta^+\ \gamma\ \ (e,\ \mathrm{X})$
(c) Electron capture	$(\gamma)\ (e)\ \mathrm{X}$
3. γ-disintegration	$\gamma\ (e,\ \mathrm{X})$

* In the absorption of positrons, γ-radiation is always produced (see p. 12).

The energy is best given in terms of the electrical potential through which an elementary electrical charge would need to fall to acquire the kinetic energy of the particle under consideration. For example, a proton has the kinetic energy of one "electron volt" (1 eV) after falling through a potential difference of one volt. In order to impart an energy of 1 eV to an α-particle it is only necessary for it to fall through 0·5 V, since it is doubly charged and the energy is given by the product of the charge and the potential. The energy of uncharged particles, such as neutrons or light quanta (photons), which cannot be electrically accelerated, can nevertheless be expressed in electron volts. One electron volt equals $1·6 \times 10^{-12}$ erg or $3·8 \times 10^{-20}$ cal. When we convert from atomic to macroscopic (chemical) magnitudes, we must multiply by Avogadro's number (6×10^{23}). Consequently, an energy change of 1 eV per atom corresponds to 23 050 cal/g-atom (23·05 kcal/g-atom).

To give an idea of the magnitude of the electron volt it may be recalled that free electrons in an electron tube are accelerated through at most a few hundred volts of anode potential, and so acquire kinetic energies of a few hundred electron volts. The energy of chemical reactions is still smaller. When two atoms form a molecule, the binding energy is not more than a few electron volts, as can be shown by employing the required conversion factors or by direct measurement in the case of electrochemical reaction. On the other hand, the energies of individual nuclear rays are generally not less than several thousand electron volts (1000 eV = 1 kiloelectron volt (keV)), and may attain several million electron volts (10^6 eV = 1 megaelectron volt (MeV)). Thus an enormous amount of energy is developed in nuclear reactions, as was pointed out on p. 2.

2.12. Induced Nuclear Reactions

Radioactive disintegrations are spontaneous reactions of unstable atomic nuclei. Other nuclear reactions are induced artificially by bombarding stable or long-lived nuclei with high-energy particles or photons. The first example of such an artificial nuclear reaction, discovered in 1919, was that of nitrogen with fast α-particles: $^{14}_{7}\text{N} + ^{4}_{2}\text{He} = ^{17}_{8}\text{O} + ^{1}_{1}\text{H}$. This process may be written $^{14}_{7}\text{N}(\alpha, p) \, ^{17}_{8}\text{O}$, with α denoting an incident α-particle and p an emitted proton. This reaction was carried out by allowing high-energy α-particles from the disintegration of radium C to impinge upon nitrogen gas. The emission of protons was observed as a consequence of this bombardment.

Induced nuclear reactions occur very rapidly after the impact of the bombarding particle, and may be regarded as practically instantaneous. Various "projectiles" may be used, especially nucleons (protons and neutrons), and lighter atomic nuclei such as deuterons (nuclei of heavy hydrogen) or α-particles (helions, nuclei of ^{4}He), as well as high-energy photons. These projectiles are also the most important products of induced nuclear reactions. Photons appear together with corpuscles when the nucleus formed by the emission of a heavy particle is initially in an excited state. If photons alone are emitted, the product nucleus, also initially in an excited state, is the addition product of the initial nucleus and the projectile. An important class of reactions of this kind is "radiative neutron capture", the (n, γ)-reaction. For example, light hydrogen captures neutrons according to the process $^{1}_{1}\text{H}(n, \gamma) \, ^{2}_{1}\text{H}$.

Nuclei produced in induced nuclear reactions may be either stable or radioactive. In the latter case they are known as artificially radioactive nuclei. An example of the formation of artificial radioactive nuclei is the process discovered in 1934 by Frédéric and Irène Joliot-Curie. Radiophosphorus was produced by bombarding aluminium with α-particles, according to the reaction $^{27}_{13}\text{Al}(\alpha, n) \, ^{30}_{15}\text{P}$.

Through reactions of this kind many important radioactive nuclides are produced. From a practical standpoint the use of charged projectiles (protons, deuterons and α-particles) suffers from a great disadvantage. Because of their positive charge, these particles are repelled by the positively charged nuclei. But they react with the nuclei only after very close approach, since the specific non-electrical attractive forces operative between elementary particles have very small range (see p. 8). Therefore, reactions with charged particles are only possible if the particles possess large kinetic energy. Nowadays such particles are mostly produced in accelerators such as the Van de Graaff machine or the cyclotron.

Even if the charged particles originally had high energy, they may lose much of this energy on passing through layers of materials, even thin layers (p. 18), and will cease being effective. They are then repelled by the Coulomb force before they can react with the nucleus, and so the yield in such processes is usually small.

Shortly after the discovery of the neutron it was shown that this difficulty does not apply to it. Since neutrons are not electrically charged they are not repelled by the atomic nucleus, and so even after the loss of practically all of their kinetic energy neutrons may still penetrate into the nucleus and cause transformations. Such neutrons are described as slow neutrons. The radionuclides most commonly used in practice are produced with slow neutrons. The formation of radiocarbon, radiosodium and radiocobalt are important examples, and the reactions may be written:

$$^{14}_{7}\text{N} + ^{1}_{0}n = ^{14}_{6}\text{C} + ^{1}_{1}\text{H}; \quad \text{or} \quad ^{14}_{7}\text{N}(n, p) \, ^{14}_{6}\text{C}$$

$$^{23}_{11}\text{Na} + ^{1}_{0}n = ^{24}_{11}\text{Na} + \gamma; \quad \text{or} \quad ^{23}_{11}\text{Na}(n, \gamma) \, ^{24}_{11}\text{Na}$$

$$^{59}_{27}\text{Co} + ^{1}_{0}n = ^{60}_{27}\text{Co} + \gamma; \quad \text{or} \quad ^{59}_{27}\text{Co}(n, \gamma) \, ^{60}_{27}\text{Co}.$$

Radionuclides obtained by neutron capture are mostly subject to β^--decay. Further details about neutrons, their sources and properties are given in Sections 6.6.3 and 6.7.1.

2.13. Nuclear Fission

A particularly important type of induced nuclear reaction, usually brought about by neutrons, is the nuclear fission of uranium. Fission is caused in the rare (0·7%) natural isotope $^{235}_{92}U$ (actinouranium) by slow or fast neutrons, in the abundant (99·3%) isotope $^{238}_{92}U$ by fast neutrons only. In fission, two heavy fragments of some-what similar masses arise. Together with these a few neutrons (averaging 2–3) are set free. This fact makes it possible to develop a chain reaction, when the neutrons produced are utilized to induce further fission. A controlled chain-reacting system is called a reactor.

For example, fission may occur according to the equation:

$$^{235}_{92}U + {}^{1}_{0}n = {}^{143}_{56}Ba + {}^{90}_{36}Kr + 3{}^{1}_{0}n$$

Numerous other fission products are also known. The fission products are mostly β^--active. They include such important radionuclides as strontium-90, iodine-131, or caesium-137.

The neutrons emitted in fission are also used for the production of radionuclides. Neutron capture in materials inserted for this purpose into reactors is the most important process in this connection (see Section 2.12).

A list of the most important radionuclides, with their characteristic properties, is given at the end of this volume (Appendix 1). The application of radioactive substances, especially of fission products, as radiation sources is treated in Volume 2.

2.14. Absorption of Radiation: Preliminary Remarks

The next three sections will be devoted to the laws governing the absorption of various types of radiation. Primarily we shall discuss the reduction in the intensity of the radiation during its passage through absorbing materials; the intensity of the radiation is here defined as the number of rays impinging per unit area per unit time. We shall discuss less extensively the loss of energy by the individual rays in passing through the absorber, since this is of secondary significance for the most important group of measuring instruments, the counters. In general, we shall consider beams of parallel rays, for which the laws of absorption take their simplest form.

It is convenient to express the thickness of an absorber in terms of weight per unit area (mg or g per cm^2). As an example, an air column of 1 cm^2 cross-section and 1 cm height contains under normal conditions 1·29 mg of air; and so a 1 cm layer of air has an "area weight" of 1·29 mg/cm^2. This way of describing thickness has the advantage that absorption in a substance is then independent of the conditions (temperature, pressure). Moreover, theory and experience show that dependence on chemical composition is also in many important cases small when area weights are used. Thus the absorption of radiation by iron is naturally much greater than by air if the thickness is expressed in centimetres; but if it is expressed in terms of area weights, the difference is nearly eliminated. The density of iron is approximately 6000 times greater than that of air, and the absorption in 1 cm of iron is similar to that in the same area weight (corresponding to 6000 cm) of air.

2.15. Absorption of α-radiation

α-particles have only small penetrating power, since they lose their energy rapidly by interaction with matter. Thus, the ranges of α-rays from natural radionuclides (with energies up to 9 MeV) are always less than 7 cm (in air), or about 9 mg/cm². α-particles possess sharply defined initial energies, but the radiation emitted by one nuclide may consist of several groups with well-defined energies. This applies whenever the disintegration produces one or several excited states of the product nucleus. The α-disintegration is then, of course, accompanied by γ-radiation.

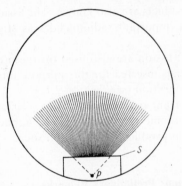

FIG. 1. Tracks of α-particles in a cloud chamber
P: Position of sample; *S*: Collimating slit

Since α-particles of the same energy lose their kinetic energy at approximately the same rate in passing through matter, they will all come to rest after traversing approximately the same path length (range). Experiments on gases with sensitive instruments show, however, a small spread in range, which is due to chance variations in the number of air molecules encountered per centimetre of path ("straggling"). When the tracks of the α-particles in the gas are made visible in a suitable way (for instance, in a Wilson cloud chamber), a picture like that in Fig. 1 is obtained, somewhat resembling the shape of a shaving brush.

Loss of energy by the α-particles is usually due to interaction with the extranuclear electrons rather than with the nucleus. The forces of electrical attraction set the electrons in motion. The energy required for this must come from the α-particles, which are consequently retarded. The electrons are either entirely removed from the atoms or molecules of the absorbing medium so that positive ions are formed, or else the electrons are raised to orbits of higher energy, the atoms thus becoming excited. Ionized and excited atoms or molecules may subsequently emit radiation.

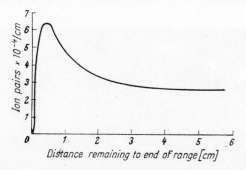

Fig. 2. Specific ionization produced by α-particles in air (Bragg curve)

Figure 2 shows how the energy loss of an α-particle per unit path length, here expressed by the number of ion pairs formed in it, depends on the length of its track remaining to the end of its range (residual range). Slow α-particles, as can be seen, lose their energy particularly easily. This curve is known as the Bragg curve.

2.16. Absorption of β-radiation

The absorption of β-rays is a more complex process than that of α-rays. In the first instance, this is due to the fact that at the time of emission β-rays do not have uniform velocity and energy. In fact, radioactive nuclei of a given type emit β-rays of energy between zero and a certain well-defined upper limit. This limiting value is quoted in the tables as the β-ray energy of the radionuclide in question. This energy distribution is due to the fact that in a β-disintegration three particles are formed at the same time: the product nucleus, the β-particle and a neutrino. The neutrino has

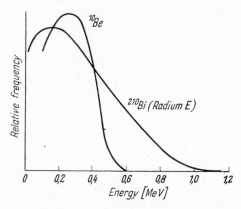

Fig. 3. Typical energy distribution of β-radiation

neither charge nor rest mass, and since its interaction with matter is extremely slight, no simple demonstration of its existence is possible. Figure 3 shows the energy distribution of β-particles from two typical emitters, ^{10}Be and ^{210}Bi (radium E).

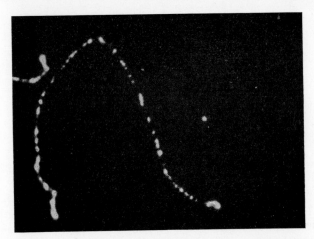

FIG. 4. Tracks of β-rays in a cloud chamber (from E. RUTHERFORD, J. CHADWICK, C. D. ELLIS, Radiations from Radioactive Substances)

Moreover, the light β-particles, unlike the heavy α-particles, may lose a great deal of their energy in single collisions with electrons. An electron may even lose its entire energy to the electron with which it collides, and so come to rest. More often the electron loses a large, but not the whole, portion of its energy and is strongly deflected

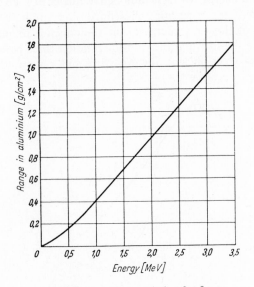

FIG. 5. Range–energy relation for β-rays

from its original direction. Consequently, the tracks of β-particles (unlike those of α-particles, see Figs. 1 and 18) are not straight lines, but are frequently strongly curved (Fig. 4). Therefore, it would be impossible to predict the ranges of individual electrons, even if their initial energies were accurately known.

Figure 5 gives the relationship between the maximum range in aluminium and the (maximum) energy of β-rays. This range (expressed as area weight in g/cm²) corresponds above 0·7 MeV to an empirical formula given by Feather:

$$R = 0.543E - 0.160 \tag{1}$$

the energy E being expressed in MeV. The lowest β-ray energy so far found is that of tritium (18 keV). High energies are observed, for example, in the β-radiation from radiosodium (^{24}Na) and radiophosphorus (^{32}P) with 1·39 and 1·70 MeV, respectively.

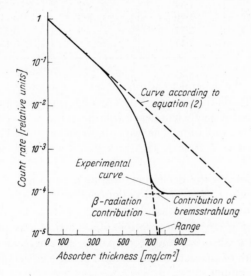

FIG. 6. Absorption of β-radiation from phosphorus-32 in aluminium

Because of the complexities of the absorption process, the number of rays in a parallel beam which penetrates a layer of given thickness cannot be calculated theoretically. Yet it has been found that within a certain range of absorber thicknesses a simple exponential expression

$$I = I_0 \, e^{-\alpha d} \tag{2}$$

often agrees well with the experimental data. I_0 is the initial intensity, I the intensity after passage through the absorber, α (the "mass absorption coefficient") a constant characteristic of the radiation and determined by its energy, and d the area weight of the absorber. The intensity may be given, for example, in terms of particles per cm² per sec. Figure 6 shows a typical β-ray absorption curve. It is seen that equation (2) is only valid within certain limits.

The mass absorption coefficients depend only slightly on the nature of the absorber (however, compounds of hydrogen are a notable exception; see Section 6.7.3.). Table 3 gives values of the mass absorption coefficients for the β-rays of a few important radionuclides. Most of the values were obtained with aluminium as absorber.

TABLE 3. MASS ABSORPTION COEFFICIENTS FOR β-RADIATIONS

β-emitter	Maximum energy (MeV)	Absorption coefficient (cm^2/g)	Half-thickness (mm Al)
Hydrogen-3	0.018	23,000	0·0001
Carbon-14	0·155	250	0·01
Sodium-24	1·39	8·1	0·32
Phosphorus-32	1·70	6·3	0·41
Manganese-56	2·87	4·9	0·64
Bismuth-210	1·17	14	0·18

The table also shows the general trend of the mass absorption coefficient, i.e., its decrease with increasing radiation energy. No exact relation between these two quantities exists, however, since the coefficient depends both on the maximum energy and on the energy spectrum of the radiation. The last column of the table gives approximate values for the "half-thickness", that is, the thickness at which the initial intensity is reduced to half.

Also in the case of β-decay the nuclei may disintegrate to the ground state or an excited state of the product. The total β-radiation then consists of several energy groups, each with its characteristic maximum energy; in this case it is of course accompanied by γ-radiation. In the absorption of β-particles, as of α-particles, X-radiation is formed in the absorber, and accompanies the emergent β-radiation. This X-radiation consists both of characteristic radiation of the elements present in the absorber, and of bremsstrahlung.

2.17. Absorption of γ-radiation

Like α- and β-radiation, γ-radiation interacts mainly with the extranuclear electrons. But in contrast to α- or β-rays, no definite range exists for γ-rays. This is because γ-rays, being uncharged, do not lose their energy through numerous individual processes along their paths. Instead, γ-rays interact with atoms relatively rarely. When such interaction does occur, however, the photon vanishes instantly, or loses at least the major part of its energy and so changes its properties fundamentally.

The intensity of the original γ-radiation therefore diminishes in passing through matter only to the extent to which such "catastrophic" interactions occur. As long as a ray is not absorbed in this manner it preserves its original energy. In this respect, γ-radiation is fundamentally distinct from α- and β-radiation, each particle of which loses energy during passage through matter gradually. This point cannot be emphasized too strongly.

The probability that any γ-ray will be absorbed in passing through a certain thickness of the layer is determined only by the energy of the radiation, and is independent of the thickness the ray has already traversed. Thus the intensity of a beam of γ-radiation theoretically never reaches zero however much the thickness of an absorbing layer is increased. Therefore, one cannot speak of a range for γ-radiation. Absorption processes of this kind can be described by an exponential function of the form

$$I = I_0 \, e^{-\alpha d} \tag{3}$$

where the symbols have the same significance as in the formally identical equation (2). However, equation (3) represents a law which is strictly valid, while the empirical rule given by equation (2), though useful in practice, is an approximation and applicable only within certain limits.

The energy lost by γ-radiation in absorption reappears predominantly as the energy of fast electrons ejected from the atoms. This may occur either through the photoelectric effect or through the Compton effect. In the former, the total energy of the photon less the binding energy appears as the kinetic energy of the liberated electron. In the latter, the photon is "scattered" by an electron, and transfers part of its energy to the electron. The scattered photon has then less energy than the primary photon. For low energies the photoelectric effect is most important, while for intermediate energies the Compton effect predominates, the relative proportions depending on the nature of the absorber.

For energies greater than 1·02 MeV, electrons may also arise in "pair formation". In pair formation the photon is converted into a positive and a negative electron. In accordance with the theory of relativity, the energy of the photon then reappears partly as the energy corresponding to the rest masses of positron and electron, and partly as their kinetic energy.

The electrons ejected or created by γ-rays are themselves subsequently absorbed in a way similar to the absorption of β-particles. The detection of γ-rays in measuring equipment mostly takes place by way of these electrons.

It should be noted that equation (3), unlike equation (2), only gives that part of the radiation which is unchanged, i.e., which emerges with the original energy. This unchanged radiation is, however, accompanied by secondary electromagnetic radiation, consisting mainly of photons from the Compton scattering, of bremsstrahlung, and, provided the energy of the photons in the primary beam was sufficient, of annihilation radiation. The intensity of the secondary radiation relative to that of the surviving primary radiation depends greatly on the geometry, i.e., on the dimensions and positions of source, absorber and radiation detector. The intensity of the secondary radiation is relatively small when a narrow beam of primary radiation falls on the absorber, and the measuring instrument subtends a small angle at the absorber ("good geometry"). On the other hand, the intensity of secondary radiation may be quite large when the beam of radiation is broad and the angle subtended by the detector at the absorber is large.

Like β-rays, γ-rays can be called "soft" or "hard" according to their penetrating power. In the energy region important in the application of radionuclides the penetrating power of γ-rays increases with increasing energy. Figure 7 gives the mass absorption coefficients in lead and aluminium as a function of energy. These values for γ-rays are much smaller, and the half-thicknesses consequently much greater, than for β-rays of equal energy.

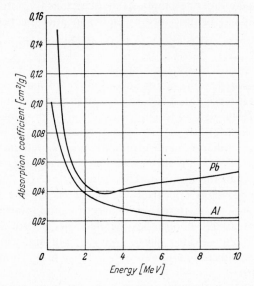

FIG. 7. Absorption of γ-radiation in lead and aluminium

2.18. Radiation Dose

As we have shown, the effect of nuclear rays on matter consists primarily in the ionization and excitation of atoms and molecules. Neutrons excite and ionize indirectly; fast neutrons transfer their kinetic energy to atomic nuclei (such as protons) in collisions, while slow neutrons induce nuclear reactions in which charged particles or photons are emitted. All rays of nuclear origin and other high energy particles (including photons) are grouped together as ionizing radiations.

The energy taken up in the absorption of radiation can reappear without production of chemical changes, e.g., as heat or light. In this case the absorber returns to its original condition after irradiation. On the other hand, chemical changes may occur as a result of ionization and excitation. The study of such changes is the object of radiation chemistry. In living systems radiation-biological effects may arise.

A suitable measure of the energy absorbed is desirable for the study of all these effects. As a measure of absorbed energy, which is independent of the nature and the energy of the radiation and the nature of the absorbing material, the "rad" is now generally used. A dose of 1 rad corresponds to absorption of 100 erg/g. This unit was recommended by the International Commission on Radiological Units in 1953.

In particular when the doses or the rates of their delivery are small, it is very difficult or even impossible to measure the absorbed energy directly. Dose measurements are therefore frequently carried out with instruments working on similar principles as the usual radiation detectors. Among these, the instruments utilizing gas ionization are particularly important (see Sections 3.1–3.4 and 13.3).

For this reason a unit based on gas ionization, the "roentgen", has found much use. By definition a roentgen (r) is that exposure to electromagnetic radiation by which positive and negative ions each with a total charge amounting to one absolute electrostatic unit are produced per millilitre of air at 0°C and 1 atmosphere (0·001293 g). Since in air one ion pair is found to be produced on the average by 34 eV of energy delivered by electromagnetic ionizing radiation, an exposure of one roentgen corresponds to a dose of 88 erg of absorbed energy per gram of air.

It must be noted that the numerical relation between the roentgen and the absorbed energy just given (1 r = 88 erg/g) is only valid for air as an absorber. Since other materials have mass absorption coefficients which differ somewhat from that of air for the same energy of radiation, irradiation of such materials with 1 r will not deliver 88 erg/g but a different amount, which will also depend on the radiation energy. For example, within a substantial energy range irradiation of water with 1 r will cause absorption of 98 erg/g (0·98 rad).

These complex relationships involving the roentgen make it desirable to express doses in terms of the actual energy absorbed, i.e., in rads. The difficult problem remains, however, to calculate the delivered doses on the basis of measurements with radiation detection instruments, or, what amounts to the same, to calibrate such instruments satisfactorily.

The chemical and biological effects of one and the same dose (in rad) may not be identical if the dose is delivered by means of radiations of different types or energies. Radiation-chemical and radiation-biological effects may depend both qualitatively and quantitatively upon the spatial distribution of the ions and excited molecules. For example, the ions and excited atoms produced by irradiation with α-rays are concentrated along short tracks, so that the spatial density there is locally very great, while that in other parts of the system is very small. For β- and γ-rays the spatial distribution is much more uniform.

2.19. Decay of Radionuclides

The basic unit of quantity of radioactive materials is the "activity", defined as the number of disintegrations taking place in a sample per unit time (cf. Section 3.1).

Up to now we have tacitly assumed that the radioactive sources show constant activities. This is a good enough approximation provided the number of atoms disintegrating in the source during the time of observation is small compared with the total number present. However, the radioactive process must result in the reduction of the number of radioactive atoms, and so of the activity. Often this reduction is observable within a very short time.

We shall need an equation for the dependence of radioactive disintegration on time. It has been shown beyond doubt that for any type of radioactive disintegration the probability of any individual nucleus disintegrating in the next unit of time is a constant characteristic of the particular nuclear species. This probability is called the "disintegration constant", λ. It then follows that the most probable value for the number of disintegrations per unit of time (the activity) must be proportional to the number of nuclei present (N). For sufficiently large numbers of nuclei, the activity approaches the calculated (most probable) value (see Section 2.21). In this case we can write for the number of disintegrations per second of the source, i.e., for the activity, A, the fundamental equation:

$$A = \lambda N. \tag{4}$$

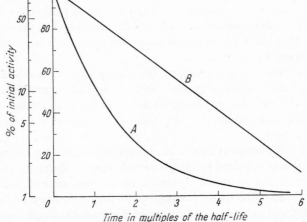

FIG. 8. Decay curve for a radionuclide with inactive daughter product
(*A*) Plot with linear scale for ordinate, (*B*) Plot with logarithmic scale for ordinate

The value of N will, of course, diminish with time, and it is possible to show that equation (4) over an extended time takes the form:

$$N = N_0\, e^{-\lambda t} \tag{5}$$

or

$$A = A_0\, e^{-\lambda t} \tag{6}$$

where N_0 is the initial number of atoms, A_0 the initial activity, and t the time elapsed. The exponential decay according to equation (6) is shown in Fig. 8.

Usually the disintegration rate of radionuclides is characterized by the half-life, τ, instead of the disintegration constant λ. The half-life is the time required for the number of active atoms, and therefore also for the activity, to drop to half the initial value.

It is seen from equation (5) that half-life and disintegration constant are related by the equation:

$$\tau = \ln 2/\lambda = 0.693/\lambda \tag{7}$$

so that equations (5) and (6) may be replaced by:

$$N/N_0 = A/A_0 = 2^{-t/\tau}. \tag{8}$$

For equations of type (5) and (6), the choice of the starting time is completely unimportant: any given instant may be chosen as zero time, provided that A_0 or N_0 are taken as the values appearing at that time.

These equations are valid when the decomposition products are inactive. This is frequently the case. For example, the β-disintegration of radiophosphorus leads to the formation of inactive ^{32}S. In other instances, particularly often with natural radionuclides, this is not true. In these cases the immediate decay product is itself radioactive, and a whole chain of radioactive disintegrations may occur. A well-known example is the naturally occurring decay series of ordinary uranium, $^{238}_{92}U$, which proceeds through several stages, including radium and radium emanation (radon), and terminates in the non-radioactive lead isotope $^{206}_{82}Pb$ (uranium series). The other natural decay series are those of thorium and actinium, starting from ^{232}Th and ^{235}U, respectively.

2.20. Radioactive Equilibrium

After sufficient time, "radioactive equilibrium" (really, a steady state) is established in such decay series. In the absence of branching, the activity is then the same for each individual nuclide in the chain. Thus, in a uranium mineral that has remained undisturbed over geological times, i.e., where no removal of any substance has taken place, the activity of radium, or radon, or any other radioactive decay product in the sample, is identical with that of uranium-238.

The explanation is obvious: if the activity of one member of the chain were smaller than that of its parent substance, the disintegration of the latter would produce an increasing amount of the daughter substance, and this would not be fully compensated by the disintegration of the daughter itself. The activity of the daughter would therefore increase until equilibrium is established through the equality of formation and disintegration. The situation would be reversed if the activity of any member of the chain were abnormally large initially.

From this equality of the activities of all the nuclides in radioactive equilibrium it is possible to calculate the amounts of the various nuclides present. The disintegration constants, and therefore the half-lives, of the various atoms differ from each other. When equilibrium exists, the number of atoms at each stage must be inversely proportional to the disintegration constant, and so directly proportional to the half-life. For instance, in an old uranium mineral in radioactive equilibrium there must be approximately three million times as many uranium as radium atoms, since the half-life of uranium (4.5×10^9 years) is three million times as great as that of radium

(1600 years). This is in agreement with the observations that one gram of radium is generally associated with three tons of uranium.

When the members of a radioactive decay series are chemically separated from each other, each individual substance will produce its daughter substance, and this in turn its own daughter substance, until radioactive equilibrium is re-established. It is easy to find a relation for this important process if the parent substance has a long half-life, and so shows practically constant activity. The activity of the separated daughter substance is given by equation (5) or (6). Furthermore, use can be made of the fact that the amount and the activity of this daughter substance in the entire system must be unaffected by chemical separation, since radioactivity is always independent of any chemical operation. Therefore, the total amount of the daughter substance must re-

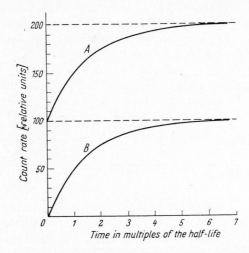

FIG. 9. Formation of a radioactive daughter nuclide from a long-lived parent nuclide
(*A*) Measuring instrument records radiation from both substances with equal yield;
(*B*) Measuring instrument records only radiation from daughter substance

main the same, and this means that the decrease in the activity of the separated daughter substance from its initial value A_0 must be compensated by a corresponding growth of the daughter in the separated parent substance. For the activity of the daughter substance within the parent substance we then have the equation:

$$A_t = A_0 - A_0\, 2^{-t/\tau} = A_0(1 - 2^{-t/\tau}). \tag{9}$$

A similar equation applies also to the amount N_t of the daughter substance within the parent substance at any time t after separation.

In Fig. 9 a graphical representation of equation (9) is given. It is seen that the rate of the re-formation is independent of the half-life of the parent substance provided this is so long-lived that it does not undergo appreciable decay during the experimental period.

Important examples of this kind of growth for both natural and artificial radionuclides are the following: Uranium-238 ($\tau = 4{\cdot}5 \times 10^9$ years) gives rise to thorium-

234 (uranium X_1; $\tau = 24\cdot1$ days); while barium-140 ($\tau = 12\cdot8$ days) produces lanthanum-140 ($\tau = 40$ hr):

$$^{238}_{92}U \xrightarrow{\alpha} {}^{234}_{90}Th \xrightarrow{\beta} {}^{234}_{91}Pa \ (\beta\text{-active}),$$

$$^{140}_{56}Ba \xrightarrow{\beta} {}^{140}_{57}La \xrightarrow{\beta} {}^{140}_{58}Ce \ (\text{stable}).$$

In the literature, equations for more complicated cases are also given, e.g., the case where the parent substance is not long-lived, or where a chain of daughter substances with similar half-lives is formed.

2.21. Statistical Fluctuations of Radioactivity

To conclude the discussion of radioactive decay, it is important to stress the statistical nature of this phenomenon. The laws of radioactive decay, as given for example in equation (4), are probability functions. Such functions give an exact description only when they are applied to a large number of events. However, the experimental values are subject to considerable deviations from the expected (most probable) values when we consider only small numbers. If a coin is tossed 1000 times, we shall obtain almost exactly 50 per cent of heads and 50 per cent of tails, but if we toss twice, the probability of obtaining a 1:1 ratio of heads to tails is only $\frac{1}{2}$, while for both heads or both tails the probability is $\frac{1}{4}$ each.

Many physical quantities, such as weight, can in principle be obtained with any desired accuracy if sufficient care is taken and suitable apparatus is used, but the situation is different with radioactive decay. With samples of low activity we observe the disintegration of relatively few atoms, as we shall show in more detail in the following chapter. A measurement may involve the detection of the disintegration of 100 radioactive atoms or less. Under such conditions statistical fluctuations are significant. Although, as we have shown, each radioactive atom is characterized by a definite probability of disintegration within a unit of time, it is impossible to predict with certainty whether the most probable number, or rather more or fewer than this, will actually disintegrate.

In actual measurements of radiations from a given radioactive sample taken over intervals of fixed length, e.g., one minute, larger and smaller values (counts) are observed. The smaller the activity of the sample, the greater the average relative deviation of the individual result from the mean value, i.e., the more important the statistical fluctuation. Naturally the greater a deviation from the mean value, the more rarely this deviation occurs. The true mean value of the measured count, free from significant uncertainty due to statistical fluctuation, can only be obtained from the observation of a great number of disintegrations, so that for a weakly active sample a long period of observation is needed.

We give now the simplest form of the equations for the calculation of the accuracy of radiation measurements by counting. The standard deviation, m, is generally taken as a measure for the dispersion of repetitive measurements. The value of m is a minimum if the deviation is reckoned from the arithmetic mean ($\overline{N}$) of the measured values under consideration, and would be increased by using any value other than $\bar{N}$ in the relation. The definition of m is:

$$m = \pm \sqrt{\frac{\sum_{1}^{n} (\bar{N} - N_i)^2}{n - 1}} \qquad (10)$$

N_i is the ith value, and n the number of measurements. The symbol $\sum_{1}^{n}$ indicates that $\bar{N} - N_i$ is summed for all measurements, i.e., from 1 to n. In words, this definition indicates that the standard deviation is given by the square root of the mean square deviation.

In radioactivity measurements by counting, a Poisson distribution of measured values is followed, for which the standard deviation of the counts accumulated in the measurement is given by the relation:

$$m = \pm \sqrt{\bar{N}} \approx \pm \sqrt{N} \qquad (11)$$

where $\bar{N}$ is the mean value (obtained from repeated measurement for a given period), and N is one of these values. The values of $\bar{N}$ and N are the number of counts, i.e., the disintegrations registered in the measuring instrument. The standard deviation m in the value of N is expressed in the same units, that is, in a number of counts. The standard deviation in the count rate, N/t, will be denoted by σ:

$$\sigma = \pm m/t \approx \pm \sqrt{\frac{N}{t^2}} \qquad (12)$$

where t stands for the duration of the measurement. Both N/t and σ have the dimension of counts per unit time, e.g., counts per minute.

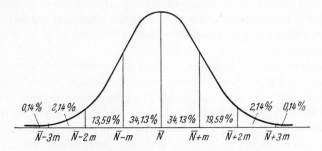

Fig. 10. Gaussian normal error distribution curve

For somewhat larger values of N (accumulated counts) the Poisson distribution assumes the form of the well-known normal distribution, the Gaussian error curve (Fig. 10), which helps in understanding the significance of the standard deviation. In the normal distribution the probability that an individual measured value will deviate from the true value by more than the standard deviation is 32 per cent, the probability of a deviation of more than twice the standard deviation is 5 per cent, and that of three times the standard deviation is 0.3 per cent. The standard deviation thus denotes the range within which the true mean value obtained in a very long measuring time will lie with 68 per cent probability. It should be noted that the equations for the calculation of errors must be applied to the number of actual counts (impulses registered), irrespective of yield in measurement.

Table 4 gives the standard deviations for some values of the total of the accumulated counts, both as absolute values and as relative values in relation to the total counts. Although the absolute deviation (in counts) increases with the counts accumulated, the relative error diminishes. Since in assessing the reliability of a result it is the latter which is significant, it is clearly necessary to register a considerable number of disintegrations. This is, as we have observed, a consequence of the random character of radioactive decay which is based on its atomistic nature.

TABLE 4. STANDARD DEVIATIONS

Number of impulses registered (N)	Standard deviation (absolute) ($\sqrt{N}$) [impulses]	Standard deviation (relative) ($100/\sqrt{N}$) [%]
100	10	10
1 000	31·6	3·16
10 000	100	1
100 000	316	0·32

For very low count rates the inaccuracy of results is still greater than is calculated from the equations just discussed. In this case, it becomes significant for the error that the count rate due to the sample is the difference between the measured count rate and the background count rate (see p. 38). The standard deviation for this difference (in counts per unit time) is given by the expression:

$$\sigma = \pm \sqrt{\frac{\overline{N}}{t_N^2} + \frac{\overline{L}}{t_L^2}} \approx \pm \sqrt{\frac{N}{t_N^2} + \frac{L}{t_L^2}} \tag{13}$$

in which $\overline{N}$ is the mean value of the measurements of the sample with a measurement period t_N, N is a corresponding individual measurement, $\overline{L}$ is the mean background for periods of measurement t_L, and L is a corresponding individual value. For the count rate of the sample as such we then have:

$$\frac{N}{t_N} - \frac{L}{t_L} \pm \sqrt{\frac{N}{t_N^2} + \frac{L}{t_L^2}} \tag{14}$$

An example will illustrate the application of this equation. A background measurement gave 600 counts in 20 min, while a measurement on the sample gave 420 counts in 10 min. Consequently, the true count rate of the sample was

$$\frac{420}{10} - \frac{600}{20} \pm \sqrt{\frac{420}{100} + \frac{600}{400}} = 12 \pm 2\cdot4 \text{ counts/min.}$$

Consequently, the relative standard deviation was $2\cdot4/12$, i.e., 20 per cent.

General References to Chapter 2

M. ARDENNE, *Tabellen zur angewandten Kernphysik*, Berlin 1956.

G. B. COOK and J. F. DUNCAN, *Modern Radiochemical Practice*, Oxford 1952.

R. EVANS, *The Atomic Nucleus*, New York 1955.

R. A. FAIRES and B. H. PARKS, *Radioisotope Laboratory Techniques*, London 1958.

W. FINKELNBURG, *Einführung in die Atomphysik*, Berlin 1962; English translation, *Structure of Matter*, New York 1964.

O. R. FRISCH (Ed.), *The Nuclear Handbook*, London 1958.

G. FRIEDLANDER and J. W. KENNEDY, *Nuclear and Radiochemistry*, New York 1955.

S. GLASSTONE, *Sourcebook on Atomic Energy*, Princeton 1958.

M. HAISSINSKY, *La chimie nucléaire et ses applications*, Paris 1957; *Nuclear Chemistry and its Applications*, Reading, Mass. 1964.

D. HALLIDAY, *Introductory Nuclear Physics*, New York 1955.

B. G. HARVEY, *Introduction to Nuclear Physics and Chemistry*, Englewood Cliffs 1962.

G. HERTZ (Ed.), *Lehrbuch der Kernphysik*, Leipzig 1958, 1961.

I. JOLIOT-CURIE, *Les radioéléments naturels*, Paris 1946.

I. KAPLAN, *Nuclear Physics*, Reading, Mass. 1955.

J. KOHL, R. D. ZENTNER and H. R. LUKENS, *Radioisotope Applications Engineering*, Princeton 1961.

R. LAPP and H. L. ANDREWS, *Nuclear Radiation Physics*, Englewood Cliffs 1963.

R. LINDNER, *Kern- und Radiochemie*, Berlin 1961.

L. MELANDER, *Isotope Effects on Reaction Rates*, New York 1960.

ST. MEYER and E. SCHWEIDLER, *Radioaktivität*, Berlin 1927.

R. T. OVERMAN and H. M. CLARK, *Radioisotope Techniques*, New York 1960.

R. T. OVERMAN, *Basic Concepts of Nuclear Chemistry*, New York 1963.

W. RIEZLER, *Einführung in die Kernphysik*, Munich 1959.

E. RUTHERFORD, J. CHADWICK and C. D. ELLIS, *Radiations from Radioactive Substances*, Cambridge 1930.

K. SCHMEISER, *Radionuclide*, Berlin 1963.

E. W. SCHPOLSKI, *Atomphysik*, Berlin 1962.

N. A. VLASOV, *Neutrons* (Russ.), Moscow 1958; German translation, Berlin–Cologne 1960.

W. J. WHITEHOUSE, Fission, in O. R. FRISCH (Ed.), *Progr. Nucl. Phys.* vol. 2, Oxford 1952.

W. J. WHITEHOUSE and J. L. PUTMAN, *Radioactive Isotopes*, Oxford 1953.

I. R. WILLIAMS and M. W. WILLIAMS, *Basic Nuclear Physics*, London 1962.

3. THE MEASUREMENT OF RADIOACTIVITY

3.1. Introductory Remarks

Nuclear radiations are measured for a number of purposes. The quantity most often required in connection with tracer methods is the activity of a sample, expressed by the number of disintegrations per unit time. This definition of activity disregards the nature and the energy of the radiation; for example, samples of radiohydrogen (^{3}H) and of radiophosphorus (^{32}P) undergoing equal number of disintegrations per unit time are regarded as having the same activity, although the energy radiated by the latter is a hundred times as great as that radiated by the former.

In other cases, measurements are carried out to determine the nature and the energy of the rays. In this way, radionuclides can be identified. In technical application it is usual to employ known radionuclides so that identification is unnecessary. However, in certain procedures discussed in this book, such as activation analysis, the identification of radionuclides may be required.

There are also cases in which the doses delivered by radiation at a particular spot have to be determined (see Section 2.18). Such measurements are often necessary for ensuring satisfactory radiation protection, but they may also play a part in the application of radioelements for the production of ions or for promoting chemical reactions.

We distinguish between absolute and relative measurements of activity. Absolute determinations are only rarely necessary. Mostly it is sufficient to determine the relative activity of a source, i.e., to compare the activity with that of a standard source emitting the same radiation. Relative determinations are, of course, much simpler to perform than absolute determinations.

In working with a counting apparatus such as the Geiger counter, the number of impulses per unit time under constant conditions is often employed as a measure of the relative activity of a source. When absolute constancy is not possible, e.g., when the thickness of the samples varies, suitable corrections must be applied (see p. 49).

The absolute activity can be calculated from the number of impulses if the measuring yield is known. For the instruments most often used, direct calculation of the yield is difficult since it depends on several factors, including the radiation energy and the composition, the shape and the arrangement of the sample. The usual procedure is, therefore, to calibrate with standard samples of known absolute activities.

The absolute activities of these standard samples can be determined with special instruments, such as counting tubes of 100 per cent yield (cf. p. 43). Sometimes they may also be calculated on the basis of the origin of the standard sample. This is the case for samples of the β-active nuclide UX_1, obtained from known amounts of ordinary uranium, with which they were in radioactive equilibrium.

Standard samples are, of course, suitable only for the determination of the measuring yield of the radionuclides they contain, since the yield depends on the nature of the radiation. In many countries, suitable standard samples of common radionuclides are now available from laboratories specializing in absolute activity measurements.

The unit of absolute activity is the curie (c). Originally, a source was said to have an activity of one curie if it gave the same number of disintegrations in unit time as one gram of radium (meaning radium-226 free from its disintegration products, which are also radioactive). In practice this definition suffered from the serious disadvantage that the disintegration constant of radium is not known with sufficient accuracy. Since it is undesirable to revise the curie each time newer and better measurements are made, the value of the curie has subsequently been fixed at exactly $3 \cdot 7 \times 10^{10}$ disintegrations per second, a figure which is close to the true activity of radium. It follows that the activity of one gram of radium is only approximately one curie. Smaller units are the millicurie (1 mc = 10^{-3} c), the microcurie (1 μc = 10^{-6} c), and the micromicrocurie or picocurie (1 $\mu\mu$c = 1 pc = 10^{-12} c).

The number of disintegrations per second per gram of any pure radionuclide is thus given by:

$$A = 3 \cdot 7 \times 10^{10} \tau_0 M_0 / \tau M \tag{15}$$

where τ and M are respectively the half-life and atomic weight of that substance, and τ_0 and M_0 are those of radium. It should be borne in mind that the number of emitted rays may not be identical with the number of disintegrations, since in the decay of an atom several rays, such as a cascade of γ-rays, may be emitted.

Instead of using the curie we may express the activity directly in terms of the number of disintegrations per second or minute (dps, dpm).

A very important concept is that of specific activity, i.e., the activity per unit weight of an element or a compound. No special unit for this has been adopted generally, but units often employed are: number of disintegrations per second per gram, curie per gram, curie per mole, etc. Specific activity has a simple relationship to the fraction (N^*/N) of active atoms in an element. For example, if the specific activity (A_s) is expressed in curies per gram, we have

$$A_s = (\tau_0 M_0 / \tau M) (N^*/N) \tag{16}$$

in which the symbols have the same significance as in equation (15).

In most methods for the detection of radioactive radiations use is made of their ability to ionize atoms and molecules, i.e., the ions or electrons formed in the sensitive volume of an instrument during the incidence of the radiation are registered in some way.

Basically the simplest technique consists in measuring the ionization produced by the rays in a gas. Use is also made of ionization in photographic methods, in which the radiations are detected by the blackening of silver halide grains in a photographic emulsion. Ionizing radiations, like ordinary light, liberate electrons from the bromide ion, the electrons are subsequently captured at active sites of the crystal, and give a latent image which may then be developed.

Scintillation counting, which has gained increased importance in recent years, depends on the registration of light emitted from excited atoms or molecules. Here as well, ionization plays an important role since the excitation is partly due to electrons liberated by the incident radiation.

We shall now give a survey of the fundamental principles of the most important measuring techniques. (The measurement of neutrons will be treated in Section 6.7.1.) Detailed descriptions may be found in the literature listed at the end of this chapter.

3.2. Ionization Chambers

In the ionization chambers the number of ions and electrons formed in a certain volume of gas is measured. With two electrodes, for example, parallel metal plates, an electrical potential is applied to a gas-filled chamber. The electrons, or the negative ions arising through the capture of electrons by certain types of atoms or molecules,

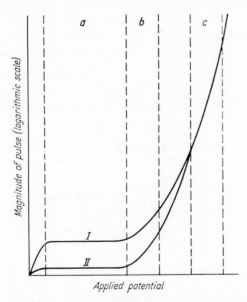

FIG. 11. Schematic current–voltage curve for gases subjected to ionizing radiation, (*I*) Curve for α-rays of a certain energy; (*II*) Curve for β-rays of a certain energy; (*a*) Region of saturation current; (*b*) Region of proportionality; (*c*) Geiger region

then move to the positive pole (anode), while the positive ions move to the negative pole (cathode). The current so produced may be measured directly by a galvanometer, or after electronic amplification. It is also possible to charge the ionization chambers to a certain electrostatic potential and then to follow the discharge with an electroscope.

Recombination of oppositely charged ions to form neutral atoms or molecules also occurs in the chamber. This process is suppressed by application of strong electric fields, since the ions then move more rapidly, and thus are more likely to reach the electrodes without recombination. Above a certain minimum value of the potential gradient, recombination is practically eliminated, and the current in the chamber is determined only by the number of ions formed in unit time. This saturation current is then a measure of the radiation intensity, provided the nature of the radiation and the position of the radiation source are fixed.

For a considerable range of the applied potential above this minimum value the current produced by a constant radiation intensity is constant, giving a long plateau (Fig. 11, part *a*). This is the voltage range used in the practical operation of ionization chambers. Using such voltages the full ionization current in the chamber is obtained, which is independent of accidental fluctuations in the voltage.

With weak radiation sources it is often advantageous not to measure the current, but instead to count the pulses which are due to the individual rays. This is possible only if the size of the pulses exceeds a certain minimum. In practice this means that pulse counting of radioactive substances with ionization chambers is restricted to α-rays. These rays have a very short range, and give up their considerable energy completely within the chamber. But even the counting of α-particles requires rather sensitive amplifiers. While counting chambers cannot be used for β- or γ-rays, current measuring (integrating) chambers are suitable for these radiations provided the intensity is not too low.

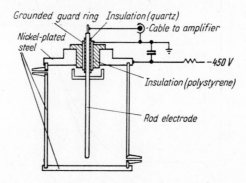

FIG. 12. Counting ionization chamber for measurement of radon and thoron

Since in counting chambers the magnitude of the individual current pulses is proportional to the energy of the α-particles, it is possible to sort out current pulses according to their magnitudes, and so to obtain an energy spectrum. This requires special electronic circuits, called pulse analysers.

In working with ionization chambers, samples in the form of a solid layer may be used (see Section 3.7). However, one of the most important applications of ionization chambers consists in the measurement of emanation, the inert gas (element no. 86), all isotopes of which are α-emitters. The emanation is introduced as such into the gas space of the ionization chamber. Figure 12 shows an ionization chamber for the measurement of gaseous α-emitters. Other radioactive gases, such as radiokrypton or radioactive carbon dioxide ($^{14}CO_2$), may also be determined with ionization chambers.

Ionization chambers are frequently employed to measure γ-ray intensities due to sources outside the instrument. Among such uses are radionuclide applications based on radiation absorption as well as dosimetry in connection with radiation protection (see Section 13.3).

3.3. Proportional Counters

When the electric field applied to a volume of gas is increased further, the end of the plateau is reached; still further increases in potential cause a rapid rise of current (Fig.11, part *b*). This increase is not due to a prevention of recombination, but to a new physical effect, ionization by collision (ion multiplication).

Electrons and ions moving to the electrodes undergo repeated collisions with neutral atoms or molecules along their path. In such collisions they lose some or all of the kinetic energy imparted to them by the field. After each collision they are again accelerated, and this process is repeated until the particles reach the electrode and are discharged.

It is the behaviour of the electrons which determines the operation of the counters. When the field strengths are high, primary electrons acquire so much energy between collisions that they ionize molecules or atoms with which they collide. The secondary electrons formed in this manner then undergo similar accelerations and collisions, so that an "avalanche" is formed. The total number of free electrons produced will of course increase with the field strength. The magnitude of the final current pulse at the anode is determined by the extent of the multiplication.

Within a certain range of voltage, the current pulse increases with voltage, while for any given voltage it is proportional to the number of primary electrons produced by the radioactive ray, and therefore to the energy given up by the ray. This is the voltage range in which proportional counters operate.

In such counters, the potential is usually applied between a metal cylinder (cathode) and a thin wire stretched along the axis of the cylinder (anode). Since the avalanche mechanism causes current amplification in the gas space ("gas amplification"), this instrument, unlike the ionization chamber, may be used to count individual β- and γ-rays. In the counting of α-rays, the electronic amplification circuit has a much lighter task than in the case of the ionization chamber. The boron chambers for neutron measurements (p. 101) are also generally operated as proportional counters.

The proportional counter, like the ionization chamber, can distinguish between rays of different energies, such discrimination also being possible for β- and γ-rays. Therefore, the proportional counter can be employed for β- or γ-spectrometry. To a considerable extent, the elimination of the background count rate is also possible by energy discrimination. As will be discussed in greater detail in the next section, the background is due to the radioactive contamination of the environment and to the cosmic radiation.

On the basis of this ability to discriminate between radiations, the proportional counter (together with the scintillation counter) finds application both in the laboratory and in industry, wherever it is necessary to distinguish between radiations coming from different nuclides and possessing different energies. Internal counters (p. 43) are often operated in the proportional region. When discrimination is not required, preference is usually given to Geiger counters, because of their simplicity, or to integrating ionization chambers, because of their stability.

3.4. Geiger Counters

3.4.1. *Principles*

When the voltage applied to a proportional counter is increased above a certain value, proportionality ceases to hold. The magnitude of the current pulse is then no longer proportional to the number of primary electrons. The pulse size still increases with potential, but the greater the primary ionization the smaller the relative increase (Fig. 11). In this way, the pulse sizes tend to be equalized. This is called the region of limited proportionality. Finally we reach the part c, where the current pulses are independent of the primary ionization. Thus all pulses are, apart from minor fluctuations, equal. This is the Geiger region in which Geiger counters operate.

The main advantage of this type of counter is the large gas amplification. Each primary ion pair formed in a Geiger counter may in practice give rise to 10^9 secondary ion pairs. Owing to this fact the external amplifier can be quite simple, and is therefore cheaper and more stable than amplifiers for proportional counters.

The Geiger counter has certain disadvantages. Since all pulses are of the same size, discrimination is impossible, and it is also impossible to distinguish "true" pulses arising from radiations emitted by the sample, and "false" pulses coming from impurities in construction materials, the surroundings, or cosmic radiation.

The correction for the false activity is obtained by a background measurement. The counter is operated under the same experimental conditions as for the measurement of the activity, but in the absence of the sample. A background is, of course, also found with ionization chambers or proportional counters, but for these instruments it may be greatly reduced by discrimination. Partial suppression of the background may be attained by surrounding the counter with plates of iron or lead. When protected by a few centimetres of lead, a typical commercial Geiger counter may show a background of 10–100 impulses/min, depending mostly on size.

Further reduction of background, which is sometimes of great importance, can be attained by the combined use of shielding and of anti-coincidence circuits. The main effect of such circuits is the elimination of the pulses due to the hard component of cosmic radiation. The measuring counter is surrounded by a number of screening counters. Hard cosmic radiation (mesons), which produces ions in the measuring counter, will also pass through one of the screening counters. Pulses will therefore be produced simultaneously in the measuring counter and in one of the screening counters. The anti-coincidence circuit then eliminates all pulses from the measuring counter which are accompanied by simultaneous pulses from screening counters.

While in Fig. 11 the magnitude of individual current pulses was shown as a function of potential, Fig. 13 gives, as a function of potential, the number of pulses (counts) per unit time that arise from a definite radiation intensity falling upon a Geiger counter. This is the "characteristic" of the counter. To obtain reliable and reproducible measurements, independence from potential is obviously desirable, since the values would otherwise be affected by accidental variations of voltage. In the voltage range of the plateau, the number of pulses is nearly independent of the potential.

The count rate obtained from satisfactory counting tubes actually shows almost complete independence of potential over a considerable range of voltages. A typical counter characteristic is shown in Fig. 13. The slope of the characteristic in the plateau range should not exceed a few per cent per 100 V, and may actually be quite negligible, e.g., less than 0·5 per cent per 100 V. As operating voltage a value about one third along the plateau is usually taken.

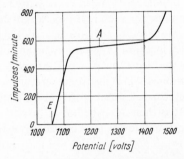

Fig. 13. Typical characteristic of a Geiger counter
(*E*) Starting point; (*A*) Suitable working point

The higher the gas pressure, the higher is the voltage at which the plateau of any given counting tube starts. Therefore very high pressures should be avoided. At very low pressures, on the other hand, no satisfactory plateaux are obtained. Suitable filling gases are hydrogen and the noble gases, while oxygen has undesirable effects even in small concentrations.

Every Geiger counter has a tendency to give multiple or continuous discharges instead of individual pulses. In view of the enormous ion multiplication in the gas space, this is not surprising. Non-neutralized electrons may produce new avalanches; ultraviolet light produced during discharge may also liberate electrons from the walls by photoelectric effect, and so initiate new avalanches. It is necessary to avoid such disturbances, and to enable the counter to recover its rest state as quickly as possible. In this way, the dead time is cut down, and the counter is quickly ready for registering further ionizing events. This is accomplished by quenching the discharge. Quenching may be brought about either electronically or by means of suitable additions to the filling gas; the two methods may also be used together. Insufficient quenching is expressed in a relatively steep characteristic.

External electronic quenching by means of a quenching circuit is accomplished by a sudden reduction of the potential as soon as a discharge occurs. Ionization by collision is thus stopped, while the electrons and ions already present are collected. The counting tube thus recovers. Internal quenching (self-quenching) is brought about by a gas, which is added to the filling and absorbs ultraviolet light. Alcohol and halogen vapours are suitable additives of this kind. A typical filling for a self-quenching counter consists of argon (80 mm Hg) and alcohol (15 mm Hg). Since organic quenchers are decomposed by ultraviolet light, the filling loses its quenching power after a certain number of discharges (around 10^9–10^{10}). Most industrial counters of this kind cannot be refilled, and therefore have a limited life. Unlike organic filling gases, halogens are not decomposed irreversibly. The halogen atoms formed by absorption of ultraviolet light recombine to form molecules so that the quenching capacity is not reduced.

From the start of the discharge to the end of quenching the counting tube is not sensitive to further rays. The existence of this dead time may lead to losses in the measurement of high radiation intensities. For a counter filled with argon and alcohol the dead time may amount to 0·2 millisecond. For older or simpler apparatus a more important limitation in the intensities that can be measured arises from the mechanical register used to count the pulses, for such registers cannot cope with high count rates. Therefore, electronic counting circuits are now usually employed. These indicate the number of pulses, practically without time-lag, by means of glow discharge tubes. In order not to enlarge unduly the electronic part of the instrument, electronic and mechanical counting may be combined. The electronic circuit then triggers the mechanical register only after a pre-determined number of pulses, such as a hundred, has been reached. The electronic part is then described as a "scaler".

If the dead time is known, small losses may be roughly estimated from the equation

$$A_0 = A/(1 - At),\tag{17}$$

in which A_0 and A are the true and the measured count rates (impulses/sec), respectively, and t is the dead time (sec).

Counting losses can also be determined experimentally. An empirical correction curve is obtained by increasing the radiation intensity acting upon the instrument by a known amount, for example, by superimposing a number of sources of known strength. The resulting increase in count rates is observed. In practice it is generally preferable not to measure high intensities, but instead to reduce the intensity by dilution of a parent solution, increase of distance or insertion of absorbers.

Geiger counters and other counting instruments may be equipped with an integrating indicator which gives the count rate directly, so that there is no need for counting a known period of time; such instruments are known as rate meters. They cannot be employed when the count rates are very low.

3.4.2. *Construction Types*

Geiger counters are in principle capable of recording α-, β-, and γ-rays, but in order to obtain satisfactory efficiencies the construction is adapted to the radiation to be measured. The efficiency of measurement is determined by several factors: the geometry of the instrument, which determines the solid angle subtended by the instrument at the sample; the probability of response to a ray entering the instrument; absorption occurring between sample and instrument, e.g., in the air or in the walls of the instrument; scattering of the rays by the backing of the sample, surrounding matter, etc. Scattering may produce either a reduction or an increase in counting yield.

Since α-rays have only small penetrating power, counters designed to measure them have a very thin window, usually made of mica, to admit the rays into the internal gas space, or the sample may be introduced into the counter in order to eliminate completely absorption by a window. (This also holds for the measurement of very soft β-radiation.) The samples that are introduced into counters may be in solid, liquid or gaseous form (see p. 43). However, ionization chambers and scintillation counters are usually preferred to Geiger counters for the measurement of α-rays.

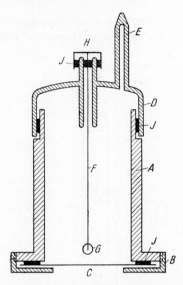

Fig. 14. Section through an end-window Geiger counter. (*A*) Brass cylinder; (*B*) Metal ring; (*C*) Mica window; (*D*) Glass cap; (*E*) Sealed-off filling connection; (*F*) Tungsten wire; (*G*) Plastic bead; (*H*) Metal cap as connector; (*J*) Plastic seals

On the other hand, the measurement of γ-rays by means of Geiger counters is sometimes difficult because of their low absorption. Detection obviously is possible only if ionization takes place, i.e., if free electrons are produced (p. 23). The probability of the liberation of an electron from the wall of the counter or from the filling gas on passage of a γ-ray is, however, only of the order of one per cent, and this can be increased only slightly by improvements in construction. Thus the counting yield for γ-rays is only 1/10–1/100 of that of a typical β-ray measurement in a similar instrument. Investigations requiring a good efficiency for γ-ray detection are therefore more suitably performed with scintillation counters.

Geiger counters are best suited to the measurement of β-rays of not too low energies. The rays from most β-emitters penetrate satisfactorily into counting tubes through windows or fairly thin walls. Typical values for the absorption of β-rays, permitting the estimation of losses in windows or walls, have already been given in Table 3.

β-rays which penetrate into the sensitive space produce, with a probability of nearly 100 per cent, at least one ion pair, thus giving current pulses which lead to their registration. Hard β-rays may therefore be measured with a yield often amounting to

30 per cent in a wall counter in which the sample lies against the metal cylinder which also serves as the cathode; with 5–20 per cent yield they may be measured with an end-window counter, also known from its shape as a "bell counter" (Fig. 14). In spite of the lower yield, the end-window counter is mostly preferred to the wall counter, since it is more stable, the arrangement of the sample relative to the counter (the counter geometry) is more reproducible, and absorbers are more easily inserted. Samples usually consist of layers of solid material. Their preparation will be discussed below.

A great variety of Geiger counters is available for various purposes, the designs generally being derived from the fundamental types of wall counter, window counter and internal counter.

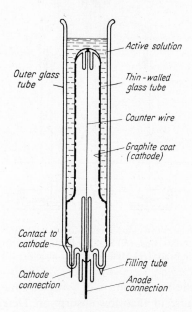

FIG. 15. Geiger counter for liquids (cup counter)

Special types include both very large and very small counters. The former are used for the measurement of large quantities of only slightly active material, such as potassium salts in mines, while the latter are used in plotting variation in activity from one point to another for extended systems, and may also be introduced into small cavities.

Mention should be made of liquid counters, which are wall counters, and not the liquid counterpart of gas-filled counters. They are used to measure the activity of liquids. Their cylindrical wall usually consists of a glass tube surrounding the cathode. Thus they can be inserted into liquids. Some counters have two concentric glass tubes, the liquid being introduced into the annular interstitial space (Fig. 15).

The liquid counter has the advantage of simplicity of operation. Moreover, good reproducibility is ensured since the liquid lies always in the same geometrical position relative to the counter. Its disadvantage is that the sensitivity is rather low if, as is normally the case, the liquids involved are solutions. Absorption of radiation in the solvent is considerable. If larger quantities of liquids are measured by inserting the counter into them, the mean distance of the radioactive atoms from the counter is greater than if the measurement were performed on the solute free of solvent. This leads to a decrease in counting efficiency.

The internal counter exists in many forms. In one the gaseous sample is introduced into the counter; β-rays can then be measured with large yield, approaching 100 per cent. This gas counter is important for the determination of the soft β-rays emitted by carbon-14 and tritium.* Working with a gas counter is, however, rather involved since it must be refilled for the measurement of each sample. When tritium is introduced as water vapour, and in some other cases, special steps may be needed to remove the last traces of highly active samples from the counter after the measurement (memory effect).

Special gas counters measure continuously the current of radioactive gas that is obtained from gas–liquid chromatograms. Usually radiocarbon and tritium are converted by combustion to carbon dioxide ($^{14}CO_2$) or water (THO) before entering the counting tube, and the carrier gas is selected so that a good plateau is obtained.

In another type of internal counter, solid samples are introduced into the tube. Among these counters are the instruments used for the determination of absolute activities, where the sample is applied to an extremely thin foil positioned within the counter. This type is called a "4π-counter", and usually has two wires (anodes), one on each side of the foil.

A third type of internal counter, the flow counter, has wider application. This instrument, primarily suitable for solid samples, consists essentially of a bell counter without window, and is not completely sealed; a suitable gas is passed through at atmospheric pressure during measurement. Change of samples is quite simple here. To avoid excessively high voltages, the counter must either be operated in the proportional region, or an expensive filling and flushing gas (consisting mainly of helium) must be used. With suitable solvents it is possible to use the flow counter for the measurement of liquid samples as well.

3.5. Scintillation Counters

Scintillation counting, which, in a primitive form, played an important part in early studies of radioactivity, has in recent years been reintroduced, and is finding wide application. Its main use is in the measurement of γ-rays, where considerably greater measuring yields than with Geiger counters are possible, and γ-quanta of different energies can be distinguished.

When suitable substances ("scintillators" or "phosphors") absorb ionizing rays, they emit part of the energy rapidly in the form of light, i.e., they show luminescence. By means of suitable instruments, the light flashes may be automatically registered and counted. The scintillators may consist either of inorganic salts, such as sodium iodide

* References relating to the measurement of carbon-14 and tritium are given at the end of Chapter 3 (page 51).

activated with traces of thallium, or of organic compounds, such as anthracene. The two main requirements of a scintillator are high light output, and rapid light emission with the least possible after-glow.

The most suitable composition and size of the scintillator will depend on the nature and the energy of the radiation to be determined. To measure hard γ-rays with a good yield, the thickest possible scintillator layer that still gives sufficient transparency should be used, since only then is satisfactory absorption of the γ-rays obtained. Large single crystals, such as the sodium iodide crystals activated with thallium already mentioned, or solutions of scintillating organic compounds in organic solvents or in plastics, may be employed. For X-rays and γ-rays of low energy, thinner layers may be used.

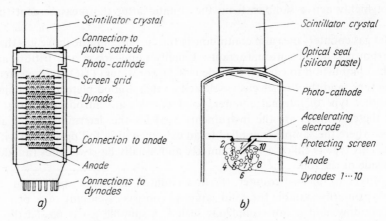

FIG. 16. Schematic diagrams of two types of scintillation counters for measuring γ-radiation

For α- and β-radiation as well thin layers are to be preferred. When discrimination between energies is not necessary, zinc sulphide is often used as a scintillator for α-rays; for β-rays, a thin layer of an organic phosphor may be applied. Under certain conditions, the measuring yield may be improved by mixing the active substance with the scintillator. Thus samples containing radiocarbon or tritium, both emitting soft β-radiation, may be brought into a suitable chemical form and then dissolved or suspended in a liquid scintillator. It must be kept in mind that the luminescence of scintillators may be suppressed by foreign substances (quenching).

A gas containing radiocarbon or tritium, as is obtained in gas–liquid chromatography (see p. 43), may be measured continuously by being passed over a solid scintillator.

The light flashes are registered by means of photoelectron multipliers. Electrons liberated by light quanta from the photocathode of such a tube are accelerated by an electrical field on to the first intermediate electrode (dynode) of the multiplier. Their energy is then sufficient to expel several secondary electrons from the dynode, which are subsequently accelerated electrically on to the next dynode. The multiplication process is continued at a number of successive dynodes. A photomultiplier may, for example, have twelve dynodes, and give a multiplication factor of 10^5–10^{10}. The current pulses at the output of the multiplier may then be further amplified and finally counted. Figure 16 shows schematically scintillation counters for the measurement of γ-radiation.

A general drawback of scintillation counters is their appreciable background, which is mainly due to spontaneous emission of electrons, owing to the thermal movement within the metal, from the electrodes of the multiplier. The effect can be reduced by taking special precautions, such as cooling of the multiplier or use of coincidence circuits.

A coincidence circuit consists of two photomultipliers that view the same scintillator and are so connected that registration occurs only when both multipliers produce current pulses simultaneously. This occurs when one and the same light flash in the scintillator is detected by both multipliers. If on the other hand a pulse appears, through spontaneous ejection of an electron, at the output of only one of the two multipliers, it is improbable that a pulse will be produced simultaneously in the second multiplier. The single current impulse is then suppressed by the electronic circuit. As with gas-filled counters, the contribution of cosmic radiation to the background may be suppressed by suitable shielding and anti-coincidence circuits.

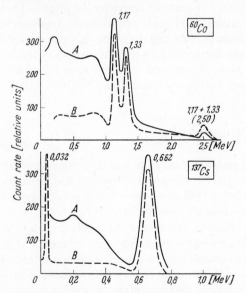

FIG. 17. γ-spectra of cobalt-60 and caesium-137, obtained with scintillation counters. (*A*) Detector: cylindrical sodium iodide (thallium activated) crystal with bore-hole: height 5·7 cm, diameter 3·8 cm, bore-hole 3·82 cm × 1·67 cm (authors' data); (*B*) Detector: cylindrical sodium iodide (thallium activated) crystal: height 10·2 cm, diameter 10·2 cm (from *Applied Gamma-Ray Spectrometry*, C. CROUTHAMEL (Ed.), London 1960) Curves A and B do not refer to samples of the same activity. Subsequently to the β-decay of cobalt-60, γ-quanta of 1·17 and 1·33 MeV are emitted in cascade. Caesium-137 undergoes β-decay to the excited isomer barium-137m (half-life 2·6 min), which on disintegration emits γ-quanta of 0·662 MeV. In 10 per cent of the disintegrations, internal conversion takes place, as a consequence of which K-X-rays of 0·032 MeV are emitted.

An important application of scintillation counters is in determining the energy of γ-rays. For this, use is made of the facts that the intensity of a light flash is approximately proportional to the absorbed energy, and the size of the current pulse from the photomultiplier is proportional to the intensity of the flash. Scintillation counters, like proportional counters, may therefore be used with special circuits as γ-ray spectrometers.

Pulses falling within a definite range (channel) may be sorted out by means of a discriminator circuit and counted separately. By moving this energy channel over the relevant energy range, the intensity of the radiation may be determined as a function of the energy. More rapid results can be obtained with the expensive multi-channel instruments which register the intensities in a considerable number of channels separately, and so record the whole spectrum simultaneously. γ-ray spectrometry is particularly useful for the identification of radionuclides and for the analysis of mixtures of nuclides. Figure 17 shows typical γ-spectra obtained with NaI(Tl) crystals. It is seen that the maxima (photopeaks) corresponding to radiations of sharply defined energies are somewhat broadened and appear as bands.

This broadening is due to the fact that in the chain of processes between the interaction of a photon with a scintillator and the occurrence of a current pulse there are stages in which the number of particles (electrons or photons) is so small that statistical deviations (see Section 2.21) must result. Such stages include the emission of photons in the scintillation process and the events at the first dynodes in the multiplier. A further factor causing broadening of the photopeaks is the fact that scintillations produced in various parts of one and the same scintillator are not registered with exactly equal efficiencies by the photomultiplier.

3.6. Photographic Detection Methods

The blackening of a photographic plate was the phenomenon that led in 1896 to the discovery of radioactivity by Becquerel. Photographic detection methods received considerable impetus from 1945 onwards, when it became possible to prepare emulsions containing 80 per cent or more of silver bromide. In such "nuclear emulsions" little radiation energy is lost by absorption in the gelatine, and the tracks of individual ionizing particles such as α-particles can be recorded clearly (Fig. 18).

The measurement of radioactivity by means of photographic effects may be applied both to (homogeneous) solutions and to materials possessing structure. For solutions, the measurement gives merely the concentration. For such a determination the emulsion is brought into contact with the solution in some convenient way, after a certain time (a few hours or days) it is developed and fixed, and either the total blackening is determined, e.g., photometrically, or the individual tracks are counted. Contact may be made with the emulsion either by allowing a drop of the solution to evaporate on the emulsion, or by immersing the emulsion for a few minutes in the solution to saturate the gelatine, and then drying the emulsion. It is also possible to fill thin glass capillaries with the active liquid and to pour the liquid emulsion over these. Such procedures are tedious and less accurate than measurements with electronic instruments, but counting the total number of individual tracks produced over a long period is an extremely sensitive method of detection. From the shape and the length of the tracks, radiations of different kinds and energies may be distinguished.

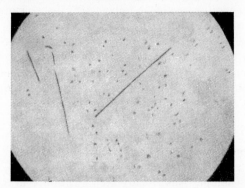

FIG. 18. Tracks of α-rays from thorium C′ in a photographic plate (magnification: 750×). (The weak tracks at the side are inclined to the plane of the picture, and are therefore only partially in focus)

The distribution of activity in solid bodies possessing structure may be determined by autoradiography. A smooth surface of the sample is pressed against the emulsion. Frequently a suitable thin film is interposed to prevent any chemical action of the

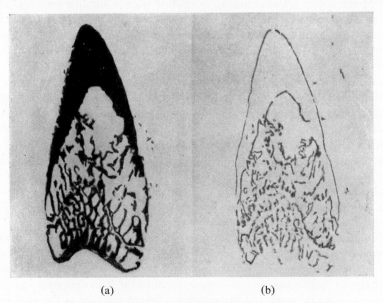

(a)   (b)

FIG. 19. (*a*) Photograph of a section through the thigh bone of a rat 1 week after injection of plutonium. Magnification: 10×
(*b*) Autoradiograph of the same section. Selective deposition of the radionuclide in certain portions of the tissue is clearly visible. Magnification: 10× [After J. HAMILTON, *Radiology* **49**, 325 (1947)]

sample. Polished surfaces of metals or minerals, or sections of living tissue are suitable samples. The distribution of blackening gives direct information as to the distribution of the radioactive substance in the sample (Fig. 19). Autoradiography will clearly give the best resolution when the rays have only short range, such as α-radiation or low energy β-radiation, like that from carbon-14 and tritium.

The radiation dose necessary for a given blackening may be reduced at least tenfold if a film of a suitable fluorescent material, such as zinc sulphide, is placed between the sample and the photographic film. The blackening is then not due directly to the ionizing radiation, but to the visible light emitted in the secondary process. Naturally the resolution is not as good as in the direct registration.

3.7. Preparation of Solid Samples

The preparation of samples has already been mentioned in connection with liquid counters. If liquid counters or gas counters cannot be used – this applies to most measurements – solid samples must be prepared in a reproducible manner. These samples are then placed under the window or the wall of a counting tube, or they are introduced into the tube. In all these cases accurate reproducibility of the position of the sample is required.

The simplest way to obtain solid samples is to take a drop of known volume of solution of the active material and to evaporate it on a suitable support, e.g., on a glass plate. Care must be taken that for all samples the drop is placed in the same position relative to the counting tube. This procedure is only suitable for solutions of high specific activity, for which a single drop contains a sufficient amount of the active material.

More often it will be necessary to concentrate the radioactive substance from a large volume of solution. The precipitation of radioactive phosphate ion in the form of $MgNH_4PO_4$ is an example. Precipitation is brought about by addition of a magnesium salt and ammonia to the phosphate solution, and the precipitate is then filtered off. In order to obtain suitable samples for counting, special filters are used (Fig. 20). It is seen that the filter paper rests on an interchangeable perforated metal plate. After filtration the precipitate together with supporting plate and paper is placed in a suitable holder, and is then brought into a reproducible position beneath the counting tube. Instead of filtration, centrifugation may be used; centrifuge tubes with interchangeable flat bottom parts are recommended.

The principal problem with solid samples is their thickness. Since the absorption of radiation in the sample itself (self-absorption) depends on its thickness (or better, on its area weight), a false result would be obtained for the amounts of radioelement present if the count rates measured on samples of different thickness were compared directly. It must also be noted that, in order to prevent changes in the area weight of samples, only dry and non-hygroscopic samples can be used.

Errors due to variation in self-absorption in thick layers can be avoided in various ways. Here suitable procedures for β-emitting samples which are most important in practice will be discussed. Samples thicker than the range of the β-particles may be used. In this case the lower part of the sample makes no contribution to the count rate, which is therefore independent of the thickness. Another method is to maintain the thickness exactly constant, but this is rather difficult in practice. It is also possible to use different sample thicknesses, and then to correct to a standard value by means of a correction curve. Such curves have to be obtained for the particular working conditions, since they depend on the instrument, the geometrical arrangement, the ma-

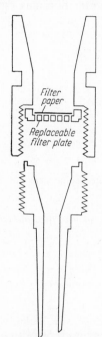

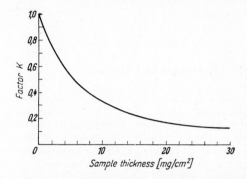

FIG. 21. Typical curve for correction for self-absorption (radionuclide: carbon-14; precipitate: barium carbonate; K: factor by which the measured count rate must be divided to obtain the count rate that would be found using the same amount of radionuclide in an infinitely thin layer)

FIG. 20. Special filter holder for radioactive precipitates

terial of the sample support, the radiation energy, etc. Figure 21 gives an example of such a correction curve.

An estimate of the self-absorption of β-rays may be obtained by using equation (2), page 21. For this purpose, the absorption coefficient is replaced by the self-absorption coefficient. This has a value of about half that of the absorption coefficient, as has been shown both by experiments and by approximate calculations.

On the basis of equation (2) it can, for example, be shown that for the β-radiation of radiophosphorus (^{32}P) and an area weight of the sample of 15 mg/cm² a self-absorption loss of about 5 per cent will occur. With β-radiation from radiocarbon (^{14}C) this fraction is lost at a sample thickness of only 0·4 mg/cm². For the β-rays from ^{14}C the absorption in the counter window and the self-absorption in the sample are so strong that only low counting efficiencies are obtained with end-window counters. Somewhat better efficiencies are obtained when solid samples are measured with a flow counter. If high yields in the determinations of ^{14}C are needed, a gas counter, e. g., with carbon dioxide as the filling gas, or a liquid scintillation counter must be used.

T.A.R. 4

α-radiation is absorbed within the samples so strongly that reproducible results can be obtained in practice only by working either with very thin or with very thick layers. Thin layers for such measurements must be still thinner than in the case of most β-radiations.

Self-absorption of γ-radiation is usually small. For example, it can be shown that a self-absorption loss of 5 per cent for the γ-radiation of cobalt-60 occurs in a sample with an area weight of about 2 g/cm². The self-absorption of γ-radiation may therefore often be neglected.

General References to Chapter 3

C.G.BELL and F.N.HAYES (Ed.), *Liquid Scintillation Counting*, London 1950.

J.B.BIRKS, *The Theory and Practice of Scintillation Counting*, Oxford 1965.

G.A.BOYD, *Autoradiography in Biology and Medicine*, New York 1955.

G.D.CHASE and J.L.RABINOWITZ, *Principles of Radioisotope Methodology*, Minneapolis 1962.

G.B.COOK and J.F.DUNCAN, *Modern Radiochemical Practice*, Oxford 1952.

C.E.CROUTHAMEL (Ed.), *Applied γ-ray Spectrometry*, London 1960.

P.DEMERS, *Ionographie*, Montreal 1958. (Describing the application of photographic measuring methods in nuclear science.)

R.A.FAIRES and B.H.PARKS, *Radioisotope Laboratory Techniques*, London 1958.

G.E.FRANCIS, W.MULLIGAN and A.WORMALL, *Isotopic Tracers. A Theoretical and Practical Manual for Biological Students and Research Workers*, London 1959.

G.FRIEDLANDER, J.W.KENNEDY and J.M.MILLER, *Nuclear and Radiochemistry*, New York 1964.

E.FÜNFER and H.NEUERT, *Zählrohre und Szintillationszähler*, Karlsruhe 1959.

D.HALLIDAY, *Introductory Nuclear Physics*, New York 1955.

E.HARBERS, Autoradiographie, in: H.SCHWIEGK and F.TURBA (Ed.), *Künstlich radioaktive Isotope in Physiologie, Diagnostik und Therapie*, Berlin 1961.

W.HARTMANN and F.BERNHARD, *Fotovervielfacher*, Berlin 1957.

L.HERFORTH and H.KOCH, *Radiophysikalisches und radiochemisches Grundpraktikum*, Berlin 1961.

G.HERMANN, *Die einzelnen Isotope und die Besonderheiten ihrer Bestimmung* in: H.SCHWIEGK and F.TURBA, *vide supra*.

I.KAPLAN, *Nuclear Physics*, Reading, Mass. 1955.

B.KARLIK, T.BERNERT and K.LINTNER, Messung radioaktiver Strahlen in der Mikrochemie, in: F.HECHT and M.ZACHERL (Ed.), *Handbuch der mikrochemischen Methoden*, vol.2, Vienna 1955.

J.KOHL, R.D.ZENTNER and H.R.LUKENS, *Radioisotope Applications Engineering*, Princeton 1961.

S.A.KORFF, *Electron and Nuclear Counters*, New York 1955.

H.LAUDA, *Photographische Methoden in der Radiochemie*, in: F.HECHT and M.ZACHERL (Ed.), *vide supra*.

G.W.O'KELLEY, *Detection and Measurement of Nuclear Radiation*, Nuclear Science Series, National Academy of Sciences, National Research Council NAS-NS 3105, Washington 1962.

R.T.OVERMAN and H.M.CLARK, *Radioisotope Techniques*, New York 1960.

W.J.PRICE, *Nuclear Radiation Detection*, New York 1958.

E.RAPKIN, *Liquid Scintillation Counting 1957–1963* (Review), *Int. J. Appl. Rad. Isot.* **15**, 69 (1964).

K.SCHMEISER, *Radionuclide*, Berlin 1963.

J.SHARPE, *Nuclear Radiation Detectors*, London 1964.

D.TAYLOR, *The Measurement of Radioisotopes*, New York 1958.

C.C.H.WASHTELL, *Radiation Counters and Detectors*, London 1958.

C.F.WEISS, G.BRUNNER and M.LEISTNER, *Radioaktive Standardpräparate. Eigenschaften, Herstellung und Aktivitätsmessung*, Leipzig 1962.

D.WEST, Energy Measurements with Proportional Counters, in: O.R.FRISCH (Ed.), *Progr. Nucl. Phys.*, vol. 3 (1953).

W. J. WHITEHOUSE and J. L. PUTMAN, *Radioactive Isotopes*, Oxford 1953.
H. YAGODA, *Radioactive Measurements with Nuclear Emulsions*, New York 1949.

Literature on the Measurement of Radiocarbon and Tritium

E. BRODA, T. SCHÖNFELD, Radiochemische Methoden der Mikrochemie, in F. HECHT, M. ZACHERL (Ed.), *Handbuch der Mikrochemischen Methoden*, vol. 2, Vienna 1955.
E. BRODA and B. KALAB, Die empfindliche Serienbestimmung von Radiokohlenstoff mit dem Gaszählrohr, *Mikrochimica Acta*, **1962**, 128.
M. CALVIN, C. HEIDELBERGER, J. C. REID, B. TOLBERT and P. F. YANKWICH, *Isotopic Carbon*, New York 1949.
J. R. CATCH, *Carbon-14 Compounds*, London 1961.
F. DRAWERT and O. BACHMANN, Neuere Methoden zur Trennung und kontinuierlichen Messung von ^{14}C-Verbindungen in der Gasphase, *Angew. Chem.* **75**, 717 (1963).
R. F. GLASCOCK, *Isotopic Gas Analysis for Biochemists*, London 1955.
A. T. JAMES and E. A. PIPER, A Compact Radiochemical Gas Chromotograph, *Anal. Chem.* **35**, 515 (1963).
E. RAPKIN, Messung mit flüssigen Szintillatoren, *Atomwirtschaft* **7**, 508 (1962).
E. SCHRAM, *Organic Scintillation Detectors*, Amsterdam 1962.
H. SIMON and F. BERTHOLD, Die Messung weicher Beta-Strahlen in der Gasphase, *Atomwirtschaft* **7**, 498 (1962).
W. G. VERLY, *Tritium: Dosage, préparation de molécules marquées et applications biologiques*, I. A. E. A., Vienna 1960.
F. WEYGAND, Isotope in der organischen Chemie, *Naturwiss.* **44**, 169 (1957).
ANONYMOUS: Tritium Tracing — a Rediscovery, *Nucleonics* **16** (3), 62 (1958).
Tritium in the Physical and Biological Sciences (Proceedings of a Symposium, Vienna, 3–10 May 1961), I. A. E. A., Vienna 1962.

4. THE PRODUCTION AND CHEMISTRY
OF RADIOELEMENTS

4.1. Production of Radionuclides

The choice of a radionuclide for a particular purpose is governed by physical factors (the half-life, the nature and the energy of radiation), and, for use as tracer, also by chemical factors. The cost, which depends primarily upon the method of production and the production yield, must be taken into account as well. In industry, artificial radionuclides are much more often employed than natural radionuclides. Nuclides obtained in accelerators are usually very much more expensive than those obtained from reactors. A list of radionuclides important as tracers is given in Appendix 1. Radiation sources used for the measurement of thickness and for the utilization of radiation effects are discussed in Volume 2.

In the production of a specific nuclide, the material to be irradiated must of course be free from impurities which would give radioactive substances on irradiation. If such impurities cannot be entirely excluded, the irradiation may be limited to so short a time that undesirable long-lived products are formed in small amounts only. Interfering short-lived products, on the other hand, may be allowed to disappear by decay before the material is used. In the same way one can discriminate between radionuclides formed from different isotopes of the same element.

In the production of artificial radionuclides usually the natural elements or their compounds are irradiated, but higher specific activities are obtained when pure isotopes are used. In this way, the production of unwanted radionuclides from accompanying isotopes is also eliminated. For example, calcium-45 produced from the pure isotope calcium-44 is 50 times as active as that obtained from the natural element, of which this isotope constitutes only 2 per cent. However, the separation of isotopes, which is generally carried out by an electromagnetic process, is expensive.

The nuclear reactor is nowadays the most important source of radionuclides. Primarily the slow neutrons are utilized. Most often the (n, γ) reaction, called "radiative neutron capture", is employed (see p. 16). The fast neutrons of reactors are also sometimes utilized, for instance, in the preparation of radiophosphorus by the reaction $^{32}_{16}S(n, p)^{32}_{15}P$. A large number of useful fission products are also obtained from reactors (see p. 17).

Because of their low intensities, natural neutron sources (see p. 85) are now little used. They may, however, still be useful in the production of very short-lived radionuclides.

Accelerators must be used when the desired nuclide cannot be made by reactions with neutrons. Thus long-lived sodium-22 is obtained by bombarding magnesium with deuterons, according to the reaction: $^{24}_{12}Mg(d, \alpha)^{22}_{11}Na$.

When a radionuclide is produced by radiative neutron capture, and is thus isotopic with the target element, its specific activity is relatively low. The attainable specific activities can be calculated from the information in Table 7 (p. 90) and Appendix 1. On the other hand, reactions in which the nuclear charge is altered lead to radionuclides of different chemical nature, and can thus be used to obtain nuclides practically carrier-free. The (n, p)- and (d, α)-reactions, as well as nuclear fission, are important in this respect. Radionuclides formed by β-decay of primary products of neutron capture can also be obtained carrier-free. An example of practical importance is the reaction chain

$$^{130}_{52}\text{Te}(n, \gamma) \, ^{131}_{52}\text{Te} \xrightarrow{\beta^-} \, ^{131}_{53}\text{I},$$

by which the most important radioisotope of iodine ($\tau = 8$ days) is prepared. Radionuclides which in practice can be obtained carrier-free (or nearly carrier-free) are indicated in Appendix 1.

(The term "carrier" denotes an inactive element or compound present in weighable amount which is identical in chemical properties with the radionuclide or compound, or closely similar to it. Identity of properties will, of course, exist when the inactive element is isotopic with the radionuclide.)

A number of radionuclides may be obtained nearly carrier-free even by radiative neutron capture. This applies when as a consequence of the neutron capture a relatively strong (covalent or complex) bond in the parent molecule is broken, and the activated atom is expelled from it, so that the chemical form of this atom is changed irreversibly. This is called the Szilard–Chalmers effect. An example is the irradiation of ethyl iodide ($C_2H_5{}^{127}I$). Here radioiodine (^{128}I, $\tau = 25$ min) appears partly in the form of free molecules or ions, which may then be separated from the ethyl iodide by shaking with dilute alkali.

4.2. General Aspects of Radiochemistry

Chemical separations and transformations of radioactive substances are often required. In principle, the radioactive isotopes behave chemically like the inactive isotopes of the element. But experimental work with them is distinguished by special features so that radiochemistry is properly regarded as a special branch of chemistry. Paneth has defined radiochemistry as the chemistry of substances which are detected through their (nuclear) radiations. Here we shall give a brief review of this field.

The high sensitivity of detection by means of radioactivity leads to stringent demands on the purity of the materials. A sample is said to be radioactively pure if it contains only a single radionuclide. Impurities which are present only in traces and have practically no effect on the chemical purity of a substance may nevertheless destroy its radioactive purity.

Hence, especially in the use of radioactive elements as tracers, determination of radioactive purity is often necessary. Such tests may be carried out by physical methods, e.g., by determining the half-life from a decay curve or by determining the energy of the radiation through spectrometric analysis or by means of absorbers. On the other hand, radioactive impurities may be detected by chemical methods when the impurities consist of foreign elements. The procedure is to perform suitable chemical separations (often after addition of carriers for the radioelement and for the suspected impurities), and then to determine the activities of the separated fractions. The removal of active impurities, consisting of foreign elements, can often be carried out in a manner analogous to this technique of radiochemical analysis.

Isotopic carriers, i.e., the inactive elements, have the general disadvantage that they cannot be removed subsequently so that the specific activity is permanently reduced ("isotopic dilution"). To avoid this, elements are used as carriers which are chemically similar to, but not identical with, the active substance; such carriers can later be removed through suitable chemical reactions. Whenever the addition of any carrier is unacceptable, special radiochemical methods are required; such carrier-free operations will be described later.

The removal of radioactive impurities can be dispensed with when the radioelement of interest and the impurities can be distinguished by means of radiation measurements. Thus it is often possible to suppress unwanted radiation with absorbers, or the intensity of a radiation which it is desired to measure may be determined as the difference between two measurements, one made with, and the other without the absorber. Short-lived impurities may simply be allowed to disintegrate before the measurements; on the other hand, a short-lived substance may be determined in the presence of long-lived impurities by taking measurements before and after the decay of the former, its activity then being obtained by difference.

In addition to "false" radioactive nuclides, "false" compounds of the correct radionuclide may also be a source of error in tracer applications. Thus a labelled detergent, whose distribution between water and an organic solvent is to be determined, may contain, from the process of preparation, a certain amount of a radioactive impurity, e.g., sulphate ion. The amount of such impurity may be small, and yet its contribution to the total radioactivity may be appreciable. In the experiment, such impurities will naturally behave quite differently from the detergent. Their presence can be determined radiochemically. Carriers are added, suitable separations are carried out and the distribution of the activity between the chemical fractions is determined.

The presence of non-radioactive impurities in the radioactive substance to be used for experimental work is a disturbing factor only if the impurities affect the system under investigation. The extent to which this applies depends on the nature of the investigation. In the measuring sample non-radioactive impurities interfere only if the self-absorption of the radiation is increased excessively.

It is a distinguishing feature of radiochemistry that the system is constantly subjected to ionizing radiation, which can produce chemical changes within it. Such effects are usually unimportant in work with radioactive tracers, where the activity employed is not higher than is necessary for convenient measurement, and the radiation intensity is thus kept below the levels at which measurable radiation-chemical effects arise.

Exceptions are systems where long reaction chains appear as a consequence of the primary radiation-chemical act, such as those containing organic substances capable of polymerization, and also certain biochemically important substances (for instance, proteins), in which a modification at one position within a giant molecule leads to a loss of their specific biological activities. For methods of detecting such effects, see Section 5.2.

Another special feature of radiochemistry is the consideration given to the time factor. For the preparation and separation of short-lived substances (for instance, formed in the course of activation analysis; Section 6.6) rapid working procedures must be developed. Such procedures also serve to suppress the undesired growth of daughter activities. Account must be taken of the change of activity with time in the evaluation of data as well. This may be done by using equations (8) or (9), or graphically.

A further important fact in radiochemistry is that radioactive elements, even of considerable activity, are often present in trace amounts only. Such traces may show a chemical behaviour quite different from that of weighable quantities. To avoid such differences, carriers may be added. Then it is possible to apply ordinary chemical procedures.

Thus in order to precipitate traces of radioiron in the form of the sulphide, inactive iron or manganese may be added to the solution as a carrier to give a visible and weighable precipitate. Iron and manganese may subsequently be separated, for example, by extracting the iron in the form of its chloride into an organic solvent.

Adsorption phenomena are particularly important in work with traces, since the amounts are small in relation to the size of the surface with which they come in contact and upon which adsorption may take place. Unless special measures are taken, serious losses may therefore occur by adsorption upon the walls of the vessels, the filter paper, or the precipitates. Such losses may be reduced by avoiding contact between the solution and surfaces of high adsorbing power, as well as with large surfaces of any kind.

More effective protection is provided by displacing the traces from the adsorption sites by means of weighable amounts of substances that are strongly adsorbed themselves. Such substances are rather loosely called "hold-back carriers". Thus the adsorption of radioiron on the walls of vessels may be suppressed by the addition of a large excess of inactive iron to the solution; then it is the inactive rather than the active iron which is adsorbed. If isotopic dilution must be avoided, we may use some other metal ion, such as manganese in the case here considered. Hydrogen ions also act as adsorption displacer so that the adsorption of cations may be reduced or suppressed by acidification.

4.3. Radiochemical Procedures

In the chemistry of inactive materials, especially in inorganic chemistry, precipitation reactions occupy a central position. In contrast, because of the complicated adsorption phenomena taking place on precipitates, in radiochemistry these procedures are increasingly avoided, and are replaced by procedures where adsorption is unimportant. These include distribution between immiscible solvents and electrochemical procedures. However, processes in which strong adsorption occurs may themselves be of great value for radiochemical separations provided the adsorption is under good experimental control, as is the case with adsorption on ion exchangers.

An example of separation with a pair of immiscible solvents is the ether extraction of iron or gallium from aqueous hydrochloric acid solution, whereby iron or gallium is taken up by the ether phase, while other cations, such as cobalt or manganese, remain in the aqueous phase. Generally, the distribution coefficient between the solvents is the same for traces as for small but weighable quantities. Another important example is the ether extraction of uranyl nitrate from aqueous solution; the uranyl nitrate is taken up by the ether phase, and the decay products of uranium and any fission products remain in the aqueous phase.

Particularly efficient extraction procedures have now been developed by using complexing agents. Thus vanadium may be separated quantitatively from chromium and manganese by extraction from potassium thiocyanate solution with methyl isobutyl ketone in the presence of oxine (β-hydroxyquinoline). The separation of uranium, plutonium and their fission products with phosphoric acid esters, especially tributyl phosphate in organic solvents, has become important. This type of separation by extraction is employed on an industrial scale for reprocessing uranium from reactors.

Procedures involving the electrochemical deposition of ions have been employed since the early days of research on radioactivity. The deposition may be carried out either with or without the use of an electrical current. In the latter case, the ions of a dissolved radioelement are allowed to deposit spontaneously on a foil or wire of a less noble metal, just as copper deposits on iron. Thus traces of radiobismuth may be deposited quantitatively on a nickel foil from solutions in hot dilute hydrochloric acid.

By employing a current, it is possible to bring about electrolytic deposition on the cathode or the anode. Many heavy metals may be deposited on a platinum sheet cathode as firmly adhering layers; a well-known case of anodic deposition is that of lead as lead dioxide from nitric acid solution. Trace amounts of radioelements may often be deposited quantitatively on a platinum foil without the appearance of any visible film.

Use can also be made of the evaporation of radioelements in the form of atoms or molecules. For example, traces of krypton and xenon may be separated by fractional condensation: xenon condenses at the temperature of an ice–salt freezing mixture while krypton requires the temperature of liquid air. Radioiodine may be distilled at slightly elevated temperatures. Many metals are volatile on heating. For example, traces of radiocadmium may be distilled from silver in which it has been formed by induced nuclear transformations.

Chromatography has proved very effective for radiochemical separations. Its main advantages are that sharp separations may be obtained, and that it is well applicable to small quantities. Column chromatography on ion exchange resins may be used for the quantitative resolution of mixtures of similar ions (such as those of the alkali elements) or of similar organic molecules (such as the amino acids). As in the distribution between immiscible solvents, the laws governing separations on ion exchange resins are substantially independent of the absolute amounts, so that procedures developed for traces may be directly applied to small but weighable quantities, and vice versa. An example of the efficiency of ion exchange chromatography is the separation of radioactive rare earths, shown in Fig. 22. Fraction collectors have now been so far developed that the radioactivity of the individual fractions of eluates can be registered automatically. The gas obtained in gas–liquid chromatography may be measured continuously (pp. 43 and 44).

Some of these advantages apply to paper chromatography, which serves to separate small amounts of metallic ions or organic compounds. Figure 23 shows a radio-

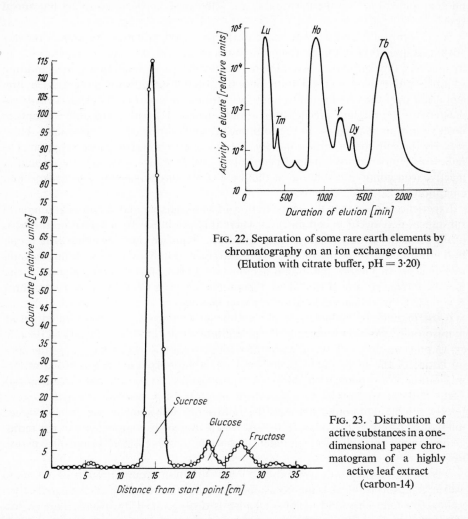

FIG. 22. Separation of some rare earth elements by chromatography on an ion exchange column (Elution with citrate buffer, pH = 3·20)

FIG. 23. Distribution of active substances in a one-dimensional paper chromatogram of a highly active leaf extract (carbon-14)

chromatogram obtained in the authors' laboratory with a mixture of radioactive glucose, fructose and sucrose. The mixture had been prepared by photosynthesis in leaves using radioactive carbon dioxide, extraction of the leaves and removal of the ionized substances with ion exchangers. The total quantity of sugars was only a few tenths of a milligram. The radiochromatogram was obtained by moving a window counter step by step along the paper with the radioactive substances, and measuring the activities. Equipment for continuous scanning of paper chromatograms is now available commercially.

The position of substances can also be determined by autoradiography (see Section 3.6). This procedure does not directly give a quantitative measure of the activity, but it is labour saving, especially for the location of substances in two-dimensional paper chromatography. The paper is simply pressed against a suitable photographic film, and the position of the substances is then shown by blackened spots.

Some mention must finally be made of the use of precipitation. In spite of the disadvantages mentioned it finds numerous applications in radiochemical separations. In many cases, the concentrations of the radioelements are so small that simple addition of a precipitant gives no precipitate, since the solubility product is not exceeded. Precipitation may then be brought about by addition of a carrier. Thus, as already indicated, for the sulphide precipitation of radioiron we may add weighable amounts of inactive iron or manganese to the solution before addition of the precipitant. Alternatively the solution of radioiron may be treated with preformed iron sulphide. The radioiron enters the precipitate, an equivalent but, of course, unweighable amount of inactive iron going into solution at the same time. This process may be called "precipitation by isotopic exchange".

Experience shows that the precipitation of unweighable and invisible amounts of substances may occur in certain cases where this would not be expected on the basis of the solubility products given in the literature. Thus we can precipitate pure radiobismuth (radium E) with ammonia from extremely dilute solutions without the addition of a carrier. The precipitation is demonstrated by the fact that the active substance may be filtered or centrifuged. This phenomenon is called "radiocolloid formation". A complete theoretical explanation is as yet lacking.

A useful guide for judging whether a radioactive element is coprecipitated with a non-isotopic carrier is provided by the precipitation rules of Fajans, Hahn and Paneth: (1) Coprecipitation will occur when the radioactive ion is incorporated into the crystal lattice of the precipitate, i.e., in the case of isomorphism. The well-known coprecipitation of radium with salts of barium is an example. (2) Coprecipitation will occur without isomorphism when there is a tendency towards formation of a poorly soluble compound between the radioactive ion and the oppositely charged ion (counter-ion) in the precipitate, i.e., when the corresponding salt of the radioactive ion would itself be precipitated if the ion were present in weighable quantities.

It is supposed that in the second case coprecipitation occurs through a kind of ion exchange adsorption, with the occasional replacement of an ion of the carrier by a radioactive ion. This kind of ion exchange is distinguished by strong, more or less specific interaction between the radioactive ion and the counter-ions. The strength of this interaction is indicated by the low solubility of the salt when present in weighable quantity, and leads to strong coprecipitation.

Other factors besides low solubility also play a part, as has been shown in particular by Hahn. Thus anions are adsorbed better by a positively charged than by a negatively charged precipitate, and vice versa. A positive or negative excess charge is found on the precipitate when the precipitation was carried out with an excess of the cation or the anion, respectively. Thus silver nitrate reacting with an excess of sodium chloride gives negatively charged silver chloride, while with silver nitrate in excess the precipitate is positively charged.

A well-studied example of coprecipitation by adsorption is the following. Although isomorphism is absent, radiolead is efficiently coprecipitated on silver bromide, because lead bromide is itself only slightly soluble. Coprecipitation is especially efficient when the silver bromide is obtained with excess bromide ions. On the other hand, radium ions are only slightly coprecipitated with silver bromide, since radium bromide is very soluble.

The precipitation rules should, of course, be applied not only when coprecipitation is desired, but also when it is to be avoided, that is, when accompanying substances are to be removed from the solution, and the coprecipitation of the radioactive substances is to be prevented.

4.4. Radiosyntheses

"Radiosynthesis" is a term used for the synthesis of chemical substances containing radioactive atoms. Even when based on ordinary synthetic methods, radiosynthesis shows certain peculiarities.

Firstly, the possibility of "radioisomerism" must be considered. Thus, while normal organic chemistry knows only one type of acetic acid molecule, four types of "radioisomeric" acetic acid molecules are possible with radiocarbon

$$CH_3COOH \quad *CH_3COOH \quad CH_3*COOH \quad *CH_3*COOH$$

(radioactive carbon being designated by $*C$). In chemical reactions (such as metabolic transformations within the animal body) these different kinds of acetic acid will often give different products, distinguished by their differing radiocarbon contents. In radiosynthesis the location of the active atoms in the molecules is therefore important.

Secondly, economic considerations make it desirable to radiosynthesize with small quantities of active material, while addition of inactive carrier must be limited in order to avoid excessive reduction in specific activity. Consequently, radiosynthesis is often carried out on a milligram scale. For such work special equipment permitting the transfer of substances from one reaction vessel to another without appreciable loss may be required. For the synthesis of organic materials it is best to use closed systems in which the reactants and products may be transferred by distillation under a high vacuum.

Thirdly, that route of synthesis will be chosen which involves as little loss of radioactive material as possible, even if this route has disadvantages in other respects. In this connection it is generally advisable to introduce the radioactive component at the latest possible stage in the synthesis, so that the yield of radiocarbon in the final product is as high as possible.

An example of a synthesis carried out in an unusual way is the preparation of labelled phenanthrene from inactive fluorene:

$(C_6H_5)_3CNa$

Na

*COOH

*CH₂OH

*CO₂   LiAlH₄   P₂O₅

*

Complicated natural compounds can often be obtained by biosynthesis. Relatively simple labelled substances, such as carbon dioxide or acetic acid, are supplied to a living organism and the labelled atoms are then incorporated into complicated compounds through metabolic processes. The preparation of labelled sugars by photosynthesis is an important example. Green leaves or algae are supplied with radioactive carbon dioxide under the influence of light, and the sugars are subsequently extracted and purified in a multistage process (see p. 57). Radiobiosynthetic compounds are often "generally labelled", i.e., radioactive atoms appear in all positions. In "uniformly labelled" compounds, the specific activity of the radioactive element is the same in all positions. Chambers for the growth of green plants in an atmosphere containing radioactive carbon dioxide will be mentioned on p. 267.

In addition to radiosynthetic procedures that are modifications of ordinary chemical methods, specific radiochemical syntheses exist which have no counterpart in ordinary chemistry. In one group of such procedures, the preformed inactive molecule is made to undergo exchange with a radioactive substance, an inactive atom being replaced by a chemically equivalent radioactive atom. Such exchange reactions are only useful if they are not reversed under the conditions under which the labelled molecule is to be employed. For instance, labelling by exchange may be carried out at elevated temperatures or in the presence of a catalyst. An example is the catalytic introduction of radiochlorine from aluminium chloride into various alkyl chlorides.

The introduction of tritium into compounds can be induced by ionizing radiations or electrical discharges. In the Wilzbach process, the substance (usually organic) to be labelled (the substrate) is kept for a few hours or days in intimate contact with tritium gas of high activity. This leads to replacement of some of the inactive hydrogen of the substance by tritium. This is due to the β-radiation from the tritium gas which acts upon the substrate and the tritium gas itself, and excites or ionizes them.

The process is much accelerated if an electrical discharge is passed through the tritium-containing gas, and it is then possible to operate with a much smaller amount of tritium. Solid substrates for tritiation may be deposited in thin layers on one of the electrodes.

Since in the Wilzbach and in the related gas-discharge processes labelled by-products are also formed, careful separation and purity control are necessary after irradiation. Furthermore, before using the labelled substance any of the tritium introduced which is easily exchanged must be replaced by inactive hydrogen.

Such methods have been used, for example, for labelling proteins and pharmaceuticals. The yield is often very good, and comparatively high specific activities may be obtained. A disadvantage is that labelling is non-specific, that is, it does not take place at definite positions in the molecules.

Radiation-chemical formation of new compounds can also be used for radiosynthesis. Through irradiation of a mixture of benzene vapour and labelled carbon dioxide by means of admixed active krypton-85, labelled benzoic acid has been made. Up to 98 per cent of the radiocarbon taken up was found in the carboxyl groups. A gas discharge may be applied in this type of radiosynthesis as well.

Another group of syntheses ("recoil synthesis") employs the energy imparted to atoms in nuclear reactions to introduce these "hot atoms" into molecules. Thus, radiocarbon atoms that are formed according to the reaction $^{14}_{7}N(n, p)\, ^{14}_{6}C$ in the reactor irradiation of aniline with slow neutrons are introduced directly with good yield into admixed molecules of pentane. This synthesis of radiopentane is simpler than any other. Labelling with tritium may be performed similarly, using the nuclear reactions $^{6}Li(n, \alpha)\, ^{3}H$ or $^{3}He(n, p)\, ^{3}H$. In the first case, the compounds are usually irradiated after addition of lithium salts in suspension or in solution.

Hot atoms may also be produced in neutron capture processes. The recoil energy of the product atoms, which is due to the photon emission in the (n, γ)-reactions, can push these atoms into neighbouring molecules. In procedures of this kind, which can be regarded as an application of the Szilard–Chalmers effect (see p. 53), practically carrier-free labelled compounds may be produced. Thus in the irradiation of a solution of iodine in benzene with neutrons, labelled iodobenzene of very high specific activity is made.

Care must be taken during storage to prevent or reduce the decomposition of labelled compounds due to self-irradiation. The presence of radioactive decomposition products may lead to wrong results when the labelled material is used. It is recommended to store labelled organic materials in the form of solutions in inert solvents or in thin layers, to keep the temperature low, and to exclude oxygen.

General References to Chapter 4

A. *General Radiochemistry, Especially of Inorganic Substances*

J.P.ADLOFF, Gas Chromatography of Radioactive Substances, *Chromatographic Reviews*, vol. 4 (1961).

S.ARONOFF, *Techniques of Radiobiochemistry*, Ames (Iowa) 1956.

R.A.BAILEY, *Paper Chromatography and Electromigration Techniques in Radiochemistry*, Nuclear Science Series, National Academy of Sciences, National Research Council, NAS-NS 3106, Washington 1962.

N.A.BONNER and M.KAHN, The Behaviour of Carrier-free Tracers (in: A.C.WAHL and N.A.BONNER (Ed.), *Radioactivity Applied to Chemistry*), New York 1951.

N.E.BREZHNEVA and S.N.OZIRANER, *Radioactive Isotopes and their Production under Neutron Irradiation*, Vienna 1961.

E.BRODA and T.SCHÖNFELD, Radiochemische Methoden der Mikrochemie, in: F.HECHT and M.K. ZACHERL (Ed.), *Handbuch der mikrochemischen Methoden*, vol. 2, Vienna 1955.

A.I.BRODSKI, *Isotope Chemistry* (Russ.), Moscow 1957; German translation: *Isotopenchemie*, Berlin 1961.

G.D.CHASE and J.L.RABINOWITZ, *Principles of Radioisotope Methodology*, Minneapolis 1962.

G.B.COOK and J.F.DUNCAN, *Modern Radiochemical Practice*, Oxford 1952.

G.B.COOK and H.SELIGMAN, Chemical Treatment of Isotopes Produced in a Nuclear Reactor, *Fortschr. chem. Forsch.* **3**, 411 (1955).

H.L.FINSTON and J.MISKEL, Radiochemical Separation Techniques, *Ann. Rev. Nucl. Sci.* **5**, 269 (1955).

H.FREISER and G.H.MORRISON, Solvent Extractions in Radiochemical Separations, *Ann. Rev. Nucl. Sci.* **9**, 221 (1959).

W.M.GARRISON and J.G.HAMILTON, Production and Isolation of Carrier-free Radioisotopes, *Chem. Rev.* **49**, 237 (1951).

I.J.GRUVERMAN and P.KRUGER, Cyclotron-produced Carrier-free Isotopes, *Int. J. Appl. Rad. Isot.* **5**, 21 (1959).

O.HAHN, *Applied Radiochemistry*, New York 1936.

M.HAISSINSKY, *Les radiocolloides*, Paris 1934.

M.HAISSINSKY, *Electrochimie des substances radioactives*, Paris 1949.

M.HAISSINSKY, *La chimie nucléaire et ses applications*, Paris 1957; *Nuclear Chemistry and its Applications*, Reading, Mass. 1964.

M.HAISSINSKY and J.P.ADLOFF, *Radiochemical Survey of the Elements*, Amsterdam 1965.

R.N.HERBER (Ed.), *Inorganic Isotopic Syntheses*, Amsterdam 1962.

J.KOHL, R.D.ZENTNER and H.R.LUKENS, *Radioisotope Applications Engineering*, Princeton 1961.

K.A.KRAUS and F.NELSON, Radiochemical Separation by Ion Exchange, *Ann. Rev. Nucl. Sci.* **7**, 31 (1957).

R.LINDNER, *Kern- und Radiochemie*, Berlin 1961.

H.A.C.McKAY, The Szilard–Chalmers Process, in: O.R.FRISCH (Ed.), *Progr. Nucl. Phys.*, vol. 1 (1950).

Y.KUSAKA and W.W.MEINKE, *Rapid Radiochemical Separation*, Nuclear Science Series, National Academy of Sciences, National Research Council, NAS-NS 3104, Washington 1962.

N.B.MIKHEEV and V.I.SPITSYN, Application of Co-crystallization and Adsorption in the Solution of Current Problems of Radiochemistry, *Atomic Energy Review* **3** (4), 3 (1965).

A.N.MURIN, V.D.NEVEDOV and I.A.YUTLANDOV, *The Production and Isolation of Carrier-free Radioactive Isotopes*, *Uspekhi Khim.* **24**, 527 (1955); English translation: AERE Lib/trans 722 (1956).

AN.N.NESMEYANOV, V.I.BARANOV, K.B.SABORENKO, N.P.RUDENKO, YU.A.PRISELKOV, *Handbook of Radiochemical Exercises* (Russ.), Moscow 1956; (Engl.), London 1964.

R.T.OVERMAN and H.M.CLARK, *Radioisotope Techniques*, New York 1960.

S.Z.ROGINSKI, *Theoretical Foundations of Isotopic Methods for the Investigation of Chemical Reactions* (Russ.), Moscow 1956; German translation: *Theoretische Grundlagen der Isotopenchemie*, Berlin 1963.

A.F.RUPP, Production of Radioisotopes, *J. Appl. Physics* **24**, 1069 (1953); Geneva Report 314 (1955), vol. 14, p. 68.

I.E.STARIK, *Principles of Radiochemistry* (Russ.), Moscow 1959; English translation, Washington 1964.

W.J.WHITEHOUSE and J.L.PUTMAN, *Radioactive Isotopes*, Oxford 1953.

The Subcommittee on Radiochemistry of the U.S. National Research Council is sponsoring a series of monographs on the radiochemistry of the elements. All elements will be covered in this series except hydrogen, helium, lithium and boron.

B. *The Synthesis of Labelled Organic Compounds (Radiosynthesis)*

H.R.V.ARNSTEIN, The Preparation and Use of Isotopically Labelled Organic Compounds, in: E.H.RODD (Ed.), *Chemistry of Carbon Compounds*, Amsterdam 1962.

R.J.BAYLY and H.WEIGEL, Self-decomposition of Compounds Labelled with Radioactive Isotopes, *Nature* **188**, 384 (1960).

M. CALVIN, C. HEIDELBERGER, J. C. REID, B. M. TOLBERT and P. F. YANKWICH, *Isotopic Carbon*, New York 1949.

J. R. CATCH, *Carbon-14 Compounds*, London 1961.

E. A. EVANS and F. G. STANFORD, Decomposition of Tritium-Labelled Organic Compounds, *Nature* **197,** 551 (1963).

G. E. FRANCIS, W. MULLIGAN and A. WORMALL, *Isotopic Tracers, A Theoretical and Practical Manual for Biological Students and Research Workers*, London 1959.

J. L. GARNETT, Catalytic Tritium Labelling Attractive for Organics, *Nucleonics* **20** (12), 86 (1962).

H. GRISEBACH, Darstellung isotop markierter Verbindungen, in: H. SCHWIEGK and F. TURBA (Ed.), *Künstlich radioaktive Isotope*, Berlin 1961.

H. A. C. MCKAY, The Szilard–Chalmers Process, in: O. R. FRISCH (Ed.), *Progr. Nucl. Phys.*, vol. 1 (1950).

A. MURRAY and D. L. WILLIAMS, *Organic Syntheses with Isotopes*, vols. 1 and 2, New York 1958.

A. QUARINO and P. A. OSINSKI (Ed.), *Conference on Methods of Preparing and Storing Marked Molecules*, Brussels 1963.

J. SIRCHIS (Ed.), *Preparation and Bio-medical Application of Labelled Molecules*, Brussels 1964.

B. M. TOLBERT, Self-Destruction in Radioactive Compounds, *Nucleonics* **18** (8), 74 (1960).

M. WENZEL and P. E. SCHULZE, *Tritium-Markierung*, Berlin 1962.

F. WEYGAND and H. SIMON, Herstellung isotopenhaltiger organischer Verbindungen, in: *Methoden der organischen Chemie (Houben-Weyl)*, vol. 4/2, Stuttgart 1955.

M. L. WHISMAN and B. H. ECCLESTON, Gas-Exposure Labelling of Organics with Tritium, *Nucleonics* **20** (6), 98 (1962).

A. P. WOLF, Labelling of Organic Compounds by Recoil Methods, *Ann. Rev. Nucl. Sci.* **10,** 259 (1960).

N. H. WOODRUFF and E. E. FOWLER, Biological Syntheses of Radioisotope-labelled Compounds, *Nucleonics* **7** (2), 26 (1950).

The Stability of Labelled Organic Compounds, Booklet Issued by Radiochemical Centre, Amersham 1965.

5. THE RADIOACTIVE TRACER METHOD

5.1. General Characteristics of the Tracer Method

Many applications of radioactivity make use of the tracer (indicator) method. In this method the radiation serves only to detect and measure the radioelements, and not to induce chemical or physical changes in materials.

The widespread application of radioactive nuclides as tracers is to be attributed both to their versatility and to the ease with which they may be applied in laboratories and plants. It is an important feature of these applications that only small amounts of the active elements are required, so that radiation protection can be provided quite simply. In this section we shall discuss the general characteristics of the tracer method.

The tracer method employs radioactivity as a means of identifying atoms, molecules or larger objects, which for this purpose must be radioactively "indicated" or "labelled" ("tagged"). The manner of labelling depends on the nature of the problem. In many cases chemical labelling is necessary, while to larger objects the radioelement may simply be attached mechanically.

As far as chemical labelling is concerned, the chemical near-identity of active and inactive isotopes has already been emphasized; disturbing isotope effects arise only rarely. An element may therefore be labelled by adding an active isotope, and its behaviour can then be determined by radiation measurements; no separation of active and inactive components will occur during any process. Chemical labelling can often be accomplished by simply mixing together active and inactive atoms. In other cases it may be necessary to incorporate the radioelement into the molecules by radiosynthesis.

One of the important advantages of the tracer method is its extreme sensitivity. Quantities as small as a few atoms may be determined, provided the radiation from their disintegration enters the sensitive space of a detection instrument. Other conditions being the same, the greater the disintegration constant, or the smaller the half-life, the greater the sensitivity expressed in terms of the number of atoms or gram-atoms.

In Table 5 are listed the quantities of radionuclides which can be determined with a rather simple instrument consisting of a Geiger counter (counting efficiency 10 per cent, background 20 counts/min) and accessory electronic equipment. If the rough assumption is made, as is frequently done, that satisfactory quantitative determinations are still possible when the count rate due to the radioactive substance equals the background count rate, a sensitivity of about 10^{-10} curie is calculated for such an instrument. With special equipment (including good shielding and anti-coincidence circuitry) much lower activities can be measured, for instance, 10^{-12} c of β-emitters.

The sensitivity of detection of a given labelled element or compound depends, of course, on the ratio of the number of active atoms to the total number of atoms of the labelled element, i.e., on the specific activity.

TABLE 5. DETECTION LIMITS OF RADIONUCLIDES (FOR AN ACTIVITY DETECTION LIMIT OF 10^{-10} CURIE)

Half-life of the radionuclide	Detection limit	
	Atoms	g-atoms
1 hour	2×10^4	3×10^{-20}
1 day	5×10^5	8×10^{-19}
1 month	$1 \cdot 4 \times 10^7$	2×10^{-17}
1 year	$1 \cdot 7 \times 10^8$	3×10^{-16}
1000 years	$1 \cdot 7 \times 10^{11}$	3×10^{-13}

The high sensitivity reached with radioactive tracers permits the application of the method where other methods fail. In the first application of the indicator method ever made this high sensitivity was also used. The solubility of the sparingly soluble salts lead chromate and lead sulphide was determined in the Vienna Radium Institute in 1913. Hevesy and Paneth* measured the activity of saturated solutions of the labelled salts. Although the labelled lead was present in the solution in unweighable quantities, the concentration could be calculated from the activity of the solution on the basis of the known specific activity of the lead. The values obtained for the solubilities in water were $1 \cdot 2 \times 10^{-5}$ g/l. for lead chromate, and 3×10^{-4} g/l. for lead sulphide.

As we have already mentioned, labelling is not restricted to atoms but may be applied to particles of practically any size. The application of the method to molecules may be illustrated by the following example. The adsorption of glucose from various solvents by charcoal may be studied. The radioactive carbon atoms of the glucose do not exchange with those of the solvent or the adsorbent so that the specific activity of the glucose remains constant during the process. Therefore, the activity of the charcoal at any time during the adsorption process or after the establishment of adsorption equilibrium is a measure of the amount of glucose adsorbed.

In labelling larger objects, such as the scrapers used in oil pipe lines (see p. 152), or small animals such as worms or insects (p. 288), sensitivity in detection is less important. In these cases radioactivity is used mainly because simple and convenient detection and identification of the labelled objects is possible; the instrument may be placed at a considerable distance from the object, or may even be separated from it by rather thick walls.

Though the sensitivity, the simplicity and the absence of interference by foreign substances result in great practical advantages, these features of the radioactive tracer method do not offer anything fundamentally new when compared with other methods of detection. Substances might be detected by other methods, such as catalytic or biochemical methods, with greater sensitivity than by nuclear tracer methods.

* G. Hevesy and F. Paneth, *Z. anorg. Chem.* **82**, 323 (1913).

In one respect, however, the radioactive tracer method, and the isotope method in general, offer a unique possibility: distinction can be made between different atoms or molecules of the same chemical nature. An example of this is found in the second indicator experiment ever to be carried out.* In this experiment, the exchange of lead atoms between a solution of a lead salt and a lead metal plate was determined. Before commencing the experiment, the lead in one of the two phases was labelled with a radioactive indicator. As the experiment proceeded, the other phase became active by exchanging some of its inactive atoms for active atoms, although the quantity of lead in each phase necessarily remained unchanged. From the values of the activity and a knowledge of the original specific activity of the lead in the first phase the extent of the exchange could be computed.

In experiments of this kind, a distinction is made between chemically identical atoms, that is, between atoms of one and the same element. Hence the movement or transport of atoms may be followed even when atoms of the same kind are already present in the system under examination. The same principle can be extended to molecules, provided that the molecules are completely stable under the conditions used, and that the active atoms do not exchange with atoms in other molecules present. By labelling only particular atoms of a molecule (labelling in definite positions) information about the participation of individual atoms in a reaction, and hence about a reaction mechanism, may be gained (see Section 9.2).

On the basis of the distinction between labelled and non-labelled atoms of the same chemical species the transport of substances can be investigated in systems which are in a stationary state as far as their chemical composition is concerned. Such transport can be considered as "metabolism" in the widest possible sense of the word, thus including non-living systems. Phenomena such as the exchange of a substance between various coexistent phases or chemical states and self-diffusion come under the term metabolism when used in this wide sense.

Those applications of labelled atoms which depend only on the sensitivity of detection may be described as "analytical", while those which depend on the distinction between labelled and non-labelled atoms may be described as "kinetic". A distinction between the two types of application may be made by applying specific activity as the criterion. In the former case the specific activity of the labelled substance remains constant in space and time within the system considered, while in the latter this is not so. In many applications of the tracer method, which will be described in Chapters 6–12, both the principal advantages of the radioactive method, high sensitivity and the possibility of distinction between active and inactive atoms, are used simultaneously.

In certain circumstances tracer experiments may be carried out by non-isotopic labelling, that is, by employing radioactive substances which are similar to but not isotopic with the element under investigation (see p. 273).

---

* G. Hevesy, *Physik. Z.* **16,** 52 (1915).

5.2. Chemical Radiation Effects as a Disturbing Factor

In the application of the tracer method it is important to know whether the chemical process under investigation may be affected by radiation emitted by the radionuclide employed. Since the magnitude of radiation-chemical effects depends greatly on the nature of the system it is not possible to give a general answer on the basis of the radiation dose (see Section 2.18).

Nevertheless it is possible to state that in the vast majority of cases no appreciable radiation-chemical effects are to be expected for the radiation doses normally encountered in tracer experiments (a few hundred rad at the most). Exceptions may be found with systems where long chemical chain reactions take place, and with certain high-molecular substances from living matter, such as enzymes or nucleic acids (see p. 54).

It is often desirable to estimate the dose which will be delivered to a particular system through the introduction of a radioactive element. For β-radiation the absorbed dose can be estimated rather easily. It is assumed that the radioelement is uniformly distributed in the system, and that the radiation is completely absorbed, i.e., that the system is large compared with the range of the radiation. Then the approximate equation

$$D = 51AE/3v\varrho \tag{18}$$

holds, where A is the activity of the substance (curie), E is the maximum energy of the β-radiation (electron volt), v is the volume of the system (ml), ϱ the density, and D the dose rate (rad/day). The numerical factor 51 is for the conversion of electron volts into rad and seconds to days, while the factor $1/3$ is the approximate ratio of the mean energy to the maximum energy of the β-radiation. A numerical example is given in Section 11.3.2.

When the radioelement emits α-rays, the factor 3 in equation (18) must be omitted. For electromagnetic radiation (γ-radiation) this factor is also omitted; however, because of its great penetrating power γ-radiation is usually not absorbed completely, and the actual dose is smaller than that estimated on the basis of equation (18).

When there is doubt whether radiation-chemical effects are produced by the given radiation dose, an experimental test may be made. The radiation dose is increased, either by increasing the concentration of the radioelement in the system, or by exposing the system to γ-radiation from outside. Then it is determined whether any chemical alteration has occurred as compared with the system that was given the original (lower) dose.

5.3. The Emanation Method

A special investigation method, the emanation method, was first employed by Otto Hahn, and has been developed by his school. The isotopes of radium — radium-226 (ordinary radium), radium-224 (thorium X) and radium-223 (actinium X) – disintegrate with the formation of radioactive inert gases which are isotopes of the element emanation with the mass numbers 222, 220 and 219, respectively. These isotopes are called radon, thoron and actinon. Among these, actinon, because of its short half-life of only 4 sec, is not suitable for the emanation method.

When the parent nuclide of radon or thoron, radium-226 or thorium X, is enclosed in a solid body, only part of the emanation produced enters the surrounding gas and can then be measured there. The proportion of gas emerging depends on the chemical and physical condition of the system. Measurement of the emanating power of a system therefore provides information about its condition; changes in this property that occur as a consequence of a particular treatment of the material give information about the process taking place in the system. The method requires only simple equipment, it is sensitive, and it may be used to follow a system continuously.

The emanating power is defined as the percentage of the emanation that is released from the solid. It is determined by two different physical processes. The first of these is true diffusion of the emanation; we may distinguish between lattice and surface diffusion, depending on whether the diffusion occurs through the grains of the material or along the surface of these grains. The second process is recoil. In the formation of an emanation atom through α-particle emission from the parent nucleus, this atom receives kinetic recoil energy. Through interaction with surrounding matter this kinetic energy is rapidly lost, but the atom may first penetrate through the surface layer. The range of recoil atoms is of the order of 10^{-2} cm in air.

In technical applications it is usual to measure the dependence of the emanating power on the state of the system rather than the absolute value of the emanating power. The distinction between the contributions of diffusion and of recoil to emanating power may be useful. Two methods have been developed for this purpose. When the condition of the system is not expected to be altered significantly by a change in temperature, we may observe the temperature dependence of the emanating power. The recoil part is independent of temperature. In contrast, the velocity of diffusion increases with temperature, and as a consequence the probability that a radioactive atom penetrates the surface during its life-time is also increased. The temperature dependence of lattice diffusion is greater than that of surface diffusion so that the latter dominates at lower temperatures, and the former at higher temperatures. In the second method, the emanating power of a given substance is determined in parallel experiments with radium-226 and thorium X. Since thoron has only a short life, diffusion plays only a small part compared with the case of radon. The emanating power for thoron thus gives directly the recoil component; this component will have nearly the same value for both thoron and radon.

More recently, the emanation method has been extended to β-active isotopes of krypton and xenon. For the purpose, suitable isotopes of the parent elements bromine and iodine (e.g., iodine-133) are introduced into the materials to be tested.

A modification of the emanation method has been proposed, which is specially suitable for investigating changes in surface layers of solids. In this method the radioactive inert gas is not produced by disintegration of a parent substance, but is introduced into the surface layers by means of a gas discharge or by perfusion of the solid at high temperature (see p. 178). Investigations of this kind have been carried out with radon and with krypton-85. After the introduction of the active gas into the solid, its release may be observed under various conditions, for example as a function of changes in temperature, under the action of gases and vapours on the surface of the solid, or during mechanical wear.

For a comprehensive discussion of the emanation method and its applications, reference may be made to the appropriate literature, listed below. Selected applications are mentioned in Section 9.1.8.

General References to Chapter 5

A. *Characteristics and Variants of the Tracer Method*

See general references to Chapters 2 and 4.

B. *Emanation Method*

O.HAHN, *Z. Elektrochem.* **29**, 189 (1923).
O.HAHN, *Liebigs Ann. Chem.* **440**, 121 (1924).
O.HAHN, *Naturwiss.* **12**, 1140 (1924); **17**, 296 (1929).
O.HAHN, *Ber. dtsch. chem. Ges.* A **67**, 150 (1934).
O.HAHN, *J. Chem. Soc.* (*London*) **1949** (*Supplement* S), 259.
O.HAHN, *Applied Radioactivity*, New York 1936.
K.E.ZIMEN, *Z. Elektrochem.* **44**, 590 (1938).
S.FLÜGGE and K.E.ZIMEN, *Z. physik. Chem.* B **42**, 179 (1939).
K.E.ZIMEN, *Z. physik. Chem.* A **191**, 1, 95 (1942); A **192**, 1 (1943).
A.C.WAHL, in: A.C.WAHL and A.N.BONNER (Ed.), *Radioactivity Applied to Chemistry*, New York 1951.
H.SCHREINER, *Österr. Chemiker-Ztg.* **53**, 233 (1952).
Proc. Internat. Symposium on Reactivity of Solids, Göteborg 1952.
N.I.SHTEINBOK, *Uspekhi fyziki* **54**, 231 (1954).
D.CHLECK, R.MAEHL and O.CUCCHIARA, *Nucleonics* **21** (7), 53 (1963).
D.CHLECK, R.MAEHL, O.CUCCHIARA and E.CARNEVALE, *Int. J. Appl. Rad. Isot.* **14**, 581, 593, 599 (1963).
(The papers by CHLECK *et al.* concern introduction of radiokrypton.)

6. APPLICATION OF RADIOACTIVITY
IN CHEMICAL ANALYSIS

6.1. Survey of the Types of Application

The great significance of radioactivity for chemical analysis is primarily due to the advantages of the tracer method. Among these are the sensitivity, the possibility of distinction between labelled and non-labelled atoms and molecules, the rapidity and the simplicity of procedures, and the frequent possibility of non-destructive measurement [1, 2, 3, 248, 350, 351, 369, 371].

Research into radioactivity soon revealed the high sensitivity of activity measurements in detecting naturally radioactive substances. Determination of short-lived natural radionuclides (such as actinium or polonium) cannot in practice be performed by any other method than by radiation measurement. For long-lived natural radio-elements (such as uranium, thorium and potassium), radiation measurement is less sensitive than available chemical methods, but even for such elements the simplicity and rapidity of radiochemical determinations afford considerable advantages. Some radiochemical methods for the determination of natural radionuclides are of industrial importance (Section 6.2).

As we have already indicated, inactive elements may be labelled by admixing their radioactive isotopes. If the specific activity is known, a measurement of the activity is sufficient for the determination of a labelled element in a sample. Of great practical importance are the cases where the specific activity is uniform throughout the system under investigation. This condition is fulfilled when the element in the labelled form, with known specific activity, is introduced into the system before commencing the determination, and any dilution by inactive atoms of the element is prevented. A single determination of the specific activity is then sufficient as a basis for any number of highly sensitive analyses by activity measurement. This analytical method is conveniently called "indicator analysis". It will be discussed further in Section 6.3.

Before the discovery of artificial radioactivity, the number of radionuclides suitable as tracers was small, and their field of application correspondingly limited. In order to extend the advantages of detection by radioactivity — particularly the high sensitivity and rapidity — to the determination of other elements, analytical methods have been developed in which radionuclides are used as reagents for other substances. Another reason for the development of this method, to be called the "radioreagent method", lies in the possibility of a radiometric determination of substances for which radioactive labelling before the start of the analytical operations is not possible. This is the case when the system, in which they are present, is not under the control of the analyst. Analyses with radioactive reagents will be discussed in Section 6.4.

70

The inaccuracy of analytical methods is often due to the fact that the substance to be determined ought to be isolated from a mixture both with 100 per cent yield and in completely pure form while in practice either purity or yield fall below these requirements. It is clear that such inaccuracies can be eliminated if the yield of the substance on separation in a pure form is known. Such a determination of yield is possible by the isotope dilution method. This method will be discussed in Section 6.5.

Increasing use is being made of activation analysis. In contrast to the analytical methods already mentioned, this does not employ previously produced radionuclides. Instead, the samples are exposed to elementary particles (often slow neutrons) which induce nuclear transformations. Usually radionuclides are formed. The induced activity is proportional to the amount of the element, which can therefore be determined by activity measurement. Major advantages of activation analysis are the high sensitivity and the speed. Section 6.6 deals with the principles and applications of activation analysis.

Finally, there are those analytical procedures in which the absorption or the scattering by the sample of radiations produced directly or indirectly in nuclear processes is measured. From the results of such measurements the content of various elements in the samples may be determined (Section 6.7).

6.2. **Determination of Natural Radioelements**

The determination of the three long-lived radioelements uranium, thorium and potassium by their radiations has acquired great significance in industry. In particular, the determination of uranium and thorium and their disintegration products is carried out at various stages of the extraction of these elements, beginning with ore prospecting and continuing right up to the analysis of waste streams. However, the production of the raw materials for the atomic energy industry is a very specialised field which, notwithstanding its importance, is of direct interest to a limited number of specialists only. Since this book is intended for a wider public, we shall not discuss this question further.

The determination of potassium by means of its radioactivity is, on the other hand, a matter of general interest. Its importance is greatest in the mining of potassium salts, but it is also employed in other industries, such as in cement factories. The natural radioactivity of potassium has been known for more than fifty years [4]. We know to-day that natural potassium contains 0·012 per cent of the isotope potassium-40, which has a half-life of $1·3 \times 10^9$ years; the other natural potassium isotopes are inactive. About 89 per cent of the disintegrations take place with β^--particle emission ($E_{max} = 1·35$ MeV), giving calcium-40. In the other 11 per cent of the disintegrations, argon-40 is formed through electron capture with the emission of γ-radiation of 1·46 MeV.

The former process is often used for the determination of potassium, since the β-rays are easily detected. Since the specific activity of potassium is small, the measurement must be carried out on as large a sample as possible, and with the best possible yield. Measurements are performed on solutions [5–7] and on powders [8–12].

Because of the absorption due to the solvent, determinations using salt solutions are less sensitive. One instrument for such measurements [5] consisted of a counting tube 45 cm long and 2·5 cm in diameter, the glass wall of the tube being 0·2 to 0·4 mm thick. A further glass cylinder surrounded the counting tube at a distance of 4 mm, and the solution was placed in the space between the two glass jackets. Under lead shielding this tube had a background count rate of about 150 per minute, while a molar potassium chloride solution (39 g K per litre) gave 400 counts/min. From these values we may estimate the measuring time necessary to attain a given accuracy (see p. 31). For example, if the relative mean error of the determination were to be only 1 per cent, a determination of a molar solution would require 10 min, and that of a 0·01 M solution about 1 hr. Changes in the density of the solution must be allowed for when evaluating the measurements. This is done by means of empirical correction curves.

Higher yields are obtained in measurements on solid samples. Various authors [8–12] have described wall counters for powdered salt or rock samples in rather thick, or "infinitely thick" layers. Some of the counters are of the double jacket type. It is possible to use commercial counting tubes designed for other purposes [8, 9]. Typical data for such counters are: length of wall 7 to 10 cm, diameter 2·0 to 2·5 cm, background under lead shielding 20 counts/min. Samples containing 1 per cent of potassium give about 20 counts/min in excess of the background in such an arrangement. The count rate can be increased more than threefold by the use of particularly large wall counters (20 cm in length and 3 cm in diameter), and the measuring time for a given accuracy reduced appreciably [10]. It has been shown that particle size and chemical composition of the samples may have some effect on the count rate.

Radiometric determination of potassium may be regarded as a suitable rapid procedure for use in industry. The accuracy is about the same as that of the gravimetric methods, but the speed is much greater. The advantages are not so great compared with flame photometry, which is finding increasing application to potassium. For serial determinations, the two methods are about equally rapid, but the flame photometry will usually be given preference when other elements are to be determined simultaneously. The simplicity of operation is, however, an important advantage of radiometry compared with flame photometry. If the counting tube is placed in a steel chamber that can be tipped and can serve also as a shield, filling and emptying takes a few seconds only. The powder to be measured is simply poured into the space around the counting tube, and is removed after measurement by tipping the entire unit.

Measurements on various crude potassium salts, flotation concentrates and finished products with the large special counting tube have shown that a measuring time of 5 min is sufficient to obtain values for the potassium contents which agree within $\pm 0·7$ per cent K_2O with gravimetric values, themselves subject to an analytical error of up to $\pm 0·4$ per cent K_2O [10]. These figures make evident that serial determinations on potassium salts may be performed by this method quickly and simply.

Battery-operated portable equipment for routine operation in mines has been developed [10]. By means of a calibrated count rate meter the potassium content can be read directly off a scale. Obviously, accuracy and sensitivity are not as good as with laboratory instruments. Equipment of this kind may also be used for potassium prospecting in mines (see Section 7.3) [13].

The determination of the lean meat in pigs by determination of the potassium with a scintillation counter will be mentioned in Section 10.8.

6.3. Indicator Analysis

The extreme sensitivity of radioactivity measurement (p. 64) makes detection of minute quantities of labelled substances possible, as the determination of the solubility of lead sulphide and lead chromate has shown (p. 65). A further example is the possibility of determining extremely small quantities of mercury vapour which might prove injurious to health (p. 228). Clearly this kind of analysis, known as indicator analysis, is capable of a great variety of applications. Many examples will be given in Chapters 7–12. All such applications require that the specific activity of the radioactive element or the labelled compound in the system under investigation remains constant and is known.

In this section we will show that radioactive tracers may also be used for testing and improving other analytical methods, and have already shown themselves indispensable for this purpose. Indicator analysis can be used, for example, to determine in the simplest possible way whether a separation has been quantitative, whether undesired materials have been occluded, whether losses have occurred in washing precipitates or liquid phases, etc. Such applications of indicator analysis can be described as radiometric testing.

Many classical analytical methods have been found to be deficient when submitted to radiometric tests. Thus, investigation of the formation of ammonium phosphomolybdate precipitates with labelled phosphate has shown that the conditions recommended by Woy result in losses up to 1·5 per cent, i.e., appreciable amounts of radiophosphorus were found in the filtrate. On the basis of further radiometric tests, improved precipitation conditions – a reduction in the nitric acid concentration to 1 per cent – have been recommended [15]. The separation of the noble metals platinum, iridium and gold has been tested with radiogold [16]. While it had been claimed that platinum and gold can be dissolved quantitatively by aqua regia from a precipitate of the three elements obtained with formic acid, it was found that in fact 3 per cent of the added radiogold remained in the precipitate. On the other hand, it was found that in the separation of gold and platinum by precipitation of gold from alkaline solution with hydrogen peroxide up to 3 per cent of the gold may remain in solution.

The separation of the rare earths has been the subject of many investigations. Because of their great similarity, this separation is difficult, and it is therefore also hard to establish by normal chemical techniques the contamination of one element by another. This is, however, easily accomplished with tracers. For instance, the precipitation of lanthanum as its double sulphate has been examined; it was found that, on the one hand, a few per cent of yttrium earths may be coprecipitated, while, on the other, a few per cent of lanthanum may remain in solution [17]. A thorough study has been made of the coprecipitation of lanthanum and yttrium with cerium(IV)-

iodate [18]. From such results it can be decided how often the precipitation must be repeated to reduce the contamination to the required level.

The separation of calcium and magnesium through oxalate precipitation has been investigated with radiocalcium. Under certain conditions considerable errors were found [19]. The precipitation of calcium oxalate and magnesium ammonium phosphate has been found to involve appreciable coprecipitation of radiosodium [20]. The separation of (radioactive) lead and barium by precipitation of basic lead chloride Pb(OH)Cl has been shown to be satisfactory [21]. Similarly, basic lead bromide and basic lead iodide are suitable for the precipitation of small amounts of lead from concentrated solutions of alkaline earths [22]. The best conditions for the separation of strontium and barium by precipitation of the barium as its chromate have been investigated with barium-140 and strontium-89 [23]. The information so obtained has made it possible to reduce appreciably the coprecipitation of strontium with the barium chromate. An investigation with zinc-65, cobalt-60 and iron-59 has indicated that these metals are often carried down with sulphides precipitated from 0·3 M hydrochloric acid, particularly with mercury and tin sulphides [24].

The precipitation of tungsten by various organic reagents has been tested with tungsten-185. While reagents often recommended, such as cinchonine and quinine, did not give quantitative precipitation, a mixture of tannin and methyl violet gave good results with respect to both yield and separation from alkaline earths and aluminium [25]. Organic reagents for the precipitation of zinc, cadmium, bismuth, indium, thallium, zirconium and hafnium were also examined by this type of radiochemical technique [26].

The washing of potassium chloroplatinate precipitates with alcohol has been tested with potassium-42 [27]. Losses up to 5 per cent have been shown to occur. A method of alkali determination commonly used in silicate analysis has been tested with radioactive isotopes of potassium, rubidium and caesium, and some sources of error were disclosed [28]. These include loss of alkali through spraying when opening up with hydrofluoric acid, through evaporation when fusing with ammonium chloride and calcium carbonate, and through occlusion and adsorption when precipitating other materials from the solution of the alkali salts.

The recovery of small amounts of beryllium from biological material has been examined with beryllium-7 [29]. Since this radioactive nuclide is available carrier-free, very small amounts can be detected. In earlier work, appreciable losses of beryllium in the course of ashing had often been observed. It has now been possible to show that such losses were not due to volatilization of the beryllium, but to the formation of practically insoluble oxide. This became apparent through the observation that no beryllium-7 activity was lost from the residue during ashing, while it was not possible to adsorb the beryllium on a cation exchanger after dissolving the ashing residue in dilute acids. Such adsorption, which is to be expected for beryllium ions, occurred only after the residue had been digested with concentrated sulphuric acid for a long period.

Another result of this work concerns the concentration of solutions of beryllium acetylacetonate in benzene through evaporation. Small but significant losses of beryllium through volatilization were observed. In consequence, the separation of beryllium by evaporation of the volatile components of the solution was replaced by a back-extraction of the beryllium from the acetylacetonate–benzene solution with strong hydrochloric acid.

The extraction of indium with ethyl ether from solutions containing iodide ions has been investigated with radioindium [30]. The best results are obtained when the concentration of the iodide in the aqueous phase was about 1·5 mole/l., and the hydrogen ion concentration lay between 0·5 and 7·0 mole/l. The extraction is not disturbed even by considerable quantities of other halide ions. A procedure for the extraction of cerium with organic solvents has been developed using tracers. Twenty-four solvents were tested with radiocerium, and the co-extraction of yttrium, samarium and ytterbium was examined with their radioactive isotopes. Good separation of cerium was obtained by extraction of the quadrivalent form from a strong hydrochloric acid solution (4 M) with ether [31].

Serious losses may occur in the course of microanalytical determinations through adsorption on walls of vessels and on filter materials. In particular, cations may be taken up by glass or paper through ion exchange. Such processes have been examined with tracers. Serious losses of radiolead were found when the lead concentration was less than 10^{-3} mole/l. [32]. The losses may be prevented by addition of other ions. The concentration required depends on the strength of the adsorption of these ions on the vessel walls or on the filtration media. Thus, a hydrogen ion concentration as low as 5×10^{-3} mole/l. protects against losses of lead by adsorption on filter paper and glass walls, while even in 1 molar solutions of alkali chlorides appreciable losses still occur. Similar work was carried out with other radionuclides [33–35]. The reduction of adsorption by coating the walls of the vessel with plastics has also been tested [36].

A particularly useful feature of indicator analysis is to be seen in the possibility of finding out whether methods apparently giving satisfactory results do so only through the compensation of several errors. For instance, seemingly satisfactory results were obtained in the determination of sulphate as 4-chloro-4'-aminodiphenyl sulphate under certain experimental conditions. A test with radiosulphur showed, however, that this was due to compensation of errors rather than to exact stoichiometric relations. Some reagent was coprecipitated, while part of the sulphate remained in solution, and a further part was lost in washing the precipitate [243].

In spectroscopic analysis, the introduction of γ-emitting radioelements into the arc makes it possible to determine the distribution of the different elements in the hot zone, and in particular to discover the position of maximum concentration. Molybdenum, zirconium, cerium, sodium, potassium and bismuth were used in quantities varying from 400 to 600 mc, and the distribution of the elements in the arc was determined by means of a sort of pinhole camera. It has been found that this distribution depends greatly on the volatility of the element. Particular interest attaches to results on the modification of the distribution through addition of carriers [37–39]. The speed of evaporation of a labelled element (indium) in the arc has also been determined [333]. Polarographic methods may be subjected to tests with radioactive tracers [344, 345].

Physico-chemical data of analytical importance may be obtained by indicator analysis. Reference has already been made to the determination of the solubility of lead sulphide and lead chromate by Paneth and Hevesy. Many other solubility determinations followed (see, e.g., [40–44, 248]). The mutual solubility of liquids, the distribution of substances between solvent phases, the complex formation constants and similar quantities may also be determined by indicator analysis (see p. 192). Present-day knowledge of the factors governing coprecipitation depends greatly on results obtained with radioelements (see, e.g. [1, 45–48, 61, 248, 340]).

Occasionally, solubilities have been determined with non-isotopic radioactive tracers [292–294]. For instance, the solubility of barium sulphate was computed from the distribution of tracer radiostrontium between the precipitate and the solution, and the solubility of potassium chloroplatinate from the distribution of radiocaesium [294].

Analyses distinguished by high sensitivity and sharpness of separation may be obtained by a combination of chromatography and indicator analysis, known as radiochromatography (see, e.g., [49–51]). The importance of radiochromatography for the separation of nearly carrier-free radionuclides and labelled compounds has already been referred to in Section 4.3.

The sensitivity and simplicity of radiometric measurement has greatly facilitated the development of new chromatographic procedures. It is often possible to measure continuously the activity of the eluate from a chromatographic column by making it flow past the window of a counting tube, e.g., in a spiral tube. Alternatively, if the radioelements present in the column emit γ-radiation or very energetic β-radiation, they may be detected there by scanning with a counter.

Radioactive tracers have been of special importance in developing the chromatographic separation of the rare earths on ion exchange columns (see p. 57). In the course of atomic energy research the necessity arose to resolve the mixture of radioactive isotopes of the rare earths produced in nuclear fission. This gave impetus to the development of chromatographic separations on ion exchange columns [53, 54]. Tracers were also used for the investigation of the separation of other substances in such columns, examples being the separation of zirconium from hafnium [55, 56], niobium from tantalum [57, 58], and rhenium from molybdenum [244].

Labelled substances have also been used in paper chromatography, in particular to detect individual compounds rapidly and simply when working out separation methods [59, 60]. The distribution of the labelled substances in the paper chromatogram can be determined by scanning with a counter or by autoradiography [50] (see p. 58).

We may show the sharpness of radiochromatographic separations by an example. Whereas previously no paper-chromatographic procedure permitting reliable differentiation between certain isomeric amino acids, such as valin and norvalin, was known this has been successfully accomplished with radioactive tracers. A pure labelled compound is mixed with the compound to be identified, and a paper chromatogram of the mixture is run. The spot on the paper chromatogram formed by the two substances is cut into thin strips at right angles to the direction of movement, and the specific activity of the amino acid is determined in each strip. Only if the value is identical in all the strips can it be said that the substances are identical [52].

6.4. Analysis with Radioactive Reagents

The analytical procedures with radioreagents worked out (mainly by Ehrenberg) before the discovery of artificial radioactivity used radiolead as the active reagent. A review of these older procedures has been published [62].

An example is the determination of chromate. The solution of the chromate is treated with an excess of a solution of a lead salt of known concentration that is labelled with radiolead (thorium B). The precipitated lead chromate is filtered off, and the activity of the filtrate measured. From the ratio of the activity of the filtrate to that of the added lead solution the amount of the precipitated lead, and therefore that of the chromate, can be calculated [63].

In order to extend the application of these methods to substances which do not give sparingly soluble precipitates with lead, procedures have been employed in which the labelled solution was added at the end of a chain of reactions. For example, the determination of chloride ions might be performed by the following sequence of reactions: precipitation of the chloride with an excess of inactive silver nitrate, of the silver with an excess of inactive chromate, and, finally, of the chromate with an excess of labelled lead nitrate [64]. Such methods are cumbersome and also inaccurate, since they involve a number of reactions. They have found little practical application.

Since the discovery of artificial radioactivity many further radioreagents have become accessible, and more single-stage determinations have become feasible. Radioreagent methods are therefore finding expanding application [1, 248]. As examples, we may mention the assay of thallium [66] and silver [67] by precipitation with radioactive iodide, of thorium by precipitation with radioactive pyrophosphate [68], and of chromate, vanadate and molybdate with radiosilver [69]. Numerous elements, including aluminium, gallium, indium, the rare earths, zirconium, bismuth and uranium, may be determined by precipitation with radioactive phosphate [70]. Sulphate is assayed by addition of a solution of barium chromate (^{51}Cr) in hydrochloric acid, neutralization with ammonia, and measurement of the activity of the chromate remaining in solution [265].

An automatic procedure for the radiometric analysis of phosphate in concentrations from one to fifty parts per million in boiler feed-water has been described. By means of a liquid counter the excess of radiocalcium remaining in solution after addition of the radiocalcium to the sample (taken automatically) is measured [65]. In order to facilitate this measurement, the precipitate formed is deposited by centrifugation on to a cylinder surrounding the solution. The liquid counter is placed along the axis of the cylinder. Since the β-radiation of calcium-45 is soft, even a small distance between the counter and the cylinder on which the precipitate is deposited is sufficient to keep rays emitted by the precipitate from reaching the counter. The apparatus performs automatically all steps necessary for analysis: drawing in of the sample, addition of the labelled precipitant, centrifugation of the precipitate, and measurement of activity in the solution.

Phosphate determinations have also been carried out with labelled cobalt salts (^{60}Co) as precipitant. Alternatively, it is possible to label the phosphate to be determined by addition of radiophosphate. A precipitant, such as a solution of barium chloride or magnesia mixture, is then added in a known amount, which must be less than the (equivalent) quantity required for complete precipitation of the phosphate. The fraction of the activity remaining in solution is measured, and from it the amount of phosphate present is calculated [266].

Various determinations may be carried out by titration [71, 248]. The activity of the solution may, for example, be measured after each addition of the labelled precipitant, the solution being sucked into a double-jacketed liquid counter through a glass sinter [72, 73]. After passing the equivalence point, the active reagent appears in the solution, and an increase in the activity is observed. Under certain circumstances two measuring points are sufficient to find the equivalence point. Magnesium, uranium, lead and thorium can be determined by titration with radiophosphate [72]. Beryllium and zirconium have also been titrated with phosphate, and for determinations of thallium labelled iodide, chromate or phosphotungstate have been employed [74]. Cobalt, zinc and copper may be titrated with potassium ferrocyanide [47, 75]. Figure 24 shows the change in the activity of a solution during the titration with a labelled precipitant.

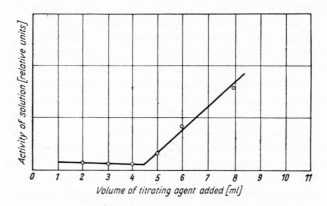

FIG. 24. Titration with radioactive reagent.
10 ml of a 0·1N sodium tungstate solution was titrated with 0·2N cobalt ammonium nitrate labelled with cobalt-60. pH = 7·4
(After D. H. BRADHURST, B. A. COLLER and J. F. DUNCAN, *J. Inorg. Nucl. Chem.* **4,** 379 (1957))

Other reactions besides the formation of sparingly soluble precipitates may be used as the basis of radioreagent methods [1]. For example, water may be determined by letting the mixture react with aluminium chloride labelled with chlorine-36, and measuring the activity of the hydrogen chloride evolved [76].

A further group of radioreagent procedures is based on the formation of complexes soluble in organic solvents. For this purpose, the metallic ion originally present in aqueous solution or the reagent itself may be labelled. For instance, zinc or mercury may be determined through the solubility of their complexes with dithizone in chloroform or carbon tetrachloride. When the metal ion is labelled, the radioactivity of the aqueous phase should become zero at the equivalence point [77, 78].

In other determinations a foreign ion, originally present in a different phase, is added. This ion must have the property of forming a water-soluble complex only after the ion to be determined has been completely used up by reaction with the complexing agent. In this way, copper may be determined by titration with ethylenediamine tetraacetate (EDTA). Only after the copper is used up will further addition of the reagent dissolve radiosilver originally present as silver iodate, and the activity of the solution will increase rapidly [79].

The determination of iodide or iodine may be carried out by oxidizing with bromine to iodate, and then treating with an excess of radioactive iodide solution. On acidification, free iodine is formed, and this is extracted with a solvent. From the activity of the extracted iodine the amount of inactive iodine originally present is calculated [80]. In a micro-method for the determination of iodine numbers, iodine monobromide (^{131}I) is used. A drop of known volume of the fat solution under examination is put on paper and the solvent is evaporated. The spot is then treated with a solution of the active reagent, and the excess of the reagent washed away. The activity remaining on the paper gives the iodine number [81].

Fatty acids may also be determined by a radioreagent method after paper-chromatographic separation. Unsaturated acids, such as oleic acid, are treated on the paper with iodine-131, the excess iodine is removed, and the remaining activity measured. Saturated acids, such as palmitic or stearic acids, are converted on the paper to their silver salts, which are then treated with radioactive iodide. The amount of fatty acid is finally calculated from the activity of the silver iodide [82–84]. Alternatively the acids are caused to react with radiocobalt [259]. Hydroxyl groups in organic substances are assayed by measurement of activity after reaction with labelled acetic anhydride [86]. Carboxyl groups in cellulose may be determined after conversion to radioactive salts (see Section 10.1), and reducing end groups in sugars after reaction with ^{14}C-cyanide [341].

For continuous production control, procedures using the liberation of radiokrypton from an inclusion (clathrate) compound with hydroquinone, followed by automatic measurement, may be suitable [87, 88]. In this manner, sulphur dioxide in a current of gas may be made to liberate chlorine dioxide from chlorite, and the strongly oxidizing chlorine dioxide will then liberate krypton. Similarly, ozone in the higher strata of the atmosphere may liberate krypton. The activity of the released krypton is measured by a counter, the result is transmitted by radio to the Earth, and there recorded automatically. The activity is not proportional to the quantity of chlorine dioxide or ozone, so that calibrations are necessary. Fluorine is also determined by an analogous method [260].

It has been found that the amount of tantalum-182 extracted from 6·5 M sulphuric acid into di-isobutyl ketone as a fluoride complex depends on the concentration of the fluoride. This concentration can consequently be computed on the basis of a calibration curve from the activity of the tantalum transferred into the organic phase [264].

Active reagents have found an interesting application in the determination of free radicals. The radical is made to react with the reagent, and it is then possible to determine its quantity and often its nature by radioactivity measurement. In some investigations the gas current containing the free radicals was passed over a deposit of labelled lead [89, 90], bismuth [91], or tellurium [92]. The radioactive compound carried away was collected in a cooling trap, and was then determined by its activity. Radioiodine may be used for the determination of individual hydrocarbon radicals [93, 94, 258]. By injection of labelled iodine into the gas current, the free radicals are converted to labelled alkyl iodides. After addition of inactive alkyl iodides as carriers, the compounds are separated by fractional distillation or gas chromatography. The activities of the individual compounds indicate which free radicals had been formed.

6.5. Isotope Dilution Methods

Through the isotope dilution method, the yield with which a substance is obtained in the pure form is determined. This is essential when quantitative separation is impossible. In this way, the accuracy of various analytical procedures can be improved greatly [1, 95, 351, 370]. A discussion of the accuracy obtained with variants of the isotope dilution method has been given [299].

The principle of the normal isotope dilution method is the following. The substance to be determined is added, in a labelled form and in accurately known quantity and specific activity, to the mixture to be analysed. After thorough mixing, the substance to be determined is separated by a suitable procedure, and the separation process is repeated until a definitely pure product is obtained. The yield is of secondary importance in this process. From the activity of the pure separated substance, both the yield in the separation process and the amount of the substance in the original mixture may be calculated.

If we denote the unknown quantity by M_1, the quantity and the specific activity of the labelled additive by M_2 and A_2, respectively, and the specific activity of the separated pure substance by A_3, we have

$$A_3 = \frac{A_2 M_2}{M_1 + M_2} \tag{19}$$

or, on rearrangement,

$$M_1 = M_2 \left(\frac{A_2}{A_3} - 1 \right).$$

If the labelled substance is added carrier-free, and therefore with a very large specific activity, we may neglect M_2 as compared with M_1, and obtain

$$M_1 = \frac{A_2 M_2}{A_3} = \frac{G_2}{G_3} M_3, \tag{20}$$

where G_2 and G_3, respectively, represent the activity of the added and the separated labelled substance, and M_3 is the separated amount of pure substance. For the case of addition of carrier-free substance, we see at once that the separation yield is given directly by the activity ratio G_3/G_2.

Stable isotopes may also be used for the isotope dilution method. The determination of the isotopic composition is usually carried out with a mass spectrometer.

The isotope dilution method is particularly suitable for mixtures of very similar substances, where no specific quantitative methods for the determination of the components are available. In resolving such mixtures, purity of components can only be attained at the expense of yield.

The isotope dilution method was invented by Hevesy [96]. In micro-determinations of lead by anodic deposition the results showed poor reproducibility. Addition of a known quantity of radiolead and measurement of the activity of the deposit permitted the determination of the deposition yield, and so, in spite of incomplete separation, an accurate analysis was obtained. A similar procedure for the determination of lead has been developed by Starik [97].

A further example of the isotope dilution method consists in the assay of potassium in mixtures of potassium and lithium salts [98]. After the addition of carrier-free radioactive potassium chloride (potassium-42) to the solution of the salts the potassium was precipitated as the perchlorate, and purified by washing and re-precipitation. From the weight of the perchlorate and the fraction of the radiopotassium precipitated, the potassium content of the salt mixture was calculated. Other elements may be determined in a similar manner, e.g., rubidium [70, 99], strontium [99], caesium [99], zinc [100], cerium [101] and ruthenium [102]. In connection with the analysis of detergents a procedure for determining pyrophosphate and triphosphate in mixtures with other phosphates has been developed; the separation of the pure components is performed by repeated fractional crystallization [103].

The isotope dilution method may be used for the assay of uranium in ores containing little or no (ordinary) thorium. The uranium-238 is in radioactive equilibrium with its decay product ionium (thorium-230). To determine the uranium, ordinary thorium (thorium-232) is added to the solution as a carrier for the ionium, the total thorium (230 and 232) is isolated, the activity of the ionium is determined, and, finally, the yield is found by measurement of the activity of the thorium-232. The measurements are carried out with a discriminating ionization chamber capable of distinguishing between the α-radiation of ionium and of thorium-232. A similar procedure may be used to find the thorium content in uranium-free ores. Here ionium, or even more simply dissolved uranium ore in which the ionium is in radioactive equilibrium with uranium, is used for the labelling and for the determination of the separation yield [104].

In contrast to the determination of elements or simple ions, it is often impossible to avoid the addition of carrier when complicated compounds are subjected to analysis by isotope dilution. In particular this is the case in the analysis of organic compounds. An example is the determination of naphthalene in the tar distillation fractions of a coking plant, for which naphthalene labelled with radiocarbon is employed [105]. A further example is the determination of glucose after hydrolysis of maize starch [106]. Applications in the pharmaceutical industry will be discussed later (p. 257).

The isotope dilution method has found a number of interesting applications in biochemistry, such as the analysis of mixtures of amino acids from the hydrolysis of proteins, and the mixture of mononucleotides from the hydrolysis of nucleic acids.

These applications go back to the pioneer work of Schoenheimer and Rittenberg [107, 108], and of Ussing [109], but cannot be further considered here [see 1, 85].

Although the isotope dilution method leads to an improvement in the accuracy of analysis, it does not increase the sensitivity of analytical methods. In the most favourable cases, the sensitivity is simply given by that of the determination methods used in the analysis, such as gravimetric or colorimetric methods. However, in the analysis of mixtures of very similar substances the sensitivity is often worse than this, since certain minimum quantities $(M_1 + M_2)$ are needed for carrying out the necessary separation. Of course, the introduction of these quantities in the form of the labelled additive could be considered. However, in micro-determinations this would mean making M_2 appreciably larger than M_1. In such a case A_3 approaches A_2, and since the activity measurements usually involve errors of a few per cent, the determination becomes increasingly inaccurate with a reduction in the ratio M_1/M_2, until finally it becomes impossible.

In some of these cases the "reverse isotope dilution method" may be applied. The substance to be determined is initially in a labelled form, the separation is then carried out after addition of a known amount of inactive carrier, and the separation yield is determined for this carrier by ordinary chemical methods.

We may illustrate this by discussing the case of trace elements in soils. It is known that ruminants do not thrive on soils deficient in cobalt (see p. 279). In this connection it is important to find out what proportion of small additions of cobalt remains in the soil after a certain time. Indicator analysis with radiocobalt is suitable for this investigation. It is, however, not possible to measure the radiocobalt directly on soil samples, since the measuring efficiency is very low owing to self-absorption, and it is not desirable to employ high activities. Therefore it is necessary to extract the cobalt from large quantities of soil before measurement. But, because of adsorption, very small quantities of cobalt cannot be extracted from the soil in a quantitative manner. Therefore, the following procedure may be adopted: A known amount of inactive cobalt is added to the soil sample, the mixture is homogenized, and then a certain quantity of a suitable cobalt compound is separated in pure form for activity measurement. The ratio of the weights of the recovered cobalt to the added cobalt gives the yield of separation. This is used to calculate the total activity and the quantity of cobalt in the original soil.

A further example is the determination of the oxidation products formed from small quantities of radioactive hydrocarbons under the action of ionizing radiation. Here it is necessary to distinguish between a considerable number of substances which are chemically very similar [110].

It may often be impossible to label the substance to be determined, since the system investigated is initially not under the control of the analyst (see p. 70). In such cases it may be possible to combine isotope dilution and radioreagent methods. A labelled reagent with high specific activity is added to the mixture. As a consequence the substance to be determined, and perhaps other substances as well, are converted to a radioactively labelled derivative. After removing the excess of reagent, the same derivative is added as a carrier in an inactive form in any desired quantity, and after thorough mixing the pure derivative is isolated. From the specific activity of this, it is possible to calculate the quantity in the mixture by the relation:

$$M_1 = M_2/([A_1/A_3] - 1). \tag{21}$$

In order to apply this equation, the specific activity of the derivative A_1 is calculated from the specific activity of the labelled reagent.

This kind of assay procedure may be suitable even for exceedingly small quantities. An example is the determination of the individual amino acids in biological materials. The amino acids are converted to their "pipsyl" derivatives, using *p*-iodophenylsulphonyl chloride labelled with radioactive iodine. These labelled derivatives are then separated chromatographically and determined individually [111; see also 1, 85].

6.6. Activation Analysis

6.6.1. *Principle of the Method*

Activation analysis depends on the following principle: The sample under investigation is irradiated with elementary particles, most frequently slow neutrons, in such a manner that the elements to be determined undergo nuclear transformations. In general it is desirable that radionuclides should be formed, which may be determined after irradiation by activity measurement. The activity is a measure of the amount of the parent nuclide. Since the elements as occurring in nature almost always show constant isotopic composition, the activity is also a measure of the amount of the element (see, however, p. 96).

In certain cases analysis is also possible where the nuclides produced in the transformations are not radioactive. It is then necessary to measure the rate of formation of one of the products during irradiation (see pp. 94, 98).

Numerous review articles and books dealing with activation analysis have been published [1, 112–116, 120, 245, 248, 256, 257, 348, 349, 367]. These contain extensive bibliographies and there is also a full bibliography available, which is periodically brought up to date [368].

6.6.2. *Direct Measurement of Activity Compared with Measurement after Chemical Separation*

Activation analysis is particularly simple when the measurement of the activity may be carried out directly on the irradiated sample, i.e., without chemical treatment. In general the most important condition for analysis by direct activity measurement is that the radiations emitted by nuclides produced by nuclear transformation of other elements do not interfere. In particular this is the case when only the element to be determined undergoes transformation into radionuclides to any appreciable extent.

But even when accompanying substances are also activated, it is frequently possible to use direct activity measurements on the samples to be analysed. For example, if the radionuclides emit β-radiation of different energies they may be distinguished by means of absorbers (see, for example, p. 92). γ-rays of different energies may be measured separately with a scintillation spectrometer (p. 46). Such equipment is therefore finding increasing application in activation analysis [117–121]. Semi-conductor detectors (lithium drifted germanium) will undoubtedly also find much use, particularly when good resolution is required [372].

Radionuclides can also be distinguished if their half-lives differ appreciably. In such cases radioactive decay curves will indicate what proportion of the activity is due to individual nuclides, and it may be an advantage to wait for the decay of short-lived nuclides. It may be also possible to suppress the formation of long-lived radionuclides by a suitable choice of the irradiation period. The activity of each nuclide produced will approach a saturation value after irradiation for a period several times greater than its half-life (see p. 89). With a suitable choice of the time of irradiation, the saturation activity of the desired short-lived nuclide is reached while long-lived nuclides formed from other elements are present only in negligible amounts.

Chemical separations of the radionuclides are necessary when the direct determination of the nuclides formed from the element of interest is impossible because of interference by other elements. A separation may also be of advantage when in the nuclear transformation of an isotope of the element to be determined an isotope of another element is formed; this nuclide may then be concentrated by separation.

These chemical separations show certain features that must be considered important advantages of activation analysis as compared with other micro-analytical methods. After irradiation, inactive carriers for all the elements to be determined may be added to the samples. The chemical separation can then be conducted with the relatively large carrier quantities, and the difficulties involved in work with micro-quantities are avoided. Moreover, quantitative separation of the individual elements is not needed. Provided that the quantity of the carrier is great compared with the quantity of the element to be determined, the separation yield is given by the ratio of the separated and of the added quantity of carrier. From this yield and from the activity measured, the total activity in the sample is calculated (reverse isotope dilution method). This is illustrated by a determination of gold in meteorites (p. 94): 30 mg of gold carrier were added to the irradiated sample after dissolution, and after chemical separation a yield of about 75 per cent was obtained. A further advantage of activation analysis is that inadvertent introduction of small quantities of the element to be determined during the separation process has no effect on the analysis. Hence no errors are introduced by the impurities in the reagents.

In activation analysis comparison methods (relative methods) are almost always used, i.e., a reference sample is irradiated under identical conditions, preferably simultaneously with the samples to be analysed. From the ratio of the activities obtained in the two samples, the content of the desired element can be calculated. If the compositions of the two samples are similar, the effective particle flux (generally neutron flux) will be practically the same in both cases.

Sometimes it is an advantage to use an internal standard as reference sample. A foreign element capable of activation is mixed with the sample, and the activity produced from it is measured independently after irradiation [125]. The ideal internal standard is the element to be determined. In this case both the standard and the sample react in the same way with elementary particles of a given energy distribution. One portion of the sample is irradiated in its original condition. To a second portion a known quantity of the element to be determined is added, and this portion is then irradiated simultaneously with the first portion ("spiking").

6.6.3. *Neutron Activation: General Remarks*

For activation analysis slow neutrons are used most frequently. There are several reasons for this. The fact that neutrons react with atomic nuclei much more easily than ions has already been referred to (p. 16). A further advantage of neutrons lies in the fact that, unlike charged particles, they easily penetrate many materials, so that nuclear reactions are not limited to the surface of the sample. For the same reason it is also possible to irradiate samples in closed vessels. In this way the operations are greatly simplified, and volatile materials may also be irradiated. Finally, in irradiation with neutrons the samples are heated much less than in irradiation with ions.

Slow neutrons may possess various energies. For activation analysis, "thermal" neutrons are preferred. These are neutrons which have lost their excess energy in collisions with atomic nuclei, and therefore have only the energy corresponding to the temperature of the ambient matter. They show a Maxwell–Boltzmann energy distribution, and have at room temperature a mean energy of 0·025 eV.

Generally thermal neutrons bring about nuclear transformations most easily, that is, their reaction cross-sections are largest (see p. 88). Moreover, thermal neutrons suffer little change in average energy on interaction with matter, and therefore the energy of the neutrons is similar in all parts of the sample, and is largely independent of its chemical composition, size and shape.

Various sources of neutrons are available for irradiations. The simplest are natural sources in which the radiation from a radionuclide liberates neutrons from nuclei in which the "last" neutron is only weakly bound. The most suitable nucleus for this purpose is that of beryllium-9; natural beryllium consists entirely of this isotope.

In α-neutron sources the reaction $^9_4\mathrm{Be}(\alpha, n)^{12}_6\mathrm{C}$ is employed. The α-particles may come from radium and its daughters, from separated radon and its daughters, from polonium or plutonium. Americium-241 is a long-lived (half-life 462 years) α-ray source which is free from hard γ-radiation [310]. The active substance is intimately mixed with beryllium powder, and the mixture placed in sealed capsules made of metal or glass.

γ-neutron sources depend on the reaction $^9_4\mathrm{Be}(\gamma, n) 2^4_2\mathrm{He}$. They must contain a nuclide which emits γ-radiation with an energy of at least 1·63 MeV, the binding energy of the last neutron in beryllium. Suitable nuclides are radium or radon in equilibrium with their daughters, or artificially produced antimony-124.

The principal advantage of natural neutron sources is the simplicity of preparation and operation. A further important point is that the emission rate of the source is not subject to irregular variations. This stability makes it possible to calibrate only occasionally during a series of activation analyses. The calibrations need not be carried out at the same time as the individual determination, as must be done with the other types of neutron sources. The major disadvantage of natural neutron sources is the low neutron output.

More neutrons may be obtained from accelerators. Nuclei of heavy hydrogen (deuterons) are the particles usually accelerated for this purpose. They are allowed to impinge on deuterium, tritium, lithium or beryllium. Neutrons are produced through the reactions $_1^2D(d, n)\,_2^3He$, $_1^3H(d, n)\,_2^4He$, $_3^7Li(d, n)\,2_2^4He$ and $_4^9Be(d, n)\,_5^{10}B$, respectively.

For use in chemical laboratories, in particular for activation analysis, relatively simple neutron generators of the accelerator type are manufactured. Generally use is made of the reaction $_1^3H(d, n)\,_2^4He$ (see, e.g., [253, 261, 367]). Portable neutron generators for use in bore-holes will be discussed in Section 7.4.6.

The strongest neutron source available to-day is the nuclear reactor. Various types of reactors have channels through which the sample may be introduced, and there submitted to intense neutron irradiation. Nuclear research reactors that produce very high neutron fluxes are known as "material testing reactors". Mobile reactors suitable for activation analysis will be mentioned in Section 7.1.1.

In all the neutron sources the neutrons produced are at first fast. For activation analysis they must generally be slowed down. This is done by means of "moderators". The neutrons are allowed to collide with atomic nuclei, and in this process some of their energy is transferred to the nuclei. The final result is the production of nearly thermal neutrons. The lighter the nucleus, the greater the average amount of energy lost in a collision. With natural sources and accelerators, hydrogen compounds (water and paraffin wax) are used as moderators. With reactors, other moderators are also applied, in particular heavy hydrogen in the form of heavy water, and carbon as pure graphite. These moderators are less efficient in the slowing-down of neutrons, but they capture slow neutrons less readily than ordinary hydrogen, and show therefore better "neutron economy".

A simple arrangement for activation analysis with a natural source consists of a paraffin wax block 20 cm long. The source is placed in its centre. The moderator scatters the neutrons in all directions, so that the entire block is filled with a "neutron gas". The flux of slow neutrons is a maximum near the neutron source itself, since neutrons diffuse back to this point from all directions. However, in this region the slow neutrons are accompanied by a large number of fast neutrons. These may not interfere, for, as has been pointed out, the activation cross-sections for slow neutrons are usually greater than those for fast neutrons. In this case, the sample is placed directly against the source. But if strong irradiation by fast neutrons must be avoided, a few centimetres of moderator are interposed between the source and the sample.

When the maximum possible slow neutron flux is required, the irradiation is performed inside a reactor. Most reactors contain so much moderator that slow neutrons predominate. If the fast neutrons in the reactor still interfere the sample must be irradiated outside the reactor, with an adequate layer of moderator placed between reactor and sample for slowing down the fast neutrons escaping from the reactor. Such a device is called a "thermal column".

Rapid activation analysis with neutrons is made possible by high neutron fluxes. In this case it is not necessary to activate to saturation. The speed may also be improved by relying on short-lived nuclides [123, 127, 271]. The γ-activities obtained after 5 min with a neutron flux of 10^8 cm^{-2} sec^{-1}, typical for laboratory accelerators, have been tabulated for many nuclides in a form suitable for work with scintillation spectrometers; for this purpose not the total γ-activities, but the emission rates of quanta of particular energies are listed [127].

Systems of instrumental activation analysis, which operate mainly with short ir-radiation periods, can lead to great savings in time and labour. In one such method a hundred-channel γ-spectrometer is used, which prints the spectra on paper. Evaluation of the spectra is carried out by comparing with reference samples, each containing known quantities of one of the elements to be determined; the reference samples are irradiated simultaneously. This method has been used on 27 different elements. Even with the relatively low flux of 10^8 cm^{-2} sec^{-1}, ten minutes are often sufficient for an analysis [122] (see also [367]).

Short high-intensity pulses of neutrons for activation studies may be obtained from certain reactors. When a Triga reactor is pulsed by rapid ejection of the main control rod, an instantaneous neutron flux of 3–6×10^{16} cm^{-2} sec^{-1} may be obtained during 10–20 millisec. For very short-lived nuclides, one such pulse can generate more activity in a sample than is possible by irradiation all the way to saturation at the normal steady power level. The method may be applied to fast as well as slow neutrons [271, 367].

Instrumental activation analysis has been further developed by recording the γ-spectrum at several times after the irradiation. Then the photopeak areas obtained after different periods of decay may be compared with standard areas obtained for 70 elements with the same time schedule. The areas under every photopeak are deter-mined by an electronic calculator capable of automatically eliminating interference by other maxima. Automatic correction for the neutron flux is also provided so that the reference sample need not be irradiated at the same time as the sample under analysis [131]. A further development provides for storage of the standard spectra in the machine, and the machine identifies the photopeaks automatically on the basis of energy and half-life. In the form described, this machine "remembers" the relevant data of 128 nuclides [124] (see also [367]).

In suitable cases, the selectivity may be improved by means of coincidence circuits. Nuclides which emit a cascade of γ-rays, or positrons (and therefore annihilation radi-ation), may be identified by coincidence spectrometry in spite of considerable γ-ray in-tensities from other radionuclides in the samples. This method has been applied to scandium, cobalt and selenium [277], copper [271, 277], and manganese [267].

6.6.4. *Sensitivity of Activation Analysis with Neutrons*

The detection limit of activation analysis depends on the fact that a certain minimum activity is needed for unequivocal detection. Obviously, the activity produced in a given sample is proportional to the neutron flux if other conditions are kept constant; the greater the flux, the lower the detection limit. In Table 6 the flux of slow neutrons provided by various neutron sources is given.

The second principal factor determining the sensitivity of activation analysis is the probability, under standard conditions, of a suitable nuclear reaction between the nuclide and the neutrons. This probability is usually expressed in terms of a "reaction cross-section", which can be imagined as the cross-sectional area through which the neutron must pass in order to bring about the nuclear reaction. However, cross-sections are areas only in a formal sense; often the cross-section exceeds the geometrical cross-section of the nucleus by several orders of magnitude. Nevertheless, the dimensions are those of a true cross-section, i.e. those of an area. A unit frequently employed for cross-sections is the "barn", which is equal to 10^{-24} cm^2. The cross-section for a (n, γ)-reaction is often called a capture cross-section.

TABLE 6. SLOW NEUTRON FLUX PRODUCED BY VARIOUS SOURCES (TYPICAL VALUES)

Source	Neutron flux (particles cm^{-2} sec^{-1})
Radium–γ–Beryllium source (1 c)	10^4
Radium–α–Beryllium source (1 c)	10^5
Accelerator (T + D, 150 kV)	10^8
Cyclotron	10^9
Reactor	10^{11}–10^{15}

In discussing the sensitivity of activation analysis it is convenient to use the "atomic" reaction cross-section, which is obtained by multiplying the reaction cross-section of the nuclide undergoing activation ("isotopic" reaction cross-section) by the abundance of the nuclide in the element (isotopic abundance). The atomic cross-section is thus a magnitude which applies to an element as a whole. As an example, we may consider the isotopic cross-section for the capture of thermal neutrons by potassium-41 with the formation of β-active potassium-42. This has the value 1·0 barn. The abundance of ^{41}K in natural potassium is 6·7 per cent so that the atomic capture cross-section, which determines the detection limit of the element, is 0·067 barn.

On the basis of the definition of reaction cross-section it is clear that for an activating period of t seconds

$$N_p = f\sigma Nt \tag{22}$$

where N_p is the number of atoms of the radionuclide produced, f is the neutron flux (neutrons cm^{-2} sec^{-1}), σ is the atomic reaction cross-section (cm^2), and N is the number of atoms of the element in the sample. If the half-life τ of the radionuclide is much greater than the irradiation time t, the number of atoms disintegrating during irradiation may be neglected. The number of active atoms present at the end of the irradiation is then equal to the number of active atoms formed. In this case the activity at the end of irradiation is given by

$$A = f\sigma Nt\lambda = 0\cdot693 f\sigma Nt/\tau \tag{23}$$

where λ is the disintegration constant.

If the irradiation period cannot be neglected compared with the half-life, equations (22) and (23) cannot be used. Since the number of atoms undergoing disintegration in unit time is proportional to the number of active atoms present, increase in activation time is accompanied by an increasing loss of active atoms. For long irradiation times the rate of loss becomes equal to the constant rate of formation of these atoms. Saturation activity is then attained in the sample.

The activity after any irradiation period is given by the equation:

$$A = f\sigma N(1 - e^{-0.693t/\tau}). \tag{24}$$

The saturation activity is then given by:

$$A_\infty = f\sigma N. \tag{25}$$

When the activity is not measured immediately after the end of irradiation, but after a time t', then we have for all irradiation times:

$$A = f\sigma N(1 - e^{-0.693t/\tau}) e^{-0.693t'/\tau}. \tag{26}$$

We may now estimate the sensitivity of activation analysis. It may be assumed that for a quantitative analysis in which the activity is measured with a Geiger counter at least 20 counts/min must be recorded. For the measurement yield a value of 10 per cent may be considered as typical. The activity A must then amount to at least 3 disintegrations/sec. When irradiation is carried to saturation activity, the detection limit, expressed in number of atoms, is:

$$N_{min} = 3/(f\sigma). \tag{27}$$

When the amount of element in the sample is expressed by its weight W (gram), the detection limit is

$$W_{min} = 5 \cdot 10^{-24} M/(f\sigma) \tag{28}$$

where M is the atomic weight of the element. The sensitivity obtained with the γ-spectrometer will be generally somewhat less.

The cross-section σ for activation by slow neutrons depends on the energy of the neutrons. In general it increases with decrease in energy. Since the cross-section is therefore usually greatest for thermal neutrons, and since these are the most numerous among the slow neutrons present under ordinary conditions of irradiation, activation by thermal neutrons often predominates. However, for certain nuclei the cross-section does not increase continuously with decreasing energy, but shows maxima for particular energies, called "resonance" bands. For such nuclei the activation does not depend on the thermal neutron cross-section only, but in any case, the thermal cross-section may be used for a rough estimate of the sensitivity.

Table 7 gives the activation cross-sections for thermal neutrons for a number of elements that can be determined by activation analysis with these neutrons. The detection limit on the basis of a thermal neutron flux of 10^{12} cm^{-2} sec^{-1} (typical for reactors) is also listed. The value of the detection limit is, of course, inversely proportional to the flux. Elements which can be determined with natural neutron sources in quantities under 1 mg are marked by an asterisk. The recent bibliographies should be consulted for complete information on particular elements (see references p. 83). Table 7,

TABLE 7. SENSITIVITY OF ACTIVATION ANALYSIS BY NEUTRON CAPTURE
(THERMAL NEUTRON FLUX $= 10^{12}$ cm^{-2}sec^{-1})

Atomic number and Element	Radionuclide formed		Atomic reaction cross-section (barns)	Theoretical detection limit (g) for irradiation period of	
	Mass number	Half-life		1 day	Saturation
11 Na	24	15 h	0·41	4×10^{-10}	3×10^{-10}
13 Al	28	2·3 m	0·21	7×10^{-10}	7×10^{-10}
14 Si	31	2·6 h	0·0049	3×10^{-8}	3×10^{-8}
15 P	32	14·1 d	0·23	1×10^{-8}	7×10^{-10}
16 S	35	87·1 d	0·011	4×10^{-6}	1×10^{-8}
17 Cl	38	37·3 m	0·14	1×10^{-9}	1×10^{-9}
18 Ar	41	109 m	0·53	4×10^{-4}	4×10^{-10}
19 K	42	12·4 h	0·06	4×10^{-9}	3×10^{-9}
20 Ca	45	152 d	0·013	3×10^{-6}	2×10^{-8}
21 Sc	46	85 d	22	1×10^{-9}	1×10^{-11}
23 V*	52	3·74 m	4·50	6×10^{-11}	6×10^{-11}
24 Cr	51	25 d	0·50	2×10^{-8}	5×10^{-10}
25 Mn*	56	2·59 h	10·7	3×10^{-11}	3×10^{-11}
26 Fe	59	46 d	0·001	1×10^{-5}	3×10^{-7}
27 Co	60	5·26 y	21·7	2×10^{-8}	1×10^{-11}
28 Ni	65	2·56 h	0·017	2×10^{-8}	2×10^{-8}
29 Cu	64	12·8 d	2·0	3×10^{-10}	2×10^{-10}
30 Zn	65	250 d	0·26	3×10^{-7}	1×10^{-9}
30 Zn	69	57 m	0·17	2×10^{-9}	2×10^{-9}
31 Ga	70	19·8 m	0·85	4×10^{-10}	4×10^{-10}
31 Ga	72	14·1 h	1·30	4×10^{-10}	3×10^{-10}
32 Ge	75	1·37 h	0·14	3×10^{-9}	3×10^{-9}
33 As*	76	1·11 d	4·2	2×10^{-10}	9×10^{-11}
34 Se	81	18 m	0·23	2×10^{-9}	2×10^{-9}
35 Br	80	18·5 m	4·1	1×10^{-10}	1×10^{-10}
35 Br	80^m	4·54 h	1·39	3×10^{-10}	3×10^{-10}
37 Rb	86	19·5 d	0·52	2×10^{-8}	8×10^{-10}
38 Sr	87^m	2·80 h	0·128	1×10^{-8}	1×10^{-8}
39 Y	90	2·54 d	1·24	1×10^{-9}	4×10^{-10}
40 Zr	95	65 d	0·073	4×10^{-7}	6×10^{-9}
40 Zr	97	17 h	0·009	7×10^{-8}	5×10^{-8}
41 Nb	94	6·6 m	1·4	3×10^{-10}	3×10^{-10}
44 Ru	97	2·8 d	0·15	9×10^{-9}	3×10^{-9}
45 Rh*	104	41·8 s	137	4×10^{-12}	4×10^{-12}
46 Pd	109	14·1 h	3·0	3×10^{-10}	2×10^{-10}
47 Ag*	108	2·44 m	23·0	2×10^{-11}	2×10^{-11}
47 Ag*	110	24·5 s	45·6	1×10^{-11}	1×10^{-11}
47 Ag	110^m	270 d	1·1	1×10^{-7}	4×10^{-10}

TABLE 7 (CONTINUED)

Atomic number and Element	Radionuclide formed		Atomic reaction cross-section (barns)	Theoretical detection limit (g) for irradiation period of	
	Mass number	Half-life		1 day	Saturation
48 Cd	115	2·25 d	0·30	7×10^{-9}	2×10^{-9}
49 In*	116^m	53·9 m	138	4×10^{-12}	4×10^{-12}
50 Sn	125	9·4 d	0·009	1×10^{-6}	7×10^{-8}
51 Sb	122	2·63 d	3·8	6×10^{-10}	2×10^{-10}
52 Te	131	25 m	0·074	9×10^{-9}	9×10^{-9}
53 I	128	24·9 m	6·25	1×10^{-10}	1×10^{-10}
54 Ba	139	85 m	0·37	2×10^{-9}	2×10^{-9}
55 Cs	134	254 d	25·6	1×10^{-8}	3×10^{-11}
57 La	140	1·67 d	7·0	3×10^{-10}	1×10^{-10}
58 Ce	143	1·4 d	0·105	2×10^{-8}	7×10^{-9}
59 Pr*	142	19·1 h	10·1	1×10^{-10}	7×10^{-11}
60 Nd	149	2 h	0·16	5×10^{-9}	5×10^{-9}
62 Sm*	153	1·96 d	72·0	3×10^{-11}	1×10^{-11}
63 Eu*	152	9·3 h	299	2×10^{-12}	2×10^{-12}
64 Gd	159	9·5 h	2·3	3×10^{-10}	3×10^{-10}
65 Tb	160	71 d	22	2×10^{-9}	4×10^{-11}
66 Dy*	165	2·42 h	725	1×10^{-12}	1×10^{-12}
67 Ho*	166	1·11 d	59·6	3×10^{-11}	1×10^{-11}
69 Tm	170	127 d	106	1×10^{-9}	8×10^{-12}
70 Yb*	175	4·2 d	22	2×10^{-10}	4×10^{-11}
71 Lu*	177	6·8 d	91·0	9×10^{-11}	1×10^{-11}
72 Hf	181	45 d	3·5	1×10^{-8}	2×10^{-10}
73 Ta	182	117 d	20·6	7×10^{-9}	4×10^{-11}
74 W*	187	24·1 h	10·2	2×10^{-10}	9×10^{-11}
75 Re*	188	18·9 h	46·5	3×10^{-11}	2×10^{-11}
76 Os	193	17 d	2·19	1×10^{-8}	4×10^{-10}
77 Ir	192	70 d	388	2×10^{-10}	2×10^{-12}
77 Ir*	194	19·0 h	79	2×10^{-11}	1×10^{-11}
79 Au*	198	2·69 d	96·4	4×10^{-11}	1×10^{-11}
80 Hg	197^m	24 h	4·5	4×10^{-10}	2×10^{-10}
81 Tl	204	3·5 y	2·2	8×10^{-7}	5×10^{-10}
82 Pb	209	3·3 h	0·0006	2×10^{-6}	2×10^{-6}
83 Bi	210	5 d	0·02	4×10^{-7}	5×10^{-8}
90 Th	233	23·3 m	7·0	1×10^{-10}	1×10^{-10}
92 U	239	23·5 m	2·65		

Notes: s = second; m = minute; h = hour; d = day; y = year; ^{m} = excited isomeric state of nucleus; * = detection limit under 1 mg when using natural neutron sources.

although restricted, shows the usefulness of activation analysis for the determination of small quantities. Many elements not included in the table because of their small industrial importance can also be determined in the reactor in minute quantities.

The sensitivities given are limiting values which may be attained under favourable conditions. The value attained in practice depends considerably on the nature of accompanying substances, the time needed for chemical separations, the self-absorption of the radiation within the sample, the measurement yield, and the half-life of the radionuclide produced.

More extensive tables and diagrams have been prepared which give the activities and the sensitivities of activation analysis after different irradiation periods, but in computing the sensitivities only some of the factors mentioned were considered [126, 276, 278]. In some tables the numerical data for activation by fast neutrons are also listed [276, 278].

If an accompanying element has an atomic number differing by only one or two units from that of the element being determined, certain nuclear reactions may interfere. The radionuclide to be measured may be produced from the accompanying material as well. An example is the determination of sodium in aluminium. The reaction $^{27}Al(n, \alpha)$ ^{24}Na is induced by fast neutrons; its product is identical with that of slow neutron capture in sodium [128].

For a number of important elements the sensitivity of activation analysis has been compared with that of other methods [129]. The errors likely in activation analysis as well as the methods for their suppression have been discussed [112, 130].

6.6.5. *Examples of Activation Analysis with Neutrons*

A number of examples will now be given to indicate the possible applications and the working technique of activation analysis with neutrons.

A determination of alkali elements without chemical separation by early techniques has been described. After activation in a reactor, traces of potassium and caesium in rubidium were determined by following the decay curve for several days [132]. Use was made of three radionuclides with half-lives suitable for discrimination: caesium-134, $\tau = 2 \cdot 8$ h; potassium-42, $\tau = 12 \cdot 8$ h; rubidium-86, $\tau = 19 \cdot 5$ days. The natural radioactivity of potassium is so small that it does not interfere with the activation analysis. The simultaneous determination of sodium and potassium without chemical separation is not possible by an analogous method because the nuclides ^{24}Na and ^{42}K have similar half-lives. Such a determination was, however, carried out on the basis of the difference in the energy of the β-radiations. One measurement was carried out with an absorber of an area weight of 700 mg/cm^2 which allows γ-radiation of both nuclides to pass without significant loss, but absorbs the β-radiation of ^{24}Na completely, and that of ^{42}K partly. A second measurement was carried out with a filter of 1700 mg/cm^2 which registered only the γ-radiation [132]. From these two results the activity of the potassium and the sodium could be calculated. It was possible to determine potassium down to 3 μg and sodium down to 0·3 μg in the nerve fibres of cuttlefish (*Sepia*) [133, 134]. Alkali carbonates were used as reference samples.

Other examples of non-destructive analysis refer to rhodium, silver and indium, which have exceptionally large capture cross-sections. A 25-mg radium–beryllium source, available relatively cheaply and giving a flux of 3×10^3 slow neutrons $cm^{-2}sec^{-1}$ is sufficient to determine 1 per cent of these elements with a relative accuracy of a few per cent. Because of the short half-lives of the radionuclides produced in the determination of rhodium and silver (2 and 4 min, respectively), quite short irradiations are sufficient. Hence appreciable activation of accompanying elements is avoided even when the cross-sections for such processes are high. The methods may be applied to any kind of sample and can be completed within a few minutes [135]. The thickness of silver on a brass support in wave guides has been measured by activation with a 200 mg radium–beryllium source [179].

The detection of arsenic in hair, a matter of importance for forensic medicine and industrial hygiene, is a further example of non-destructive activation analysis. Activation of single hairs in a reactor has made it possible to determine not only the total amount of arsenic, but, by scanning with a counter, its distribution within the hair [136].

Similarly, neutron activation of paper chromatograms, followed by scanning with a counter or by autoradiography, can be used for the location of substances containing atoms with large capture cross-sections [137]. Irradiation of ground surfaces of minerals or metals makes it possible to activate selectively individual components or trace impurities, and to reveal their distribution by means of autoradiography [138, 139] (see p. 47).

Chemical separation is necessary if other radionuclides interfere with the measurements. As a first illustration of analysis with chemical separation the alkali elements will again be discussed. The following methods have been developed [140]: The sample is irradiated and dissolved. Carriers are then added for the alkali elements to be determined and for other elements that are present in small quantities and can be activated. Heavy metals and alkaline earths are removed by precipitation with ammonium sulphide and ammonium carbonate, so that only the alkali elements remain in solution. If it is necessary to separate the alkali elements from each other, this is done either by precipitation or by chromatography.

Precipitation methods are used for sodium and potassium. Sodium is precipitated with excess uranyl acetate after driving off the ammonium salts by heating. To avoid interference of the decay products of uranium in the activity measurement, the precipitate is not counted directly. The uranyl acetate is washed with alcohol and ether, dried, and treated with hydrochloric acid in butyl alcohol. Sodium chloride precipitates out and is measured. In the analysis of potassium present in magnesium and lithium salts, the potassium is precipitated as the chloroplatinate, and this precipitate is measured directly (see [1]).

Chromatographic separation of the alkali cations can be performed by adsorption on a cation exchange column and elution with very dilute hydrochloric or perchloric acid [141, 142]. The eluate is then led through a counter, and small fractions are collected. The fractions in which the elements are found are indicated by the count rate. All fractions containing the same element are then combined, and their activity is measured in a liquid counter, and compared with the activity of reference samples. If necessary, the solution is first concentrated and then measured. All the alkali elements can be determined in this way, with the exception of lithium which gives no suitable radioisotope on neutron irradiation. Estimation of the yield of the chemical separation is unnecessary in this process, since separation on ion exchange columns can be carried out without appreciable loss. Chromatographic separation on ion exchange columns may also be used for the activation analysis of mixtures of the rare earths [142].

A further example of activation analysis using chemical separation is the determination of gold in meteorites [143]. After irradiation in a reactor the sample is dissolved, gold carrier is added, and the gold chloride is extracted with ethyl acetate from a 10 per cent hydrochloric acid solution. The chloride is then reduced with hydroquinone to metallic gold; this is filtered off, and its activity is measured (see p. 84).

A novel method has been worked out for the determination of zirconium in zirconium–hafnium mixtures [144]. Here, the difficulty of distinguishing between the activities induced in the two elements by neutron capture, or of chemically separating zirconium from hafnium had to be overcome. However, the radionuclide zirconium-95, which is produced by neutron irradiation, undergoes β-decay to niobium-95, which is itself β-active. Therefore, instead of separating zirconium from hafnium, the much simpler separation of niobium from zirconium and hafnium is carried out. The activity of the niobium-95 is then measured.

A good example of trace analysis by activation is provided by the examination of electrolytic magnesium [145]. The sample was submitted to a neutron flux of $5 \cdot 10^{11} \text{cm}^{-2}$ sec^{-1} for 4 weeks, and the radionuclides produced were isolated with carriers. The following impurities were found, the figures giving the contents in parts per million (ppm) by weight; arsenic 0·13; calcium 1·3–1·7; chromium 0·1–0·4; copper 7·7–8·0; phosphorus 2·2; potassium 1·2–1·4; strontium 1·1–2·1. In alloy steel, 16 elements have been determined by activation [269]. An irradiation of 30 sec was sufficient for 0·6 ppm of vanadium or 2 ppm of aluminium in iron [273]. Aluminium [273, 313] and zirconium [273] as well as beryllium [272] of very high purity have also been tested.

Activation analysis is particularly suitable for very small amounts of impurities in semi-conductors (germanium and silicon) [1, 3, 117, 146–150, 331, 338, 366] (Section 8.6).

For the determination of impurities in silicon carbide, the neutron-activated material was first treated with chlorine and then with oxygen at elevated temperatures to volatilize the silicon and carbon. The substances condensed in the cooler parts of the apparatus or remaining in the residue were dissolved in acid, heated to dryness in a platinum dish, and submitted to activity measurement [151].

The examples so far given depend on activation by slow neutron capture. Other nuclear reactions induced by slow neutrons are used less frequently. Thus for the detection of very small quantities of nitrogen in metals or organic compounds the reaction $^{14}\text{N}(n, p)$ ^{14}C is suitable [152]. Uranium may be determined by irradiation with neutrons and measurement of a radionuclide formed in nuclear fission (fission product). Thus the radioisotopes of barium, tellurium or xenon that are produced in this process in good yield may be separated chemically and then determined by activity measurement [153, 154, 268].

It is also possible to determine uranium by counting the number of fissions during irradiation. This is done by introducing a thin sample into an ionization chamber and irradiating with neutrons, the amplifier being so biassed that it will count only fission fragments and not α-particles [155, 156]. Nuclear emulsions of selective sensitivity may also be employed for fission counting; they are pressed against the sample during irradiation [157]. In all these determinations the evaluation is carried out by comparison with reference samples of known uranium content.

Similar photographic methods are suitable for lithium [158–160] and boron [161–163]. On neutron irradiation these elements do not form radionuclides which could be measured, but they give α-particles of high energy according to the reactions $^6\mathrm{Li}(n, \alpha)$ $^3\mathrm{H}$ and $^{10}\mathrm{B}(n, \alpha)$ $^7\mathrm{Li}$, respectively. The α-particles may again be detected by nuclear emulsions. In the reaction $^{10}\mathrm{B}(n, \alpha)$ $^7\mathrm{Li}$, the nucleus $^7\mathrm{Li}$ is first formed in an excited state, which decays to the ground state by emission of 0·48 MeV γ-rays. This radiation has been made the basis of determination methods for boron in explosives (cartridges) [358], in solutions of boric acid [359] and in synthetic detergents [357].

In mixture with water or in solids containing oxygen, lithium may be estimated by the reaction chain $^6\mathrm{Li}(n, t)$ $^4\mathrm{He}$ and $^{16}\mathrm{O}(t, n)$ $^{18}\mathrm{F}$; the positron-active fluorine is measured by coincidence scintillation spectrometry [342] (see p. 97).

Fast neutrons can be applied to induce (n, p), (n, α) and $(n, 2n)$ reactions in many substances [271]. Small amounts of phosphorus, sulphur and chlorine have been detected in paper chromatograms. The paper strips were inserted into a beryllium capsule which was bombarded with deuterons in a cyclotron. Fast neutrons were produced by the reaction $^9_4\mathrm{Be}(d, n)$ $^{10}_5\mathrm{B}$, and these induced the following nuclear reactions in the substances on the paper strip: $^{31}\mathrm{P}(n, p)$ $^{31}\mathrm{Si}$; $^{32}\mathrm{S}(n, p)$ $^{32}\mathrm{P}$; $^{35}\mathrm{Cl}(n, p)$ $^{35}\mathrm{S}$. Only the last of these three reactions is brought about by slow neutrons as well. The various radionuclides produced were distinguished on the basis of their half-lives and radiation energies [164].

Fast neutrons with energy exceeding 14 MeV, from the reaction $^3_1\mathrm{H}(d, n)$ $^4_2\mathrm{He}$, have been used for the determination of the elements just referred to, and also of oxygen. The half-lives of the nuclides produced are in some cases so short, e. g., in the case of nitrogen-16 from the reaction $^{16}\mathrm{O}(n, p)$ $^{16}\mathrm{N}$ only 7·3 sec, that activation and measurement require special techniques [127, 165, 166, 187]. The method is finding increasing application for the determination of oxygen [281, 282, 346, 363, 367]. Measurement is usually by means of the high-energy (6–7 MeV) γ-radiation emitted by $^{16}\mathrm{N}$. 0·001 per cent oxygen in beryllium may be determined. (Other methods for determining oxygen by activation analysis are based on the reactions $^{16}\mathrm{O}(t, n)^{18}\mathrm{F}$ and $^{16}\mathrm{O}(\gamma, n)^{15}\mathrm{O}$ (see p. 98). A survey of the various methods of the analysis of oxygen by activation has been given [280].)

The formation of $^{16}\mathrm{N}$ may also be used for the activation analysis of fluorine through the reaction $^{19}\mathrm{F}(n, \alpha)$ $^{16}\mathrm{N}$. Oxygen does not interfere with this determination if neutrons produced by bombarding beryllium with 2 MeV deuterons, i.e., neutrons having a not too high energy, are applied [167].

The feasibility of further determinations by fast (14 MeV) neutron activation has been shown: Aluminium can be determined using the process $^{27}\mathrm{Al}(n, p)^{27}\mathrm{Mg}$ and silicon by the process $^{28}\mathrm{Si}(n, p)^{28}\mathrm{Al}$. In both cases, the characteristic γ-rays emitted by the product nuclides are measured [363].

It is a general advantage of activation with fast neutrons that accompanying substances which absorb slow neutrons strongly do not interfere much [168]. This was already seen in connection with the determination of sulphur through the reaction $^{32}S(n, p)$ ^{32}P where activation of arsenic and chromium was avoided. However, it must be remembered that the activation cross-sections for fast neutrons are generally considerably lower than those for slow neutrons. The sensitivity of activation analysis with fast neutrons is thus correspondingly less. Though accelerators are commonly used as sources of fast neutrons, in certain cases reactors may be preferable [271].

Inelastic scattering of fast neutrons is a further nuclear process that can be utilized. Samples are bombarded with fast neutrons and the characteristic prompt γ-rays from short-lived excited states are detected by γ-spectrometry. Such techniques have been found applicable for carbon and oxygen determinations in coals [363] (see also Section 7.4.6).

Finally, it should be mentioned that activation analysis with neutrons can also serve the determination of the isotopic composition of an element. Thus, uranium-238 may be determined in mixtures with the isotopes 235 or 233 by the formation of the β-active uranium-239 through neutron capture. After irradiation, natural uranium is added as carrier and separated chemically from the fission products [121]. On the other hand, uranium-235 can be determined in uranium by slow neutron fission [169]. The abundance of isotopes in lead [170], bromine, ruthenium, hafnium, tungsten and osmium [171] has also been determined by activation. In certain cases, activation analysis has advantages compared with mass spectrometry.

A few elements emit delayed neutrons after irradiation with neutrons. Their flux, determined with neutron counters (boron chambers), with monitor foils consisting of elements that are readily activated, or with scintillation counters containing phosphors loaded with boron or lithium (see p. 100), is then a measure of the amount of the element present. In this way, better than 10^{-7} g uranium was detected with a thermal flux of 4×10^{12} cm^{-2} sec^{-1}, and 10^{-6} g thorium with a fast neutron flux of $1\cdot 4 \times 10^{12}$ [279]. Lithium in aqueous solution may be determined on the basis of the reaction sequence $^{6}Li(n, t)^{4}He$, $^{18}O(t, \alpha)^{17}N$; the nitrogen-17 emits delayed neutrons with a half-life of $4\cdot 1$ sec [263].

6.6.6. *Activation with Ions*

In comparatively few analytical procedures use is made of activation directly by charged particles. As sources, natural radionuclides, accelerators or, indirectly, reactors can be used. In nuclear reactions of protons, deuterons and helium nuclei (α-particles) radionuclides are produced that generally differ from those obtained with neutrons. For this reason these particles may sometimes be used for the activation of elements that are not satisfactorily activated by neutrons. As in the case of neutrons, analyses have also been carried out by measuring radiations emitted during the reaction with the projectiles.

Several procedures for the determination of traces of carbon in iron with charged particles have been described in the literature; they are of practical interest. By bombardment with deuterons or protons carbon is converted into β-active nitrogen-13 (half-life 9·9 min) according to the reactions $^{12}C(d, n)$ ^{13}N or $^{12}C(p, \gamma)$ ^{13}N, respectively. It is possible to measure the activity of the nitrogen directly on the iron sample [172–175]. A more sensitive method provides for the dissolution of the activated sample and the isolation of the nitrogen as ammonia [176]. For the detection of ^{13}N it is advantageous to measure the annihilation radiation due to the emitted positrons. This has an energy of 0·51 MeV. Two scintillation counters with channels adjusted to the range 0·4 to 0·6 MeV are placed on opposite sides of the sample, and are arranged in coincidence. This arrangement shows high selectivity for the annihilation radiation. The background count rate is therefore small, and it is possible to detect 3×10^{-4} per cent carbon [177]. Alternatively, the prompt γ-radiation emitted in the $^{12}C(p, \gamma)^{13}N$ reaction may be measured [352]. For boron, the reaction $^{11}B(p, n)^{11}C$ may be used [274]. In all these procedures reference samples are used for comparison.

Because of the low penetrating power of ions, the nuclear reactions mentioned take place only in very thin surface layers. For this reason, slight carbonaceous impurities on the surface can produce misleading results. Precautions must therefore be taken against fat or oil layers on the metal.

On the other hand, the interaction of ions with thin surface layers can be applied to the analysis of these layers. Carbon, nitrogen, oxygen, fluorine and sodium can be determined with a sensitivity of 10^{-8} to 10^{-6} g/cm^2 of surface. Variations in layer thickness can be detected with a resolving power of 10^{-2} μ. Similarly local variations in concentration within a surface layer can be studied. In some cases, the activity of radionuclides formed on irradiation is utilized, in other cases the radiation emitted promptly in the nuclear reaction is measured (see also p. 103) [178].

The liberation of neutrons from beryllium in its reaction with α-particles is used for the determination of this highly toxic element in air, a matter of importance in industrial hygiene. A known volume of air from the plant is drawn through a filter, the dust separated is submitted to α-radiation from polonium, and the 4·5 MeV γ-radiation emitted in the nuclear reaction $^9Be(\alpha, n\gamma)$ ^{12}C is measured with a scintillation spectrometer [179].

Alternatively, the neutrons emitted in this reaction are counted. In one investigation, the powdered sample (beryllium ore) was exposed as a dry solid layer to the α-rays from several hundred millicuries of polonium [317]. To a lesser extent, neutrons are produced in the (α, n) reaction on fluorine so that fluorite can also be assayed [317]. Solutions of beryllium, fluorine or boron compounds have been similarly analysed by exposing them to an external polonium source [319].

Improved selectivity is obtained through measurement of the prompt γ-rays of characteristic energies which are emitted by the excited nuclei produced in the reactions of the α-rays. For instance, in the irradiation of beryllium γ-rays of 4·45 and 7·65 MeV are emitted (see above), in that of boron γ-rays of 2·3 and 3·8 MeV, and in that of fluorine mainly γ-rays of 1·24 MeV [322, 323]. Positron emitting nuclides formed in α-ray bombardment may also be utilized [318].

It may be added that the simple device built for the analysis of solid powders by the (α, n) reaction may also be used to determine minerals, such as diamond or scheelite, by the radioluminescence induced by the polonium α-rays. The light intensity, estimated

visually or measured with a photomultiplier, is a linear function of the concentration
of the relevant mineral in the sample [321].

Oxygen is detected down to concentrations of 10^{-4} per cent with the high-energy
tritium ions (tritons) from the nuclear reaction $^6Li(n, \alpha) \, ^3H$ (see p. 95). An intimate
mixture of the substance under analysis with a lithium compound or a suitable solution is irradiated with slow neutrons in a reactor. Some of the tritons react with oxygen
according to $^{16}O(t, n) \, ^{18}F$. ^{18}F has a half-life of 112 min, and can, for example, be
detected with a scintillation spectrometer by measuring the annihilation γ-radiation
due to its positrons. In some investigations, fluorine has been separated chemically
to avoid interference from other radionuclides. The method can be used for oxygen in
zirconium, titanium, aluminium, lithium, silicon and nickel [120, 165, 180, 254, 283 to
286]. This method is interesting in that the high flux of slow neutrons available in
reactors is utilized to carry out irradiations with charged particles. (For the determination of lithium by the same nuclear reaction, see p. 95.) Irradiation with tritons
may also be performed with accelerators [280]. Other charged particle reactions have
likewise been employed for oxygen determinations, although to a smaller extent than
the process $^{16}O(t, n) \, ^{18}F$ [280].

Oxygen-18 in water may be assayed by irradiation with fast neutrons. The recoil
protons induce the reaction $^{18}O(p, n) \, ^{18}F$, and the positrons from the fluorine are
measured by coincidence scintillation spectrometry. Care must be taken that the sample
is not markedly enriched in deuterium so that the density of the protons is too low.
Any excess deuterium is easily removed by exchange with ammonia, which is subsequently swept out [343].

6.6.7. *Activation by γ- and X-radiation*

Irradiation with γ-rays has been used primarily for the detection of beryllium, i.e.,
beryllium-9 [181–186, 275, 297, 317, 324], and deuterium [187]. Only these two nuclides react with photons from natural radioactive elements (maximum energy 2·2MeV)
to give neutrons by a (γ, n) process ("nuclear photo-effect"). The radiation source
may consist, e.g., of radium with its daughter products, or of antimony-124 (see p. 85).
The flux of neutrons produced during irradiation of the sample is a measure of
the quantity of deuterium or beryllium present. Since slow neutrons can be measured with appreciably better yield than fast neutrons, the sample is surrounded
by a moderator. The neutrons are counted by one of the methods mentioned on
p. 100.

The γ-radiation of sodium-24 is distinguished by its high energy of 2·75 MeV. These
rays eject photoneutrons from D_2O, and the flux of these neutrons is a measure of
the amount of sodium-24 in a sample. Fractions of a microgram of sodium may thus
be determined by neutron irradiation and subsequent measurement of the neutron flux
induced in D_2O. Few foreign elements other than gallium interfere [262]. The principle
is also applicable to some other elements [353].

Irradiation with X-rays from a betatron (15 MeV) may be used for the activation
of metal surfaces for autoradiography; photons of this energy give rise to β-active
nuclides from many elements by (γ, n) reactions. Variations in the period of irradi-

ation and of the cooling period after irradiation allow determination of several elements in the same sample [188].

A method for determining oxygen also makes use of high energy photons; the reaction is $^{16}O(\gamma, n)$ ^{15}O. The emitted neutrons or the radiation from the positron emitter ^{15}O (half-life 124 min) may be registered [288–291].

Iodine has been determined in biological materials by irradiating samples with high energy bremsstrahlung from a 22 MeV electron accelerator. The characteristic γ-rays from iodine-126 formed by γ, n-reaction were measured [364].

According to a new principle of activation analysis, nuclides and elements can be determined through the excitation of nuclei by intense bremsstrahlung. The nuclei then return to the ground state, emitting γ-rays (γ-disintegration, see Section 2.9). The intensity of this γ-radiation is measured and compared with that of a reference sample. The half-lives of excited nuclei (nuclear isomers) may amount to seconds, minutes, or even hours. Discrimination between γ-rays from different elements on the basis of their different energies is possible. This method may be applied to selenium, strontium, silver, cadmium, indium, lutetium, hafnium, iridium, gold and other elements. Even where the sensitivity is less than that for activation by slow neutrons, the procedure may still be of advantage whenever its selectivity is superior [246].

6.7. Analysis by Absorption or Scattering of Nuclear Rays (Absorption Analysis)

Of the rays emitted by atomic nuclei in transformations, neutrons and β- and γ-rays are suitable for absorption analysis. For these radiations the essential requirement for absorption analysis may be fulfilled, that is, the rays are absorbed to very different extents by different substances. The absorption of X-rays emitted as a consequence of radioactive decay also finds application in analysis. Finally, analysis may be carried out by measuring scattered radiations (consisting of neutrons, β-, γ- and X-rays) or characteristic fluorescence radiation emitted from the extranuclear regions of the atoms on exposure to nuclear radiation.

6.7.1. *Analysis by Neutron Attenuation*

Neutron absorption analysis is based on the considerable differences between the interaction probabilities of neutrons, generally slow neutrons, with different nuclides. (Surveys of the method have been published [189–191] (see also [1, 248])). Such probabilities can be expressed in terms of cross-sections, as discussed on p. 88. However, cross-sections used in activation analysis refer to particular nuclear reactions (partial cross-sections), while the attenuation of a neutron beam depends on the total cross-section or attenuation cross-section. This is the sum of the cross-sections of all reactions taking place, and of the scattering cross-section. By averaging over all the isotopes of an element, the attenuation cross-section of that element (atomic attenuation cross-section) is obtained. The attenuation of a well collimated beam of neutrons of uniform energy on passage through a layer of material is then given by the expression

$$\frac{f_d}{f_0} = e^{-d(\sigma_1 n_1 + \sigma_2 n_2 \cdots)}, \qquad (29)$$

where f_0 denotes the neutron flux (cm^{-2} sec^{-1}) before entry into the layer, and f_d the flux after passing through a layer of thickness d (cm); $\sigma_1, \sigma_2, \ldots$ are the atomic attenuation cross-sections (cm^2) of the individual elements in the layer for the neutrons used, while $n_1, n_2, \ldots$ are the concentrations of these elements (atoms·cm^{-3}).

We shall now consider the differences that occur between the attenuation cross-sections of the individual elements. For fast neutrons the cross-sections of all elements are similar, and are less than 10 barn. Many elements have cross-sections for slow neutrons of about the same magnitude. However, some elements have much greater cross-sections for slow neutrons – up to 10^5 barn. The value of the cross-section depends on the energy. High values are often found in the thermal (energy) region, and sometimes resonance peaks appear in the epithermal region, as reported on p. 89. Only elements with high cross-sections are susceptible to neutron absorption analysis.

The method is not of practical importance for all elements for which it is in principle suitable. The high attenuation cross-sections depend in the majority of cases on high neutron capture cross-sections, that is, cross-sections for the (n, γ)-reaction. Now in neutron capture radionuclides are often formed, so that activation analysis and absorption analysis compete. Since activation analysis is more sensitive and more convenient, it will usually be preferred. However, there are elements which yield no radionuclides suitable for activation analysis although they absorb neutrons readily; for such cases absorption analysis is important.

Several types of equipment are used for measuring slow neutron fluxes, particularly monitor foils and neutron counters [247]. The principles of measurement will be given here, and more references will be found in connection with the application to soil science (Section 12.8).

Neutrons are uncharged particles. Therefore they do not themselves ionize, and cannot be measured directly. In all methods of measurement, the slow neutrons are therefore allowed to fall upon substances with which they react; as a consequence of this reaction, radiation is emitted. Because of the energy dependence of the cross-sections of these nuclear reactions, the sensitivity of the instrument depends, among other factors, on the energy of the neutrons.

Monitor foils for the detection of slow neutrons consist of substances with high cross-sections for activation by slow neutrons. The foils are introduced into the neutron beam to be measured for a certain time, and the induced β- or γ-activity is measured subsequently. Substances used for this purpose include indium or rhodium metal and manganese dioxide powder. Dysprosium oxide gives particularly high activity. Unlike the neutron counters (see below), the monitors do not measure the instantaneous flux but give an integrated value over the exposure time. Thus they do not permit immediate or continuous registration. It is also seen that a correct mean value is only obtained when the half-life of the induced activity is long compared with the exposure time.

For instantaneous neutron counting the reaction $^{10}B(n, \alpha)$ ^{7}Li is much used. The instruments contain boron compounds, and the neutrons are counted through the energetic α-particles (helions) and lithium nuclei produced. Boron fluoride counters are most common. They are built like counting-tubes, but are filled with boron tri-fluoride gas and are operated in the proportional region. The number of impulses per unit time is a measure of the flux of slow neutrons with a definite energy spectrum. For high sensitivity it is best to use the fluoride of the pure isotope boron-10, of which natural boron contains only 20 per cent. In other neutron counters, the boron is applied as a solid coating on the wall.

Another type of compact instrument for counting slow neutrons provides for neutron capture in cadmium and registration of the emitted γ-radiation by a Geiger counter. Unlike boron counters, these instruments do not need high gain amplifiers or high operating potential [192, 309]; they are, however, less sensitive. It is also possible to let the slow neutrons react with boron (enriched if desired) embedded in a scintillator, and to count the light flashes in the usual way [193]. Instead of the boron-loaded, lithium-loaded scintillators may also be used. A suitable crystal consists of lithium iodide (preferably enriched in the isotope lithium-6) activated with europium [194]. Alternatively cerium-activated silicate glass containing lithium may be used [329]; this is resistant against moisture and most corrosive agents. The slow neutrons induce the reaction $^{6}_{3}Li(n, \alpha)$ $^{3}_{1}H$. More energy is released in this reaction than in that with boron, and therefore stronger light flashes are obtained. In both types of scintillation counters for neutrons, the background may be reduced considerably by discrimination. Absolute measurements of slow neutron fluxes are difficult. Such measurements are best made with boron fluoride counters, but they are rarely necessary in neutron absorption analysis.

The analyses are carried out by measuring attenuation, i.e., by comparing the flux in absence and in presence of the sample, and evaluating through comparison with reference samples having similar composition. Evaluation of attenuation measurements on the basis of tabulated cross-section values is much less accurate since many factors are involved.

Cadmium is of great importance for the investigation of neutron absorption. The absorption cross-section of this element (more precisely: of cadmium-113) is very large below 0·3 eV, but falls to a low value for higher energies. Thus it is possible to absorb selectively thermal neutrons with rather thin cadmium foil (0·5 mm). Such foils are used to single out the effects of the thermal neutrons. The difference between the activities induced in the presence of a surrounding cadmium foil and in its absence is due to the thermal neutrons, and is called the "cadmium difference".

When the neutron attenuation occurs mainly through absorption, as is usually the case, poor geometry may be accepted. This means that the sensitive part of the neutron detector (neutron counter or monitor foil) may subtend a large solid angle at the absorbing sample under investigation. For example, an indium foil may be placed simply on the sample; the solid angle subtended then approaches 2π (see Fig. 25). On the other hand, in measurements of neutron attenuation due to scattering, as in hydrogen determinations (see p. 103), good geometry is essential, and the neutron beam must be narrowly collimated between the sample and the detector. Only in this way is it possible to prevent scattered neutrons from being registered by the instrument. Obviously it is necessary to use much stronger neutron sources with good geometry than with poor geometry.

For industrial laboratories absorption analysis is most useful when it can be carried out with comparatively simple equipment, particularly when the slow neutron flux from natural sources is sufficient. This is the case when the element of interest has a high cross-section, when a broad spectrum of slow neutrons consisting mainly of thermal neutrons may be used, and when poor geometry is permissible. A simple arrangement for such determinations is shown in Fig. 25. The cadmium foil in the paraffin wax block prevents the thermal neutrons from reaching the monitor foil (dysprosium) by any other route than through the sample under analysis.

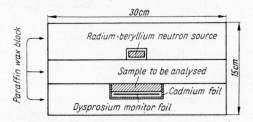

FIG. 25. Simple arrangement for neutron absorption analysis

In absorption analysis, the constancy of the neutron flux from natural sources is of particular advantage. The sensitivity and precision of absorption analysis are essentially limited by the accuracy of the determination of attenuation, and this, in turn, by the accuracy of the flux measurements and by the constancy of the flux. The flux from natural sources is sufficiently large to reduce the statistical error of flux measurements to a very small value. In going to strong sources (accelerators or reactors), the decrease in constancy of flux may exert greater influence on the accuracy of attenuation measurement than the further reduction in statistical error. Thus absorption analysis with strong sources may show lower sensitivity than that with the very constant natural sources. But even if this is not the case, only small gains in sensitivity or accuracy of absorption analysis are possible by increasing the neutron flux. This is, of course, in contrast to activation analysis, where sensitivity is proportional to flux.

The following elements are capable of the most sensitive determination: lithium (total cross-section for thermal neutrons 70 barn), boron (720 barn), cadmium (2470 barn), samarium (8900 barn), europium (4800 barn), gadolinium (42000 barn), and dysprosium (1150 barn). Under certain conditions, quantities as small as a few milligrams can be detected.

For industry, the determination of boron is useful [199]. It has been used for glasses [195, 196], other silicates [197], boron carbide [189], synthetic detergents [357] and rocks containing boron [198]. Cadmium may be assayed with high sensitivity in zinc [200]. On the basis of neutron absorption, the thickness of thin layers of cadmium, silver and gold on substances of low cross-section may be measured.

Small amounts of hydrogen in fluorocarbon compounds have been determined by neutron attenuation [189]. Since the fairly high attenuation cross-section of hydrogen is mainly due to scattering, good geometry and a strong neutron source are needed. More recently, hydrogen has been determined similarly in hydrocarbons. Either thermalized neutrons from a plutonium–beryllium source or slow neutrons of selected energies from a reactor were employed. A collimated beam was directed at an aluminium cell containing the sample, and the transmitted neutrons were measured with a boron trifluoride counter. The sensitivity was 0·05 per cent hydrogen under the best conditions [328].

Elements with strong resonance absorption may be determined selectively on the basis of the energy dependence of neutron attenuation in the appropriate energy region. In work of this kind foreign elements generally do not interfere since the resonance peaks only rarely overlap. These methods have as yet found little application. The selection of neutrons of well-defined energy requires complicated equipment, and only a small proportion of the neutrons have the particular desired energy, so that a powerful neutron source such as a cyclotron or a nuclear reactor must be used. Neutron absorption spectroscopy may be of interest for determinations of indium in tin, hafnium in strontium, tantalum in niobium, and manganese in aluminium and iron. It may also be used for the analysis of mixtures of rare earths, and for thickness measurements of thin layers of silver, gold, rhodium and cadmium on any substrate [189, 190].

6.7.2. *Analysis by Slowing-down of Neutrons or Ions*

Hydrogen and its compounds may be detected through their strong moderating action (see p. 86). A suitable arrangement consists of a natural neutron source and a neutron detector. This may be a monitor, such as a cylinder of rhodium foil, or a neutron counter. This unit is embedded in the sample under analysis. It is of advantage to work with a γ-free polonium–beryllium source. The slow neutron flux in the source and its surroundings is determined by the concentration of substances with very low atomic weight, particularly of hydrogen. The detector responds practically to slow neutrons only.

The method is suitable for the rapid measurement of the water content or mineral oil content of earth layers [201–207, 309, 314]. Its applications in petroleum technology and in agriculture will be discussed in Sections 7.4 and 12.8, respectively. It is also possible to determine the moisture content of cement [208] (see p. 248) and, with moderate accuracy, the hydrogen content of hydrocarbons, even in pipes or vessels from outside these [209, 315, 316]. Special equipment has been built for the determination of moisture in objects accessible from one side only, such as a flat surface of hardened concrete [311]. In all these procedures, the presence of substances which absorb slow neutrons strongly, such as chlorine, manganese and boron, is a source of error [196].

The scattering of fast ions by atoms in thin surface layers may be used for the analysis of the composition of such layers, since the energy loss in scattering depends, in addition to its dependence on the direction of scattering, on the mass of the scattering nucleus. The determination of the energy of the scattered particles requires very good resolving power, and therefore highly specialized and complicated equipment. Descriptions have been given of the determination of oxygen, aluminium, silicon, sulphur, calcium, iron, copper, silver, barium and lead [178] (see also p. 97).

6.7.3. *Analysis by Absorption and Scattering of β-rays*

The attenuation of β-rays on passing through materials occurs through electrical interaction with the electrons (see p. 20). The binding energy of the electrons in the atoms, ions, or molecules has little influence on these interactions so that the absorbing power of a layer of material is nearly proportional to the number of electrons per unit area. For most elements, the ratio of atomic weight to atomic number (the latter being equal to the number of electrons in the atom) is between 2 and 2·5, so that the absorption coefficient for β-radiation does not depend greatly on the nature of the absorbing material, provided that the thickness is expressed in terms of area weight, that is, if the mass-absorption coefficient in units of cm^2/g is used (see p. 22).

The one major exception to this rule is provided by hydrogen, for which the ratio of atomic weight to atomic number is only 1. Consequently, the absorption per unit mass is about twice as great as that for other elements. If the substance under investigation contains only one other element in addition to hydrogen, the absorption of β-radiation by a sample of known mass then gives the hydrogen content with great accuracy. In this case, hydrogen determination provides a complete elementary analysis.

The method is suitable for liquid hydrocarbons. A fixed measuring cell is used, and the mass of the sample filling the cell is determined by a density measurement. Pure hydrocarbons are used for calibration. Instruments for such determinations are available commercially [210–213] (see also [325, 335]). Some of these use strontium-90 (with its daughter yttrium-90) as radiation source. The β-rays from this source have a maximum energy of 2·18 MeV. There is no γ-radiation, so that radiation protection for a 10–25 mc source is simple.

One instrument of this kind (Fig. 26) contains a single strontium–yttrium source which is placed between two thin mica foils [211–213]. In one direction, the β-radiation passes through an absorber of fixed thickness and then directly into an ionization chamber. In the other direction, the β-particles pass first through the measuring cell, then through an absorber of variable thickness, and finally into an ionization chamber. The variable absorber is wedge-shaped, i.e., the thickness is adjusted by shifting the absorber in the same way as in some colorimeters. The two ionization chambers are arranged in a compensation circuit. By means of an amplifier and a galvanometer that position of the variable absorber is found for which the radiation intensities falling on the two ionization chambers are equal. This gives the absorption in the measuring cell. The measuring cell is in communication with a space which is also filled with the sample, and in which the density is measured with a sensitive hydrostatic balance. Because the density is obtained for the actual conditions of the absorption measurement, no thermostatic control is needed. With such equipment the C–H determination may be carried out in 5 min with an accuracy, for the hydrogen content, of ± 0.02 relative weight per cent.

In other types of equipment (see, e.g. [210]) two strontium–yttrium sources are provided. Radiation from the one goes through a cell containing a reference liquid, while that from the other passes through the measuring cell. The two radiation beams then go into identical ionization chambers, and the difference in the currents from the two chambers is measured. The density is determined pyknometrically.

With such instruments hydrogen determinations are also possible for liquids other than hydrocarbons, but, for precision, corrections for the content of other elements must be introduced [210, 212].

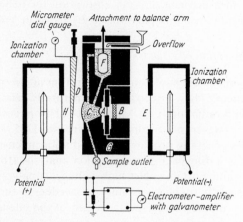

FIG. 26. Apparatus for determination of carbon and hydrogen by β-ray absorption [212] (*A*) β-ray source; (*B*) Absorber of constant thickness; (*C*) Cell for sample; (*D*) Wedge-shaped absorber; (*E, H*) Windows of ionization chambers; (*F*) Float of the buoyancy balance; (*G*) Copper block enclosing source and cell

Similar equipment is suitable for the continuous determination of the composition of many binary liquid mixtures. Furthermore, the concentration of substances of high atomic weight in certain solvents can be determined in this way [214]. The instruments developed for such analyses can be used for the automatic control of mixing processes.

In order to eliminate the effect of density variations on hydrogen determinations, instruments have been constructed in which the radiation source is connected with a float in such a way that the area weight of the absorbing layer of liquid is automatically adjusted to a pre-determined value [215, 362].

It has later been found that the intensity of back-scattered β-radiation, which also depends on the number of electrons in unit volume, is less dependent on the density of the liquid than that of the transmitted radiation. Equipment for C–H determinations based on the measurement of back-scattered radiation therefore requires only rough temperature constancy, and the density determination can also be less accurate [216–218].

Liquids containing three light elements (such as hydrogen, carbon, nitrogen, oxygen, and fluorine) may be analysed by measuring the density, the transmission and the back-scattering of β-radiation. The liquid may consist of a single compound or a mixture. Only 20–30 minutes are required for the analysis [218] (see also [354]).

Measurement of back-scattered β-radiation has been used in many other analytical methods (see [248]), for instance, to find the composition of chromium–nickel alloys [221], or the content of substances of high atomic number (such as vanadium, copper, nickel and lead) in aqueous solutions or in paraffin suspensions [222]. A similar method has been applied to the determination of metals in pharmaceuticals [301].

It has also been suggested that the energy of the back-scattered β-radiation, which depends on the atomic number of the substances in the sample, might be used for analysis [223].

Application of the measurement of β-ray absorption for the determination of the area weight and of the density of liquids will be discussed in Volume 2.

6.7.4. *Analysis by Absorption of γ- and X-rays*

Many analytical methods are based on the absorption of electromagnetic radiation from radioactive sources. These procedures are naturally related to the analytical methods operating with radiation from X-ray tubes or from accelerators such as the betatron. These will, however, not be discussed here (see [295, 334]).

Radioactive sources generally provide lower radiation intensity than X-ray tubes or accelerators. This is a drawback for absorption analysis. However, these sources are cheap, compact, and portable. No high voltage supply, no attention during operation, and no specially trained personnel are needed. A further decisive advantage is the constancy of the energy spectrum and of the intensity of the radiation [295, 360].

In the X-ray methods of analysis with radioactive sources, that is, in the absorption methods discussed in this section and in the methods based on induced X-ray emission (Section 6.7.5), no use is made of diffraction by crystals. These methods may thus be called "non-dispersive" [337]. However, many of the methods make use of energy spectrometry, in which case scintillation spectrometers or proportional counters serve as radiation detectors. Some energy discrimination can also be obtained with suitable absorbers. Geiger counters and ionization chambers are employed in a number of methods where no energy spectrometry is required.

γ- and X-radiations interact with absorbers in three principal ways: by the photo-electric effect, by the Compton effect, and by pair formation (see p. 23 and [334]). In absorption analysis, the differences in absorption due to the photoelectric effect or to the Compton effect are exploited.

In the low energy region (below about 200 keV) appreciable differences in absorption by photoelectric effect are found among the various elements. The dependence of the absorption coefficient on the energy shows characteristic edges for each element. Increasing energy of the radiation leads at particular energy values to a sudden stepwise increase in the absorption coefficient to a maximum. A further increase in energy results in a gradual decrease of the absorption coefficient. These edges correspond to the energies necessary to remove an electron in a given shell from the atom (K-edge, L-edge, etc., see p. 6). The characteristic energies of the edges increase with the atomic number. Examples of K-edges are: sodium 1·07 keV, copper 9·0 keV, iodine 33 keV, lead 89 keV, uranium 117 keV. As a consequence of this relationship between the positions of the edges and the atomic numbers, heavy elements usually absorb more strongly per unit mass in the energy range where the photoelectric effect predominates. This applies with particular force when the radiation energy exceeds that of the K-edge for all elements under consideration.

For radiation of higher energy, especially in the case of lighter elements, the Compton effect becomes important. The probability of absorption by the Compton effect is independent of the nature of the element, and is simply proportional to the number of electrons per unit mass. Consequently, the mass absorption coefficient due to the Compton effect increases with the ratio of atomic number to atomic weight, as is true for the mass absorption coefficient for β-rays. The absorption of energetic electromagnetic radiation can then be exploited like that of β-radiation.

Several types of sources of low-energy photons are available. A few nuclides emit soft monochromatic γ-radiation directly, such as thulium-170 and americium-241. Capture-active nuclides emit the characteristic X-rays of the elements formed, with rays of one energy usually strongly predominating in this radiation. For instance, iron-55 decays to stable manganese-55 by K-capture with a half-life of 2·9 years, and this nuclear transformation is followed immediately by emission of the K-lines of manganese (energy about 6 keV). Similarly, caesium-131 gives monochromatic X-rays of 28·5 keV, and tungsten-181 of 56 keV.

A principle of more general application for the production of soft radiation is to expose a material (target) to radiation, especially β-radiation, from a radionuclide. X-ray emission, either as characteristic radiation or as bremsstrahlung (with a continuous energy distribution), is then induced. Various types of such X-ray sources have been studied [224, 227–232, 336]. Yields up to 0·1–0·2 photons per β-particle have been obtained. The primary emitters mostly used in such sources are tritium, krypton-85, strontium-90-yttrium-90, promethium-147, thallium-204 and americium-241 [229, 327, 330, 347]. Tritium sources are relatively cheap and long-lived. Generally the tritium is chemically combined as a hydride with the metal serving as the target (titanium or zirconium). The X-radiation emitted by such tritium sources consists mainly of bremsstrahlung [196].

By suitable construction of the sources either low or quite high ratios of bremsstrahlung to characteristic X-radiation may be obtained. Monochromatic radiation may be obtained from bremsstrahlung by various techniques. For instance, the primary electromagnetic radiation may be used to excite secondary (monochromatic) radiation by fluorescence [179]. Relatively strong γ-ray excited X-ray sources have also been developed [355].

Sources of high-energy (hard) γ-radiation usually consist of nuclides directly emitting such radiation, e.g., of cobalt-60 or of caesium-137.

Critical edge absorptiometry with the characteristic X-radiation from antimony, excited by nickel-63 β-rays, has been used for the highly selective determination of silver, in order to find the thickness of photographic emulsions. The absorption edge of silver is 25·5 keV, the characteristic antimony X-ray 26·4 keV. The radiation dose is so low that the emulsion is not fogged [179].

The less specific absorption of the monochromatic γ-radiation (60 keV) from americium-241 may be used for the rapid determination of uranium or other heavy elements in solution [226, 249, 250, 302, 303, 305, 326]. Impurities of low atomic weight interfere only if present in large excess. However, the γ-active fission products may be present only with small activities. Uranium in flat fuel elements has been assayed through the absorption of the 0·34 MeV γ-rays from europium-152, 154 [296]. Lead has been measured in ore samples with the X-radiation from lead or uranium targets exposed to strontium–yttrium-90 β-rays, the difference in the absorption of the two kinds of radiation being sensitive to lead content [304, 347]. X-radiation from iron-55 is used to determine argon in the nitrogen–hydrogen gas mixtures for the synthesis of ammonia [306], and tritium bremsstrahlung to estimate salts of sodium, potassium, calcium or lead in solution [339].

The routine determination of sulphur in hydrocarbons with radioactive X-ray sources is important [225, 233, 234, 251, 252, 295]. 4 mc of iron-55 may be used as the source. For this radiation, the mass absorption coefficient of sulphur is much greater than that of carbon or hydrogen (for sulphur 200 cm^2/g, for carbon 10 cm^2/g, and for hydrogen 0·5 cm^2/g). Even low sulphur contents therefore give appreciable absorption, and sensitive determinations are possible. The limit of detection lies at a few hundredths of 1 per cent.

The equipment is quite simple. The X-rays pass through the sample, which is placed in a cell with beryllium windows. The intensity of the transmitted radiation is measured with a Geiger counter. To compute the sulphur content from this value, the density of the liquid, and, because of the difference in their mass absorption coefficients, the ratio of the carbon and hydrogen contents must be known, the last, however, not with great accuracy. (If the carbon–hydrogen ratio varies, it may be determined by the β-absorption method described above, using the same cell and a strontium-90-yttrium-90 source [196].) It has also been shown that in certain cases the necessary corrections for density and hydrogen content can be made on the basis of an absorption measurement with electromagnetic radiation of higher energy ($\sim$70 keV) [361]. Another method is to adjust the area weight of the absorbing layer to a constant value by placing the radiation source on a float (see p. 105) [362]. The content of other elements should not exceed certain limits.

Instead of the radiation emitted by iron-55 (or more correctly, manganese-55), the bremsstrahlung from a tritium–zirconium source [196, 233, 251, 255, 335] or from a promethium-147–aluminium source [337, 347] may be applied. Tritium sources are used for the continuous automatic determination of sulphur in oil fractions in refineries [235]. Sulphur may also be assayed by a fluorescence method (see p. 109) with tritium–titanium bremsstrahlung [332].

Elementary analysis of organic compounds consisting only of carbon, hydrogen and oxygen may be carried out by measuring the absorption of monochromatic X-rays of three different energies. Use is made of the fact that the mass absorption coefficients of the three elements depend in different ways on the wavelength (energy) of the radiation. The three absorption measurements thus provide three equations with three unknowns. The monochromatic radiations have been obtained from the secondary targets selenium, rubidium and zirconium, whose fluorescence was excited either by

β-ray excited bremsstrahlung or by X-radiation from a tube. The radiation is measured with a proportional counter and a discriminating circuit. The accuracy has not reached that of chemical methods but the procedure is rapid and can be carried out by untrained personnel [179].

The determination of hydrogen is possible on the basis of the fact that its mass absorption coefficient for γ-radiation of 1 MeV is about twice that of other elements. This is due to the predominant role of the Compton effect in radiation attenuation at this energy (see p. 23). Again a density measurement is needed (see p. 104). In a suitable instrument a radiocobalt source of 0·5 c and a sample layer thickness of 1 m are used [225]. The radiation intensity can be measured with a Geiger counter.

The method has certain disadvantages compared with β-absorptiometry. The strong source makes rather heavy shielding necessary, and because of the weak absorption of the radiation long paths and therefore large samples are needed. But in contrast to the β-absorption method, no correction need be applied for the oxygen or sulphur content, and because of the good penetration of the γ-radiation, liquids flowing through pipe lines or stored in containers may be analysed there directly.

It has been proposed to determine hydrogen, particularly in organic liquids, by measuring the Compton scattered radiation (for instance, at right angle to the incident radiation) instead of the transmitted radiation [316]. A similar method may be used to measure the thickness of a hydrogen-containing layer (polystyrene) on Teflon [297].

6.7.5. *Analysis by Induced X-ray Emission*

A further group of analytical methods is based on the measurement of the intensity of X-rays that are emitted by the element to be determined when this is exposed to nuclear radiation. Electromagnetic or β-radiation may be applied. The characteristic radiation of the particular element is then measured selectively with a discriminating proportional counter or with a scintillation spectrometer [236, 237, 337, 360, 365]. Like the absorption methods discussed above, these emission methods show analogies to analysis with X-rays from tubes. In particular, they are related to the method of X-ray fluorescence analysis which is finding increasing use [334].

The radiation intensities available with radionuclide sources are much lower, so that the sensitivity is less. Moreover, owing to the relatively poor resolution of the radiation analysers (proportional counters or scintillation spectrometers) as compared with crystal spectrometers, distinction between two elements of very similar atomic number is not possible, unless the spectrum is evaluated by special techniques [312]. The principal advantage of analysis with radionuclide sources lies in the simplicity and convenience of operation, as already indicated in the previous section.

Two of the important problems of the emission method with radionuclide sources are to prevent radiation from the source from passing directly to the radiation detector, and to eliminate scattered radiation. This is not always easy, since it is desirable to keep the distances between the source and the sample as well as between the sample and the radiation detector small, so that the radiation emitted by the source is utilized efficiently. The advantages and disadvantages of various arrangements and measuring instruments have been discussed [236, 237, 360, 365].

For the fluorescence method it may be of advantage to irradiate the sample with monochromatic X-radiation, and so eliminate the continuous spectrum (bremsstrahlung) as far as possible in order to excite the element under determination selectively. Some analyses may be carried out with capture-active sources of less than a hundred microcuries [239]. Sources emitting γ-rays may be preferable for excitation when deeper penetration into the sample is required; iridium-192 (γ-ray energies 0·31 and 0·47 eV) is an example [297].

A few applications of X-ray emission methods with radionuclide sources will now be mentioned. Some methods refer to the analysis of material in bulk, others to the measurement of the thickness of coatings. A list of the applications to date has been given [337].

In favourable cases (such as those of molybdenum or tungsten in steel) concentrations of the order of 0·1 per cent may be determined, and measurable characteristic X-rays may be obtained from 10 μg of an element [240, 327]. The determination of lead dust deposited on a paper filter by sucking through air from a factory can be carried out within a few minutes. Uranium K-radiation excited by irradiation with β-rays from strontium-90–yttrium-90 has been employed [179]. Tungsten-181 has been used to determine the molybdenum content of a catalyst employed in the oil industry, and caesium-131 for the determination of the thickness of titanium oxide layers of about 3 mg/cm^2 [240]. Iron or cobalt in oils [307, 327, 347] as well as zinc in ores and concentrates [347] and lead mixed with quartz [297] have been estimated. Analysis of cores from bore-holes in an iron ore mining area have also been carried out by measurement of X-ray fluorescence. For excitation a tritium–titanium source was used, for measurement a proportional counter. A two-channel pulse height analyser permitted simultaneous determination of iron and calcium, and 3 m of core were scanned per hour [300].

In certain cases, Rayleigh-scattered X-radiation, i. e., radiation that has suffered no change in energy, contributes appreciably to the measured radiation. This may be an advantage when elements of high atomic number are to be determined, since these have high scattering cross-sections for X-rays. The effect has been utilized in a method for determining uranium in aluminium. The radiation source consisted of a krypton-85 clathrate mixed with uranium oxide powder. Both characteristic X-rays and bremsstrahlung were emitted. The signals from the detector (scintillation counter) were discriminated in such a manner that only radiation of 85–116 keV energy was counted. In this way Rayleigh-scattered and fluorescent radiation were registered while Compton-scattered radiation was excluded [298].

Excitation by the direct action of β-radiation on the sample under analysis has been used, for example, for the determination of calcium and iron in ores [236], of lead in air filters [179], and of tungsten in iron [219, 220].

Emission methods are also suitable for the determination of the thickness of thin surface layers of such metals as chromium, tin, nickel, copper, zinc, cadmium, silver and gold [236, 237, 239, 241, 297, 308]. In some cases, the measurement of the fluorescence radiation from the base is an alternative. The analysis actually makes use of the absorption, in the covering layer, both of the radiation falling on the sample and of the fluorescence radiation from the base [327]. A tritium–zirconium bremsstrahlung source has been used to determine tin layers in tinplate [238, 239]. Measuring times as short as half a minute gave an accuracy of 1 per cent. Chromium on nickel has been measured in a similar way [239]. Determinations of the thickness of surface layers, such as in tin plate, have also been carried out with γ-ray excited X-ray sources [356].

6.7.6. *Analysis by Luminescence Quenching*

Oxygen may be determined in a novel way through the quenching of the luminescence of a liquid scintillator. The gas to be analysed is first saturated with the solvent employed for the scintillator, and is then led through the scintillator solution. This is subjected to the β-radiation from strontium-90. Oxygen contents from 0·1 to 100 per cent may be measured continuously in this way [242].

References to Chapter 6

1. E.BRODA and T.SCHÖNFELD, Radiochemische Methoden der Mikrochemie, in: F.HECHT and M.K.ZACHERL (Ed.), *Handbuch der mikrochemischen Methoden*, vol. 2, Vienna (1955).
2. T.SCHÖNFELD and E.BRODA, *Atompraxis* **3**, 77, 163, 217, 295 (1957).
3. Collections of references: W.W.MEINKE, *Anal. Chem.* **28**, 736 (1956); **30**, 686 (1958); **32**, 104 R (1960); G.W.LEDDICOTTE, *Anal. Chem.* **31**, 143 R (1962); **36**, 419 R (1964).
4. N.R.CAMPBELL and A.WOOD, *Proc. Cambridge Philos. Soc.* **14**, 15 (1906).
5. R.B.BARNES and D.J.SALLEY, *Anal. Chem.* **15**, 4 (1943).
6. I.GÜBELI and K.STAMMBACH, *Helv. Chim. Acta* **34**, 1245 (1951).
7. S.I.KRITSHMAR and L.G.KAISTRA, *Zavod. Lab.* **24**, 925 (1958).
8. A.M.GAUDIN and J.H.PANNEL, *Anal. Chem.* **20**, 1154 (1948).
9. O.J.RUSSELL, *Brit. J. Appl. Phys.* **3**, 47 (1952).
10. K.E.SCHEEL, *Angew. Chem.* **66**, 102 (1954).
11. H.FRIEDMANN, *Eng. Mining J.* **152**, 90 (1951).
12. M.RÖSSELER, *Kernenergie* **3**, 388 (1960).
13. J.CZUBEK, B.DZIUNIKOWSKI, L.JURKIEWICZ, J.KRZUK, J.NIEWODNICZANSKI, T.OWSIAK, K.PRZEWLOCKI and A.ZUBER, Geneva Report 1591 (1958), vol. 3, p. 83.
14. Comprehensive review, see [1].
15. N.FERLA, *Ann. Chim. Appl.* **28**, 331 (1938).
16. O.ERBACHER and K.PHILIPP, *Angew. Chem.* **48**, 409 (1935).
17. J.BEYDON, *Compt. rend.* **224**, 1715 (1947).
18. W.F.BOLDRIDGE and D.N.HUME, *Nat. Nucl. Energy Series*, vol. 8, p. 679, New York (1950).
19. V.P.SHVEDOV, *Zhur. Anal. Khim.* **3**, 147 (1948).
20. V.P.SHVEDOV, *Vestnik Leningrad Univ.* **1947** (1).
21. V.P.SHVEDOV, *Zhur. Obshch. Khim.* **17**, 33 (1947).
22. V.P.SHVEDOV, E.O.GOLDSHTEIN and I.N.SELEKTOVA, *Zhur. Anal. Khim.* **3**, 109 (1948).
23. V.B.MILLER, M.B.NEIMAN and L.A.SAZONOV, *Zhur. Anal. Khim.* **7**, 269 (1951).
24. N.A.RUDNEV, *Zhur. Anal. Khim.* **8**, 3 (1953).
25. V.I.KUSNETSOV, V.N.OBOSHIN and E.S.PALSHIN, *Zhur. Anal. Khim.* **9**, 199 (1954); **10**, 32 (1955).
26. V.I.KUSNEZOV, Paris Report 46, vol. 2, p. 264.
27. G.HEVESY and L.HAHN, *Kgl. Danske Vidensk. Selsk. Biol. Medd.* **16**, 1 (1941).
28. W.GEILMANN and A.GÄNSSLE, *Angew. Chem.* **66**, 453 (1954); *Glastechn. Ber.* **27**, 80 (1954).
29. T.Y.TORIBARA and P.S.CHEN, *Anal. Chem.* **24**, 539 (1952).
30. H.M.IRVING, T.J.ROSOTTI and J.G.DRYSDALE, *Nature* **169**, 649 (1952).
31. D.I.RYABCHIKOV and M.M.SENYAVIN, in: *Conference on the Application of Labelled Atoms in Analytical Chemistry*, Acad. Sci. U.S.S.R., Inst. Geochem. and Anal. Chem. (Russ.), Moscow 1955.

32. T. SCHÖNFELD and E. BRODA, *Mikrochemie* **35-36,** 485 (1951).
33. P. C. TOMPKINS, O. M. BIZZELL and C. D. WATSON, *Nucleonics* **7** (2), 42 (1950).
34. L. O. MORGAN, *Anal. Chem.* **22,** 200 (1950).
35. H. M. HERSHENSON and L. B. ROGERS, *Anal. Chem.* **24,** 219 (1952).
36. B. A. RUBIN, *Science* **110,** 425 (1949).
37. Yu. I. BELAYEV and A. N. SNIDEL, *Zhur. Anal. Khim.* **12,** 1 (1957).
38. E. E. VAINSHTEIN and Yu. I. BELAYEV, *Int. J. Appl. Rad. Isot.* **4,** 179 (1959).
39. E. E. VAINSTEIN, L. I. PAVLENKO and Yu. I. BELAYEV, Paris Report 47, vol. 2, p. 242.
40. B. N. CACCIAPUOTI, *Ann. Chim. Appl.* **29,** 166 (1939).
41. M. HAISSINSKY and R. BOVY, *Bull. soc. chim. France* **17,** 827 (1950).
42. R. RUKA and J. E. WILLARD, *J. Phys. Colloid Chem.* **53,** 351 (1949).
43. A. N. NESMEYANOV (Ed.), *Radiochemistry* (Russ.), Moscow 1952, pp. 83, 91, 99, 107, 111.
44. M. B. NEIMAN, M. B. MILLER and A. I. FEDOSSEYEVA, *Doklady Akad. Nauk SSSR* **75,** 719 (1950).
45. O. HAHN, *Applied Radiochemistry*, New York 1936.
46. V. KHLOPIN and M. MERKULOVA, *Izvest Akad. Nauk SSSR, Otd. Khim. Nauk,* **1949,** 460.
47. I. P. ALIMARIN, Geneva Report 706 (1955), vol. 15, p. 60.
48. T. SCHÖNFELD, *Mikrochimica Acta* **1956,** 1050.
49. S. LISSITZKY and R. MICHEL, *Bull. Soc. Chim. France* **1952,** 891.
50. H. WEIL and T. I. WILLIAMS, *Angew. Chem.* **63,** 457 (1951).
51. V. V. RATSHINSKI, *Uspekhi Khim.* **19,** 445 (1950).
52. S. UDENFRIEND, *J. Biol. Chem.* **187,** 65 (1950).
53. *J. Amer. Chem. Soc.* **69,** 2769–2881 (1947).
54. B. K. PREOBRAZHENSKII, A. V. KALYAMIN and O. M. LILOVA, *Zhur. Neorg. Khim.* **2,** 1164 (1957).
55. E. H. HUFFMAN and R. C. LILLY, *J. Amer. Chem. Soc.* **71,** 4147 (1949); **73,** 2902 (1951).
56. K. A. KRAUS and G. E. MOORE, *J. Amer. Chem. Soc.* **71,** 3263 (1949).
57. K. A. KRAUS and G. E. MOORE, *J. Amer. Chem. Soc.* **71,** 3855 (1949); **73,** 2900 (1951).
58. N. P. RUDENKO, in: *Conference on the Application of Labelled Atoms in Analytical Chemistry*, Acad. Sci. USSR, Inst. Geochem. and Anal. Chem. (Russ.), Moscow 1955.
59. D. KRITCHEVSKY and M. CALVIN, *J. Amer. Chem. Soc.* **72,** 4330 (1950).
60. F. P. W. WINTERINGHAM, A. HARRISON and R. G. BRIDGES, *Nature* **166,** 999 (1950).
61. N. A. RUDNEV and A. A. MAZUR, *Zhur. Anal. Khim.* **12,** 433 (1957); *J. Anal. Chem. USSR* (English translation) **12,** 449 (1957).
62. R. EHRENBERG, in: *Physikalische Methoden der analytischen Chemie* (W. BÖTTGER, Ed.), Leipzig 1933.
63. R. EHRENBERG, *Biochem. Z.* **164,** 183 (1925).
64. R. EHRENBERG, *Biochem. Z.* **183,** 63 (1927).
65. B. F. SCOTT and W. J. DRISCOLL, Copenhagen Report 202, vol. 2, p. 339.
66. H. MOREU, P. CHOVIN and R. DAUDEL, *Compt. rend.* **219,** 127 (1944).
67. P. SUE, *Bull. Soc. Chim. France* **13,** 102 (1946).
68. T. MÖLLER and G. K. SCHWEITZER, *Anal. Chem.* **20,** 1201 (1948).
69. J. GOVAERTS and C. BARCIA-GOYANES, *Anal. Chim. Acta* **6,** 121 (1952).
70. I. V. TANANAYEV, in: *Conference on the Application of Labelled Atoms in Analytical Chemistry*, Acad. Sci. USSR, Inst. Geochem. and Anal. Chem. (Russ.), Moscow 1955.
71. see I. P. ALIMARIN, *Chem. Anal. (Warsaw)* **2,** 297 (1952).
72. A. LANGER, *J. Phys. Chem.* **45,** 639 (1945).
73. A. LANGER, *Anal. Chem.* **22,** 1288 (1950).
74. I. P. ALIMARIN, I. M. GIBALO and I. A. SIROTINA, *Int. J. Appl. Rad. Isot.* **2,** 117 (1957); see also *Zavod. Lab.* **21,** 1022 (1955), and **23,** 412 (1957), also *Zhur. Anal. Khim.* **12,** 367 (1957).
75. I. M. KORENMAN, F. R. SHEYANOVA, E. A. DEMINA and M. I. SHAPOSHNIKOVA, *Zavod. Lab.* **32,** 1143 (1956).
76. C. H. WALLACE and J. E. WILLARD, *J. Amer. Chem. Soc.* **72,** 5275 (1950).
77. I. M. KORENMAN, F. R. SHEYANOVA, N. M. MESINA and M. I. OSTASHEVA, *Zhur. Anal. Khim.* **12,** 48 (1957).
78. J. F. DUNCAN and F. G. THOMAS, *J. Inorg. Nucl. Chem.* **4,** 376 (1957).
79. T. BRAUN, I. MAXIM and I. GALATEANU, *Nature* **182,** 936 (1958).

80. M.S.RABEN, *Anal. Chem.* **22,** 480 (1950).
81. H.P.KAUFMANN and J.BUDWIG, *Fette u. Seifen* **53,** 253 (1951).
82. A.Z.BUDZYNSKI, Z.J.ZUBRZYCKI and I.G.CAMPBELL, *Nukleonika* **3** *(special issue),* 133 (1958).
83. A.Z.BUDZYNSKI, Z.J.ZUBRZYCKI and I.G.CAMPBELL, *Nature* **182,** 178 (1958).
84. A.Z.BUDZYNSKI, Z.J.ZUBRZYCKI and I.G.CAMPBELL, Geneva Report 1588 (1958), vol. 24, p. 274.
85. E.BRODA, *Radioactive Isotopes in Biochemistry,* Amsterdam 1960.
86. R.H.BENSON and R.B.TURNER, *Anal. Chem.* **32,** 1464 (1960).
87. D.J.CHLECK and C.A.ZIEGLER, Copenhagen Report 199, vol. 2, p. 361.
88. D.J.CHLECK and C.A.ZIEGLER, *Int. J. Appl. Rad. Isot.* **7,** 141 (1959).
89. P.A.LEIGHTON and R.A.MORTENSEN, *J. Amer. Chem. Soc.* **58,** 448 (1936).
90. M.BURTON, J.E.RICCI and T.W.DAVIS, *J. Amer. Chem. Soc.* **62,** 265 (1940).
91. G.M.HARRIS and A.W.TICKNER, *J. Chem. Phys.* **15,** 686 (1947).
92. D.M.MILLER and C.A.WINKLER, *Can. J. Chem.* **29,** 537 (1951).
93. R.W.DURHAM, G.R.MARTIN and H.C.SUTTON, *Nature* **164,** 1052 (1949).
94. G.R.MARTIN and H.C.SUTTON, *Trans. Faraday Soc.* **48,** 823 (1952).
95. I.P.ALIMARIN and G.N.BILIMOVICH, *Int. J. Appl. Rad. Isot.* **7,** 169 (1960).
96. G.HEVESY and R.HOBBIE, *Z. Anal. Chem.* **88,** 1 (1932).
97. I.E.STARIK, *Problems of Soviet Geology* (Russ.) **3,** 70 (1933).
98. P.SUE, *Bull. Soc. Chim. France* **1947,** 405.
99. A.A.SMALES, D.MAPPER, J.W.MORGAN, R.K.WEBSTER and A.J.WOOD, Geneva Report 282 (1958), vol. 2, p. 242.
100. K.THEURER and T.R.SWEET, *Anal. Chem.* **25,** 119 (1953).
101. A.J.FREEDMAN and D.N.HUME, *Anal. Chem.* **22,** 932 (1950).
102. M.A.EL GUEBELY, *Anal. Chim. Acta* **15,** 580 (1956).
103. O.T.QUIMBY, A.J.MABIS and H.W.LAMPE, *Anal. Chem.* **26,** 661 (1954).
104. L.E.HOWARD, *Nucleonics* **16** (2), 112 (1958).
105. W.S.MACDONALD and H.S.TURNER, *Chem. and Ind.* **1952,** 1001.
106. J.C.SOWDEN and A.S.SPRIGGS, *J. Amer. Chem. Soc.* **76,** 3539 (1954).
107. R.SCHOENHEIMER, S.RATNER and D.RITTENBERG, *J. Biol. Chem.* **130,** 703 (1939).
108. D.RITTENBERG and G.L.FORSTER, *J. Biol. Chem.* **133,** 737 (1940).
109. H.H.USSING, *Nature* **144,** 977 (1939).
110. W.H.CLINGMAN and H.H.HAMMEN, *Anal. Chem.* **32,** 323 (1960).
111. S.F.VELICK, L.F.WICKS and S.UDENFRIEND, *J. Biol. Chem.* **190,** 721, 741 (1951).
112. E.N.JENKINS and A.A.SMALES, *Quart. Rev. Chem. Soc.* **10,** 83 (1956).
113. T.I.TAYLOR and W.W.HAVENS, *Physical Methods in Chemical Analysis* (Ed. W.G.BERL), vol. 3, New York 1956.
114. D.H.ATKINS and A.A.SMALES, *Adv. Inorg. Chem. Radiochem.* **1,** 315 (1959).
115. Bibliography: D.GIBBONS, B.A.LOVERIDGE and R.J.MILLETT, *Radioactivation Analysis,* Atomic Energy Research Establishment, Harwell, England, Report 1/R 2208 (1957) and Supplement (1960).
116. R.C.KOCH, *Activation Analysis Handbook,* New York 1960.
117. G.H.MORRISON and J.F.COSGROVE, *Anal. Chem.* **27,** 810 (1955); **28,** 320 (1956); **29,** 1017 (1957).
118. A.A.SMALES, Geneva Reports 766 and 770 (1955), vol. 9, p. 273 and vol. 15, p. 73.
119. I.FINEMAN, K.LJUNGGREN, L.G.ERWALL and T.WESTERMARK, *Svensk Papperstidning* **60,** 132 (1957).
120. G.W.LEDDICOTTE, W.T.MULLINS, L.C.BATE, J.F.EMERY, W.A.BROOKSBANK and R.E.DRUSCHEL, Geneva Report 927 (1958), vol. 28, p. 478.
121. R.E.JERVIS and W.D.MACKINTOSH, Geneva Report 189 (1958), vol. 28, p. 470.
122. V.P.GUINN and C.D.WAGNER, *Anal. Chem.* **32,** 317 (1960).
123. W.W.MEINKE, Copenhagen Report 283, vol. 2, p. 277.
124. W.E.KUYKENDALL, R.E.WAINERDI, Copenhagen Report 198, vol. 2, p. 233.
125. G.LELIAERT, J.HOSTE and Z.EECKHAUT, *Nature* **182,** 600 (1958).
126. W.W.MEINKE, *Anal. Chem.* **31,** 792 (1959).
127. O.U.ANDERS, *Nucleonics* **18** (11), 178 (1960); *Anal. Chem.* **33,** 1706 (1961).
128. R.C.PLUMB and R.H.SILVERMAN, *Nucleonics* **12** (12), 29 (1954).

129. W.W. MEINKE, *Science* **121,** 77 (1955).
130. R.C.PLUMB and J.E.LEWIS, *Nucleonics* **13** (8), 42 (1955).
131. O.U.ANDERS and W.H.BEAMER, *Anal. Chem.* **33,** 226 (1961).
132. G.E.BOYD, *Anal. Chem.* **21,** 335 (1949).
133. R.D.KEYNES and P.R.LEWIS, *Nature* **165,** 809 (1950); **168,** 153 (1951).
134. P.R.LEWIS, in: *Radioisotope Techniques*, vol. 1, London 1952.
135. W.W. MEINKE and R.E.ANDERSON, *Anal. Chem.* **25,** 778 (1953).
136. H.GRIFFON and J.BARBAUD, *Compt. rend.* **232,** 1455 (1951).
137. F.P.W.WINTERINGHAM, *Nature* **168,** 153 (1951).
138. A.KOHN, *Rev. Métallurgie* **48,** 219 (1951).
139. F.MONTARIOL, P.ALBERT and G.CHAUDRON, *Compt. rend.* **253,** 477 (1952).
140. M.T.KELLEY, G.W.LEDDICOTTE and S.A.REYNOLDS, *International Congress on Analytical Chemistry*, Oxford 1952.
141. G.KAYAS, *J. Chim. Phys.* **47,** 408 (1950).
142. W.A.BROOKSBANK and G.W.LEDDICOTTE, *J. Phys. Chem.* **57,** 819 (1953).
143. H.BROWN and E.GOLDBERG, *Anal. Chem.* **22,** 308 (1950).
144. J.E.HUDGENS and H.J.DABAGIAN, *Nucleonics* **10** (5), 25 (1952).
145. G.J.ATCHISON and W.H.BEAMER, *Anal. Chem.* **24,** 1812 (1952).
146. A.A. SMALES and B.D.PATE, *Anal. Chem.* **24,** 717 (1952).
147. G.SZEKELY, *Anal. Chem.* **26,** 1500 (1954).
148. J.V.JAKOVLEV, Geneva Report 632 (1955), vol. 15, p. 54.
149. J.A.JAMES and D.H.RICHARDS, *Nature* **175,** 769 (1955).
150. G.H.MORRISON and J.F.COSGROVE, *Anal. Chem.* **28,** 320 (1956).
151. L.F.LOWE, H.D.THOMPSON and J.P.CALI, *Anal. Chem.* **31,** 1951 (1959).
152. E.BRODA and G.ROHRINGER, *Naturwiss.* **40,** 337 (1953).
153. A.A.SMALES and A.P.SEYFANG, *Analyst* **77,** 778 (1952); **78,** 394 (1953); **80,** 74 (1955).
154. C.FISCHER and J.BEYDON, *Bull. Soc. Chim. France* **1953,** C 102.
155. U.FACCHINI and L.ORSONI, *Nuovo Cimento* (*Ser. 9*) **6,** 241 (1949).
156. R.L.MACKLIN and J.H.LYKINS *J. Chem. Phys.* **19,** 844 (1951).
157. I.CURIE and H.FARAGGI, *Compt. rend.* **232,** 959 (1951).
158. E.PICCIOTTO and M.V.STYVENDAEL, *Compt. rend.* **232,** 855 (1951).
159. P.JANSSENS, *Compt. rend.* **232,** 825 (1951).
160. W.HERR, *Z. Naturforsch.* **8a,** 305 (1953).
161. H.FARAGGI, A.KOHN and J.DOUMERC, *Compt. rend.* **233,** 714 (1952).
162. M.HILLERT, *Nature* **168,** 39 (1951).
163. G.MAYR, H.D.BRUNER and M.BRUCER, *Nucleonics* **11** (10), 21 (1953).
164. K.SCHMEISER and D.JERCHEL, *Angew. Chem.* **65,** 366, 490 (1953).
165. A.A.LBOV and I.I.NAUMOVA, *Atomnaya energiya* **6,** 468 (1959); *Kernenergie* **3,** 276 (1960).
166. R.F.COLEMAN and J.L.PERKIN, *Analyst* **84,** 233 (1959).
167. O.U.ANDERS, *Anal. Chem.* **32,** 1368 (1960).
168. D.GIBBONS and H.SIMPSON, Copenhagen Report 7, vol. 2, p. 269.
169. S.MAY and P.LÉVÊQUE, Paris Report 49, vol. 2, p. 180.
170. G.W.REED, K.KIGOSHI and A.TURKEVICH, Geneva Report 953 (1958), vol. 28, p. 486.
171. E.MERZ and W.HERR, Geneva Report 984 (1958), vol. 28, p. 491.
172. M.v.ARDENNE and F.BERNHARD, *Z. Physik* **122,** 740 (1944).
173. W.RIEZLER, *Z. Naturforsch.* **4a,** 545 (1949).
174. I.CURIE, *J. Physique Radium* **13,** 497 (1952).
175. I.CURIE, *Bull. Soc. Chim. France* **1953,** C 94.
176. P.ALBERT, G.CHAUDRON and P.SUE, *Bull. Soc. Chim. France* **1953,** C 97.
177. J.J.POINT, Paris Report 48, vol. 2, p. 180.
178. S.RUBIN, T.O.PASSELL and L.E.BAILEY, *Anal. Chem.* **29,** 736 (1957).
179. L.REIFFEL, Geneva Report 827 (1958), vol. 19, p. 278.
180. H.J.BORN and N.RIEHL, *Angew. Chem.* **72,** 559 (1960).
181. A.M.GAUDIN and J.H.PANNELL, *Anal. Chem.* **23,** 1261 (1951).
182. C.P.VICTOR, *J. Physique Radium* **8,** 298 (1947).

183. B.S.AIDARKIN, G.V.GORSHKOV, A.G.GRAMMAKOV, W.S.TSADIN and A.G.KOLTSHINA, *Tr. Radievogo Inst. Akad. Nauk SSSR* **5,** 89 (1957).
184. "Beryllometer", see *Nucleonics* **18** (4), 107 (1960).
185. F.H.HALE and H.BISBY, Copenhagen Report 40, vol. 2, p. 291.
186. KH.B.MEZHIBORSKAYA, *Atomnaya energiya* **6,** 567 (1959); *J. Nucl. Energy* **12**A, 123 (1960).
187. C.P.HAIGH, *Nature* **172,** 359 (1953); *Radioisotope Conference* 1954, vol. 2, p. 101, London 1954.
188. W.W.SCHULTZ, H.D.BRIGGS, R.A.DEWES, E.E.GOODALE, D.H.MORLEY, J.P.NEISSEL, R.S.ROCHLIN and V.V.VERBINSKY, Geneva Report 819 (1958), vol. 19, p. 112.
189. T.I.TAYLOR, R.H.ANDERSON and W.W.HAVENS, *Science* **114,** 341 (1951).
190. T.I.TAYLOR and W.W.HAVENS, *Nucleonics* **5** (6), 4 (1949); **6** (2), 66 (1950); **6** (4), 54 (1950).
191. T.I.TAYLOR and W.W.HAVENS, *Physical Methods in Chemical Analysis* (Ed. W.G.BERL), vol. 3, New York 1956.
192. V.A.EMELYANOV and V.E.NESTEROV, *Atomnaya energiya* **6,** 573 (1959); *Kernenergie* **3,** 198 (1960).
193. *Nucleonics* **18** (4), 107 (1960).
194. R.STEDMAN, *Rev. Sci. Instr.* **31,** 1156 (1960).
195. J.GOVAERTS, *Experientia* **6,** 459 (1950).
196. J.L.PUTMAN, Geneva Report 283 (1958), vol. 19, p. 22.
197. J.MARTELLY and P.SUE, *Bull. Soc. Chim. France* **1946,** 103.
198. See *Atomnaya energiya* **2,** 292 (1957); see also *Atompraxis* **4,** 61 (1958).
199. D.D.DE FORD and R.S.BRAMAN, *Anal. Chem.* **30,** 1765 (1958).
200. P.SUE and J.MARTELLY, *Bull. Soc. Chim. France* **1946,** 400.
201. E.BRUNNER and E.S.MARDOCK, *Amer. Inst. Mining Met. Engrs., Petroleum Technol.* **9** (2), Tech. Pub. 1986 (1946).
202. L.B.LIPSON, *U.S. Patent* 2462270 (1949).
203. D.J.BELCHER, T.R.CRYKENDILL and H.S.SACK, *Nucleonics* **8** (4), 78 (1951).
204. W.GARDNER and D.KIRKHAM, *Soil. Sci.* **73,** 391 (1951).
205. J.SHARPE, *Brit. J. Appl. Physics* **4,** 93 (1953).
206. A.H.KNIGHT and T.W.WRIGHT, Radioisotope Conference 1954, London 1954, vol. 2, p. 111.
207. J.W.SPINKS, D.A.LANE and B.B.TORCHINSKY, *Can. J. Technol.* **29,** 371 (1951).
208. J.W.SPINKS, Geneva Report 216 (1958), vol. 19, p. 13.
209. P.MARTINELLI and M.H.RICCI, Copenhagen Report 90, vol. 2, p. 129.
210. V.N.SMITH and J.W.OTVOS, *Anal. Chem.* **26,** 359 (1954).
211. R.B.JACOBS and L.G.LEWIS, *Oil Gas J.*, 28 Sept. 1953.
212. R.B.JACOBS, L.G.LEWIS and F.J.PIEHL, *Anal. Chem.* **28,** 324 (1956).
213. R.ROWAN, *Anal. Chem.* **31,** 558 (1959).
214. E.CANALS, R.MARIGNAN and L.BARDET, *Ann. Pharmac. Franc.* **11,** 588 (1953).
215. R.BERTHOLD, Geneva Report 983 (1958), vol. 19, p. 288.
216. P.R.GRAY, D.H.CLAREY and W.H.BEAMER, *Anal. Chem.* **31,** 2065 (1959).
217. R.H.MÜLLER, Copenhagen Report 203, vol. 2, p. 65.
218. P.R.GRAY, D.H.CLAREY and W.H.BEAMER, *Anal. Chem.* **32,** 582 (1960).
219. J.FODOR and C.VARGA, Geneva Report 2241 (1958), vol. 19, p. 215.
220. J.FODOR, *Acta Chim. Hungarica* **19,** 327 (1959).
221. N.A.BOGDANOV and V.V.FUNKE, *Zavod. Lab.* **21,** 181 (1955).
222. J.KOHL, *Chem. Eng. Progr.* **48,** 611 (1952).
223. S.A.HUSAIN, Geneva Report 1408 (1958), vol. 19, p. 213.
224. P.LÉVÊQUE, P.MARTINELLI and R.CHAUVIN, Geneva Report 383 (1955), vol. 15, p. 142.
225. D.E.HULL and B.A.FRIES, Geneva Report 166 (1955), vol. 15, p. 199.
226. R.E.CONNALLY, *Nucleonics* **17** (12), 98 (1959).
227. L.REIFFEL, *Nucleonics* **13** (3), 22 (1955).
228. J.G.KEREIAKES and A.T.KREBS, Geneva Report 809 (1958), vol. 20, p. 234.
229. J.F.CAMERON and J.R.RHODES, Copenhagen Report 14, vol. 2, p. 23.
230. J.F.CAMERON and J.R.RHODES, *Int. J. Appl. Rad. Isot.* **7,** 244 (1960).
231. J.G.KEREIAKES, G.R.KRAFT, O.E.WEIR and A.T.KREBS, *Nucleonics* **16** (1), 80 (1958).
232. G.J.MATLACK, J.W.T.MEADOWS and G.B.NELSON, *Anal. Chem.* **30,** 1753 (1958).

116 *Application of Radioactivity in Chemical Analysis*

233. H.K.HUGHES and J.W.WILCZEWSKI, *Anal. Chem.* **26**, 1889 (1956).
234. W.R.DOUGHMAN, A.P.SULLIVAN and R.C.HIRT, *Anal. Chem.* **30**, 1924 (1958).
235. R.E.PEGG and J.S.POLLOCK, Copenhagen Report 11, vol. 2, p. 137; *Erdöl und Kohle* **14**, 367 (1961).
236. P.MARTINELLI and G.SEIBEL, Copenhagen Report 108, vol. 2, p. 41.
237. C.E.MELLISH, *Research* **12**, 212 (1959).
238. J.F.CAMERON and J.R.RHODES, *Brit. J. Appl. Phys.* **11**, 49 (1960).
239. G.B.COOK, C.E.MELLISH and J.A.PAYNE, Geneva Report 285 (1958), vol. 19, p. 127.
240. C.E.MELLISH and J.A.PAYNE, Copenhagen Report 21, vol. 2, p. 55.
241. G.B.COOK, C.E.MELLISH and J.A.PAYNE, *Anal. Chem.* **32**, 590 (1960).
242. D.J.CHLECK, J.BRINCKERHOFF, M.HADLEY and C.A.ZIEGLER, *Rev. Sci. Instr.* **30**, 37 (1959).
243. W.GEILMANN and W.GEBAUHR, *Angew. Chem.* **66**, 453 (1954).
244. D.I.RYABCHIKOV and L.V.BORISSOVA, *Zhur. Anal. Khim.* **13**, 155 (1958).
245. W.SCHULZE, *Neutronenaktivierung als analytisches Hilfsmittel*, Stuttgart 1962.
246. H.R.LUKENS, J.V.OTVOS and C.D.WAGNER, *Int. J. Appl. Rad. Isot.* **11**, 30 (1961).
247. W.D.ALLEN, *Neutron Detection*, London 1960.
248. L.M.MIKHEYEVA and N.B.MIKHEYEV, *Radioactive Isotopes in Analytical Chemistry* (Russ.), Moscow 1961; German translation, Berlin 1962.
249. F.J.WOODMAN, T.G.CLINTON, W.FLETCHER and G.A.WELCH, Geneva Report 1453 (1958), vol. 28, p. 423.
250. S.J.BRODERICK and J.C.WHITMER, *Anal. Chem.* **33**, 1314 (1961).
251. A.F.PYRAH, R.S.ROBERTSON and J.WISEMAN, *Anal. Chem.* **33**, 1355 (1961).
252. G.BRUNNER, *Isotopentechnik* **1**, 148 (1961).
253. W.W.MEINKE and R.W.SHIDELER, *Nucleonics* **20** (3), 60 (1962).
254. W.LEONHARDT, *Kernenergie* **5**, 166 (1962).
255. M.M.KANNUNA and J.F.CAMERON, *Int. J. Appl. Rad. Isot.* **2**, 76 (1957).
256. R.E.WAINERDI and N.P.DuBEAU, *Science* **139**, 1027 (1963).
257. H.J.M.BOWEN and D.A.GIBBONS, *Radioactivation Analysis*, Oxford 1963.
258. R.A.HOLROYD and G.W.KLEIN, *Int. J. Appl. Rad. Isot.* **13**, 493 (1962).
259. R.OTTO, *Atompraxis* **7**, 209 (1961).
260. C.O.HOMMEL, F.J.BROUSAIDES and R.L.BERSIN, *Anal. Chem.* **34**, 1608 (1962).
261. E.N.WISE, *J. Chem. Educ.* **39**, A 771 (1962).
262. S.AMIEL and M.PEISACH, *Anal. Chem.* **35**, 1072 (1963).
263. S.AMIEL and Y.WELWART, *Anal. Chem.* **35**, 566 (1963).
264. F.L.MOORE, *Anal. Chem.* **35**, 1032 (1963).
265. W.J.ARMENTO and C.E.LARSON, *Anal. Chem.* **35**, 918 (1963).
266. L.ADAM, *Isotopentechnik* **2**, 46 (1962).
267. D.C.BORG, R.E.SEGEL, P.KIENLE and L.CAMPBELL, *Int. J. Appl. Rad. Isot.* **11**, 10 (1961).
268. L.A.HASKIN, H.W.FEARING and F.S.ROWLAND, *Anal. Chem.* **33**, 1298 (1961).
269. I.J.GRUVERMAN and W.A.HENNINGER, *Anal. Chem.* **34**, 1680 (1962).
270. *Production and Use of Short-lived Radioisotopes from Reactors*, Symposium, I.A.E.A., Vienna 1963.
271. V.P.GUINN, see [270].
272. J.PETIT and C.ENGELMANN, *Int. J. Appl. Rad. Isot.* **13**, 528 (1962).
273. P.ALBERT, N.DESCHAMPS, L.FOURNET and M.DEYRIS, *Int. J. Appl. Rad. Isot.* **13**, 517 (1962).
274. H.ROMMEL, *Kernenergie* **5**, 859 (1962).
275. C.A.LEVINE and J.P.SURLS, *Anal. Chem.* **34**, 1614 (1962).
276. E.N.WISE, *J. Chem. Educ.* **39** A, 771 (1962).
277. K.LJUNGGREN, Copenhagen Report 79, vol. 2, p. 199.
278. F.BAUMGÄRTNER, *Kerntechnik* **3**, 356 (1961).
279. S.AMIEL, *Anal. Chem.* **34**, 1683 (1962); *Atomwirtschaft* **7**, 217 (1962).
280. L.C.BATE, *Nucleonics* **21** (7), 72 (1963).
281. D.J.VEAL and C.F.COOK, *Anal. Chem.* **34**, 178 (1962).
282. E.L.STEELE and W.W.MEINKE, *Anal. Chem.* **34**, 185 (1962).
283. A.A.SMALES, *Ann. Rep. Progr. Chem.* **46**, 285 (1950).

284. R. G. OSMOND and A. A. SMALES, *Anal. chim. Acta* **10**, 117 (1954).
285. H. J. BORN and P. WILKNISS, *Int. J. Appl. Rad. Isot.* **10**, 133 (1961).
286. W. LEONHARDT, *Kernenergie* **5**, 166 (1962).
287. R. F. COLEMAN, *Analyst* **87**, 590 (1962).
288. R. BASIL *et al.*, *Compt. rend.* **239**, 422 (1954).
289. D. B. BEARD, R. G. JOHNSON and W. G. BRADSHAW, *Nucleonics* **17** (7), 90 (1959).
290. P. ALBERT *et al.*, *Compt. rend.* **254**, 119 (1962).
291. A. KH. BREGER *et al.*, *Zhur. Neorgan. Khim.* **2**, 696 (1957).
292. I. M. KORENMAN, F. R. SHEYANOVA and M. A. POTAPOVA, *Zhur. Obsh. Khim.* **26**, 2114 (1956).
293. I. M. KORENMAN, *Uspekhi Khim.* **22**, 936 (1957).
294. N. B. MIKHEEV, *Int. J. Appl. Rad. Isot.* **5**, 32 (1959).
295. H. A. LIEBHAFSKY, H. G. PFEIFFER, E. H. WINSLOW and P. D. ZEMANY, *X-Ray Absorption and Emission in Analytical Chemistry*, New York 1960.
296. L. C. NELSON, *Nucleonics* **21** (6), 88 (1963).
297. See report in *Nucleonics* **21** (6), 100 (1963).
298. C. A. ZIEGLER and J. C. MCCUE, *Int. J. Appl. Rad. Isot.* **12**, 1 (1962).
299. H. WEILER, *Int. J. Appl. Rad. Isot.* **12**, 49 (1961).
300. G. SEIBEL and J. Y. LE TRAON, *Int. J. Appl. Rad. Isot.* **14**, 259, 365 (1963).
301. P. SCHILLER, *Kernenergie* **6**, 514 (1963).
302. D. H. THURNAU, *Anal. Chem.* **29**, 1772 (1957).
303. W. L. MADDOX and M. T. KELLEY, *Talanta* **3**, 172 (1959).
304. B. DZIUNIKOWSKI, T. FLORKOWSKI, L. JURKIEWICZ and B. TURKOWA, *Nukleonika* **7**, 561 (1962).
305. J. BUBERNAK, M. S. LEW and G. M. MATLACK, *Anal. Chem.* **34**, 585 (1962).
306. K. HOFFMANN and F. HERRE, *Chem. Ing. Techn.* **31**, 399 (1959).
307. T. FLORKOWSKI and J. GILEWICZ, *Nukleonika* **7**, 793 (1962).
308. P. LÉVÊQUE, R. HOURS, P. MARTINELLI, S. MAY, J. SANDIER and J. BRILLIANT, Geneva Report 1231 (1958), vol. 19, p. 34.
309. V. SCHURICHT, *Isotopentechnik* **2**, 101 (1962).
310. *Nucleonics* **20** (11), 90 (1962).
311. V. SCHURICHT, *Isotopentechnik* **2**, 296 (1962).
312. J. Y. LE TRAON and G. SEIBEL, *Int. J. Appl. Rad. Isot.* **14**, 365 (1963).
313. W. KIESL, H. BILDSTEIN and H. SORANTIN, *Monatsh. Chem.* **94**, 151 (1963).
314. L. I. KOROTKOV, *Handbook (spravochnik) of Radioisotope Instruments* (Russ.), Moscow 1963.
315. R. TORNAU and K. H. WAECHTER, *Chem. Ing. Technik* **34**, 35 (1962).
316. K. H. WAECHTER, *Atomwirtschaft* **8**, 538 (1963).
317. I. N. PLAKSIN, V. N. SMIRNOV and L. P. STARCHIK, *Doklady Akad. Nauk SSSR* **127**, 618 (1959); **150**, 1270 (1963); *Atomnaya Energiya* **9**, 361 (1960).
318. I. N. PLAKSIN, V. N. SMIRNOV and L. P. STARCHIK, *Doklady Akad. Nauk SSSR* **128**, 1208 (1959).
319. I. N. PLAKSIN, M. A. BELYAKOV, V. L. RENTYRGIN and L. P. STARCHIK, *Doklady Akad. Nauk SSSR* **139**, 424 (1959); *Radiokhimiya* **4**, 581 (1962).
320. I. N. PLAKSIN, N. G. MALYSHEVA and L. P. STARCHIK, *Doklady Akad. Nauk SSSR* **141**, 1158 (1961)
321. I. N. PLAKSIN, M. A. BELYAKOV and L. P. STARCHIK, *Atomnaya Energiya* **11**, 548 (1961).
322. I. N. PLAKSIN, M. A. BELYAKOV and L. P. STARCHIK, *Doklady Akad. Nauk SSSR* **141**, 921 (1962); **142**, 374 (1962).
323. I. N. PLAKSIN, M. A. BELYAKOV and L. P. STARCHIK, *Atomnaya Energiya* **13**, 374 (1962).
324. KH. B. MEZHIBORSKAYA, *The Photoneutron Method of Beryllium Determination* (Russ.), Moscow 1961.
325. T. BALINT, *Acta Chim. Hung.* **39**, 161, 171 (1963).
326. S. J. BRODERICK, *Anal. Chem.* **34**, 295 (1962).
327. J. F. CAMERON and J. R. RHODES, *Nucleonics* **19** (6), 53 (1961).
328. H. L. FINSTON and E. YELLIN, *Anal. Chem.* **35**, 336 (1963).
329. F. W. FIRK *et al.*, *Nucl. Instr. Methods* **13**, 313 (1961).
330. F. HARTMANN and W. SCHURICHT, *Isotopentechnik* **1**, 225 (1961).
331. H. JASKOLSKA and L. WODKIEWICZ, *Chem. Anal.* (Warsaw) **6**, 161 (1961).
332. C. BURCKHARDT, A. GRÜTTER and H. STOESSEL, *Nature* **196**, 825 (1962).

333. K. KIMURA, Geneva Report 1061 (1955), vol. 15, p. 220.
334. G. L. CLARK, in: W. G. BERL (Ed.), *Physical Methods in Chemical Analysis*, vols. 1 and 3, New York 1960, 1956.
335. L. WIESNER, *Atomwirtschaft* **6**, 278 (1961).
336. D. MÜLLER and G. BRUNNER *Isotopentechnik* **2**, 257 (1962).
337. G. SEIBEL, *Int. J. Appl. Rad. Isot.* **15**, 26 (1964).
338. R. S. RYCHKOV and N. A. GLUKHAREVA, *Zavod. Lab.* **27**, 1246 (1961).
339. W. KÜHN and F. HERRMANN, *Kerntechnik* **2**, 268 (1960).
340. E. E. PICKETT and B. E. HANKINS, *Anal. Chem.* **30**, 47 (1958).
341. J. D. MOYER and H. S. ISBELL, *Anal. Chem.* **30**, 1975 (1958).
342. H. J. BORN and D. C. AUMANN, *Naturwiss.* **51**, 159 (1964); *Radiochim. Acta* **3**, 62 (1964).
343. D. C. AUMANN and H. J. BORN, *Naturwiss.* **51**, 159 (1964).
344. D. L. LOVE and A. E. GREENDALE, *Anal. Chem.* **32**, 780 (1960).
345. J. BLAŽEK and D. W. WAGNEROVÁ, *Coll. Czech. Chem. Comm.* **29**, 915 (1964).
346. J. WING, *Anal. Chem.* **35**, 559 (1964).
347. T. FLORKOWSKI, *Kerntechnik* **7**, 172 (1964).
348. W. S. LYON (Ed.), *Guide to Activation Analysis*, New York 1964.
349. D. TAYLOR, *Neutron Irradiation and Activation Analysis*, London 1964.
350. A. J. MOSES, *Nuclear Techniques in Analytical Chemistry*, Oxford 1965.
351. D. A. LAMBIE, *Techniques for the Use of Radioisotopes in Analysis*, London 1964.
352. T. B. PIERCE, P. F. PECK and W. M. HENRY, *Nature* **204**, 571 (1964).
353. S. AMIEL, Geneva Report 825 (1964).
354. R. P. GARDNER, J. W. DUNN, *Anal. Chem.* **37**, 528 (1965).
355. J. S. WATT, *Int. J. Appl. Rad. Isot.* **15**, 617 (1964).
356. J. A. HOPE and J. S. WATT, *Int. J. Appl. Rad. Isot.* **16**, 9 (1965).
357. K. LJUNGGREN and R. CHRISTELL, *Atompraxis* **10**, 259 (1964).
358. E. D. JORDAN, *Trans. Amer. Nucl. Soc.* **5**, 199 (1962).
359. J. LAUNE, *J. Physique Radium* **23**, 238 (1962).
360. G. BRUNNER, *Z. Chemie* **4**, 266 (1964).
361. E. DAHN and G. BRUNNER, *Chem. Technik* **16**, 112 (1964).
362. E. DAHN, *Chem. Technik* **16**, 174 (1964).
363. T. C. MARTIN, S. C. MATHUR and I. L. MORGAN, *Int. J. Appl. Rad. Isot.* **15**, 331 (1964).
364. P. F. MULVEY, J. A. CARDARELLI, R. A. MEYER, R. COOPER and B. A. BURROWS, *Radioisotope Sample Measurement Techniques in Medicine and Biology*, Symposium in Vienna, I.A.E.A., Vienna, 1965.
365. W. KÜHN, *Kerntechnik* **6**, 240 (1964).
366. J. P. CALI (Ed.), *Trace Analysis of Semiconductor Materials*, Oxford 1964.
367. V. P. GUINN, Geneva Report 197 (1964).
368. W. BOCK-WERTHMANN and W. SCHULZE, *Atomkernenergie-Dokumentation beim Gmelin-Institut*, AED Information Service, Section 14—Activation Analysis, Frankfurt 1961, 1963, 1964.
369. L. G. ERWALL, H. G. FORSBERG and K. LJUNGGREN, *Industriell Isotop-Teknik*, Copenhagen 1962; *Industrial Isotope Techniques*, Copenhagen 1964.
370. *Radioactive Isotope Dilution Analysis*, Booklet Issued by Radiochemical Centre, Amersham 1965.
371. *Radiochemical Methods of Analysis*, Symposium at Salzburg, I.A.E.A., Vienna 1965.
372. G. L. SCHROEDER, H. W. KRANER, R. D. EVANS and T. BRYDGES, *Science 151*, 815 (1966).

7. APPLICATION OF RADIOACTIVITY IN MINING AND OIL PRODUCTION

7.1. Mining

7.1.1. *Analysis and Classification of Ores*

Natural radioactivity may be used for detecting and investigating ore deposits, particularly those of the radioactive elements uranium, thorium and potassium. The methods for uranium and thorium prospecting have reached a high stage of development and are employed on a large scale. However, as has already been indicated in the chapter on chemical analysis, a discussion of these methods is outside the scope of this book. The investigation of potassium deposits will be treated in Section 7.3 (see also Section 6.2). Methods for studying conditions around bore-holes, among them those in ore deposits, by means of radioactive radiation sources will be discussed in Section 7.4.

Artificial radioactivity may be used to detect several important elements in rock samples during prospecting or in mining operations. The fundamentals of the relevant methods, among which activation analysis is of particular importance, have been discussed in Chapter 6.

Among the technically important elements which are easily activated to give β- or γ-emitting radionuclides are, for example, arsenic, manganese, copper, tungsten and gold. For a rapid analysis of rocks, e. g., at the mine, natural neutron sources may be employed, preferably the γ-free polonium–beryllium sources [2]. Induced activity is best measured with portable scintillation spectrometers [2]. An increase of the neutron flux, and therefore of the induced activity, by several orders of magnitude may be attained by using sub-critical assemblies. In these devices the natural sources are made to induce sub-critical (convergent) chain reactions. For this purpose, a portable system containing enriched uranium and ordinary water may be used [3]. Provided the system is properly constructed, the reaction cannot become divergent. The development of a self-perpetuating chain reaction would, of course, be disastrous.

X-ray fluorescence analysis with radionuclide sources (see Section 6.7.5) may also be used for ores. A rapid analytical method of this kind has been developed for iron and calcium in iron ores. The X-radiation of the two elements is measured separately with a proportional counter and pulse height analyser. The method may be used for recording the distribution of the elements in drill cores [234] (see p. 110).

The distribution of elements in rocks may also be investigated by autoradiography of a highly polished sample after activation [7]. The procedure resembles the autoradiography of alloys (Section 8.3).

The suggestion has been made that ores could be separated from gangue automatically on the basis of induced radioactivity. The principle is that the material to be sorted is placed on a transporter belt which passes first a suitable radiation source and then a radiation measuring instrument. This instrument operates a mechanical selector which sorts the rock pieces according to their activity, thus removing the pieces of high activity or of low activity from the belt [4].

Equipment for automatic ore analysis has been described in some detail. Although designed for naturally radioactive ores (mainly uranium ores), such equipment could, with some modification, be applied to artificially activated ores [1, 5, 6]. A detailed survey covering the various aspects of radiometric ore sorting methods as applied to uranium and to other ores has been published [304].

In practice it is necessary to use penetrating radiation for activation. Activation by slow neutron capture seems to offer the greatest promise. Under given conditions, the greater the reaction cross section (p. 88) and the more favourable the half-life of the nuclide produced, the stronger is the activation. By "favourable" is meant that the half-life is, on the one hand, so short that an appreciable fraction of the saturation activity (p. 89) is attained during short irradiation periods (a few seconds or a few minutes at the most), while, on the other hand, it is so long that the activity does not decrease too much during passage from the radiation field to the measuring instrument. Furthermore, the radiation must be measurable easily, and must therefore not be too soft.

The activation of the gangue is usually of little importance. The majority of the elements in gangue, such as silicon, oxygen, calcium, magnesium and carbon, are hardly activated by slow neutrons. Only aluminium, which is often present in the rocks in the form of silicates (clays, etc.), is activated easily. But since the half-life of this activity is 2·3 min only, it is eliminated by allowing 10–20 min between the end of the irradiation and the measurement.

For ore sorting of this type large quantities of rock would have to be handled. Therefore strong radiation sources with extended radiation fields are needed. In most cases probably only a reactor will be adequate [4].

A special case is that of copper ore [238, 239]. By activation with slow neutrons positron-active copper-64 is formed, and therefore two quanta of annihilation radiation appear in each disintegration. They are registered by two plastic scintillators with a coincidence circuit (see p. 97). The influence of variations in the sizes of the ore pieces is taken into account by measuring the total radiation intensity from the pieces as well; this is found to be practically proportional to size. The coincidence rate is then compared by the instrument to the total counting rate, and automatic sorting follows on the basis of this ratio.

Beryllium is another special case. Photons of comparatively low energy liberate neutrons from this element, as they do from deuterium (p. 98). In the case of beryllium, the energy threshold is 1·63 MeV. Neutron emission occurs instantaneously during irradiation. Therefore, the measuring instrument is so placed that the neutrons are detected during irradiation.

It has been suggested that the separation of ores from gangue could also be performed by exploiting differences in the adsorption power for labelled substances. The rock would be passed through a solution of an active substance which is adsorbed either by the ore or by the gangue. The rock would then be led past a measuring instrument coupled with a device for separating and collecting the ore [8]. Adsorption of labelled substances also plays an important part in investigations of flotation (p. 125).

In the grinding of ores or other minerals, it is of interest to know the rate at which grains of a given size are reduced on further grinding to smaller grain sizes, or may aggregate to larger particles. This process may be studied by sieving off the particles of a particular size after partial grinding, and replacing this material by the same quantity of radioactively labelled but otherwise identical mineral of the same fineness. Further grinding follows, and the distribution of radioactivity over the various grain sizes subsequently present is determined. The labelled mineral of the desired fineness is also obtained by grinding and sieving [9, 266].

7.1.2. Radionuclides in Coal Mining and Coke Production

The possibility of using radioactivity in coal mining has been the subject of several reviews and bibliographies [10–17, 32, 244]. The application of radioactivity for the investigation of bore-holes (logging) in coal mines will be discussed in Section 7.4.

Layers of clay often show higher contents of natural radionuclides than the coal itself (see Section 7.3). Automatic guide systems for seam cutting machines may therefore work on the principle that the machine turns away from the stronger radioactivity present at the edge of the seam and follows the seam itself. However, automatic guide systems utilizing the differences in the back-scattering of γ-radiation by different layers seem more promising; in particular, the count rates arising in such equipment can be made much higher (see p. 123).

Radioactivity may also be applied in various ways to improve safety in mines [255]. The air supply to the various parts of coal mines and the effectiveness of ventilation may be checked with radiokrypton [10]. Radioactive methyl bromide has been used to follow turbulent diffusion in the air space of experimental galleries in mines [20], and to investigate the movement of the type of respirable dust cloud produced when explosives are fired in ventilated mine workings [241]. Undetonated explosives may be discovered by radiation measurement if the explosive, such as dynamite, is labelled. Only a few microcuries of antimony-124 (half-life 60 days) per cartridge are required [19].

The speed of single grains in the pneumatic transportation of coal within a mine has been measured by selective labelling of grains of a definite size with ammonium bromide (bromine-82). The coal contained very fine particles as well as lumps up to a diameter of 1 cm. Many tons were transported per hour. Measurements were carried out at various heights, from 8 to 310 m, above the base level. The velocity was determined by registering the γ-radiation emitted from individual particles, using two counters 2 m apart from each other. The time interval between the passage – typical values being about 70 millisec – was recorded with an automatic chronometer (see also Section 9.3.4) [24, 25].

Lignite particles have been labelled to find their velocity in tube driers. The particles were first impregnated with sodium chloride or gold chloride, and then activated in a reactor. The γ-radiation was measured with counters [26].

The apparent density, and thence the grain size and the moisture content of stored coal, peat and coke may be determined by means of radiation measurements [21–23, 244]. In one method of density determination the back-scattered γ-radiation of caesium-137 was measured, the direct radiation from the source being shielded off by means of lead. The moisture content was obtained by measuring the slowing-down of neutrons due to the hydrogen; the flux of the slow neutrons was measured with a boron chamber (see Section 6.7.2) [21]. The apparent density may, of course, also be determined through γ-ray absorption.

The methods described in Section 9.3.3 for level detection may be applied to coal dust, coke and the like, provided due regard is paid to the possibility of surface unevenness [32]. Control of filling and alignment and the operation of safety relays by radiation, as mentioned in the same section, may also be employed [32], and the uniformity of a mixture of coals may be checked [259] (see also p. 212).

A good deal of attention has been paid to the determination of ash contents of coals by absorption and scattering of radiation [32, 255, 264]. In one group of such methods the absorption of soft electromagnetic radiation, e.g., from thulium-170 ($E_\gamma = 84$ keV), in ground coal is measured [230, 248, 263]. The elements present in ash (silicon, aluminium, oxygen, sodium and calcium) have greater atomic numbers than carbon; their K-edges are therefore nearer the radiation energy used than that of carbon, so that they absorb the radiation more strongly (see p. 106). Therefore the ash content may be found from the weight of coal in the cell and the attenuation of the radiation; a calibration curve is used. The heat of combustion of the coal can also be correlated empirically with the attenuation. Appreciable amounts of water in the coal may interfere seriously with the application of the method. However, in one modification of the method, the absorption is measured with the interstices between the coal particles filled with water [248].

Methods have also been proposed for analysing larger coal pieces of varying sizes by γ-absorptiometry. If such methods are to work automatically, the thickness of the coal piece which is crossed by the radiation beam must also be obtained by the instrument. One solution of the problem is to measure the absorption of the radiations from two different radionuclides, i.e., of different energy, when going through the coal piece along the same path. From the measured absorption values, both the thickness and the composition of the coal are obtained. If this is to be done automatically, special circuits are needed [249].

In another method the back-scattering of β-radiation by the coal sample is measured, the coal again being placed in a cell. This method makes use of the fact that the intensity of back-scattering by an "infinitely thick" layer increases with the mean atomic number of the sample. Investigations have shown that quantitative ash determination by a method of this kind is only possible if the type of impurity present is known. The radiation source used consisted of strontium-90–yttrium-90 [231, 236].

Measurement of the back-scattering of soft electromagnetic radiation by coal has been studied in some detail as to its suitability for ash determinations. Thulium-170 has been mostly used as the source. The basis of this technique is as follows: The intensity of the back-scattered radiation depends on two factors. Firstly, on the strength of scattering per unit volume, mainly due to Compton effect. Secondly, on the absorption of the incident and of the back-scattered radiation within the sample, in which the photoelectric effect plays the main part. For the radiation energies used, the absorption effects predominate, so that coal with high ash content shows smaller back-scattering intensity than coal with low ash content. This relationship, which follows from the considerations discussed in connection with the absorption method (see Section 6.7.4), has been checked in a number of preliminary investigations [232, 233, 244].

Measurements on powdered coal in a cell using this principle have shown that acceptable accuracy can only be obtained when the density of the coal in the cell is held constant, or is also determined. At higher ash contents (more than 10 per cent), the accuracy of the determination is considerably less than at smaller ash contents [237]. This measurement principle is also of great interest for direct measurements on lumps of coal, as has been pointed out by several authors [232, 233, 244]. The suggestion has been made that sorting machines for the separation of coal from gangue might be controlled by such an instrument. But so far, development work on, or testing of, such equipment has not been reported.

In a feasibility study it was shown that activation analysis with fast neutrons and fast neutron scattering can be used to determine the following elements in coal: carbon, oxygen, aluminium, and silicon [303].

The measurement of the back-scattering of low-energy γ-radiation, as mentioned, has also been applied to a coal sensing unit in connection with coal cutting machinery for thin seams ("midget miner") [246, 247]. There has been great need for such a sensing unit, since the operator of a coal cutting machine for thin seams (thicknesses less than approx. 80 cm) should know about the conditions 3 or 4 m ahead of him in a restricted, unilluminated space. The machine has to be steered vertically in such a way that it cuts only coal and does not cut into the rock forming the bottom or the roof of the seam. In order to inform the operator of the vertical position of the cutting machine, a sensing unit has been constructed which measures the amount of coal left on the seam bottom. The unit, which is installed in the leading edge of the skids on which the machine moves forward, consists of a source of thulium-170 (original activity 125 mc) and of three Geiger counting tubes with their amplifying circuits as radiation detectors. The count rate is indicated on a meter that is mounted near the operator and is usually calibrated directly in units (in.) of coal thickness. Coal layers up to a thickness of about 3 in. can be measured with an accuracy of about ± 0.5 in. The accuracy of measurement is naturally better for thin coal layers.

Such sensing units have led to an appreciable improvement in the maintenance of the cutting horizon. It is reported that the operators now place complete reliance on the meter reading. As they have various tasks and cannot watch the meter of the sensing unit continuously, fully automatic steering units are now being designed. Here the signals from the sensing unit will actuate electrohydraulically the steering jacks which regulate the vertical movement of the coal cutting machine. The application of coal sensing units to other types of coal cutting machines is being considered.

Radionuclides are also employed in connection with the application of coal, especially with the production of coke [32]. For example, the processes involved in the thermal degradation and coking of coal [27], and the movement of coal [265] and of gases [29] within coking ovens have been studied (see p. 160). Radiometric control methods, including methods of level detection, have also been applied to coking ovens [32, 242].

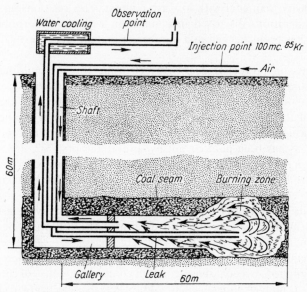

FIG. 27. Schematic diagram of underground coal gasification system [229] (after [18])

An interesting investigation has been devoted to the settlement of an old technological dispute. Is it the organically combined sulphur or the pyrite sulphur in coal which remains to a greater extent in the coke produced, and thus contributes to the unwanted sulphur content of pig iron? The question was answered by introducing 1 kg of pyrite labelled with radiosulphur into 12 tons of coal. The coal was processed in an industrial coking oven. The specific activity of the sulphur in the coke was then measured, and it was calculated whether a larger or a smaller portion of the radiosulphur, compared with inactive sulphur, remained in the coke. It was found that pyritic (labelled) sulphur appeared in the coke to the same extent as organic sulphur. Consequently, both forms are equally harmful, and in the purchase of coking coal for iron production only the total sulphur content should be considered [28]. Other work suggests, however, that the situation may be more complicated [27, 30, 32].

For the underground gasification of coal, several tunnels or shafts are dug, which must meet. Procedures have been developed to determine the distances between tunnels and shafts by the absorption of γ-rays from cobalt-60 [18, 33–35].

Leaks occurring during the underground gasification of coal can be detected with a radioactive gas (krypton-85). If a short-circuit, by-passing the ignition zone, exists between entry and exit shafts, part of the krypton injected into the former shaft appears abnormally quickly in the latter shaft [18, 33] (see also p. 121). The time interval between the injection and the appearance of the first activity peak is a measure of the distance between the injection point and the short-circuit point, while the area under the peak is a measure of the seriousness of the short-circuit. The enlargement of the combustion space itself due to the progress of the reaction can be determined by the increase in the time interval between the injection and the appearance of the main part of the radioactive gas in the exit shaft. Moreover, the main activity peak is broadened as the combustion space is enlarged [18] (Fig. 27).

Reference to hydrological work in connection with lignite mining will be made in Section 12.3.

7.1.3. *Ore Dressing*

The behaviour of ore particles of definite composition and size during dressing operations may be followed in the actual plant by radioactive labelling of the relevant constituent similarly as in the study of grinding (p. 121). The labelling may be carried out, for example, by activation or by selective adsorption of dissolved radioactive substances on the minerals.

The adsorption phenomena which underlie flotation procedures have been studied with a variety of labelled substances [12, 36–40, 42, 49, 53, 58, 250, 254, 300, 301, 307].

The detailed distribution of adsorbed labelled substances can be investigated by a micro-autoradiographic technique, which may be coupled with photometry of the images [39–42, 250, 254]. The technique has been employed in connection with the flotation of sulphide ores, such as galena, sphalerite, pyrite, pyrrhotite, etc., in order to obtain the distribution of labelled collector substances (^{35}S-xanthates) over particles of different kinds and sizes. Such studies have proved useful in investigating the concentration and distribution on the surface as a function of the composition of the mineral, the pH value of the solution, the length of the non-polar chains in the xanthates, the concentration of oxygen, and other variables [38–40, 42–51, 250–252].

The adsorption of xanthate is depressed by chromate ion. Investigations with labelled chromate have shown that this effect is due to the formation of chromate layers on the grain surface [40, 52, 53]. On the other hand, frothing agents such as pine oil increase both the amount of the labelled xanthate adsorbed and the uniformity of the adsorption layer [40]. Instead of measuring directly the adsorption of labelled xanthate, the displacement of other (labelled) ions by inactive xanthate may be observed. It was shown that those parts of surfaces of pyrite particles, which had been treated with xanthate, did not adsorb lead-212 (thorium B). Thus it is possible to determine the hydrophobic character given to minerals by comparing autoradiographs of untreated material and of similar material after treatment with the collector [39].

The adsorption of labelled anions (laurate) and cations (sodium, barium, dodecylamine and tridecylamine) on quartz, fluorite and calcite, and of labelled anions (tridecoate) on fluorite and rare earth minerals have been determined in further flotation studies [40, 54–56, 253, 254]. Labelled kerosene has also been used [254]. Other investigations refer to the flotation of metals, such as copper, silver and gold [40, 43, 57].

The effect of activating cations, such as copper, calcium or iron, is due to improved adsorption of the collector. Partial activation of the surface, corresponding to 20 to 40 per cent of a monolayer, is sufficient. Depending on the type of mineral, the decisive factor for the interaction may be chemisorption, heterogeneous chemical reaction, ion exchange or electrostatic sorption [58].

7.2. Oil Prospecting

On the basis of extensive measurements of the low radiation intensities due to the natural radioelements in the surface layers of the earth, certain relationships between this intensity and the presence of petroleum deposits have been found. In many cases the radiation intensity immediately above the most productive zone was low, while above-average values were found over the edges of such a zone. The deposit is thus surrounded by an "activity halo". Since the first reports on this phenomenon [59–61] numerous petroleum deposits as well as regions where oil prospecting was in progress have been investigated in this way [60, 62–78]. Often the portable scintillation counters developed for uranium and thorium prospecting were used. Increasingly, mobile equipment installed in motorcars [74, 78] or in low-flying aircraft [69, 75] is employed. The relationship just mentioned between radiation intensity and the presence of petroleum has been shown to apply in 60 to 70 per cent of the cases [79]. On this basis radiometric surveys of territories may often be regarded as a suitable method for petroleum prospecting. Similar anomalies have also been found over natural gas deposits, and the radiometric method has already led to the detection of such deposits [69].

The origin of the activity halo over petroleum deposits has been the subject of many investigations in recent years [67, 68, 72]. Determination of individual radionuclides in rock samples [72], together with γ-spectrometric measurements using special equipment [74, 80], have shown that the anomalies found above petroleum deposits can be attributed to the distribution of members of the uranium–radium series. The elements of the thorium series do not show this characteristic distribution. It has also been found that various non-radioactive trace elements such as manganese, cobalt, nickel, vanadium and chromium, show anomalous distributions over petroleum deposits similar to those of the members of the uranium series [72]. Thus, the behaviour of the radioelements is only a special case of a general geochemical phenomenon. It is also of interest that uranium and radium are present in rocks over petroleum deposits predominantly in exchangeable form, so that these elements can be desorbed, and are thus capable of migration.

Two reasons for this anomalous distribution have been proposed: either that the adsorption of the trace elements in the surface layers is affected by gases rising from the oil deposits, or — less likely — that these elements are brought into the surface layers by water from greater depths, and are then concentrated there [68, 72]. Investigations on the influence of gases and vapours on ion adsorption at mineral surfaces support the first mechanism.

In laboratory investigations it has been found that hydrocarbons with more than six carbon atoms significantly increase the desorption of certain ions from clays by dilute hydrochloric acid or ammonium chloride solution [72]. This effect may be due to adsorption of the hydrocarbons on active centres, so that hydrophobic qualities are introduced. It is also possible that hydrocarbons rising from a petroleum deposit cause desorption of the trace elements in the layers through which the hydrocarbons pass, and that these elements are then redeposited in peripheral zones.

The use of aircraft in radiometric petroleum prospecting permits large areas to be surveyed in a comparatively short time. The outlay therefore seems worthwhile even though radioactive anomalies appear only over some of the deposits. It has been reported that a single aircraft can investigate an area of 50,000–60,000 square kilometres (20,000–25,000 square miles) in 5–6 months [69].

A systematic method for the analysis of trace elements in (crude) oil by activation with neutrons has been given [262]. Activation analysis has also been applied to many other products of the oil industry [302, 306].

7.3. Bore-hole Investigations by Measurement of Natural Radioactivity (Gamma-Logging, GL)

Investigations of bore-holes by measurement of γ-radiation from naturally radioactive substances are carried out on a large scale. The objectives of such investigations have mostly been:

(1) Search for uranium and thorium ores;
(2) Search for potassium salts; and
(3) Differentiation between various geological strata distinguished by their trace contents of natural radioelements.

As we have already indicated, prospecting for uranium and thorium will not be further discussed here. GL measurements in potassium deposits have proved very suitable for the detection of strata containing potassium, and for discovering their extent and potassium content. Such methods are now increasingly used instead of the investigation of drill-cores [81–83, 258], because in potassium deposits it is generally difficult to obtain cores for which unequivocal assignment to definite strata is possible.

GL is extensively used in petroleum bore-holes. The first investigations of this kind were conducted in 1937 [84]. On the basis of the gamma-logs it is possible to distinguish between various types of rock strata. In general, slate shows comparatively large activity, followed by clays with intermediate activity, and by sandstone and limestone with only small activity [85–90]. The activities are mainly due to uranium and thorium. Measurement of γ-radiation in petroleum bore-holes is therefore suitable for detecting slate formations and for estimating clay contents.

GL has also been found suitable for the investigation of bore-holes in other formations. Measurements on palaeozoic bauxite deposits, in which aluminium is primarily present as $Al_2O_3 \cdot H_2O$, have shown that owing to their greater content of natural radioelements the bauxite layers have a higher radiation intensity than the surroundings [91].

Various automatic instruments have been developed for use in GL [92–103]. Measuring instruments may be Geiger counters, high pressure ionization chambers [104] or scintillation counters. With scintillation counters it is possible to obtain γ-spectra in the bore-holes and so to determine the contributions of the different radioactive decay series [99–103]. This is complicated, however, by the fact that a large portion of the γ-quanta reaching the instrument consists not of primary but of scattered radiation. Transistors are now increasingly employed in logging equipment [105].

Recent equipment is often constructed in such a way that GL is carried out simultaneously with neutron logging (see Section 7.4.1.) [106].

7.4. Bore-hole Investigations with Radiation Sources

Logging methods where a radiation source is introduced into the bore-hole have in recent years acquired considerable importance, and are constantly being extended. The starting point of this development were investigations by Pontecorvo, in which a neutron source was introduced into the bore-hole, and the γ-radiation emitted on neutron capture was recorded [107]. The considerable scope of the application of this type of logging can be judged by the fact that as early as 1957 a total length of 8 million bore-hole metres was investigated in the U.S.S.R. The scope of such work in the United States is assumed to be even greater [224].

Before discussing individual logging methods with radiation sources in detail, a short review will be given. Suitable primary radiations are fast neutrons and γ-rays. Neutron methods may be distinguished according to the kind of radiation recorded. The most important groups are:

(1) Measurement of slowed-down neutrons (neutron-neutron-logging, NNL);
(2) Measurement of capture γ-radiation (neutron-gamma-logging, NGL);
(3) Measurement of radiation, particularly γ-radiation, from radionuclides produced through neutron irradiation (activation logging, AL).

Several variants of these methods exist according to the kind of radiation measuring method used; selective recording of radiation of particular energy is of importance in this connection.

In methods using sources of electromagnetic radiation (γ- or X-rays), it is usual to measure the scattered radiation (γ-γ-logging, GGL). The methods can be varied by applying radiation sources of different energies.

Until a few years ago, the only sources available for bore-hole logging were those in which the relevant primary logging radiation is emitted directly by a radionuclide, or is induced by the radiation from a radionuclide. In recent years, small accelerators for introduction into bore-holes have been developed. These are particularly suitable as neutron sources, but can also be employed to produce electromagnetic radiation. Special equipment for the latter purpose is at present being developed. Bore-hole accelerators have the following advantages as neutron sources:

1. They give a higher neutron flux.
2. Because of the greater neutron energy, the depth of penetration, i.e., the rock zone actually investigated, is increased.
3. By pulsed operation new investigation methods become possible.

Up to now, logging with radiation sources has been used primarily in petroleum bore-holes. There are two main objectives of such investigations:

(a) Evaluation of the porosity of petroleum-, gas- and water-bearing layers, and especially of the petroleum content of porous layers.

(b) Location of boundaries between petroleum-, gas-, and water-containing layers, especially the position of oil–water interfaces.

Logging with radiation sources is also used, to a lesser extent, for the investigation of other types of borings, as in coal mining, potassium mining, and prospecting for various ores. The discussion of such applications will be given in connection with each type of method after the description of petroleum bore-hole investigations.

A number of reviews on bore-hole investigations with radiation sources have been published. The principal difficulties and limitations of these methods, arising mainly from the complex conditions prevailing in bore-holes, are discussed in these publications in greater detail than is possible here [66, 71, 123, 136, 224, 240]. These reviews as well as other publications [267–270] contain much information on the radiation detection equipment used in bore-hole logging with radiation sources.

Logging results are affected by a great number of parameters, including: (1) bore-hole diameter; (2) position of the probe in the bore-hole; (3) composition of the bore-hole filling with respect to density, salt content, etc.; (4) penetration of bore-hole liquid into surrounding rock layers; (5) deposition of solid material from the bore-hole filling or penetrating liquid on the wall of the bore-hole; (6) thickness and composition of the bore-hole cementing (see [224]). Under practical operating conditions these quantities may show considerable deviations, and reliable data for them are hard to get. Interpretation of logs is then complicated, or may even be impossible. The applicability of a logging method therefore often has to be judged on the basis of practical experience, by comparing a great number of nuclear logs with information obtained by other techniques. A certain procedure may turn out to be suitable for particular geological or technological conditions, but quite unsuitable for others. In any case, in order to arrive at reliable data on the conditions in bore-holes it is advisable not to rely on a single nuclear logging technique but to supplement it by other methods of investigation, based either on nuclear phenomena or on other principles.

7.4.1. *Neutron-Neutron-Logging* (NNL)

To explain the principles of neutron-neutron-logging, we shall consider the behaviour of fast neutrons emitted from a source placed in a bore-hole. The fast neutrons collide with atomic nuclei in the surrounding materials, including the contents of the bore-hole, the material of the casing, the cement and the rock layer, and are thus slowed down. Hydrogen, in whatever chemical state it may be present, is by far the most effective moderator (see p. 86). The larger the hydrogen content in the surrounding layers, the nearer the source the neutrons are slowed down. The spatial distribution of slow neutrons therefore depends in the first instance on the hydrogen concentration, i.e., on the oil and water content. If this concentration is great, the slow neutron flux reaches high values near the source and diminishes rapidly with increasing distance from the source. On the other hand, if the hydrogen content is low, the flux near the source is comparatively small, diminishes much more slowly with distance, and at a great distance exceeds the value which would be obtained with higher hydrogen content. There is therefore a point with intermediate distance from the source (30–40 cm) at which the slow neutron flux is substantially independent of the hydrogen content of the medium. The hydrogen content may be determined by measuring the flux either near the source (less than 25 cm) or at a greater distance (more than about 50 cm). Such measurements are usually carried out with boron fluoride filled proportional counters (p. 101). Scintillation counters with boron or lithium loaded scintillators are also used (see p. 101).

However, the neutron flux in a medium does not depend only on the moderator properties of the medium which are due predominantly to its hydrogen content. It is also affected by neutron capture in the medium which is due to elements with appreciable capture cross-sections for slow neutrons. In bore-hole logging, the elements principally responsible for neutron capture are hydrogen and chlorine. As far as hydrogen is concerned, its role in neutron capture may be considered as secondary to its effect as moderator and may thus be treated in combination with that effect. Changes in the capacity for neutron capture are then mainly due to the chlorine content of the layers around the hole and of the filling of the bore-hole.

Chlorine has a very large capture cross-section (33 barns) for thermal neutrons, which is mainly due to the isotope chlorine-37. Chlorine occurs in certain rocks, but in the study of petroleum bore-holes the sodium chloride content of the ground water, which may reach high values, is most important. The presence of chlorine always reduces the slow neutron flux. Thus the slow neutron flux around the neutron source is determined by the hydrogen and chlorine contents. Neutron distribution in and around bore-holes as a function of the various parameters has been the object of extensive theoretical studies [119, 240, 267, 276–282].

The purpose of NNL is either to obtain information on the liquid content of the strata, that is, their porosity (see in particular [108–111, 124, 240, 267, 269, 288, 289]), or to locate the position of the oil–water interface. The conditions for the measurement of the slow neutron flux will depend on which of these two problems is considered. For the determination of the porosity, the influence of the capture cross-section of the surrounding medium on the measured flux must be reduced as far as possible, while for the detection of the oil–water interface this effect should be as great as possible.

When registering thermal neutrons, even the use of a probe of optimum dimensions does not result in complete elimination of the effect of the capture cross-section of the surrounding medium. Nevertheless many useful bore-hole investigations have been carried out by NNL with registration of thermal neutrons. However, practically complete elimination of the effect of neutron absorption in the medium is possible, if the flux of epithermal neutrons, that is, of incompletely slowed-down neutrons, is measured instead of that of thermal neutrons [108–111]. Since the capture cross-section for neutrons generally diminishes with increase in neutron energy, the effect of such neutron-absorbing materials as chlorine on the life-time of epithermal neutrons is much less than on the life-time of thermal neutrons. The flux of such neutrons therefore depends practically only on the moderator properties of the medium, and thus predominantly on its hydrogen content.

For the measurement of epithermal neutrons it is usual to employ one of the normal neutron detectors, which is, however, surrounded by cadmium or boron to shield against thermal neutrons. When cadmium is used, neutrons of energy greater than ca. 0·3 eV are recorded (see p. 101). Experiments with model set-ups resembling boreholes with surrounding layers have shown that with a probe of this kind the measured neutron flux is practically independent of the salt content of the layer. The influence of the type of detector, the length of the probe, the diameter of the bore-hole, the nature of the casing, the cementing and other factors on the results has been investigated [111, 119, 267, 283], but a number of other factors still await study.

For the determination of the porosity, the strongest possible dependence of the measured neutron flux on the hydrogen content, with simultaneous elimination of the effect of other factors, is required. The influence of the porosity on the measured flux can be increased by pressing the probe against the wall of the bore-hole, by making the water layer (the bore-hole filling) around the probe as small as possible, and by using a long probe [109]. A further increase in the effect of the porosity on the measured flux can be attained by surrounding the probe with a neutron shield made of a paraffin wax–boron mixture which has collimation openings near the source and the detector; these openings are directed towards the wall of the bore-hole against which the probe is pressed [112].

With these considerations in mind, probes have been developed which show a strong dependence of the measured flux on the porosity, and so give comparatively good accuracy in the determination of the porosity. When suitable calibration curves are used which take account of the conditions in the bore-hole and the nature of the surrounding rock, a relative accuracy of porosity determinations of around 10 per cent is attainable [111]. Thus it was found under certain conditions that an alteration in porosity from 15 to 30 per cent caused a change in the recorded flux of 30 per cent, the error in the flux measurement being about ±5 per cent. Porosity determinations may also be carried out in cased bore-holes, but the accuracy here is lower than in uncased bore-holes.

For NNL using measurement of epithermal neutrons stronger sources are necessary than when thermal neutrons are registered. This arises from the fact that the flux of epithermal neutrons is lower, and neutrons of this energy are measured with considerably lower yield by the detectors generally employed. A certain increase in the sensitivity of the detector for epithermal neutrons is attained by placing a paraffin wax layer within the cadmium or boron shield which keeps off thermal neutrons coming from outside.

NNL with epithermal neutrons is the best method for determining porosity as long as porosities are small. For larger values it is sometimes possible to obtain greater accuracy by GGL (see Section 7.4.4). A difficulty in all porosity determinations by neutron-logging arises from the fact that hydrogen may be present in rocks in other forms than that of oil or water filling the pores. Especially in the case of clays hydrogen may be present in the form of chemically combined water. This hydrogen obviously slows down neutrons in the same way as hydrogen in the pores. Porosity determinations in clay-containing strata are therefore more difficult than in carbonate strata which are largely free from clay. Occasionally the clay content of strata has been determined by measuring the natural γ-radiation (see Section 7.3), and these data were then used in evaluating the NN-logs.

Since NNL with epithermal neutrons is in effect a determination of hydrogen content, this method has also been found convenient for locating the gas–liquid interface [113]. The main problem in this application of NNL is the elimination of the effect of liquids present in the bore-hole, or pressed from the bore-hole into the rock. This is achieved by using probes with comparatively large distance between source and detector [114, 115], since with this type of probe the measured flux depends to a greater extent on the composition of the deeper layers.

For NNL with thermal neutrons, systematic investigations of the roles of certain parameters have also been carried out, and improved probes have been proposed on this basis [116–118]. Thus the effect of variations in the composition of the bore-hole filling and in the bore-hole diameter may be reduced by using a probe pressed against the wall of the bore-hole, shielded against the open space of the bore-hole by means of boron or cadmium. In all variants of NNL the bore-hole diameter has a strong influence on the result, especially in the case of bore-holes filled with water. This effect has also been investigated [119].

In the determination of porosity NNL is much superior to NGL, which has also been used for this purpose. With the latter, it is impossible to obtain the strong dependence on hydrogen content which is attainable with NNL. Moreover, the natural radioelements in the rock do not interfere in NNL and this method may also be applied to bore-holes where investigations have been carried out by introducing radioactive materials (see Section 7.5).

Under certain conditions NNL may also be used to locate the oil–water interface. However, the method is generally less sensitive in this respect than NGL, since only a relatively small change in the measured value is observed when the probe passes through the interface. The use of NNL for locating the oil–water interface depends on the salt content of the ground water. As stated before, the life-time of the thermal neutrons, and therefore the flux of these neutrons, are reduced by the salt. The neutron flux observed in water-containing strata is therefore less than the corresponding value in oil-containing strata. The change on passing through the interface may amount to about 30 per cent in dry bore-holes and with high salt concentrations, but in water-containing bore-holes it may be as small as a few per cent [120]. Poor results are obtained in perforated bore-holes [121]. The change in flux when the probe passes the interface depends upon the length of the probe. Working with models built to represent typical bore-hole situations, an optimum probe length (distance between source and detector) of 25–30 cm has been arrived at [122]. However, as the values obtained depend also on the porosity of the layer, it is best to choose the probe length in such a way that this influence is reduced as much as possible. During experiments with models it has been found that under typical conditions this influence is a minimum with a probe length of 15–20 cm [122].

Experiments have shown that changing the position of the probe within the bore-hole and changing the thickness of the cementing lead to large variations in the value of the measured flux. The value observed also depends on the water content and on the salt content of the cement. These effects are more pronounced with NNL than with NGL [124].

Besides being used in petroleum bore-holes, NNL has also been applied to the investigation of deposits which contain strongly neutron-absorbing materials such as boron or manganese [240, 284–286]. Moreover, it has been used to detect water-containing layers, such as layers in potassium deposits which contain water of crystallization [110].

7.4.2. *Neutron-Gamma-Logging* (NGL)

In this type of logging γ-radiation from neutron capture (n, γ-reaction) in the materials surrounding the probe is measured. The measured radiation intensities are a function of the spatial distribution of the capture processes. In oil fields this spatial distribution depends in the first instance on the hydrogen content of the medium. In zones with high hydrogen content the neutrons are slowed down near the source and then captured by nuclei of the medium; the capture is due mostly to hydrogen and chlorine. However, other factors, including the number of γ-quanta emitted per capture and the energy of the quanta, also affect the count rates. The greater this energy, the lower is the absorption in rock, and therefore the greater the yield with which the capture processes are registered by the γ-ray detector. In the applications of NGL the differences between neutron capture in hydrogen (^1H) and chlorine (^{37}Cl) as to quantum yield and energy of emitted γ-radiation may play an important part. The most important difference is due to the fact that the radiation emitted on neutron capture by chlorine-37 has much greater energy. Simplified theoretical calculations for the relationships in NGL have been presented (see [240]). The influence of various parameters, such as those concerning the construction of the probe, the dimensions and filling of the bore-hole and the composition of the rock strata have been studied by special experiments [135, 240, 267].

NGL has been used extensively for locating oil–water interfaces [120–122, 124–128, 175, 240, 267, 290]. This method is based on the fact that neutron capture in chlorine leads to emission of high energy γ-radiation; the interface is located on the basis of a rise in the measured radiation intensity as the probe passes from the oil-bearing to the water-bearing strata. The change in radiation intensity during the passage through the interface therefore increases with the salt content of the water. With low salt contents it is difficult or impossible to locate the interface by NGL.

In the earliest NGL probes, the γ-radiation was measured with Geiger counters. To locate the oil–water interface, a distance between source and counter of about 50 cm was used. Under typical conditions, with such equipment a change in count rate of about 10–15 per cent is observed during the passage through the interface [120]. This change is somewhat increased (by about 20 per cent, relative), and the effect of the borehole diameter is at the same time diminished, when the probe is not placed in the middle of the bore-hole, but is pressed against the wall [127].

The effect of the filling of the bore-hole and of the layers close to it on the radiation intensity at the detector may be reduced when the latter is surrounded by a shield containing boron, such as boric acid in paraffin wax, with a thickness of 0·5 to 1 cm [122]. The boron greatly reduces the slow neutron flux in the probe and its surroundings, and so diminishes the effect of changes in the composition of the surrounding layers. Furthermore, in the reaction of neutrons with boron only comparatively soft γ-radiation is emitted, so that this process is only recorded with small yield. To reduce the effect of the bore-hole filling, probes with the largest possible diameter have also been used.

With probes containing a detector with boron shield the oil–water interface may in certain circumstances be located even when water from the bore-hole has already penetrated into the surrounding rock layers [128].

NGL generally gives good results on non-perforated bore-holes with large porosity (exceeding 15 per cent) of the strata. With ordinary methods, the detection of the interface in perforated bore-holes is difficult since the perforation often leads to a substantial penetration of water from the bore-hole into the rock strata. The investigation of some perforated bore-holes has, however, been possible by a procedure where liquid is pumped out of the bore-hole while NGL is carried out [121].

By employing scintillation detectors in NGL, considerable improvements in locating oil–water interfaces can be brought about. Two characteristics of scintillation detectors are important in this connection. In the first place they are much more sensitive for γ-radiation than Geiger counters. Secondly they can be operated with energy discrimination or even as γ-spectrometers (p. 46). Since the radiation emitted on neutron capture in chlorine is, as has already been mentioned, of comparatively high energy, it is possible to measure this radiation selectively by employing energy discrimination, registering only impulses above a certain magnitude. The relative change in the count rate which occurs when the probe passes through the interface is thus increased, and the sensitivity in locating the interface is improved. Under typical conditions the change in count rate observed at the interface may be increased to 50 or 60 per cent, which is several times the change attainable with Geiger counters [67, 120]. It is best to set the discriminator so that only γ-radiation of more than ca. 3 MeV is recorded, so that even the most energetic radiation emitted on neutron capture by hydrogen ($E_\gamma = 2\cdot2$ MeV) as well as the natural γ-radiation of the rock are eliminated [103, 120, 129]. Comparatively large scintillator crystals are needed for measuring high energy γ-rays with sufficiently high yield. A NG-log obtained with a scintillation detector using discrimination is shown in Fig. 28.

The porosity of the strata in oil fields has also been determined by NGL [128, 130 to 136, 240, 267, 269]. Various difficulties arise in such determinations. They are mainly due to the disturbing effect of the salt content, to the dependence of the results on the composition of the rocks, and to the relatively small dependence of the measured radiation intensity on the hydrogen content.

In carbonate rocks a smaller influence of chlorine is observed than in sandstone formations. This is primarily attributed to the lower content of bound water and to the generally lower porosity of the carbonate formations [130]. Porosity determinations by NGL can therefore be applied best to sandstone formations with low salt contents and to carbonate formations. The use of long probes (80–90 cm) is recommended for these determinations. If the chlorine content is high but its concentration in the water is constant, porosity determinations in sandstone strata may be carried

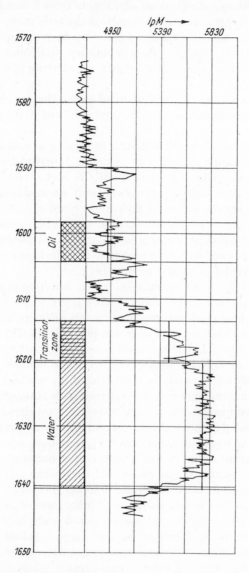

Fig. 28. Differentiation between oil-bearing and water-bearing layers by NGL (employing a scintillation counter with energy discrimination) [122]

out with short probes (20–25 cm). Such methods exploit the dependence of the measured radiation intensity on the chlorine content, or, more precisely, on the volume concentration in the rock [130].

Because of the various factors influencing the measured radiation intensities in porosity determination with NGL, special calibration methods have been worked out [131–135]. Probes with two detectors arranged at different distances from the neutron source have also been suggested [136]. Changes in the ratio of the intensities recorded by the two detectors would indicate changes in the composition of the strata.

In spite of the introduction of special calibration methods and improved probe construction, NGL is less satisfactory for porosity determinations than NNL with epithermal neutrons.

NGL has also been used elsewhere than in oil fields. The search for layers containing water either chemically bound or as a liquid is related to the porosity determinations discussed above.

The detection of chemically combined water by logging techniques has proved useful for finding the stratification in potassium deposits. In particular it was easy to distinguish between sylvine (KCl) and carnallite (KCl $\cdot$ MgCl$_2$ $\cdot$ 6 H$_2$O) [83]. The measurements were carried out with short probes (23 cm). Because of their high water content carnallite strata are recognised by high count rates.

Mesozoic bauxite deposits are a second case where chemically combined water is found by logging. In these deposits the aluminium is mainly present as Al$_2$O$_3$ $\cdot$ 3 H$_2$O. The NG-logs were obtained with long probes so that the layers rich in water of crystallization were detected by intensity minima [91].

Furthermore, NGL has found application for the detection of water-bearing layers to be exploited in wells and water supply systems [139].

NGL may also be used in prospecting for elements distinguished by strong neutron absorption. Most work has been done on boron [91, 137, 138, 285, 286]. Here a special technique has proved useful. The radiation intensity is measured simultaneously at two different distances (12·5 cm and 40 cm) from the neutron source (polonium–beryllium). Since only soft γ-radiation is emitted in the reaction between boron and neutrons, intensity minima appear in both detectors in boron-containing strata. On the other hand, in hydrogen-containing strata the inversion already referred to occurs, the count rate increasing in the near detector and diminishing in the distant detector. For boron contents up to about 10 per cent B$_2$O$_3$ semi-quantitative results have been obtained [91]. The great sensitivity of the detection of boron by NGL is certainly of interest. In one investigation it was established that boron concentrations down to 0·2 or 0·3 per cent in sands could readily be detected [138].

NGL has been used for the determination of other elements which have large capture cross-sections for neutrons, but unlike boron emit hard γ-rays as a result of neutron capture. In this way, manganese-containing strata were detected by intensity maxima, and the manganese content was estimated (for manganese: $\sigma = 13\cdot3$ barn) [91, 140]. Here use was made of the fact that capture γ-radiation from manganese consists in part of much harder rays than radiation from hydrogen.

Attempts to use NGL to investigate coal fields have also been reported. When the probe enters the coal, the count rate goes down [91, 141, 168, 240]. The changes are, however, less than the corresponding effects obtained by GGL, so that NGL has no advantages in connection with coal mining.

7.4.3. *Activation Logging* (AL)

Activation logging (AL) is a form of activation analysis in which a relatively long-lived activity produced by neutron bombardment is measured *in situ*. The specific technique to be used in applying AL to a particular problem depends mainly on the activation cross-section of the element in question, the half-life of the nuclide produced and the strength of the neutron source.

Up to now, activation logging has primarily been used to locate the oil–water interface in oil fields [126, 142–154, 240, 290, 305]. In these investigations natural neutron sources of the greatest possible strength have been used and the induced activity of sodium-24 or chlorine-38 has been measured. Because of the salt dissolved in the water, the induced activities are greater in water-containing than in oil-containing strata. For activation, the source is held in a fixed position. At the end of the irradiation, radiation measuring equipment is placed at the point previously occupied by the source. In one probe constructed for this purpose, the source and the measuring instrument are 4 m apart. After the end of the irradiation the probe must be lowered into the bore-hole by this amount. For satisfactory accuracy the positions of the source and of the detector must coincide within less than 5 cm. Equipment has also been constructed for the simultaneous introduction of several sources into the bore-hole, so that several points may be irradiated simultaneously [147].

In most cases the location of the oil–water interface is determined by the induced sodium-24 activity. In view of possible interference by other induced activities it is always necessary to check whether the radiation recorded in AL determinations is actually due to the radionuclide in question. In the case of sodium-24 several methods are available for identification. The radiation intensity may be measured over a long period of time. The contribution of the sodium-24 to the intensity can then be determined from the decay curve. However, rather long measuring periods (between 4 and 15 hr) are necessary because the activity of manganese-56 (half-life 2·58 hr) must first be allowed to decrease sufficiently. A separate estimation of the intensities due to manganese-56 and to sodium-24 may in certain cases require a careful analysis of the decay curves [150].

Using a scintillation counter with discriminator, the sodium-24 activity may be determined much more quickly. The discriminator is set to register the 2·74 MeV γ-radiation from sodium-24 while the γ-radiation of manganese-56 is eliminated almost completely [103, 152, 153]. With this technique no decay curve need be obtained, and much time is saved.

Measurement of the activity of chlorine-38 (half-life 37·3 min) is in practice of interest only for uncased bore-holes. Steel tubes normally contain so much manganese that a strong manganese-56 activity arises during neutron irradiation, and this masks the activity of chlorine-38 in the rock. In cased bore-holes it is therefore necessary to measure the activity of sodium-24.

It has also been proposed to measure the activity of manganese-56 which is induced in the bore-hole steel casing [151]. This activity is a measure of the slow neutron flux (mainly that of the thermal neutrons), and is therefore larger in oil strata than in water strata provided other conditions, in particular composition of rocks as well as composition and thickness of cementing, are similar. In this procedure an induced activity is measured, but the relationships are really those characteristic of NNL.

Detailed investigations of AL, especially with regard to the location of oil–water interfaces, have been described in several publications [146–154, 240, 290]; the sources of error and the limitations of the method have also been discussed there. The following factors are of particular importance in this connection:

(1) The depth of penetration achieved with ordinary neutron sources amounts to 15–20 cm only. Consequently the radiation intensity measured after activation is determined by the composition of a layer of this thickness around the bore-hole, the nearest parts making the largest contribution. If this layer has a composition different from that of the layers further away from the bore-hole, perhaps because of cementing or the penetration of liquid, AL does not give the information desired.

(2) The count rate measured in AL due to radiation from the relevant radionuclide is not only a function of the volume concentration of the activated element (usually sodium), but is also strongly affected by such parameters as porosity of strata and composition of rocks, these factors having an important influence on the neutron distribution. The effect of changes in porosity on the count rate measured in AL is particularly strong if the porosities are relatively low (0 to 15 per cent).

In principle, a reduction in the effect caused by layers very close to the bore-hole can be obtained by surrounding the neutron source with a good absorber for slow neutrons, such as boron or cadmium. The slow-neutron flux in the bore-hole and its immediate neighbourhood is thus decreased considerably. But clearly flux reduction occurs also in more remote layers, so that the applicability of this method is necessarily limited.

Typical data in connection with a point irradiation for detecting the oil–water interface are: emission from the source $5–10 \times 10^6$ neutrons/sec; irradiation period 5 to 10 hr. It can be seen that AL needs long working periods even with relatively strong neutron sources (5–10 c polonium–beryllium). Nevertheless AL may be regarded as a practicable method for locating the interface. In some cases it has been applied successfully where NGL and NNL methods have failed, generally owing to the low salt content of the ground water. In typical cases, the radiation intensities from sodium-24 that are measured in a water-containing stratum are two to three times as great as those in the corresponding oil-containing stratum.

It follows from what has been said that the investigation of oil fields with AL using point-by-point irradiation depends primarily on the formation of sodium-24, chlorine-38, and, in special cases, manganese-56.

Other elements may also be detected by AL, and this technique is therefore not limited to oil fields. From known nuclear data it is clear that the method may prove suitable in particular for aluminium, manganese, vanadium, indium, copper, silver and gold. Experiments in appropriate bore-holes have confirmed the applicability of AL to some of these elements [91, 140, 240]. Point-by-point activation in bore-holes in manganese, copper and aluminium ore beds gave values for the contents of these elements which agreed at least approximately with the results of chemical analysis [91, 140]. The examination of manganese deposits was carried out with neutron sources emitting 10^7 neutrons/sec; the irradiation times were 0·5 to 2 hr.

"Continuous activation logging" is carried out with a continuously moving probe containing a neutron source and a radiation measuring instrument [91, 292]. The procedure is particularly relevant for short-lived nuclides (half-lives less than about 10 min). The distance between the neutron source and the radiation detector is usually made so large that the results are not significantly affected by capture γ-radiation; if such effects were large, one would be carrying out NGL rather than AL. Continuous AL has been described for bauxite deposits; the activity of aluminium-28 (half-life 2·3 min) was measured [91]. The speed of movement of the probe in the experiments was between 8·4 and 91 m/hr. Satisfactory logs were obtained with a speed of about 30 m/hr and a probe length of 2 m. Activities amounting to 7 per cent of the saturation value were reached with these operating conditions.

The induced aluminium-28 activity depends, of course, on the slow neutron flux in the stratum. It has, therefore, been suggested that measurements of this radionuclide could be used to locate the oil–water interface [155]. Since the chlorine in the ground water reduces the neutron flux in water-containing layers in comparison with that in oil-containing layers, the former would show lower aluminium-28 activity.

For nuclides with longer half-lives continuous AL is practicable only with powerful radiation sources, i. e., with bore-hole accelerators (neutron production of the order of 10^9 neutrons/sec). However, serious interference by short-lived activities may then arise. As yet there is little experience with the elimination of such interference.

A number of AL methods developed recently depend on irradiation with high energy neutrons (14 MeV). These methods will be described in connection with the use of bore-hole accelerators (Section 7.4.6).

7.4.4. *Gamma-Gamma-Logging* (GGL)

Gamma-gamma-logging is carried out with a probe containing a source and a detector for electromagnetic radiation, direct penetration of the radiation from the source into the detector being prevented as far as possible by a shield in the probe. The detector thus records the intensity of scattered radiation at a particular point in the bore-hole. This intensity depends primarily on the distance from the source, the density and the composition of the layer surrounding the probe, and the energy of the radiation emitted [156–160, 240]. The dependence of the intensity of the scattered radiation on the composition of the layer is greatly affected by the distance between source and detector. When the distance is small, absorption of emitted and scattered radiation does not play an important part. The intensity increases with an increase in the scattering power of the surrounding material, and thus in general with the electron density of this material. The count rate therefore increases with the density of the layer. On the other hand, with comparatively great distance between source and detector, absorption of the emitted and scattered radiation plays a decisive part. This can readily be seen from the fact that the proportion of the radiation which penetrates a layer of given thickness without being absorbed diminishes exponentially with an increase in density, while the scattering power only increases in proportion to the density. Therefore, with large probe lengths the radiation intensity at the detector decreases with increasing density of the surrounding material. It is usual to operate with these longer probes.

The sensitivity to changes in rock density increases with the probe length. There are obviously practical limits to such an increase, primarily because the intensity at the detector diminishes with increase in probe length. Furthermore, the density obtained is an average value for the layer penetrated by the radiation. If the length is too great, local density changes cannot be detected any more. The penetrating depth of GGL first increases with increase in probe length, but later diminishes again. The size and place of the shield in the probe also affect the sensitivity. Experiments have shown that it is advantageous to place the shielding partly near the source and partly near the detector [160]. If the shielding is too light, the sensitivity is reduced.

Already early investigations of GGL with an axially symmetrical probe have shown that the measured radiation intensity depends greatly on the position of the probe in the bore-hole and on the bore-hole diameter. The poor reproducibility with this type of probe is due mainly to the fact that the position of the probe in the bore-hole arises more or less by accident and cannot be determined by the operating personnel.

In improved probes the radiation detector has been placed close to one side of the probe and shielded against radiation coming from other directions. By means of suitably placed springs this probe was pressed against the wall of the bore-hole in such a way that the detector lay directly against the wall [157, 161, 162, 240]. The probe casing was constructed as lightly as possible so as to reduce radiation absorption in the casing to a minimum; aluminium was found suitable. Even with this type of probe, the diameter of the bore-hole has an effect on the result, and this must be taken account of in evaluating the logs [160, 162].

In some probes the radiation is collimated both on leaving the source and on entering the measuring instrument; in this way the sensitivity is improved [136, 163, 164]. The application of detectors with energy discrimination (scintillation spectrometers) may also be of advantage [165].

In oil fields GGL can be used to find the density, and consequently the porosity, of rocks [160, 162, 240]. In density determinations an accuracy of 0·03 to 0·05 g/cm³ can be attained. This corresponds to an accuracy in the porosity of 2–3 per cent [160]. For low porosities (1–10 per cent) it seems that NNL with epithermal neutrons is generally more accurate, while GGL is superior for greater porosities. Under some conditions, the density change at the oil–water interface is sufficiently large to be detected by GGL [166].

Moreover, GGL may give information about the liquid present in bore-holes [163]. Here it is advisable to construct the probes in a different manner than for density determinations of rock strata. In one type of special probe [163] the liquid to be determined enters the probe itself. Thulium-170, which emits very soft γ-radiation, is used as radiation source. The logging results therefore depend only on the properties of the immediate surroundings of source and detector, and no interference arises from the rock layers surrounding the bore-hole, or from cementing, etc. With probes of this kind, a change in count rate of about 40 per cent occurs in passage from oil to water.

GGL may also serve to determine the height of the cementing around cased bore-holes [160, 163, 164, 167] and to locate casing sleeves [157, 160, 166]. Small probe lengths are suitable for this purpose [157, 166].

GGL has given satisfactory results in coal fields [91, 168–170, 273–275]. To obtain good sensitivity in the detection of density changes, and to eliminate the effect of bore-hole diameter as far as possible, these investigations were carried out with fairly long probes. One group of workers [168] used probes 75–80 cm long, another group [169] probes 40–60 cm long. With both these probes absorption effects predominate over scattering effects, so that coal layers having relatively low density are detected by high radiation intensity. The differentiation may be improved by shielding the detector against soft radiation with, for example, a thin lead plate. This is found to be effective in reducing the influence of the bore-hole filling. Typical GGL probes contain 5–10 mc of cobalt-60 as radiation source.

To detect the presence of thin layers, such as insertions in coal seams, a special GGL apparatus has been developed in which two detectors are placed at different distances from the source, the distance between the two detectors amounting to about 10 cm [168]. With this probe, the difference between the signals from the two detectors is recorded. This depends primarily on the density of the layer lying between the two detectors.

GGL has also been used to elucidate the stratification in potassium deposits [83]. In particular, carnallite layers are detected through high count rates.

With low energy sources (E_γ less than about 100 keV), pronounced differences appear between the mass absorption coefficients of different elements. At these energies, the mass absorption coefficients of heavy elements are in general much greater than of light elements (see Section 6.7.4). Thus, while at high radiation energies GGL results depend essentially only on the density of the layer, and not on its chemical composition, at low energies the results strongly depend on the content of heavy elements [171, 172]. GGL with low energy radiation is therefore described as "selective gamma-gamma-logging" (SGGL).

The applicability of SGGL was first investigated on models in the laboratory [171, 172]. Experiments on sands containing small quantities of lead were carried out with a probe containing 1 mc of selenium-75 ($E_\gamma = 0·26$ MeV) as radiation source. The distance between source and counter was 20–40 cm, and the counter was shielded against the source by means of a lead cylinder. The lead in the sand caused a reduction in count rate, and as little as 1·5 per cent lead was clearly detectable. By modifying the probe and by using sufficiently strong sources the following detection limits were reached; for heavy elements such as tungsten, mercury, lead, bismuth and uranium (atomic numbers around 80), ca. 0·2 per cent; for medium-heavy elements such as antimony, tin, molybdenum (atomic number around 50), ca. 0·6 per cent. Estimates of the contents of heavy and medium-heavy elements by this method are possible, but of course only the total content of such elements is measured. As in other logging procedures, the position of the probe in the bore-hole has a considerable effect on the SGGL results so that the probe should be pressed against the wall, as in the case of GGL.

SGGL has been field tested primarily in deposits of lead, tungsten, mercury, iron and manganese [91]. It was possible to locate the lead-containing layers exactly, and to obtain an estimate of the lead content. Sources of 2–5 mc selenium-75 and a detector distance of 20–25 cm were used. The sensitivity obtained (0·2 per cent lead) corresponded to the results with the models. For the precise evaluation of the SGGlogs, the correlation with GG-logs and with measurements of the diameter of the same bore-hole proved useful.

An interesting possibility consists in the investigation of the energy of scattered radiation by spectrometric techniques to obtain data on the quantities of individual elements present [173].

7.4.5. *Gamma-Neutron-Logging* (GNL)

The nuclear photo-effect, that is, the (γ, n)-reaction, can also be employed in bore-hole investigations [91, 240, 293]. The energy of the γ-radiation emitted by radio-nuclides is sufficient for nuclear photo-effect only with very few nuclides, but high energy electromagnetic radiation produced by accelerators can induce the effect in many kinds of nuclei.

The most important element interacting in this way with γ-radiation from radio-nuclides is beryllium. GNL for beryllium is actually a special form of the nuclear assay method of this element, discussed on p. 120. A probe for detecting beryllium by GNL contains a suitable radiation source (such as antimony-124) and a neutron detector, which may be surrounded by a moderator. With point-by-point measurements in a bore-hole, it was possible to establish the presence of beryllium satisfactorily in concentrations down to ca. 0·2 per cent [91].

GNL methods with high energy γ-radiation will be treated in connection with bore-hole accelerators. Reference should also be made to a theoretical treatment of various aspects of GNL [240, 294].

7.4.6. *Bore-hole Accelerators*

The bore-hole accelerators developed in recent years are of great importance for the improvement and extension of logging procedures. These accelerators usually employ the (D + T) reaction, i.e., deuterons bombard a tritium-containing target. They induce the reaction ^{3}H(d, n) ^{4}He, and neutrons with an energy of 14·1 MeV are set free [174–187, 240, 271, 272]. The essential part of most bore-hole accelerators is a discharge tube that is filled with a gas mixture containing deuterium and has the tritium target (usually consisting of tritium chemisorbed on zirconium or titanium) at one end. A potential of at least 100 kV, usually 150–200 kV, is applied to the tube by a high voltage unit, which is placed next to the mouth of the bore-hole. Deuterons are produced by a discharge in the gas phase. In other accelerators deuterons are produced by heating in a special ion source. The neutron emission obtainable with the bore-hole accelerators now available is of the order 10^8–10^9 neutrons/sec. This is about 100 times more than the emission of strong (several curies) polonium–beryllium sources. But even though rapid progress has been made in the development of bore-hole accelerators, apparently some unsolved problems in connection with the routine operation of such equipment remain. Logging procedures with bore-hole accelerators are therefore still in the development and testing stage.

Because of the comparatively high neutron emission of these sources, it is possible to obtain a log more rapidly than with the usual logging methods; the higher radiation intensities falling on the detector make it possible to move the probe with greater speed. Even more important is the fact that fundamentally new logging methods are possible with such neutron generators. These depend either on a pulsed operation of the accelerator, or on the much higher neutron energies compared to those from natural neutron sources.

With pulsed operation it is possible to determine the variation of radiation intensity (neutrons or γ-rays) with time, or to limit the intensity measurement to a certain fixed time interval after emission. The significance of such measurements can be seen from a consideration of the scattering processes and the nuclear reactions to which the emitted neutrons are subject (slowing-down and diffusion of neutrons) [188, 191, 240]. The fast neutrons emitted by the source are first slowed down by elastic and inelastic scattering. Slowing-down by elastic scattering is primarily due to hydrogen, though carbon and oxygen also have some effect. Inelastic scattering is important only as long as the neutron energy exceeds 2 MeV, and in rock takes place mainly on calcium, iron and other medium-heavy elements. The possibility of a direct utilization of inelastic neutron scattering for bore-hole investigations will be treated later.

The time needed for the slowing-down of neutrons depends on the composition of the surrounding layer. The following figures give an indication of the periods involved in practice. Slowing-down of 14 MeV neutrons to 2 MeV requires 10^{-8}–10^{-7} sec, slowing-down to 1 eV 10^{-6}–10^{-5} sec, and slowing-down to thermal energies 10^{-5} to 10^{-4} sec.

In rocks, the major part of the neutrons become slow at a distance of less than 50 cm from the source. The slow neutrons then spread out through the rock by diffusion. The speed of the diffusion of the slow neutrons is determined by the presence of strongly scattering nuclei, especially those of hydrogen. The greater the concentration of such nuclei, the slower the diffusion.

Capture by nuclei of the medium has no significant influence on fast neutron distribution. In contrast, the disappearance of the slow neutrons owing to capture is superimposed upon their diffusion.

After reaching a maximum after a pulse, the number of slow neutrons (or of the thermal neutrons taken alone) diminishes exponentially. The mean-life $\bar{\tau}$ (the time needed for the concentration to fall to the part $1/e$ of any initial value) is determined by the composition of the rock, in particular by its chlorine content; it is often between 100 microsec and a few millisec.

The porosity (hydrogen concentration) and salt content (chlorine concentration) of the layers therefore have most influence on the time change in neutron flux after emission of a pulse. Hence by observing this change it is possible to obtain information about these concentrations. It is of advantage to arrange the equipment in such a way that the neutron detector lies at a greater distance from the source than the region in which the neutrons are slowed down. Neutrons then reach the detector only by diffusion. The change in slow neutron flux in such a detector is given schematically in Fig. 29.

It can be shown that the neutron flux $n(t)$ for large values of t after the emission of the pulse (t many times greater than t_{max}) depends mainly on the neutron life-time $\bar{\tau}$ and thus on the chlorine content of the medium. On the other hand, the value of t_{max}

is primarily determined by the diffusion velocity of the neutrons in the medium (D). When the neutron flux is measured in a short time interval Δt, the time of measurement t_v being much greater than t_{max}, a measure of the chlorine content is therefore obtained. A determination of the value of t_{max} itself gives a measure of the porosity (D), and thus of the hydrogen content. The determination of $\bar{\tau}$ by measuring $n(t)$ is very accurate compared with other methods, as the relationship between the neutron flux $n(t)$ and the mean life $\bar{\tau}$ is exponential. This relationship serves as the basis for a useful procedure for locating the oil–water interface which has already been tested in practice. Between the values of $n(t)$ ($t_v \gg t_{max}$) in an oil-saturated layer and the corresponding value in a saltwater containing layer, a difference arises which is much greater than the change in count rate obtained with other logging procedures for locating this interface.

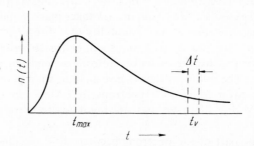

FIG. 29. Thermal neutron flux as a function of the time interval after emission of a fast neutron pulse (schematic diagram) [188]. (Neutron source and detector are some fixed distance apart)

The results obtained with this kind of pulse technique are, of course, influenced to some extent by the liquid in the bore-hole and by the cementing. The presence of hydrogen and chlorine in the bore-hole diminishes the zone where neutrons are slowed down, and therefore decreases the neutron flux at the detector. In this way, complicated changes in $n(t)$ and t_{max} are caused. However, it can be shown theoretically that the measurements can be carried out in such a way that these changes do not prevent the distinction between oil-containing and water-containing strata. Salt present in the bore-hole liquid or in the cementing causes the neutrons to have a shorter life in these regions than in rock. When the measurement of the neutron intensity, $n(t)$, is delayed considerably, the time of measurement, t_v being arranged to be several times greater than the mean life of the neutrons in the bore-hole and in the cementing, the measured neutron intensity is primarily determined by the neutron flux penetrating from the rock into the bore-hole. The absolute values depend, of course, on the composition of the bore-hole liquid and the cement, but the great difference between the values obtained in oil-bearing and water-bearing strata is not eliminated by this, and the decay curves for the neutron flux are primarily determined by the composition of the layers further away from the bore-hole.

By proper selection of the distance between neutron source and detector the effect of the bore-hole on the value of t_{max} can be reduced. If the composition of the various regions is such that $D_{\text{bore-hole}}$ is much less than D_{rock} and $\bar{\tau}_{\text{bore-hole}}$ is less than $\bar{\tau}_{\text{rock}}$, then the neutrons diffusing in the bore-hole, because of their strong absorption, reach the detector only in small yield. This absorption effect increases with an increase in the distance between source and detector. The role of the more deeply situated layers in determining t_{max} increases therefore with increasing distance between the source and the detector.

Investigations carried out on models [189] have shown that the procedure just described for distinguishing between water-bearing and oil-bearing strata has the predicted high efficiency (Fig. 30). An accelerator using the $(D + T)$ reaction, with a

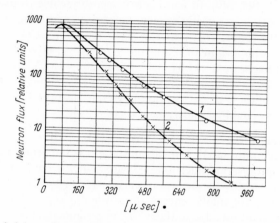

FIG. 30. Recorded thermal neutron flux as a function of the time interval after emission of a fast neutron pulse [189]. (The diagram shows results obtained on model assemblies resembling conditions in cased bore-holes.)
(*I*) Sandstone saturated with oil; (*2*) Sandstone saturated with salt water (200 g salt/l.)

yield of about 10^7 neutrons/sec, was employed in these experiments. The duration of the pulse was 5 microsec, and the pulse frequency 300 per sec. The neutron flux was measured after a delay time of 500–1000 microsec. When the sodium chloride concentration was 200 g/l. and the delay time 800 microsec, the count rate in a dry "bore-hole" next to an aqueous layer was only one-tenth of that next to the oil-containing stratum. With a measurement period of 10 microsec, the recorded count rate was only of the order of 10 counts/min, but was sufficient for continuous logging. In practical logging, it is possible to increase both the duration of the pulse and that of recording, so that the count rate can be increased [79, 272, 298].

According to recent information [79, 272], logging has been carried out successfully in bore-holes with pulses of 100 microsec, and an equally long recording period. The pulse frequency was 400 per sec. The measurements were carried out with a counting tube 25 cm long, the distance between the target and the counter being around 15 cm. The logging probe used in these investigations (consisting of accelerator, detector, etc.) had a total length of 2·9 m and a diameter of 10 cm.

Further logging methods with pulsed neutron sources have been proposed but reports on the practical development of these methods have not yet been given. One of these methods is based on the measurement of the epithermal neutron flux to determine the porosity (hydrogen concentration). The measurement of the fast neutron flux over a very short period immediately after the pulse may serve the same purpose [188]; the rate of reduction in the fast neutrons flux depends primarily on the hydrogen concentration in the immediate neighbourhood of the source.

Neutrons produced by bore-hole accelerators through the $(D + T)$ reaction have such high energy that they interact with atomic nuclei in the surrounding layers in processes that do not occur with the neutrons of lower energy from natural sources (see Section 6.6.5). Such scattering processes and nuclear reactions may also be used in logging [131, 163, 195, 240]. In particular it seems possible to use the γ-radiation emitted in such processes, especially by inelastic neutron scattering, to identify various elements through the characteristic energy of the radiation. A preliminary investigation of the elements important in sedimentary rocks has given the following characteristic energies: magnesium-24 1·37 MeV, silicon-28 1·78 MeV, hydrogen-1 2·2 MeV, sulphur-32 2·25 MeV, calcium-40 3·73 MeV, carbon-12 4·5 MeV, oxygen-16 6·7 MeV [163]. On the basis of these characteristic energies, it has been suggested that the following investigations could be undertaken:

(1) Determination of carbon content in rocks [131, 188], or determination of the carbon:oxygen ratio [163]. For this purpose it is important that the cross-section for the process in which the 4·5 MeV γ-ray is emitted, i.e., for inelastic scattering of 14 MeV neutrons on carbon-12 nuclei, is comparatively large (0·25 barn). Rays of similar energy are emitted in interactions with silicon and iron, but the count rate due to them may in certain circumstances be subtracted as constant background. By determining the carbon content or the carbon: oxygen ratio, it is possible to distinguish between limestone and sandstone strata, even when they contain much water. Oil-bearing and water-bearing strata can also be distinguished. Laboratory investigations have shown that the ratio of the relevant intensities undergoes a change of 20 per cent at the oil–water interface under typical conditions.

(2) Distinction between dolomite and limestone. For this purpose the 1·37 MeV γ-radiation of magnesium may be used [136, 163].

(3) Location of silicate-containing strata. The characteristic 1·78 MeV emission from silicon may be employed [136, 163].

(4) Location of sulphur-containing layers in dry formations [136, 163].

Interference with the measurement of this type of γ-radiation by capture γ-radiation may largely be avoided by pulsed operation [188, 240, 299]. Neutron capture takes place only after the neutrons are slowed down, thus with a certain delay. The capture γ-rays can therefore be eliminated by irradiating with neutron pulses of less than 10 microsec, and by measuring the radiation intensity only during the period of the pulse. The time interval between pulses must be so long that all the neutrons produced in the previous pulse have disappeared, for which an interval of several millisec is required. Calculations show that this logging method can have practical usefulness only if powerful accelerators with approximately the following characteristics are available:

With a pulse frequency 10^3 per sec and a pulse duration 10 microsec, a neutron emission of 10^{11} neutrons/sec during the pulse would be required.

The 14-MeV neutrons produced by bore-hole accelerators can also be used for activation logging [136, 163, 190, 191, 240, 292, 299]. Preliminary work with this type of logging in oil bore-holes has been carried out. The method seems most suitable for the determination of aluminium, silicon and oxygen, with the nuclear reactions ^{27}Al(n, α) ^{24}Na, ^{28}Si(n, p) ^{28}Al and ^{16}O(n, p) ^{16}N as basis. It appears possible to distinguish between oil-bearing and water-bearing strata by measuring the radiation from nitrogen-16 ($E_\gamma = 6\cdot6$ and 7 MeV; half-life $7\cdot3$ sec) produced in this manner.

Finally, bore-hole accelerators for the production of high energy γ-radiation are now being developed. Such accelerators would make it possible to determine certain elements (in addition to beryllium) by gamma-neutron-logging [131, 190, 191].

7.5. Bore-hole Investigations by Introduction of Radionuclides

In this section methods of bore-hole investigation will be discussed in which radioactively labelled solutions or suspensions are introduced into the bore-hole, and the position of these liquids is then determined by radiation measurement.

Bore-holes, particularly in limestone formations, are often treated with acid to make the rock layers more permeable. In such operations it is desirable to know the places where the acid has acted. This information may be obtained by radioactive labelling of the acid, as with a mixture of fission products or with other suitable γ-emitting nuclides.

When the acid is pumped into the bore-hole, the level reached can be determined by radiation measurement. The acid is then forced into the rock by an increase in pressure. Following this essential step, the acid still present in the bore-hole may be flushed out, and the distribution of the acid which was forced into the rock may be determined by γ-logging [192–195]. Special probes have been developed for this purpose, which have counters about $1\cdot5$ m long and are capable of withstanding concentrated acids and high pressures up to some hundreds of atmospheres [192].

Various investigations of the extent and condition of cementing of bore-holes are possible by introduction of radionuclides. If the cement is labelled, e. g., by addition of a mixture of fission products, the level of the cement behind the casing may be determined [195–197]. The intensity at a given height then depends on the thickness of the cement ring at that point, so that γ-logging can give an approximate picture of the cement distribution [198–201, 297]. The distribution of cement around the bore-hole is obtained more accurately when the measurement is carried out with a special probe possessing a collimator at the detector which may be rotated [202, 203]. In this way, the cement ring can be scanned, and cavities or local reductions in thickness can be detected. If the cement ring has a thickness between $1\cdot5$ and 10 cm fairly accurate thickness measurements are possible.

Fractures in the cementing (leaks) may be determined by forcing radioactive solutions into bore-holes [195, 199, 204, 205]. The active solution enters the rock layer through the fractures in the cement ring. The active solution remaining in the bore-hole is then removed by thorough flushing. γ-logging now reveals the place of the fracture. In a similar way, it is also possible to discover fractures in the bore-hole casing or to locate perforations [199].

A similar method may be employed in uncased bore-holes to detect porous layers [127, 201, 205]. Radioactive solutions or suspensions are used. Special equipment with a rotating collimator around the detector, similar to that used for the investigation of cementing, shows the preferred direction of penetration of the radioactive liquid into the porous layers [206].

To determine the zones where liquids forced in under high pressure have caused hydraulic fracturing, radioactive sand is employed [195, 199, 201, 204, 207, 267, 295, 296]. When the liquid penetrates into the layers the sand is at least partially held back by filtration. It therefore, remains very close to the bore-hole and may be detected by radiation measurement. The sand is usually labelled through adsorption of radio-elements and subsequent heating (see Section 12.7). In some cases the sand grains were covered by a suitable varnish to prevent desorption of radioactive ions. The labelled sand is introduced into the bore-hole towards the end of hydraulic fracturing. In one series of tests, 1–2 kg of sand with an activity of around 3 mc/kg gave satisfactory results. After forcing in the sand in the hydraulic fracturing operation, the bore-hole is well rinsed and the distribution of the activity is then determined.

Introduction of radionuclides into the bore-hole may also be used to locate the oil–water interface. Radioactive materials are introduced either in water-soluble or in oil-soluble form so that they go preferentially into the one or into the other type of layer [88, 122, 125].

Investigations on the transport of liquid or gas over large distances in rock layers are of particular interest. Radioactively labelled liquid or gas is introduced into a bore-hole at a certain depth, and the appearance of this material in neighbouring bore-holes, which may be specially drilled for this purpose, is determined by activity measurement on samples taken at regular intervals.

In wells where the gas pressure has been exhausted, it is common practice to force water into auxiliary bore-holes in the neighbourhood of the production well, in order to force the oil towards this well and obtain the best possible yields. Radioelements may be used to gain detailed knowledge of the movement of the water towards the production well. On this basis the exploitation may be made more efficient. In the first work of this kind, the water was labelled with iodine-131 in the form of iodide ion [195, 208, 209], which is poorly adsorbed by the minerals in the strata (see p. 300). Activity measurements which were carried out in the production well as a function of depth, made it possible to determine both the speed with which the water appeared, and the strata through which it entered the well. Strata with high permeability, which in consequence take up much water, can then be sealed with cement. The water consumption is then reduced, and the oil production at the same time increased [209]. Activity measurements carried out in the bore-holes, through which the labelled water is forced in, can be carried out as part of the same investigation. They give an indication of the water uptake at various depths [210]. The method used is similar to those already described for the investigation of the movement of acids and for the location of porous layers.

Studies with surface active agents are also related to problems involved in using pressurized water [209]. In laboratory experiments the adsorption of labelled (^{14}C) detergents (derivatives of polyethylene oxide) on sand layers has been studied. Layers containing oil have also been tested.

The movement of pressurized water has also been followed by adding tritium-labelled water (HTO). In one such investigation [211–213], three "injections", each of 1 c tritium in a cubic metre of water, were applied. Water samples were taken from three surrounding bore-holes located at distances of 80, 118 and 150 m. After each injection, inactive water was introduced into the same bore-hole. The rate of movement to the three surrounding bore-holes could then be determined. The values obtained were 40, 12 and 13 m/day. Moreover, the maximum amount of tritium was pumped from that bore-hole to which the active water penetrated most quickly. In an investigation at another site, in which samples were taken from four surrounding bore-holes, the labelled water appeared in two holes only. This was interpreted as being due to a discontinuity in the strata owing to tectonic dislocation.

In a further investigation [214] with tritium-labelled water, samples were taken from three bore-holes at distances of 105, 290 and 335 m from the bore-hole into which the labelled water had been introduced by breaking a sealed glass tube by means of a special device introduced into the bore-hole. On the basis of information about the thickness of the stratum (3–6 m), its mean porosity (21 per cent), and also the amount of water forced in and pumped out, a water speed of 1·9–2·2 m/day was estimated, uniformity of the layer being assumed. However, some tritium was detected in the exit bore-holes much earlier than would be expected from this speed. This rapid movement manifested itself by several short activity peaks, followed by periods during which no tritium was detected. In two of the exit bore-holes, a large increase in the tritium content occurred at the time expected for a uniform layer. This was followed by a slow, though not very regular, decrease. The early activity maxima were explained by the existence of paths of greater permeability, by which small portions of the tritium introduced could penetrate quite quickly to the exit bore-holes (cf. p. 301). The principal maximum with a subsequent slow decrease was attributed to comparatively uniform flow of the liquid through the stratum.

Tritium-labelled water has also been used to investigate vertical connections between strata of productive zones [214]. About 10 m^3 of tritium-labelled water of fairly low specific activity (5×10^{-6} c/l.) were forced through a perforation in the bore-hole lining at a certain depth. The active water remaining in the bore-hole was then removed by flushing with inactive water and the perforation was closed again with cement. The tightness of the sealing of the rock layers against the bore-hole was checked with solutions of suitable radionuclides such as iron-59 or zinc-65. The lining of the bore-hole was then perforated again some distance above the injection level, and water was pumped out of the stratum through this perforation. The activity of this water was measured frequently. When this method was applied to a productive zone with a thickness of more than 200 m, all the tests on successive levels of the zone gave positive results, since an appreciable activity appeared within a few days in the water pumped out. This was evidence of a vertical connection between the individual strata through the whole zone.

The movement of water forced into the rock may, in principle, also be studied on the basis of the natural tritium content of fresh water (see Section 12.5). Since very low tritium contents are involved, special methods for enriching and measuring tritium are necessary. When such methods are employed, it seems possible to obtain information about the direction of movement of the water forced in and about possible connections between various strata, as well as other information about the water movement [214]. It is an advantage of this approach that no special techniques are needed when forcing in the water. The method may thus be used even for oil fields where fresh water was pressed in some time before. The presence of fresh water can be detected by activity measurement even after years, the period of course being limited by the decay of the tritium.

The penetration of natural gas through a productive layer was investigated with ^{14}C-methane [215]. Exit bore-holes were placed at distances of 200 to 1500 m. The results indicated the existence of regions of higher and of lower gas permeability.

A special method has been developed for measuring the speed of the flow of liquid in a bore-hole [216]. A probe containing an injection device is used. On receiving an electrical impulse from a control board, a small volume of labelled solution is injected into the bore-hole filling. Some distance away from the site of injection, a radiation detector for measuring the activity of the solution flowing close by is mounted in the probe. From the time interval between the moment of injection and the appearance of maximum count rate in the instrument the speed of flow may be calculated. If the volume flow is known, information about the dimensions of the bore-hole may also be obtained.

7.6. Application to Oil Pipe Lines

Oil pipe lines are often used to transport different kinds of oils or oil products in succession. It is then important to know the position of the boundary between two products during the flow. These boundaries may be detected by radioactively labelling the first portion of a new oil entering the pipe line [217–223, 235]. Such labelling may be carried out by dissolving or suspending γ-emitting radionuclides. Suitable oil-soluble substances include barium alkyl phenolates, cobalt naphthenate and triphenyl stibine. The radiation may then be detected from outside the pipe line simply and efficiently.

For the injection of the radioelements into the oil special equipment has been developed. Radiation measuring instruments are placed along the pipe line and give signals as the labelled boundary approaches. These signals may also be made to start up auxiliary pumps along the pipe line. Such pumps are operated only intermittently. They would be filled with the wrong oil after the passage of a boundary, unless they are put briefly into operation at the right moment.

The spreading out of the radioelement through the oil is a direct measure of the mixing of the two oils. The extent of this mixing may therefore be determined by activity measurements. The mixing is minimal when the flow is turbulent rather than laminar. Under this condition the width of the active zone, or boundary, increases with the cube of the distance from the starting point. The distribution of the activity corresponds to a Gaussian probability curve and is symmetrical, in contrast to the distribution for laminar flow [225]. Detection of the boundary by this technique is in constant use with several pipe lines. Especially where refined products are being transported, considerable savings are made.

As an example for the detection of a boundary with radioactive nuclides, data obtained on an oil pipe line almost 900 km long may be mentioned. The boundary was labelled with 12 mc of antimony-124 in the form of triphenyl stibine. The radiation was measured with counters mounted in a ring around the pipe line. The boundary could be identified up to the end of the pipe line [222, 223]. Typical results obtained with another pipe line are given in Fig. 31.

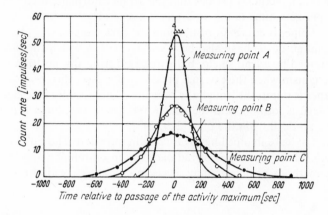

FIG. 31. Radioactive interface labelling in an oil pipe line [217]. The results show the spread of active substance with the advance of the interface. Location of measuring points:
A 22·1 km; B 69·1 km; C 173·7 km

The disadvantages connected with any addition of radioelements to products may be avoided if the products pumped through in succession differ considerably in their hydrogen contents. As a consequence of a change in hydrogen content the capacity of the materials to slow down, back-scatter and absorb neutrons is changed. Boundary detection is then possible by placing a neutron source close to the pipe and measuring the flux of the slow neutrons emerging from the pipe line with a boron counter [226]. If the hydrogen content does not change sufficiently for this technique to be applied, the boundary may be labelled by injecting inactive substances that absorb neutrons strongly, such as boron. The presence of these substances is then detected through the changes in slow neutron absorption [226].

The methods given in Section 6.7.4 are under certain circumstances also suitable for the detection of boundaries in pipe lines. In particular, differences in density or composition (above all, in the carbon: hydrogen ratio) can be found by measuring the γ-ray absorption. Provided the products differ sufficiently in one of these quantities, the position of the boundary can be observed by such a technique [229, 243, 256, 260, 261].

Techniques for locating the propeller-shaped scrapers in pipe lines are useful. These "go-devils" are forced through new pipe lines by means of compressed air to remove obstacles, such as pieces of metal. Later they are employed from time to time to scrape from the walls solid deposits which may be formed during operation. Unfortunately, scrapers occasionally get stuck during their passage through the pipe lines. It was difficult to locate them until scrapers labelled with radionuclides were used. The labelled go-devils may be located through soil, mud or water layers a metre or more thick [227, 228, 243]. In the case of the thicker layers, considerable activities are needed (200 to 1000 mc).

In work with sources of this strength careful radiation protection is needed. Special methods have therefore been developed to reduce the radiation dose to the operating personnel. One such method provides that the scraper normally used is inactive; only when this scraper gets stuck in the pipe line, is a second scraper, this time radioactive, put through the pipe. It comes to rest behind the first scraper, whose position is thus revealed. Special go-devils have also been constructed in which the radiation source is usually contained by a lead shield, but is released from this position by means of a hydraulic mechanism when the external pressure increases; this is, of course, the case when the scraper is pumped through the pipe line. The pressure is released as soon as the stuck go-devil is located, and the source returns to the shielded position before removal of the go-devil from the pipe [229, 243].

The detection of leaks in pipe lines by forcing in radioactive liquids will be discussed in Section 9.3.6. The applications of radioactivity in oil refining and in petrochemistry, including methods of determining levels in containers, will also be discussed in Chapter 9.

References to Chapter 7

1. C.M.LAPOINTE and R.D.WILMONT, *Mines Branch Memorandum Series, No.* 123, Ottawa (1952).
2. D.I.LEIPUNSKAYA, S.E.GAUER and G.N.FLEROV, *Atomnaya Energiya* **6**, 315 (1959).
3. T.A.LOPAVOK, *Atomnaya Energiya* **8**, 158 (1960).
4. F.E.SENFTLE and A.M.GAUDIN, *Nucleonics* **8** (5), 53 (1951).
5. L.N.POSIK, S.I.BABICHENKO and R.A.GRODKO, *Atomnaya Energiya* **8**, 425 (1960).
6. A.H.BETTENS and C.M.LAPOINTE, *Mines Branch Technical Paper No.* 10, Ottawa (1955).
7. C.GOODMAN and D.C.PICTON, *Phys. Rev.* **60**, 688 (1941).
8. T.G.CHURCH, *Can. J. Res.* **28** *A*, 164 (1950).
9. G.F.HÜTTIG, W.SIMM and G.GLAWITSCH, *Mh. Chem.* **85**, 1124 (1954).
10. G.FLÜGGE, *Atompraxis* **4**, 6 (1958).
11. Soviet Bibliography by H.MARTIN, *Glückauf* **92**, 1297 (1956).
12. Soviet Bibliography by H.MARTIN, *Atomkernenergie* **5**, 187 (1960).
13. V.G.SEGALIN, *Improvement in Analysis of Coal Deposits* (Russ.), Moscow 1959.
14. See also V.D.GOROSHKO, *Vestnik Akademii Nauk SSSR* **1956** (2).
15. See also A.S.KULISHENKO, *Koks i Khimiya* **1958** (4) 10.
16. V.D.GOROSHKO, in: *All-Union Conference on the Application of Radioactive Isotopes and Nuclear Radiations* (Russ.), Moscow 1957.
17. I.N.PLAKSIN *Tr. Inst. Gorn. Dela Akad. Nauk SSSR* **4**, 209 (1957).
18. C.G.CLAYTON, *Int. J. Appl. Rad. Isot.* **4**, 256 (1959).
19. G.G.EICHHOLZ, A.O.SMITH and A.BAUER, *Can. Min. Met. Bull.*, March 1957, p. 117; *Nucleonics* **15** (11), 170 (1957).

20. J.R.HODKINSON, *Int. J. Appl. Rad. Isot.* **2**, 97 (1957).
21. R.L.CARVER, *Nucleonics* **17** (11), 189 (1959).
22. W.KÜHN, *Atompraxis* **5**, 133, 335 (1959).
23. I.G.POLOVCHENKO, *Stal* **1959**, (3) 211.
24. K.SAUERWEIN, R.HOSSNER and W.ROTTER, *Atomwirtschaft* **1**, 71 (1956).
25. K.SAUERWEIN and R.HOSSNER, Geneva Report 987 (1958), vol. 19, p. 338.
26. H.K.ROTHE and H.LANGER, *Isotopentechnik* **1**, 11 (1960).
27. K.P.MEDVEDEV and V.M.PETROPOLSKAYA, *Koks i Khimiya* **1958** (3), 25.
28. S.E.EATON, R.W.HYDE, B.S.OLDS and M.H.ROOD, *Metals Technol.* **15**, 2463 (1958); *Anal. Chem.* **21**, 1063 (1949).
29. I.M.KHANIN, V.A.YAREMCHUK and I.G.KUPRIENKO, *Koks i Khimiya* **1957** (10), 20.
30. A.S.KULISHENKO and K.P.MEDVEDEV, *Izvest. Akad. Nauk SSSR, Otd. Tekhn. Nauk* **1955** (7), 145.
31. K.P.MEDVEDEV and A.S.KULISHENKO, *Khim. i Tekhnol. Topliv i Masel* **3** (9), 62 (1958).
32. K.P.MEDVEDEV, *Application of Radioactive Isotopes in the Coke-Chemical Production* (Russ.), Moscow 1962.
33. J.D.COCKCROFT, *J. Inst. Prod. Eng.* **32**, 342 (1953).
34. K.A.KUSNETSOV, *Podzemn. Gazifikatsiya Uglei* **1959** (3), 58.
35. D.A.SOKOLOV and B.I.ROGOV, *Podzemn. Gazifikatsiya Uglei* **1958** (1), 60.
36. A.M.GAUDIN, Radioactivity in Mineral Dressing, *Bull. Inst. Min. Met.*, No. 552 (1952).
37. A.M.GAUDIN, *Flotation*, New York 1957.
38. G.G.EICHHOLZ and W.N.ROBERTS, Geneva Report 217 (1958), vol. 19, p. 240.
39. L.G.ERWALL, Geneva Report 165 (1958), vol. 19, p. 107.
40. I.N.PLAKSIN, Geneva Report 2199 (1958), vol. 19, p. 249.
41. L.G.ERWALL and T.WESTERMARK, *Research* **4**, 290 (1951).
42. I.N.PLAKSIN, S.F.ZAITSEVA, G.A.MYASNIKOVA, L.P.STARCHIK, V.I.TYURNIKOVA, G.N.KHA-ZHINSKAYA and R.SH.SHAFEEV, *Trans. Inst. Min. Met.* No. 611, 1 (1957).
43. I.N.PLAKSIN and S.P.ZAITSEVA, *Doklady Akad. Nauk SSSR* **101**, 727 (1955).
44. I.N.PLAKSIN and G.N.KHAZHINSKAYA, *Doklady Akad. Nauk SSSR* **97**, 1045 (1954).
45. I.N.PLAKSIN, G.N.KHAZHINSKAYA and V.I.TYURNIKOVA, *Izvest. Akad. Nauk SSSR, Otd. Tekhn. Nauk* **1954**, 123.
46. I.N.PLAKSIN, S.P.ZAITSEVA and R.SH.SHAFEEV, *Doklady Akad. Nauk SSSR* **119**, 551 (1958).
47. I.N.PLAKSIN, L.P.STARCHIK, O.V.TRETYAKOV, V.I.TYURNIKOVA and R.SH.SHAFEEV, *Zavod. Lab.* **23**, 313 (1957).
48. I.N.PLAKSIN and G.A.MYASSNIKOVA, *Tsvetn. Metal.* **31** (2), 7 (1958).
49. I.N.PLAKSIN, *Freiberger Forschungsh.* **A 49**, 5 (1957).
50. I.N.PLAKSIN, S.P.ZAITSEVA, G.A.MYASSNIKOVA, L.P.STARCHIK, V.I.TYURNIKOVA and G.N. KHAZHINSKAYA, *Izvest. Akad. Nauk SSSR, Otd. Tekhn. Nauk.* **1957** (3), 187; (4), 164.
51. See also S.I.MITROFANOV, *Tsvetn. Metal.* **1958**, (4).
52. I.N.PLAKSIN and G.A.MYASSNIKOVA, *Doklady Akad. Nauk SSSR* **117**, 864 (1957).
53. I.N.PLAKSIN and G.A.MYASSNIKOVA, *Freiberger Forschungsh.* **A 120**, 5 (1959).
54. A.M.GAUDIN and P.L.DEBRUYN, *Trans. Can. Inst. Mining Met. Engrs.* **52**, 331 (1949).
55. A.M.GAUDIN and C.S.CHANG, *Mining Engng.* **4**, 193 (1952).
56. A.M.GAUDIN, H.R.SPEDDEN and P.A.LAXEN, *Mining Engng.* **4**, 693 (1952).
57. I.N.PLAKSIN, S.V.BESSONOV and V.I.TYURNIKOVA, *Doklady Akad. Nauk SSSR* **102**, 331 (1955).
58. O.S.BOGDANOV, V.J.HAINMAN, N.A.YANIS and A.K.PODNEK, Paris Report 72, vol. 1, p. 441.
59. T.LUNDBERG, *Oil in Canada*, 16 June 1952.
60. J.W.MERRITT, *Wld. Oil*, 1 July 1952, p. 78; 1 August 1954, p. 107; 1 August 1955, p. 84.
61. M.V.SCHERB, *Oil Forum*, March 1953.
62. Moscow Atomic Energy Conference 1955, Session of the Technical Sciences Division.
63. F.A.ALEKSEEV, A.P.GRUMBKOV and YU.S.KIRSHFELDT, in [62], p. 253.
64. V.I.ERMAKOV and A.N.SHATSOV, *Neft. Geol.* **1957** (8), 34.
65. F.A.ALEKSEEV, V.I.ERMAKOV and A.I.LAUBENBAKH, *Novosti Neft. Tekhn. i Geol.* **1957** (6), 28.
66. Reports of the Scientific and Technical All-Union Conference on the Application of Radioactive and Stable Isotopes and Radiations in the National Economy and in Science (4–12 April 1957), *Prospecting and Exploitation of Mineral Resources* (Russian), Moscow 1958.

67. G.N.FLEROV, F.A.ALEKSEEV and B.G.EROSOLIMSKII, in [66], p. 17.
68. F.A.ALEKSEEV, in [66], p. 51.
69. A.I.LAUBENBAKH and L.I.SKOSIREVA, *Neft. Geol.* **1958** (2), 27.
70. V.I.ERMAKOV, M.G.OVANESOV and YU.A.ROMANOV, *Novosti Neft.Tekhn. i Geol.* **1958** (10), 36.
71. F.A.ALEKSEEV (Ed.), *Nuclear Geophysics* (Russ.), Moscow 1959.
72. F.A.ALEKSEEV, in [71], p. 3.
73. V.I.ERMAKOV, A.I.LAUBENBAKH, N.G.OVANESOV, YU.A.ROMANOV and L.I.SKOSIREVA, in [71], p. 264.
74. A.P.GRUMBKOV, V.V.MATVEEV, G.S.SEMENOV and A.D.SOKOLOV, in [71], p. 279.
75. V.V.MATVEEV and A.D.SOKOLOV, in [71], p. 290.
76. W.CREWS, *Oil Gas J.* **57** (21), 391 (1959).
77. V.I.BARANOV, N.G.MOROSOVA, K.G.KUNASHEVA, E.V.BABITSHEVA and B.V.KARASEV, *Geokhimiya* **1959** (6), 530.
78. A.P.GRUMBKOV, V.V.MATVEEV, G.S.SEMENOV and A.A.SOKOLOV, *Neft. Gas Geol.* **1960** (3), 33.
79. G.N.FLEROV, Copenhagen Report, vol. 1, p. 117.
80. A.P.GRUMBKOV, in [71], p. 300.
81. J.CZUBEK *et al.*, *Nukleonika* **3**, (1958), special issue.
82. Z.WERNER, *Freiberger Forschungshefte* **A 14,** (1959).
83. J.CZUBEK *et al.*, *Acta Geophys. Polonica* **8,** 73 (1960).
84. A.SPAK, *Doklady Akad. Nauk SSSR* **16.** 109 (1937).
85. W.L.RUSSELL, *Geophysics* **9,** 180 (1944).
86. V.N.DAKHNOV, *The Interpretation of Logging Diagrams* (Russ.), Moscow 1948, paragraphs 30–33.
87. S.G.KOMAROV, *Geophysical Methods for the Investigation of Petroleum Bore-holes* (Russ.), Moscow 1952, pp. 85–102, 294–303.
88. V.N.DAKHNOV, in [62], p. 228.
89. E.N.TIRATSOO, *Petroleum* **12,** 117, 166, 313 (1949).
90. J.V.MERCIER, *Oil Weekly* **123,** (7), 56 (1946).
91. YU.P.BULASHEVICH, G.N.VOSKOBOINIKOV and L.V.MUSYUKIN, Copenhagen Report 309, vol. 1, p. 101.
92. H.J.DI GIOVANNI, R.T.GRAVESON and A.H.YOLI, *Nucleonics* **11** (4), 34 (1953).
93. G.H.WESTBY and S.A.SCHERBATSKOY, *Oil Gas J.*, 22 February 1940.
94. W.G.GREEN and R.E.FEARON, *Geophysics* **5,** 272 (1940).
95. R.E.FEARON, *Nucleonics* **4** (4), 67 (1949).
96. J.BERBEZIER, R.CHAMINADE and C.LALLEMANT, *Ann. Geophysique* **8,** 260 (1952).
97. J.BERBEZIER, *L'Onde Electrique* **33,** 553 (1953).
98. B.G.EROSOLIMSKII and D.F.BESPALOV, in [62], p. 320.
99. H.R.BRANNON and J.S.OSABA, *J. Petrol. Technol.* **8** (2), 30 (1956).
100. J.A.S.ADAMS and C.E.WEAVER, *Bull. Am. Assoc. Petrol. Geol.* **42** (2), 387 (1958).
101. V.M.ZAPOROZHETS and YA.YA.GORSKI, in [66], p. 195.
102. D.F.BESPALOV, in [71], p. 27.
103. F.A.ALEKSEEV, S.A.DENISIK, V.V.MILLER and V.P.ODINOKOV, in [71], p. 134.
104. L.G.HOWELL and A.FROSH, *Geophysics* **4,** 106 (1939).
105. F.E.ARMSTRONG, *Nucleonics* **15** (10), 100 (1957).
106. G.SWIFT, *Geophysics* **17,** 387 (1952).
107. B.PONTECORVO, *Oil Gas J.* **40,** 18, 32 (1941).
108. C.W.TITTLE, H.FAUL and C.GOODMAN, *Geophysics* **16,** 626 (1951).
109. F.T.KRON, V.P.ODINOKOV, M.G.OVANESOV and V.G.SHCHERBINSKII,*Neft. Geol.* **1957** (10), 52.
110. F.T.KRON and V.P.ODINOKOV, in [66], p. 111.
111. B.M.BUROV, G.N.DARVOID, F.TS.DENISIK, V.P.ODINOKOV and V.G.SHCHERBINSKII, in [71], p. 121.
112. C.W.TITTLE, *U.S. Patent* 2 769 918 (1956).
113. B.M.BUROV, G.N.DARVOID and F.T.KRON, *Neft. Geol.* **1957** (12), 60.
114. M.GROSSMANGIN and E.B.WALKER, *J. Petrol. Technol.* **9** (5), 140 (1957).
115. B.H.BAILEY, H.L.BRYANT and N.L.POWER, *Oil Gas J.* **55** (46), 368 (1957).

116. J.TITTMAN, *J. Appl. Phys.* **26**, 394 (1955).
117. H.B.FREY and J.TITTMAN, *U.S. Patent* 2778950 (1957).
118. J.TITTMAN, *U.S. Patent* 2778951 (1957).
119. S.A.KANTOR, *Prikl. Geofiz.* **23**, 174 (1959).
120. V.P.ODINOKOV, S.A.DENISIK and YU.S.SHIMELEVICH in [71], p. 154.
121. I.L.DVORKIN, A.SH.GALYAVICH and B.M.ORLINSKII, *Neft. Khoz.* **1959** (6), 50.
122. A.I.KHOLIN, in [62], p. 267.
123. *The Application of Radioactive Isotopes and Radiation in the Petroleum Industry, Collected Volume* (Russ.), Reports on the Conference of 14–19 March 1956 (Moscow 1957).
124. N.K.KUKHARENKO, A.G.SERDII and V.P.ODINOKOV, in [123], p. 34.
125. V.N.DAKHNOV, in [123], p. 25.
126. L.S.TSLAV, in [71], p. 228.
127. V.P.IVANKIN, in [66], p. 123.
128. YU.V.GALUZO, in [66], p. 137.
129. D.B.SMITH and G.R.CHURCH, AERE-I/R 1688 (1955).
130. V.V.LARIONOV, *Neft. Geol.* **1957** (9), p. 52.
131. V.M.ZAPOROZHETS and V.V.SULIN, in [66], p. 85.
132. V.V.LARIONOV and A.I.KHOLIN, *Neft. Khoz.* **1959** (9), 35.
133. A.A.BROWN and B.BOWERS, *Can. Oil Gas Ind.* **11** (3), 59 (1958).
134. A.A.BROWN and B.BOWERS, *Petrol. Engng.* **30** (5), 30 (1958).
135. YU.A.GULIN, in [71], p. 201.
136. R.L.CALDWELL, *Nucleonics* **16** (12), 58 (1958).
137. V.F.IVANOVA, *Razvedka i Okhrana Nedr* **1958** (6), 41.
138. YU.V.GALUZO, *Neft i Gaz* **1958** (1), 41.
139. V.A.RYAPOLOVA, in [66], p. 62.
140. I.N.SENKO-BULATNII, *Izvest. Akad. Nauk SSSR, Ser. Geofiz* **1959** (3), 476.
141. S.PLEVA, *Nafta* (Polish) **13** (10), 286 (1957).
142. N.K.KUKHARENKO, V.P.ODINOKOV and YU.S.SHIMELEVICH, in [62], p. 284.
143. F.A.ALEKSEEV and YU.S.SHIMELEVICH, in [123], p. 43.
144. YU.S.SHIMELEVICH, in [66], p. 132.
145. E.B.BLANKOV, in [66], p. 220.
146. F.A.ALEKSEEV, V.P.ODINOKOV and YU.S.SHIMELEVICH, in [71], p. 65.
147. S.M.AKSELROD, in [71], p. 100.
148. R.A.RESVANOV, in [71], p. 103.
149. T.N.BLANKOVA, in [71], p. 110.
150. E.B.BLANKOV, in [71], p. 170.
151. E.B.BLANKOV, A.M.BLYUMENTSEV and T.N.BLANKOVA, *Razved. i Promisl. Geofiz.* **21**, 82 (1958).
152. SH.A.GUBERMAN, in [71], p. 146.
153. E.B.BLANKOV and T.N.BLANKOVA, *Razved. i Promisl. Geofiz.* **21**, 91 (1958).
154. A.I.SOLOMASOV, *Neft. i Gaz Geol.* **1956** (6), 48.
155. L.V.TOELKE, see [79].
156. I.G.DYADKIN, *Izv. Akad. Nauk SSSR, Ser. Geofiz.* **1955** (4).
157. E.M.FILIPPOV, in [123], p. 150.
158. E.M.FILIPPOV, *Priklad. Geofiz.* **17**, (1957).
159. E.M.FILIPPOV, in [66], p. 213.
160. E.M.FILIPPOV, in [71], p. 306.
161. G.R.NEWTON, J.E.SKINNER and D.SILVERMAN, *Geophysics* **19**, 636 (1954).
162. J.L.P.CAMPBELL and J.C.WILSON, *J. Petrol. Technol.* **10** (7), 11 (1958).
163. R.L.CALDWELL and R.F.SIPPEL, *Bull. Am. Assoc. Petrol. Geol.* **42** (1), 159 (1958).
164. R.L.CALDWELL, *Wld. Petrol.* **27** (4), 59 (1956).
165. P.E.BAKER, *J. Petrol. Technol.* **9** (10), 289 (1957).
166. R.F.SIPPEL and O.HODGES, *Petrol. Engng.* **30** (4), B 118 (1958).
167. F.G.BAYEMBITOV, YU.A.GULIN and I.G.DYADKIN, *Razved. i Promisl. Geofiz.* **32**, 38 (1959).
168. YU.P.BULASHEVITCH, E.P.DIDENKO, I.N.SENKO-BULATNII and A.P.FISENKO, in [66], p. 29.
169. S.M.SHITNIKOVA and I.A.SAVINETS, in [66], p. 57.

170. I.A.GARKALENKO, *Doklady Akad. Nauk Ukr. SSR*, **1958** (8), 874.
171. G.M.VOSKOBOINIKOV, *Izvest. Akad. Nauk SSSR, Ser. Geofiz.* **1957** (3), 351.
172. G.M.VOSKOBOINIKOV, *Atomnaya Energiya* **4**, 359 (1958).
173. M.M.SOKOLOV, A.A.OTSHKUR, A.A.FEDOROV and N.I.KARBANOV, *Atomnaya Energiya* **2**, 65 (1957).
174. *Nucleonics* **13** (11), 22 (1955).
175. G.N.FLEROV and F.A.ALEKSEEV, in [62], p. 302.
176. *Oil Gas J.*, **54** (28), 136 (1955).
177. *Nucleonics* **15** (9), 192 (1957).
178. C.GOODMAN, *U.S. Patent* 2 816 242.
179. O.REIFENSCHWEILER and A.C.VAN DORSTEN, *Angew. Chem.* **69**, 760 (1957).
180. C.GOODMAN, *U.S. Patent* 2 842 695 (1958).
181. D.F.BESPALOV and A.I.KHAUSTOV, in [71], p. 346.
182. B.G.EROSOLIMSKII, L.I.BONDARENKO, L.R.VOITSIK, YU.S.SHIMELEVICH and L.I.YUDIN, in [71], p. 351.
183. E.A.AB, V.M.ZAPOROZHETS, R.I.PLOTNIKOV and L.A.KHUTSIVILI, *Prikl. Geofiz.* **23**, 226 (1959).
184. E.A.BURRILL and M.H.MACGREGOR, *Nucleonics* **18** (12), 64 (1960).
185. O.REIFENSCHWEILER, *Nucleonics* **18** (12), 69 (1960).
186. A.H.FRENTROP and H.SHERMAN, *Nucleonics* **18** (12), 72 (1960).
187. B.J.CARR, *Nucleonics* **18** (12), 75 (1960).
188. B.G.EROSOLIMSKII, L.R.VOITSIK, I.V.POPOV and A.S.SHKOLNIKOV, *Neft. Khoz.* **1958** (11), 21.
189. B.G.EROSOLIMSKII and A.S.SHKOLNIKOV, in [71], p. 337.
190. V.M.ZAPOROZHETS and E.M.FILIPPOV, *Prikl. Geofiz.* **20**, 234 (1958).
191. V.M.ZAPOROZHETS and V.V.SULIN, *Izv. Tomsk. Politekhn. Inst.* **1959** (1), 96, 110.
192. *Nucleonics* **9** (4), 77 (1951).
193. *Chem. Engng. News* **20**, 3856 (1953).
194. A.E.SERCHIKOV, *Neft. Geol.* **1958** (3), 49.
195. R.L.CALDWELL, *Nucleonics* **19** (2), 58 (1961).
196. L.G.HOWELL and A.FROSH, *Amer. Inst. Mining Metallurg. Eng., Techn. Publ.* 1113 (1939).
197. W.J.JACKSON and J.L.P.CAMPBELL, *Amer. Inst. Mining Metallurg. Eng., Techn. Publ.* 1923 (1951).
198. R.G.NORELIUS, *Petrol. Engng.* **29** (12), 1395 (1957).
199. A.SH.GALYAVICH, in [66], p. 183.
200. S.M.AKSELROD, in [123], p. 61.
201. D.M.SREBRODOLSKII, in [66], p. 39.
202. S.M.AKSELROD, *Prikl. Geofiz.* **18**, 210 (1958).
203. S.M.AKSELROD, *Razved. i Promisl. Geofiz.* **24**, 37 (1958).
204. N.I.KIM and A.SH.GALYAVICH, *Neft. Khoz.* **1958** (6), 36.
205. S.PLEWA and T.ROKOSZ, *Nafta* (Polish) **14**, (2), 34 (1958).
206. W.T.CARDWELL and S.B.JONES, *U.S. Patent* 2 856 536 (1958).
207. V.M.ZAPOROZHETS, in [123], p. 54.
208. J.W.WATKINS and E.S.MARDOCK, *J. Petrol. Technol.* **6**, 117 (1954).
209. J.W.WATKINS and H.N.DUNNING, Geneva Report 161 (1955), vol. 15, p. 32.
210. J.M.EDWARDS and L.E.HOLTER, *Oil Gas. J.* **53**, 29 November 1954, 60; *Mines Mag.* **44**, 149 (1954).
211. F.A.ALEKSEEV, V.N.SOIFER, V.A.FILONOV and YA.B.FINKELSHTEIN, *Neft. Geol.* **1958** (12), 47.
212. F.A.ALEKSEEV, V.N.SOIFER, V.A.FILONOV and YA.B.FINKELSHTEIN, *Atomnaya Energiya* **4**, 298 (1958).
213. YA.B.FINKELSHTEIN, V.A.FILONOV, V.N.SOIFER and M.P.OBUKHOVA, in [66], p. 191.
214. F.A.ALEKSEEV, G.R.GOLBEK, V.N.SOIFER, N.A.VASILEVA, V.N.MAIDEBOR, E.V.SOKOLOVSKII and N.N.SHANGIN, Copenhagen Report 318, vol. 1, p. 519.
215. W.ENGELHARDT and K.MÜLLER, *Erdöl und Kohle* **9**, 674 (1956).
216. S.M.AKSELROD and L.A.PUTKARADSE, *Novosti Neft. Tekhn. i Geol.* **1959** (3), 30.
217. D.E.HULL and J.W.KENT, *Ind. Eng. Chem.* **44**, 2745 (1952).
218. D.E.HULL, *Conf. Atomic Energy in Industry*, Nat. Ind. Conf. Board, New York 1952.

219. W.G.DAVIDSON, *Petrol. Engng.* **26** (1), E-1 (1954).
220. D.E.HULL and B.A.FRIES, Geneva Report 166 (1955), vol. 15, p. 199.
221. D.E.HULL, *Nucleonics* **13** (4), 18 (1955).
222. B. S. VOTLOKHIN, A. S. DOROGOCHINSKII and N. P. MELNIKOVA, *Atomnaya Energiya* **4**, 475 (1958).
223. B.S.VOTLOKHIN, in [66], p. 240.
224. J.G.BECKERLEY, *Ann. Rev. Nucl. Sci.* **10**, 425 (1960).
225. G.TAYLOR, *Proc. Roy. Soc.* **223 A**, 446 (1954).
226. D.B.SMITH and G.R.CHURCH, *Nature* **176**, 232 (1955).
227. D.B.SCOTT, *Nucleonics* **9** (3), 68 (1951).
228. *Radioactive Markers in Go-devils; Safety Precautions*, H.M.S.O., London.
229. J.L.PUTMAN, *Isotopes*, London 1961.
230. J.KAKAS, M.NAGY, K.VARGA, A.BISZTRAY-BALKU and A.LEVAI, *Isotopentechnik* **1**, 144 (1961).
231. E.DAHN, *Isotopentechnik* **1**, 150 (1961).
232. J.L.PUTMAN, Geneva Report 463 (1955), vol. 15, p. 119.
233. *Nucleonics* **13** (1), 71 (1955).
234. C.FISHER, *Atomwirtschaft* **6**, 481 (1961).
235. J.FODOR, A.PÉCELI and L.VAJTA, *Isotopentechnik* **2**, 77 (1962).
236. E.DAHN and G.BRUNNER, *Isotopentechnik* **2**, 201 (1962).
237. S.KOCH and W.LIEBIG, *Isotopentechnik* **2**, 353 (1962).
238. A.M.GAUDIN and H.F.RAMDOHR, *Can. Metal Quart.* **1**, 173 (1962).
239. H.F.RAMDOHR, *Kerntechnik* **5**, 204 (1963).
240. E.M.FILIPPOV, *Applied Nuclear Geophysics* (Russ.), Moscow 1962.
241. S.J.LEACH and G.L.WALKER, *Int. J. Appl. Rad. Isot.* **12**, 42 (1961).
242. J.HEINECKE, *Kerntechnik* **5**, 343 (1963).
243. S.JEFFERSON, *Radioisotopes, A New Tool for Industry*, London 1957.
244. M.QUESSON, in: P.LÉVÊQUE (Ed.), *Les applications industrielles des radioéléments*, Paris 1962.
245. L.I.KOROTKOV, *Handbook (spravochnik) of Radioisotope Instruments* (Russ.), Moscow 1963.
246. A.E.BENNETT and L.J.MILLS, *Mining Engineer* **1961**, (6) 485.
247. L.R.COOPER, *Brit. Communic. Electronics*, March 1961.
248. V.D.GOROSHKO and L.P.NIKANOROVA,*Izvest.Akad. Nauk SSSR, Otd. Tekh. Nauk, Metallurgiya i Toplivo* **1960** (1), 152.
249. V.D.GOROSHKO, O.M.TODES and A.Z.YUROVSKI, *Izvest. Akad. Nauk SSSR, Otd. Tekhn. Nauk, Metallurgiya i Toplivo* **1960** (4), 185.
250. I.N.PLAKSIN and R.S.SAFEEV, *Freiburger Forschungsh.* **A 163**, 48 (1960).
251. I.N.PLAKSIN and R.SH.SHAFEEV, *Doklady Akad. Nauk SSSR* **135**, 140 (1960).
252. I.N.PLAKSIN and R.S.SHAFEEV, *Doklady Akad. Nauk SSSR* **142**, 131 (1962).
253. I.N.PLAKSIN and S.P.ZAITSEVA, *Doklady Akad. Nauk SSSR* **144**, 857 (1962).
254. I.N.PLAKSIN, S.P.ZAITSEVA, G.N.KHAZHINSKAYA and R.SH.SHAFEEV, Copenhagen Report 308, vol. 1, p. 483.
255. L.ŠIMON, *Applications of Radioactive Isotopes to Mining* (Czech), Prague 1961.
256. J.F.CAMERON, unpublished, see [257].
257. J.THIERY, in: P.LÉVÊQUE (Ed.), *Les applications industrielles des radioéléments*, Paris 1962.
258. I.WENDT, *Geol. Jahrbuch.* **70**, 385 (1955); *Kerntechnik* **2**, 1 (1960).
259. I.L.LIPLAVK and E.P.BOLITER, *Zavod. Lab.* **25**, 1127 (1959).
260. I.POENARU, *Petrol si Gaze* **9**, 513 (1958).
261. P.GERKE, *Atompraxis* **6**, 380 (1960).
262. U.P.COLOMBO, G.SIRONI, G.B.FASOLO and E.MALVANO, *Anal. Chem.* **34**, 802 (1964).
263. S.KOCH and R.WINDELBAND, *Kernenergie* **7**, 176 (1964).
264. S.KOCH, *Bergbautechnik* **13**, 648 (1963).
265. C.H.LEWIS, *Gas Council Research Comm. G.C.* 19, Nov. 1954, London.
266. A.M.GAUDIN, H.R.SPEDDEN and D.F.KAUFMAN, *Mining Engng.* **3**, 969 (1951).
267. O.A.BARSUKOV et al., *Radioactive Investigations of Oil and Gas Wells* (Russ.), Moscow 1958; English translation, Oxford 1964.
268. S.F.VYBORNIKH, *Equipment and Instruments for Industrial Geophysics* (Russ.), Moscow 1958.

269. S.G.KOMAROV, *Techniques of Industrial Geophysics* (Russ.), MOSCOW 1958.
270. S.G.KOMAROV *et al.*, *Automatic Instruments for Geophysical Investigations of Bore-holes* (Russ.), Moscow 1958.
271. E.A.AB, G.M.ANDRIANOVA, R.I.PLOTNIKOV and L.I.KHUTSIVILI, *Pribory i Tekhn. Eksperim.* **1961** (1), 129.
272. F.A.ALEKSEEV *et al.*, in [290], p. 3.
273. YU.P.BULASHEVITCH and G.M.VOSKOBOINIKOV, *Izvest. Akad. Nauk SSSR, Ser. Geofiz.* **1957** (1), 109.
274. G.M.VOSKOBOINIKOV and L.I.DEEV, *Razvedka i Okhrana Nedr* **1956** (10), 38.
275. I.A.GARKALENKO, *Prikl. Geofiz.* **25**, 234 (1960).
276. A.E.GLAUBERMAN and I.I.TALYANSKII, *Atomnaya Energiya* **3**, 23 (1957).
277. I.I.TALYANSKII, *Atomnaya Energiya* **4**, 372 (1958).
278. I.I.TALYANSKII, B.F.BILENSKII and YA.P.DRAGAN, *Prikl. Geofiz.* **25**, 223 (1960).
279. E.M.FILIPPOV, *Prikl. Geofiz.* **27**, 201 (1960).
280. A.E.KULINKOVICH, *Prikl. Geofiz.* **22**, 187 (1959).
281. J.A.CZUBEK, *Nukleonika* **7**, 745 (1963).
282. C.W.TITTLE, *Geophysics* **26**, 27 (1961).
283. O.A.BARSUKOV, in [66].
284. V.I.BARANOV and V.K.KHRISTIANOV, *Geokhimiya* **1958** (7), 680.
285. V.F.IVANOVA and V.K.KHRISTIANOV, *Geokhimiya* **1956** (2).
286. I.I.FELDMAN, in [290], p. 181.
287. YU.A.GYULIN, in [66].
288. R.E.BUSH and J.C.STICK, Proc. Fourth World Petroleum Congress, Section 2, p. 171, Rome 1955.
289. J.H.CASTEL, Proc. Fourth World Petroleum Congress, Section 2, p. 223, Rome 1955.
290. *Nuclear Geophysics in Prospecting for Minerals* (Collective volume (Russ.)), Moscow 1960.
291. A.N.MAKAROV, in: *Problems of Geophysics* (Russ.), Moscow 1959.
292. YU.P.BULASHEVITCH and S.A.SHULYATEV, *Izvest. Akad. Nauk SSSR, Ser. Geofiz.* **1960**, (2), 253.
293. I.A.BOBER, N.I.DRAGOMOSHCHENKO, I.P.KOSHELEV, YU.S.STARTSEV and L.I.SHMOLIN, *Tr. Kazakh. Nauch.-Isled. Inst. Min. Syrya* **1959** (1), 45.
294. E.M.FILIPPOV, *Geol. i Geofiz., Akad. Nauk SSSR, Sibirsk. Otd.*, **1960** (6), 94.
295. I.G.ZHUVAGIN and YU.A.AKTSHASYANOV, *Neft. Khoz.* **1960** (6), 7.
296. A.A.KORSHEV, in [66].
297. S.M.AKSELROD, *Prikl. Geofiz.* **18**, 210 (1958).
298. S.L.ABRAMYAN *et al.*, *Azerb. Neft-Khoz.* **1960** (11), 9.
299. I.V.POPOV, in: *Neutron Generators* (Collective volume (Russ.)), Moscow 1962.
300. I.N.PLAKSIN, S.P.ZAITSEVA, G.A.MYASNIKOVA, V.I.TYURNIKOVA, G.N.KHAZHINSKAYA, *Application of Radioactive Nuclides to the Investigation of Flotation Processes* (Russ.), Moscow 1963.
301. I.N.PLAKSIN and R.SH.SHAFEEV, *Trans. Inst. Min. Metall., Lond.*, **72**, 715 (1963).
302. D.E.HULL and J.T.GILMORE, *Anal. Chem.* **36**, 2072 (1964).
303. T.C.MARTIN, S.C.MATHUR and I.L.MORGAN, *Int. J. Appl. Rad. Isot.* **15**, 331 (1964).
304. K.KÖHLER, *Radiometrisches Klauben von Uranerzen und anderen Rohstoffen des Bergbaus*, Leipzig 1963.
305. E.M.LOBANOV, A.P.NOVIKOV and A.A.KHAIDAROV, *Activation Analysis in Bore-holes* (Russ.), Tashkent 1963.
306. V.P.GUINN, Geneva Report 197 (1964).
307. I.N. PLAKSIN, *Flotation*, New York 1963.

8. APPLICATION OF RADIOACTIVITY IN THE METALLURGICAL, ENGINEERING AND ELECTRICAL INDUSTRIES

8.1. Metallurgy

In recent years the applications of labelled atoms to problems of metallurgy have become extremely numerous (for surveys see [1–4, 10, 376, 380]).

8.1.1. *Blast Furnace Operation*

The refractory linings of furnaces, such as blast furnaces, are gradually worn out during operation. It is of the utmost importance that the contents of the furnace, such as hot metal and slag, should not come into contact with the metal of the furnace wall, or else the walls would be ruptured and serious damage would result. In industrial operation it is therefore usual to interrupt the operation of the furnace fairly frequently to examine the linings. For complete safety the linings are renewed long before corrosion has worn them off. This is also true for other than metallurgical furnaces, such as rotary kilns used for burning magnesite or making cement.

It is now possible to add long-lived γ-emitters, such as radiocobalt, to the refractory material, and to measure the radiation intensity from outside without interrupting the operation of the furnace. Dangerous corrosion at any point is revealed by a reduction of the intensity, so that the furnace can be taken out of operation in time. Instead of labelling the lining uniformly, it is possible to insert cobalt cartridges at selected places [5–7, 340, 341]. The removal of the cobalt can also be established by the fact that the product, such as pig iron, becomes radioactive. A more detailed picture of the wearing out of the lining can, of course, be obtained if the lining is labelled at different places with different radionuclides, which can be distinguished by their radiation energies [8, 300].

In this type of procedure, care has to be taken that workers at the furnace, or in the plants receiving the metal produced, are not exposed to appreciable radiation doses. It is also important to prevent radioactive contamination of scientific and industrial research laboratories, which would greatly hinder measurements of radioactivity. For this reason it has been suggested that in many cases relatively short-lived γ-active nuclides, such as iron-59 ($\tau = 45$ days), antimony-124 (60 days) or tantalum-182 (115 days), should be used in preference to cobalt-60 (5·2 years) [9].

The spreading-out of the active material in the lining, which has been observed in certain cases, can make it difficult to observe the disappearance of the source as corrosion progresses, and may also lead to undesirable contamination. Special sources have been developed where the active substance (cobalt-60) is inserted in a refractory ceramic material, so that the activity does not spread even at very high temperatures [9, 128, 300].

(The radiocobalt control method has also been used in the refractory ladles for pouring metals [372] and in electric furnaces for the production of phosphorus from phosphate rock and coke [318].)

The rate of movement of the charge in a blast furnace as a function of the distance from the axis of the furnace was measured by labelling one or the other of the several constituents (ore, coke and limestone) with γ-emitters, and then determining the radiation penetrating to the outside of the furnace with a scintillation counter; the activity of the pig iron and the slag after leaving the furnace may also be measured. On the basis of such investigations the construction of blast furnaces may be improved [11–13, 131, 306, 328, 336–338].

The height of the charge within the blast furnace may be estimated by radiation absorption. A radiocobalt source is arranged over the top of the furnace, and a series of cooled radiation measuring instruments are placed at various heights outside the furnace wall. The radiation intensity diminishes very strongly when it has to pass through the charge (see Section 9.3.3). Other methods for the determination of the height of the charge had not given satisfactory results [14].

Fine ore is easily blown out of the furnace top. To estimate the extent of the loss, several kilograms of fine ore were activated in a reactor, mixed with 22 tons of equally fine ore and 54 tons of coarse ore, and the mixture introduced into the blast furnace. After the material had passed through the furnace an activity balance was drawn up, and in this particular case it was found that the fines had only been used to the extent of 60 per cent [15]. It has also been found that the dust content of the blast furnace gas is much higher when cold-pressed ore rather than agglomerated ore briquettes are used [16].

A question of great practical importance concerns the path of the gases through the blast furnace. The capacity of the furnace is utilized more efficiently, the more uniformly the gas moves, and the fewer pockets with abnormally small gas transport are formed. Earlier it had been shown that in a wind tunnel the mixing of gases, after introduction at a constant rate, can be followed by measuring the distribution of a radioactive gas (radon) [32, 316].

To elucidate the gas flow in a blast furnace under operating conditions, a pulse method has been adopted. Several millicuries of radon were rapidly injected–best by breaking mechanically nicked gold seeds [18]–into a furnace which had been charged in the usual way. Gas samples were then taken in intervals of 1 sec, both in the centre and at the sides, from the top of the furnace, and were then submitted to measurement. It was found that considerable pockets were formed; the time required for the largest amount of radon to appear in the furnace top (4–5 sec) was greater than had been expected [17] (see also [20]). The method has later been perfected to measure gas speeds within furnaces and stacks, to find leaks and to measure infiltration [18, 19, 348, 349]; such methods will be treated in more detail in Section 9.3.4. It is undoubtedly possible to reduce pocket formation by modifying construction and operation of furnaces on the basis of such data.

The measurement of the velocity of ore particles and of the spongy iron produced from them in a continuous reduction furnace is a difficult matter, since air must be excluded. It has been done by adding small fire-clay balls containing γ-active iridium wire; they were located with a scintillation counter [53] (see also [339]). The speed of vanadium ore particles in a sintering kiln was measured after they had been tagged with sodium-24 sulphate [7]. The moisture in ores for agglomeration may be controlled on the basis of measurement of the slowing-down of neutrons [324].

A review of the applications of radionuclides to the control of the blast furnace process has been published [374].

8.1.2. *Steel Production*

A monitoring system for an oxygen steel furnace is based on the indication of a β-ray gauge applied to the flame. The density of the flame is inversely proportional to temperature, and is in general independent of the composition of the gas. The density is affected by dust only in proportion to the amount of the material. The end point of the blow is recognized by the change in temperature, and therefore in density [326].

The transfer of material between the metal and the slag phases, for example during the operation of a steel furnace, can be followed in a simple way with radioactive tracers. Thus the thermodynamics and the kinetics of metallurgical reactions may be investigated. The high sensitivity of radiation measurement permits determination of any minute impurities of interest. Radiophosphorus and radiosulphur have been used to determine the speed and completeness of the removal of these undesirable elements from the metal through the interface. Of course, the dependence on the composition of the slag may also be examined [1–4, 21–30, 51, 323, 332].

With radioactive phosphorus it has been shown that this element reaches an equilibrium distribution within 10–15 min at the usual operating temperatures (ca. 1600 °C). It may therefore be assumed that after a smelting process of this duration the specific activity of the phosphorus will be equal throughout. The ratio of the activities in the two phases then indicates the phosphorus distribution between the two phases. It was also found that at 1660 °C 10 per cent more phosphorus remains in the metal (in the form of phosphide) than at 1608 °C. The phosphorus content, and thus the value of slag as a fertilizer, may be obtained rapidly when the phosphorus is radioactive; 50 mc radiophosphorus per ton of pig iron is sufficient [34].

Using radioactive sulphur the absorption of this element from the fuel in the open-hearth furnace has been measured. A great deal was found to be absorbed, but the use of oxygen for the combustion leads to an improvement [31, 35, 36, 323, 332].

Tracer methods have also been used to find the distribution of niobium (as an alloy component) [37], arsenic (as an impurity) [37], and calcium [38, 39] between the metal and the slag. Even under strongly reducing conditions too little calcium to be measured (less than $6 \cdot 10^{-5}$ per cent) was taken up by iron from a slag containing calcium, aluminium and silicon. The transfer of the iron itself between steel and slag [1, 360] and the penetration of iron into refractory [371] was studied by similar techniques.

The speed of distribution of iron and other elements within the steel depends on convective mixing (turbulent diffusion, mass transport), and may be followed with radioiron [41], radiocobalt [48] or radiophosphorus [33, 42, 46]. Such investigations are usually carried out in connection with the experiments on slag formation [1, 12, 43–47]. Other investigations have been devoted to the rate of interaction between pig iron, scrap and slag in the open-hearth furnace [47, 48], and the rate of the absorption of ferrous alloys (ferrochrome) by molten steel [49].

Special problems involve rates of diffusion within slags [363] and the extent to which transfer through the phase boundary or diffusion within the slag phase is the rate-determining process for the reaction. As a result of kinetic investigations of these problem with radionuclides, an appreciable reduction in the smelting period in open-hearth furnaces has been brought about, and the output has been raised [44, 50].

Determination of the distribution of undesirable impurities by radiochemical techniques is possible not only in technological research, but also during production. It can therefore be employed for routine technical control, such as that of phosphorus elimination. The sulphur and phosphorus contents of slag or metal may instead be determined by one of the standard chemical methods, but these methods require much time, while the measurement of radioactivity may be carried out in a few minutes after sampling. As soon as saturation activity is attained in the slag or the iron phase, the smelting may be discontinued.

Provided the radioactive element used is almost entirely taken up by the slag, it is also possible to determine the amount of slag by isotope dilution ("slag weighing"). After the addition of a known amount of the radioelement the activity of a sample of given mass (that is, the specific activity) is smaller, the greater the total slag quantity. The term isotope dilution indicates the similarity of this procedure with the isotope dilution method of chemical analysis (p. 80), where, after the addition of a known quantity of labelled material, the specific activity of a sample isolated from the mixture is smaller, the greater the total amount of the substance in question. In open-hearth furnaces such investigations have been carried out with lanthanum-140, or with barium-140–lanthanum-140; the specific activity given to the slag was between 0·2 and 2 mc/ton [52, 53, 328].

The use of such methods in industrial practice is restricted by the radiation hazard. It is hardly possible to admit routine methods which would involve the introduction of several curies of radionuclides. Amounts of this order would be necessary, for example, to determine the very small residue of phosphorus in iron by direct activity measurements on this phase. Rapid chemical separation procedures may, however, make it possible to reduce the amount of radionuclide required. Thus, if the iron is dissolved, and the phosphorus is then precipitated with carrier, the activity may be measured with much better yield because of the greatly reduced self-absorption. The amount of the radioactive element introduced may then be cut down.

The rate of crystallization of steel may be observed by adding radioiron to the crystallizing melt and measuring its distribution after cooling. Measurements of this kind are carried out most easily by autoradiography. Since the diffusion of the added radioiron is rapid in the liquid, but very slow in the solidified material, sharp boundaries are found for the active regions, and these indicate the portion already crystallized at the time of addition of the radionuclide. By this method the course of crystallization under different technical conditions may be compared [63, 188, 306]. Under certain circumstances, other radionuclides, such as radiophosphorus, may be used [64, 180, 342]. Radiocobalt wire covered by tungsten may be dropped into the crystallizing steel, and it is then possible to determine the depth of the zone which is still liquid [64].

In industrial practice carbon-poor steel parts may be immersed into salt melts containing sodium cyanide, sodium cyanate and sodium carbonate at temperatures near 900°C. Under these conditions the surface layers take up carbon, and a material with high bulk tensile strength and a hard and wear-resistant surface is produced. This carbonization has been followed with radiocarbon, and it has been shown that the carbon taken up is derived mainly from the cyanide [40].

8.1.3. *Extraction of Non-ferrous Metals*

The applications of tracer methods to non-ferrous metals are also numerous, and the procedures used in iron metallurgy may often be employed – where necessary in a modified form [3].

The Bayer process is used as a first step in the production of aluminium, to make alumina from bauxite. Here it is important to know what happens both to the bauxite and the aluminate solution in the autoclave. To follow the course of the process, the bauxite (or, more accurately, its iron content) has been activated with neutrons, radioactive phosphate being simultaneously added to the solution [20]. The most favourable conditions for isolating gallium by the amalgam–electrolytic method from the aluminate solution have been found using gallium-72 [276].

In the electrolysis of a melt of alumina and cryolite, ion transport plays a decisive role. This has been investigated with sodium-24, fluorine-18 and the long-lived isomer aluminium-26. It has been found that the current is mainly carried by the aluminium but a part is carried by a complex anion containing aluminium, oxygen and fluorine. The experimental results did not depend on whether the membrane used consisted of strongly sintered alumina or of boron nitride [54].

An isotope dilution method (see p. 162) has been described for the rapid determination of metallic aluminium present at any time in the electrolytic cell; instead of an aluminium isotope, gold-198 (half-life 2·7 days) was used [55–57]. The casting of aluminium has also been studied with active or inactive gold. In the latter case, the solidified metal was subsequently activated with neutrons. The distribution of the gold showed how far the liquid aluminium extended at the time of adding the gold [58]. In this way, the most favourable cooling conditions for continuous casting could be ascertained.

The purification of antimony by a modified Groschuff procedure (a multi-stage process starting with the pentachloride) has been studied by radiochemical methods. The changes in concentration of the impurities were not only unexpected quantitatively, but it appeared that in some stages of the process the content of foreign metals was increased rather than decreased [59].

After activation with reactor neutrons, the movement of nickel–iron lumps in a rotary kiln (see p. 246) has been followed from outside in relation to various technical parameters [320].

8.1.4. *Investigation of Metals (Analysis, Detection of Inclusions,*
        Investigation of Plastic Deformation and Welding)

Finished metals may conveniently be tested for purity by activation analysis [2, 379]. Thus, an analytical procedure has been given for aluminium in which 45 elements possibly present as impurities are tested for [60, 310, 362], tungsten in steel is conveniently measured by activation with neutrons and γ-spectrometry [317], and oxygen in steel may be determined with fast neutrons [375]. More references to activation analysis in metallurgy have been given in Section 6.6.

Non-metallic inclusions in metals are harmful. After labelling of slag or refractory (e.g., with radiocalcium or radiolanthanum), the origin of the inclusions and their distribution in the metal may be determined, for instance, by autoradiography [3, 10, 65–71, 306, 323, 327, 328, 343–347]. If the slag is radioactive, inclusions in rolled steel can be detected without delay with the Geiger counter rather than by stopping the mill and cutting strips for visual inspection [373].

The presence of hydrogen in metals — for example, aluminium, beryllium and uranium — can lead to brittleness. The hydrogen may be determined by activity measurement after interaction with radioactive hydrogen: If the tritium undergoes complete exchange with the hydrogen in the metal, the amount of the latter may be calculated from the reduction in the specific activity of the hydrogen in the gas phase. Thus an isotope dilution method is employed. Errors due to adsorbed water must be avoided [72–74]. The tritium in aluminium may be located by autoradiography [331].

Whenever liquid or solid metals are made to flow or to undergo plastic deformation, as in casting, rolling and extrusion, the path of flow is a matter of great interest. Before suitable radionuclides became available, metal blocks were labelled at certain places by insertion of foreign materials, and the distribution of these materials was studied after flow. However, the introduction of foreign materials is suspect since they may affect the course of the flow. Moreover, chemical analysis of the large number of samples required in such studies was troublesome. Labelling by means of radioisotopes of the metallic element in question is, however, simple and free from any source of error. The distribution of activity after the flow process may be determined directly by autoradiography. The important question of the influence of foreign atoms on the flow of the metal may be examined by this technique. The radioactive material may be introduced as pins into cylindrical holes of the proper size [61, 62.]

Welding involves complicated processes which were investigated in detail by the introduction of several radionuclides. It has been shown that labelled carbon was concentrated in those regions of the steel that were rich in carbide-forming alloy components. In the same study the distribution of labelled chromium, manganese and hydrogen in the weld was also investigated. It is a particular advantage of such tracer work that the distribution of the element in question arising from its introduction with bulk metal, welding wire, or welding powder can readily be compared [75]. The elucidation of the complex processes taking place at the iron–tin boundary in the production of tinplate has been attempted with labelled tin [20].

Investigations of the phases in alloys will be treated in Section 8.3, where the autoradiography of metals will be discussed further.

8.2. Diffusion in Metals

An important application of radionuclides to metallurgy is in the study of diffusion. This plays a part in many important technical processes, including welding, annealing, tempering, ageing, sintering, hardening, recrystallization, creeping and corrosion. The suitability of radionuclides for diffusion research arises, on the one hand, from the sensitivity and the simplicity of detection, and, on the other hand, from the possibility of distinction between labelled and unlabelled atoms.

In investigating the diffusion of foreign atoms, only the high sensitivity and the simplicity of detection are called into play. But even so the work is simplified so much that these processes are studied more and more with labelled atoms.

Using isotopes, self-diffusion, i.e., diffusion of atoms within a chemically homogeneous body, may also be measured. Before the discovery of isotopy this process could not be investigated. In the studies of self-diffusion, part of a homogeneous substance is activated, and the rate is determined at which the active atoms move into the originally inactive zone.

Self-diffusion has been measured in many systems — gases, liquids and solids. The solids include metals, salts, glasses, plastics, etc. We shall now give a brief outline of the measurement of diffusion in solids, and shall then mention some results on self-diffusion of importance in metallurgy. Other classes of materials will be referred to in the relevant sections. Several reviews and literature surveys on diffusion studies with radionuclides are available [1–3, 10, 76–93].

The determination of diffusion in solids (foreign or self-diffusion) may be carried out either by dividing the test sample into sections after diffusion, and determining the activity of each section, or by measuring the distribution of activity without destruction of the sample.

The earliest measurements of self-diffusion (in liquid lead) were carried out in 1920 by Hevesy [95]. Later a solid lead bar, one half active and the other half inactive, was prepared by welding [96]. The bar was heated for a definite time to a temperature a little below its melting point and was cut into sections. The activity of the lead was then determined as a function of the distance from the weld. The self-diffusion coefficient found was surprisingly small, and also much smaller than the diffusion coefficient of gold into lead, which had been determined before by chemical methods. Hevesy explained that the foreign atoms disturb the crystal lattice and are therefore able to move more rapidly in the dislocations so produced [98]. The methods for sectioning test samples have since been perfected [291–293]. Electrolytic polishing has been found particularly useful, and as little as 5μ may be taken off at a time [97, 309, 314]. In some methods the activity measurement is carried out not on the material removed, but on that remaining. This is to be recommended in the case of brittle materials [294, 295].

In more recent methods involving sectioning of test samples, the active substance is applied to the sample only as a thin layer. This is also done in the procedures based on radiation absorption which will now be discussed.

To measure the self-diffusion of lead at low temperatures, sensitive methods had to be developed. One such method provides for the application of a thin layer of radiolead on the end of a lead rod, and for the measurement of the radiation emitted from that end as a function of time. This radiation is subjected to increasing absorption as the radiolead atoms diffuse more deeply into the rod. The method is more sensitive, the more easily the radiation is attenuated in the sample. α-rays and recoil nuclei are particularly strongly absorbed [98, 325]. Various forms of this absorption technique have been described [99–101, 291, 296].

When diffusion needs to be measured with only moderate sensitivity, autoradiography may be used [102, 103, 290]. In such cases the distribution of radioactive atoms within a metal body is determined by pressing a section or ground surface against a photographic emulsion.

Self-diffusion has been measured for numerous metals and under varied experimental conditions. It has been learned that self-diffusion depends greatly on crystal structure. For iron it has been reported that at the transition temperature (910 °C) the rate of self-diffusion in α-iron is a hundred times larger than in γ-iron [104]. This was found by measuring the diffusion velocity of α-iron between 715° and 887 °C, that of γ-iron between 935° and 1112 °C, and then extrapolating from both sides to the transition temperature. Such a relationship between the two diffusion coefficients had already been expected on the basis of earlier work on the diffusion of molybdenum in iron. However, other authors later obtained quite different values [105–108]; the cause of these discrepancies has been discussed [10].

Self-diffusion in γ-iron increases with its carbon content [109]; this is also true in the presence of 20–25 per cent nickel [110]. The effect of other alloying metals on the self-diffusion of iron, often quite complicated, has been investigated [97, 111, 112, 289, 364], and the diffusion velocities of the alloying metals in iron and steel have been measured [113]. The diffusion of carbon in iron has been determined by tempering the iron in contact with radiocarbon, dividing into thin sections, and determining the distribution of the radiocarbon by autoradiography or by an absorption method [102, 107, 114, 115, 365, 366].

Much research has, of course, also been done with non-ferrous metals. The diffusion of copper or zinc in β-brass may be mentioned as an example [116]. The self-diffusion of uranium in alloys containing 10 per cent of molybdenum at 1000 °C is 200 to 300 times slower than in pure uranium, which is in harmony with the increased creep resistance of these alloys [117].

Reproducible results in measuring diffusion velocities can only be expected if the contribution of grain-boundary diffusion is constant. This condition is best fulfilled when grain-boundary diffusion amounts to either 0 or 100 per cent of total diffusion.

Grain-boundary diffusion and lattice diffusion can be distinguished by observing the temperature dependence of the diffusion. The logarithm of the diffusion coefficient obtained in such experiments is plotted against the reciprocal of the absolute temperature. If both mechanisms contribute appreciably, the curve is found to have two straight parts and a curved section joining these together. The straight parts show that at low temperatures grain-boundary diffusion is the predominant process, while at high temperatures lattice diffusion is more important. By extrapolation the contribution of each mechanism may be estimated in that range of temperature where it plays only a minor role. Thus in silver at 500 °C grain-boundary diffusion is about 10^5 times more rapid than lattice diffusion [118]. Grain-boundary diffusion and lattice diffusion have also been distinguished in other metals, including iron [80, 108, 119–121]. Another possibility of distinguishing grain-boundary diffusion and lattice diffusion is to determine the spatial distribution of active atoms diffusing into an originally inactive zone; this can be done by autoradiography (see [10]). The relative role of the two kinds of diffusion in the movement of rare gas atoms within metals has been examined by the emanation method [122].

The ratio between grain-boundary diffusion and lattice diffusion depends strongly on the chemical composition of the alloy, on particle size and on ageing (recrystallization) processes. This has been demonstrated for a number of technically important alloys [121, 124]. That grain-boundary diffusion may not take place with a single activation energy has been shown with polycrystalline cadmium [125]. From the relationship between the diffusion velocity and the extent of plastic deformation it is possible to throw light on this process [126].

From the speed of diffusion in liquid binary alloys the presence of compounds may be inferred, since for the alloy compositions corresponding to true compounds the diffusion velocities of the components will show minima, and their activation energies maxima. Thus, the diffusion of iron in liquid iron–nickel and iron–molybdenum alloys has been measured [127]. Further investigations of diffusion in liquid metals [10, 282 to 284, 299] and the interesting phenomenon of two-dimensional diffusion in metal surfaces [10, 134, 285–288, 358, 359] can only be mentioned here.

Critical tables of the velocities of self-diffusion and foreign-atom diffusion obtained by radiochemical methods, including velocities of lattice, grain-boundary and liquid diffusion are found in the book by Leymonie [10].

In some interesting experiments the mass of the diffusing isotope was altered, while all other conditions were kept identical. The simultaneous diffusion of iron-55 and iron-59 in the same test bodies of copper or silver was measured, and an attempt was made to use the observed small difference to arrive at a mechanism of diffusion [94].

The methods of measuring diffusion in metals may be applied to the study of the electrical (electrolytic) transport of substances in alloys, such as that of carbon, iron, chromium, molybdenum and tungsten in steel. It has been shown that the dissolved carbon in austenite is transported to the cathode, and the charge on the carbon ion has been calculated [107].

8.3. Composition of Alloy Phases

The affinities with which alloy constituents are bound may be determined from their partial pressures. This quantity may be determined in a very sensitive way by labelling the element (see p. 194). But even with such techniques measurements are mostly restricted to high temperatures.

The use of autoradiography to determine the distribution of labelled elements over larger pieces of metal (macro-distribution) has already been mentioned in Sections 8.1.2–8.1.4. Autoradiography is also eminently suitable for detecting and measuring segregation in alloys, that is the micro-distribution of the elements over the various phases [2, 10, 114, 129, 130, 132, 274, 297, 306, 311].

Fine-grained emulsions may be applied to a ground surface of the alloy either in the form of a liquid or as stripping film. Often it is an advantage to leave the emulsion permanently bonded to the surface, and to develop and fix the autoradiograph *in situ*. Interposition of a thin protecting layer between the sample and the emulsion is recommended to prevent chemical action of the metal on the emulsion. After fixing, the etched figures may be compared directly with the autoradiograph. Because of the smallness of depth of focus of the microscope, the metal surface and the autoradiograph may be observed separately.

It is also possible to detach inclusions from ground metal surfaces by etching techniques similar to those used in electron microscopy [130]. The inclusions released in this manner can then be irradiated separately and studied subsequently by autoradiography.

Since the resolving power of autoradiography is reduced by the fact that the radiation comes from various depths of the sample, thin layers should be used [132], or else only a thin surface layer should be activated. This can be done by dipping the ground surface into a solution of radioactive ions, which are selectively adsorbed on one of the phases [133]. It is also possible to utilize selective adsorption from the gas phase [134]. (Such activation by adsorption may, of course, be applied equally well to mineral surfaces.) The heating of alloys activated by adsorption may be tested. The active substance will diffuse more rapidly in "softer" than in "harder" phases. When a surface layer is then removed, only the "soft" phases show appreciable activity.

In 1933 Tammann [135] determined the solubility of lead in metals by saturation with labelled lead and autoradiography. Lead was found to be soluble to a considerable extent in thallium and magnesium, while with tin, bismuth and gold it accumulated preferentially at the grain boundaries. It remained in these sites when the metals underwent changes in crystal structure. When iron crystallizes, the lead separates out with the impurities, while on crystallization of aluminium the lead goes with the aluminium oxide [133]. Tungsten has been found to accumulate at the grain boundaries of its alloys with nickel and chromium [61]. The distribution of phosphorus [123, 137] and of copper, chromium, manganese, tungsten and molybdenum [138] in steels has been studied by these methods. With radiosodium it has been shown that a small addition of sodium to aluminium–silicon alloys is taken up without being segregated in subsequent heat treatment [140], though segregation does occur on larger additions [139].

Small contents of lead have deleterious effects in the rolling of austenitic stainless steel. To investigate the part played by the lead, ground surfaces of steel-containing radiolead were submitted to autoradiography [135, 141, 142]. The etched surface was then compared with the autoradiograph. The lead was found between the dendrites, that is, in the portion of the steel which crystallized last. The lead appeared practically pure in spots. The specific activity of the lead being known, the size of these lead grains could be estimated by counting the α-rays emitted by them. The diameter was found to be about 1 μ. The α-rays observed were actually emitted from the daughter products (thorium C and thorium C′) of the lead isotope used for labelling, thorium B.

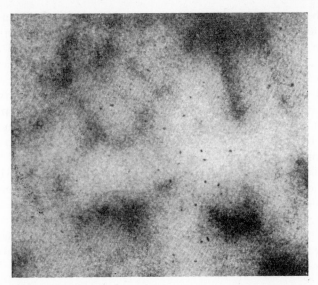

FIG. 32. Distribution of copper in an aluminium–copper alloy containing 4 per cent copper. Irradiation with neutrons, followed by autoradiography (after the decay of the activity induced in the aluminium). The dark spots correspond to copper-rich zones. Magnification: 50× (A.B. MICHAEL and M.B. BEVER, *Trans. Amer. Inst. Min. Met. Engrs.* **200**, 47 (1954))

It is often an advantage not to add radionuclides to the metal melts, nor to treat the samples with radionuclides, but to activate the finished samples by nuclear reactions, so using a form of activation analysis (see p. 93). This technique is, for example, useful when the element to be studied has only short-lived radioisotopes, and its distribution must be investigated in samples crystallizing only slowly. Activation with

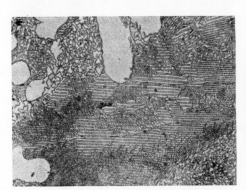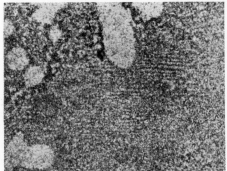

FIG. 33. Distribution of boron in steel. Photographic record of the nuclear reaction
$$^{10}B(n, \alpha)\,^{7}Li$$
Left: microphotograph of the etched surface.
Right: photographic record of the nuclear reaction on the same part of the surface.
Magnification: 147× [148]

neutrons has been used to study the distribution of aluminium in silicon [143], and of tungsten in alloys containing nickel and chromium, or cobalt and chromium [144]. Phases rich in copper [145] or zinc [146] have also been examined by activation (Fig. 32). The activation can in certain cases also be carried out with energetic photons from a betatron [147] (see Section 6.6.7).

The distribution of boron, which has no useful radioisotopes, has been determined in alloys with iron by pressing a ground surface against a photographic plate and submitting this combination to slow neutrons. Through the nuclear reaction $^{10}B(n, \alpha)$ ^{7}Li, fast ions are produced, and the emulsion is blackened (Fig. 33; see also p. 95). In this way it has been found that boron is practically insoluble in iron, and that it occurs mainly in the form of the compound Fe_2B or as the eutectic mixture [148, 149].

With suitable techniques the distribution of several elements in the same sample can be determined. Elements activated at the same time can often be distinguished by choosing a suitable activation time and "cooling" time after the end of irradiation [147]. It is also possible to detect one or more elements in a sample by previous labelling, and then to locate further elements by activation after the decay of the added tracers.

8.4. Abrasion and Wear of Metals

The products of the metallurgical industry are subject both to mechanical and to chemical attack. Both kinds of attack may be studied with radioactive tracers. Reviews of these types of investigation have been published [3, 150–152, 378].

Wear arises when solid surfaces rub against each other. Tracer methods are well suited to the investigation of these processes. In the first place, because of the great sensitivity of detection, the transfer of extremely small quantities of radioactive metal (down to fractions of a microgram) from one surface to another may be determined and measured. Because of this sensitivity, results are obtained within a short time. In the second place, it is possible to measure the transfer of material from one surface to another which is chemically identical. This is impossible by other methods. Such measurements are of great technical importance, the measurement of the transfer between two iron parts being an obvious example.

The metal can be activated before the piece to be tested is shaped. More frequently, the piece is first prepared and is then covered with an active surface layer, e.g., by an electrolytic procedure [153]. In many cases the piece may also be simply dipped into a radioactive bath. If the bath contains radioactive ions isotopic with those of the metal of the piece, labelling occurs through local exchange (see p. 176). Deposition of material vaporized in electric arcs has also been suggested. By tempering, diffusion of the isotope into the metal may be speeded up. Labelled surface layers of different composition may also be applied, for example by dipping iron into a radioactive phosphate solution [154]. In certain cases a radioactive metallic test piece may be inserted into the metal. Finally, it is possible to activate the completed piece as a whole with neutrons. This method is particularly useful for complicated shapes. For a survey of methods of activation see references [301, 321].

The material transferred may be measured by ordinary counting methods, or, if a direct picture of distribution rather than great accuracy is wanted, by autoradiography. Instead of measuring the surface, the activity of circulating lubricants may be measured, if these are employed (Section 8.4.3).

8.4.1. *Investigations on Models with Simple Surfaces*

For fundamental research into friction and wear careful removal of impurities from the surfaces is needed. It has been shown with tracers that some substances, such as fatty acids, cling very tenaciously to metal surfaces [313].

In experiments designed to elucidate the fundamentals of wear processes, radioactively labelled flat surfaces over which small spheres or hemispheres of various materials could be slid (not rolled) have been used [155]. The pressure on the spheres and the rate of movement could be varied. When a radioactive copper–beryllium alloy was used as the flat surface, the transfer of as little as 10^{-10} g of copper to the rider could be measured. The amount of material transferred was proportional to the load and to the distance of travel. Even riders made of materials as soft as lead or cadmium take up radiocopper. Clearly material transfer occurs in both directions.

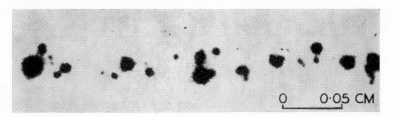

Fig. 34. Autoradiograph of radioactively labelled metal transferred by friction. (A radioactive copper point was drawn over a steel surface [161])

In other experiments inactive base surfaces (steel, copper or lead) were used, while the rider was radioactive [156, 157]. It was found that the transfer of material depends to a large extent on the pre-treatment of the surface, in particular on the manner of polishing. A certain amount of transfer may be observed already when the sphere is pressed against the base without being moved. Autoradiography of the surface after displacing the sphere tangentially along the surface confirms the older opinion that the movement of the metal is not strictly continuous, but takes place intermittently in small jumps (see Fig. 34). Through good lubrication these jumps can to a large extent be avoided, and a great reduction in the transfer of metal may be achieved [155, 156, 158, 159].

These results suggest [298, 302, 319] that local welds are formed and subsequently broken down when relatively soft metals are rubbed against each other in the absence of a lubricant. On the other hand, hard test pieces which are inadequately polished "plough" through a softer plate, breaking out pieces. An important part is also played by oxidation through local overheating.

From the sizes of the radioactive spots on the plate, it has been possible to determine the size distribution of the metal pieces broken away. In experiments with a copper test sphere and a steel plate (see Fig. 34) about 10^{-7} g was found to be the most commonly occurring weight [160, 161]. It was concluded that the most frequent diameter of the local welds is about 4×10^{-4} cm. The smaller particles are most numerous, but the larger ones make the major contribution to wear. In the same group of experiments a linear relationship was found between the amount of copper worn away and the pressure. Increase in pressure primarily increases the number of welds and their sizes only secondarily [162].

It should be pointed out that measurements of friction do not give satisfactory information on wear. Two lubricants, which reduce friction to the same extent, can have quite different protective effects on the metal. In one case, a reduction in the coefficient of friction by a factor of 5 corresponded to a decrease in wear by a factor of 400. Clearly in technical practice wear is a greater danger than friction. Measurement of wear therefore gives more significant information about the quality of lubricating oils and the suitability of additives than can be obtained by measurement of friction.

Special equipment has been constructed for the determination of the thickness of layers of radioactive lubricating oils by radiation measurement. The main result of one such investigation was that the viscosity of the oil affected the layer thickness directly only when all other factors were held constant, and that even this effect diminished as the layer thickness was reduced [165].

Some of the work mentioned [160, 164] and also other work [163, 166–168, 319] has been concerned with the mechanism of the formation of the surface layers responsible for lubrication. The more noble metals tend to physical adsorption of hydrocarbons, fatty acids, alcohols and esters, while less noble metals, such as zinc, cadmium and copper, combine with fatty acids chemically. On treating labelled base metals with a fatty acid as a lubricant, a unimolecular layer of radioactive soap is formed, which may subsequently be removed by suitable solvents. No active material is removed after similar treatment of the noble metal, or from any metal after treatment with alcohols. Alternatively, the reaction of lubricants with the surface may be studied with inactive metals and labelled lubricants. After the treatment the excess of lubricant is dissolved away, and the surface submitted to autoradiography [169]. These methods are so sensitive that even a unimolecular layer on a surface area of 1 mm^2 can be detected.

The results obtained with radioactive metal surfaces are in good agreement with those obtained by electron diffraction and friction measurements. In particular, it has been found that good lubrication and minimum wear are obtained with lubricant molecules containing polar groups, but these are only effective below a certain transition temperature. This transition temperature lies near the melting point of the lubricant, or the melting point of the soap formed by reaction with the metal.

Experiments with labelled sodium-24 stearate have been used to study lubrication under extreme pressures, as in drawing steel rods. By increasing the pressure, the thickness of the layer was gradually reduced from 1000 to 600 Å. This latter thickness corresponds to the unevenness of the surface [270].

Additives facilitate the formation of firmly held surface layers of oil on metals (or glass). For example, with sulphonated olefins a thin transparent lubricant layer is obtained, which persists even after treatment with solvents. According to experiments with radiosulphur, the surface layer is formed at room temperature in the course of a few days, but more rapidly on warming [170]. The favourable effect of these additives may well depend on several factors, including prevention of immediate contact between oil and metal and therefore of catalytic decomposition of the oil by the metal.

The uptake of radionuclides (^{14}C, ^{32}P, ^{35}S, ^{65}Zn) by metals from additives has been determined under operating conditions [353, 356]. The conditions at the teeth of operating gear wheels were simulated by heating a wire intermittently with an electric current to 700 °C while the mass of the lubricant remained at a lower temperature [271].

8.4.2. *Investigations of Metal Working Processes*

Dies of cemented carbide (tungsten carbide with cobalt) have been investigated [175]. Copper wire drawn through activated dies was examined by autoradiography or by winding it around a wall type counting tube. In the latter case only the total activity could be measured, and no information about the distribution of activity along the wire was obtained. It was found that with respect to cobalt the wear took place uniformly, while the tungsten was torn from the die in fragments. Within certain limits, the rate of drawing had only a slight effect. Wear amounted to 10^{-7}–10^{-8} g/m. By this method information about the behaviour of a particular tool is obtained within a few minutes. Other methods are very protracted. In another investigation, the influence of various lubricants in the drawing of steel wire was investigated (cobalt-60) [312, 322].

In connection with the drawing of seamless tubes, the behaviour of a lubricant consisting of sodium stearate has been studied after activating the sodium with neutrons. An amount of lubricant corresponding to less than a unimolecular layer could be determined [270] (see p. 172).

Other work has been concerned with the wear of tools of metal working machines [151, 184, 200–205]. Carbide tips were activated in a reactor. Mainly cobalt-60, tungsten-185, tungsten-187 and tantalum-182 were formed. (Tungsten-187 is γ-active and decays rapidly. For studying the transfer of tungsten it is therefore convenient to wait until this nuclide has decayed, and then to measure only the β-active tungsten-185 [207].) Measurements of the activity of the turnings, for which a counting tube or, preferably, a scintillation counter is used, may be carried out within a few seconds after the machine has started. The saving of time compared with other procedures for measuring wear is therefore very great. In the course of this work it has been shown that considerable local welding of the tool with the piece is unavoidable, even when a good cutting oil such as carbon tetrachloride is used. The radioactive substance torn away remains on the turnings to the extent of at least 95 per cent. By this method the quality of the cemented carbide and of the cutting oil as well as the suitability of the tool shape are tested. The dependence of wear on the cutting speed may also be observed. In the case of some steels it was found that wear was diminished when the speed was increased from 25 to 100–200 m/sec, while above this latter value a new increase in wear occurred [61]. Wear depends greatly on the chemical or mechanical pre-treatment of the object being worked. Thus, the treatment of copper with fine glass paper increased the wear of the tool, while application of protective layers diminished it [209]. Wear on metal cutters and punches has also been measured after activation of the tools [210, 315].

The grinding and polishing of metals has been studied with tracers. Scratches on metal surfaces may be detected by a method derived from older procedures, in which the surface was treated with a fluorescent material. The surface is rubbed with a radioactive paste, then cleaned carefully with cloth, and finally submitted to autoradiography. The paste in the scratches then shows up by fine lines [272].

Cracks may be revealed by dipping the object into active solutions, or, in the case of larger objects, by brushing them with such solutions [211–213]. Solutions of radium salts or alcoholic solutions of radiocaesium chloride are suitable. After immersion for a few minutes, the solution is evaporated, the surface lightly polished to remove the excess of radioactive substance, and the sample autoradiographed. From the extent of the blackening, the depth of the crack is estimated. Even cracks with a depth of only 10^{-4} cm, not detectable under a microscope, yield to this procedure, which is in any case less tedious than the microscopic method.

The porosity of magnesium alloys was determined similarly by autoradiography after treatment with oil containing palladium-109; pores as small as $1·5 \times 10^{-5}$ cm^2 were detected [213]. In a method for finding holes in protective layers (titanium dioxide on aluminium, or chromium on iron) the reaction of the underlying metal with radioactive sulphur dioxide is employed; sulphur-35 is taken up by the base [214]. Other methods depend on the exchange between an underlying metal previously made radioactive and a solution of the same substance [215].

8.4.3. *Investigations on Machines under Operating Conditions*

The possibility of continuous automatic measurement of wear in machines on testing stands, or even during actual operation, is of particular importance, since in this way the operation of the machine is not disturbed. Studies on automobiles in motion are a good example. Because of the high sensitivity of radiation detection, results are obtained in a very short time, and the measurements are therefore economical. Furthermore, the change in wear due to changes in working conditions may be observed. A further saving in time and cost results from the fact that the machine need not be dismantled to carry out the measurements, and the possibility of faults arising in dismantling or subsequent re-assembly is eliminated. Various methods of activation are available (see p. 170).

Such studies of wear under working conditions involve the measurement of the radiation from particles detached during operation, and transported out of the machine [171–173, 208]. The measurements may, for example, be carried out directly on the oil in a closed circuit system [367, 368], or on the metal dust removed from the oil by filtration [172]. When testing the oil, the detector (scintillator) must be protected against heat (see [354]). The sensitivity of wear detection is improved if the oil flowing back to the sump is used for measurement rather than that present in the sump [186]. Arrangements can be made for a signal to be given automatically as soon as the wear reaches a certain point [174]. By labelling different parts of the motor with different isotopes, which can be distinguished with the scintillation spectrometer, wear of these parts can be followed simultaneously [355].

Wear of piston rings has been examined after activation with a layer of radioactive chromium or zinc [150, 177, 178], or by inserting pieces of radioactive metal, such as zinc or cobalt [179]. The strongest radioactivity due to the chromium or zinc was found on the cylinder wall near the upper limit of the ring travel. This may be connected with the fact that the smallest quantity of lubricant is found at this point. When three activated piston rings were employed simultaneously, the deposits due to them were seen separately in the autoradiograph [177].

Piston rings may also be activated as a whole by neutron irradiation [150, 164, 178, 179, 181–185, 307, 329, 333], among other nuclides (often cobalt-60) iron-55 and iron-59 being formed. Instead of activating the piston rings, portions of the cylinder wall may be labelled [168]; this method has also been applied to diesel motors [189]. By mounting the equipment on a car, the influence of various conditions on wear may be determined directly, such as change from city to country driving [186, 353]. The presence of sulphur in the fuel has been found to increase the wear of engines considerably [164]. Up to one-third per cent of radiosulphur originally present in diesel oil was detected, after combustion, as sulphur dioxide in the lubricant [196]. The effect of the quality of the lubricating oil on wear was tested with labelled piston rings [185, 187] (see p. 172).

For determining oil consumption, the oil or one of its components has been labelled with tritium [190] or zinc [189]; in the latter case an additive containing radiozinc was used. Activity measurements were performed on the exhaust gas or on a filter collecting the dust from this gas.

Studies under normal working conditions have also been performed on entire transmission gears. The activity of the lubricating oils due to radioiron or radiochromium has been determined continuously [191, 369]. Wear in ball-bearings [150, 192, 193, 308] and also of steel balls in ball mills [194] has been examined. In the case of bearing metals it has been found, as expected, that wear is much increased by dust in the lubricating oil [195].

If continuous control of the activity of the oil is not required, radioactive engine parts need not be used. The oil can be subsequently activated with neutrons, and the activity induced in the metallic wear particles measured [147]. Costs of activating engine parts and of any radiation protection measures in the test area are thereby saved.

Methods for the determination of deposit formation in internal combustion engines have been developed. The thickness of the deposits may be obtained by measuring the attenuation of nuclear radiations emitted from the surface under investigation. Depending on the thickness of the deposit expected, the surface (or more usually a plug inserted into the surface) is activated with emitters of more or less penetrating radiation. The deposition in the combustion chamber, in the intake lead and in the carburettor under various operating conditions may be found. A window counter may be used [197].

A different technique has been used to locate carbonaceous deposits and to find their origin. Either the lubricant or the fuel (or only a component of the fuel) was made radioactive. After the test period, the engine was dismantled, the carbon from various parts burned, and the activity of the carbon dioxide measured with an ionization chamber [303].

After introduction of radiolead into lead tetraethyl used as an anti-knock agent, lead deposited in the cylinder of a petrol engine may be located, and the quality of additives designed to prevent such deposition tested [198]. Ethylene chloride proved effective. Moreover, the distribution of the fuel over the cylinders of an internal combustion engine was measured. The fuel was labelled with radiocarbon, and the activity of samples of the combustion gases from the different cylinders was measured. Because of the danger of affecting the operation of the engine, the analysis of the total exhaust gas from the cylinders had not been considered satisfactory [199]. Tests of the effectiveness of air filters for engines will be discussed on p. 226.

The wear in the bearings of water turbines in relation to the working conditions has been determined through the activity of the metal dust held back by special filters [176]. The wear of the nose cone of rockets on passage through air has been followed in this way: 1 mc radiocobalt was added to the coating material, and the γ-radiation measured during the flight by means of a scintillation counter, the count rate being transmitted by radio [273]. Similarly, the wear of space rockets due to micrometeorites could be determined by making the rocket shell radioactive, and deducing the loss of material from the reduction in activity during flight [216].

8.5. Corrosion and Scaling of Metals

Reviews of the application of radioactivity to studies of corrosion have been given [2,10, 217, 277, 334].

The experiment of Hevesy described on p. 66 contributed greatly to an understanding of the chemical corrosion of metals, revealing the surprising extent of recrystallization under the influence of an aqueous solution of the ions. The exchange of lead between a metal foil and a solution of its ions took place so rapidly that in the course of a few minutes the lead initially present in solution penetrated several hundred atomic layers deep into the metal. Since diffusion is far too slow to account for so rapid a penetration process, it has been concluded that the formation of local galvanic elements must be responsible. Metallic lead goes into solution wherever, owing to lattice distortion etc., it is particularly reactive and therefore shows a greater tendency to give off electrons. Consequently the foil acquires a negative surface charge. Lead ions are therefore attracted from the solution and are taken up into stable positions (positions of larger binding energy, and therefore lower chemical reactivity) on the lead surface. Presumably the attack on metals by other solutions than those of their own ions is also influenced by the existence of more or less reactive spots on the metal surface. In particular, Haissinsky has stressed the importance of differences in the chemical reactivity at various places of the same metal surface [217–219].

Quantitative factors have been investigated [2, 217–219]. It has been found that the exchange rate depends on a number of variables, including surface condition, temperature, acidity and concentration. Simultaneous corrosion of the metal caused by adding acid to the solution increases the rate of exchange of the metal ions. It is remarkable that the rate of exchange and its temperature coefficient depend strongly on the nature of the anion. Thus, radiocopper is deposited, under certain conditions, from a bromide solution a hundred times faster than from an acetate solution [277 to 279].

If metal surfaces are so lacking in uniformity that large regions have greater or smaller reactivity than others, the zones may be revealed by treatment with a solution of radioactive ions of the same element, and subsequent scanning with a counter or application of autoradiography [217, 220, 221, 279]. It is also possible to use ions of more noble metals for this purpose, and it will be indicated on p. 196 that even ions which are less noble than the metal under investigation may be adsorbed on the surface in traces.

The elucidation of corrosion in multi-phase systems is facilitated by autoradiography. Thus, an alloy of zinc, lead and aluminium was treated with radiolead, which accumulated at the grain boundaries. The maximum corrosion (in this case due to water vapour) occurred in the boundary layers, so that the autoradiograph coincided with the "corrosion picture" [222].

The corrosion of aluminium has been examined with radioactive tracers [223]. The following method was used to show the nature of the process at a single localized corrosion pit: After treatment with phosphoric acid, the test sample was introduced into mains water containing chloride which served as the corroding liquid, and corrosion was initiated at a number of places by damaging the surface with a needle. The samples were then kept for several hours or days in the water. Finally they were placed for 10 min in a solution containing cobalt-60 or lead-210 (radium D), and washed. The distribution of the radionuclide plated out was then determined by autoradiography. The pits were found to be surrounded by rings where deposition had occurred. They were followed by outer rings where no radioelement had been taken up. This was clearly due to the rapid formation of a protective layer of aluminium hydroxide.

Starting from the assumption that the formation of sulphide surface layers takes place in a way similar to that of oxide layers, the reaction of copper and platinum with aqueous solutions of thiourea has been studied radiochemically [238]. The corrosion of metals by hydrogen sulphide (^{35}S) has also been examined [239–241].

Layers developed for corrosion resistance have been investigated with tracers. The adsorption of radiochromium as chromate by surfaces of metallic chromium or iron surfaces was studied with a view to obtaining information about passivation [2, 10, 224–226, 236, 377]. At low chromate concentrations, insufficient to produce passivity, chromate taken up is distributed irregularly, and much of it may be wiped off. In contrast, at concentrations sufficient to produce passivity, a uniform and tenaciously held chromium-containing layer is formed, this deposited chromium not exchanging with chromium in solution in either the ter- or hexavalent form. The kinetics of passivation were examined in the presence or absence of oxygen, and after preheating in air. Anions (sulphate, chloride and hydroxide) compete with chromate ions for adsorption sites on the surface. In further investigations with radiophosphorus, the nature of the films formed on iron in passivation with phosphate was studied [350, 351].

It had been predicted on theoretical grounds that pertechnate in aqueous solution would act as a corrosion inhibitor. This prediction has been experimentally confirmed by following the formation of the protective layer through activity measurements [231, 232]. The results obtained with chromate, pertechnate, sulphate and perrhenate (negative in the cases of sulphate and perrhenate) may well be used as a starting point for a general theory of passivation by anions [10, 232].

In a special method for detecting passivity, a surface layer of about 1 $\mu g/cm^2$ was labelled through bombardment with radon or xenon-131 by means of a high frequency discharge between the sample and an auxiliary electrode. The radionuclides entered the surface and were held there. The surface activity was then measured, by counting or autoradiography, before and after treatment with corrosive agents [227] (see also p. 201). This principle has been used to examine the passivation of iron or zinc by chromate.

Activation analysis has advantages for determining the thickness of protective layers, such as those produced by electroplating. This applies particularly when the activity induced in the base is slight or is easily eliminated during measurement, making non-destructive determination possible (see p. 83).

It has already been mentioned that corrosion in engines may be decreased by adding inhibitors to the oil. With labelled additives (sulphur-35, phosphorus-32, carbon-14) the growth of the protective layers may be followed, as has been done in the study of lubrication [13, 183, 228, 229] (p. 172). The part played by carbon disulphide in preventing corrosion in fire-extinguishers made of brass and containing carbon tetrachloride has been elucidated; it has been shown using labelled carbon disulphide that even small additions of this compound, accompanied by small amounts of alcohol give firmly adhering surface layers [15]. To gain a better understanding of the mechanisms of their action, the thickness of surface layers of various corrosion inhibitors, including vapour phase inhibitors, on metal surfaces has also been measured radiochemically [277, 361].

Zirconium reduces the corrosion of steel by liquid bismuth. This is important for the LMFR-reactor, where liquid nuclear fuel is employed. It has been found using radio-zirconium that the surface of the metal is covered by a layer of zirconium carbide or nitride [230].

A number of tracer investigations on the formation of oxide or sulphide layers on metals started from the theory of Wagner that the growth of the layers is determined by the movement of cations and anions across the layers. The method used is similar to that employed for studying diffusion in solids, the progress of diffusion being followed by sectioning or by absorption methods. However, in the heterogeneous system consisting of metal base and oxide layer the preparation of reproducible test samples is difficult, and a further problem arises from the fact that oxygen can only be labelled with the stable isotope oxygen-18 [10, 277, 278].

Radionuclides have been used to study the oxidation of metals by oxygen gas [2, 87, 233]. In one investigation [136], a radioactive platinum salt was applied in several thin streaks across both faces of thin discs of cobalt. The discs were then oxidized almost to completion at 1200°C in pure oxygen. After oxidation, they were mounted and sectioned, and autoradiographs were taken to locate the chemically inert platinum. It has been concluded that the cobalt is oxidized by outward diffusion of cobalt metal through the oxide.

Another experimental technique led to similar results. The metal (copper) was covered by a chemically identical radioactive surface layer and oxidized by heating. The oxide layer was then dissolved off step by step, and the activity measured each time [234, 235, 237].

Investigations of the growth of a sulphide layer on brass placed in liquid sulphur at 444 °C with radiosulphur and radiozinc have led to the conclusion that outward diffusion of copper ions and electrons through lattice defects in the copper sulphide and inward diffusion of sulphur through cracks in the sulphide layer are the mechanisms responsible for this growth [280]. The formation of nickel sulphide in sulphur vapour at 600 °C depends only on the diffusion of nickel ions [281]. The growth of sulphide layers on silver exposed to liquid sulphur has also been investigated with tracers [304].

In other work with radiosulphur in various chemical forms, and as a gas, the competition between sulphur and oxygen in the corrosion of iron was studied, and it is reported that sulphur will attack only surfaces free from oxygen. The fixation of the sulphur depended on the orientation of the iron crystals. Three stages of attack were observed: a physical stage where adsorption is easily reversed; chemisorption of a nearly monoatomic layer; and finally chemical reaction, or corrosion in the strict sense [357].

8.6. The Electrical Industries

Tracer tests for air- und liquid-tightness will be discussed more generally in Section 9.3.6, but we will mention here some procedures useful in the electrical industries-

At certain distances, repeaters (electronic amplifiers) are built into submarine cables. The repeaters are housed in pressure-proof steel shells of 8–15 mm thickness. These shells and the glands by which the cables enter were tested for water-tightness by exposing them to a soda solution activated with 50 mc of sodium-24 for 5 hr at 400 atm [242]. After the treatment they were washed thoroughly with inactive soda solution and the residual activity, due to any sodium which had penetrated the shell, was measured. The insulating glass beads contained in the equipment had been protected by coating against uptake of radiosodium through exchange.

Alternatively, these repeaters were tested by placing them in water containing tritium (5 mc/ml), and applying high pressure. This method is reported to be so sensitive that any leaks which would disturb the operation of the unit during the assumed time of service (20 years) are revealed within one hour [243, 305].

Similar tests of tightness on hermetically sealed relays, amplifying tubes, transistors, etc., have been carried out with labelled gases, in particular with krypton-85. Many similar units are exposed simultaneously to the gas, surface absorption of the gas being prevented by removal of grease. The sensitivity of the method is impressive. Instead of determining the penetration of the gas into the units, the loss of labelled gas from the units after prior introduction may be measured, but this procedure is usually less convenient [244, 245].

Jute-covered, lead-clad telephone cables, which are laid in the ground and filled with nitrogen, have been tested for leaks. The lead cladding must be moisture-proof. For testing, the cables are usually put under pressure, but additional tests may be made with a radioactive gas. Although xenon-135, which was tried first, has a suitable half-life and emits sufficiently penetrating radiation, it is not really suitable for such tests. It escapes too quickly from the ground, and therefore cannot be measured with sufficient sensitivity. Methyl bromide labelled with radiobromine has, however, been found suitable. The test is carried out by burying the cable in the ground and searching the surrounding earth for activity with a portable instrument after flushing the cable with inactive nitrogen. The activity developed at faulty places is so great that the measurement can be carried out while walking briskly [242]. More recently, the use of radon for the same purpose has been described, and it is reported that the radon is retained sufficiently by moist earth [246, 305].

Radionuclides may also be used in investigating amplifier tubes where the behaviour of the cathode is determined by the evaporation of strontium oxide. The vapour pressure (P) was determined, at temperatures (T) between 1290° and 1650°K, by collecting the radiostrontium evaporated from a platinum wire and measuring its activity [247]. The pressure (in atm) followed the equation:

$$\log_{10} P = 1\cdot44 + 1\cdot908 \log T - 25950/T.$$

The dependence of the evaporation on the strength of the emission current and on the age of the oxide cathode was also determined [248] (see also [352]). In other investigations, the behaviour of very thin layers of oxides of the alkaline earths, used to depress the work function for electron emission at the cathode, has been studied. In particular, the undesirable spreading of labelled strontium and barium to other parts of the tube was followed [249, 250], by finding where the decomposition products of components of the amplifying tube were deposited [251]. With radioactive carbon dioxide the parts of a cathode ray tube which take up traces of this gas [252] have been identified.

Tungsten spirals used for heating cathodes are covered by cataphoresis with aluminium oxide for insulation. The alumina particles, suspended in methanol, are given a positive charge by the addition of tervalent cations. The adsorption of these ions by the alumina has been investigated with radiocerium [250]. The thickness of thin layers deposited from vapours (such as antimony [253], bismuth [254], and gold [255]) which find application in the electrical industries has been determined with high sensitivity by labelling these elements to a known specific activity. Alternatively, activation analysis or absorption analysis may be used (see Chapter 6). For example, silver coatings with thicknesses around 0·0025 mm have been measured by activation [256].

The presence of very small quantities of arsenic and antimony is of great significance for the electrical properties of the semi-conductor germanium, which is used in transistors. These and other impurities may be determined by activation (see p. 94). The distribution of antimony in germanium bars has been obtained autoradiographically after radioactive labelling of the antimony, and the antimony was found to be concentrated in those parts of the bar which crystallize last [250, 257, 275]. In a further investigation [258], the uptake of traces of metal from a graphite crucible by molten germanium was measured after irradiation of the graphite with neutrons. The distribution coefficient of indium between liquid and solid germanium has been determined using radioindium [259].

The phosphorus present as impurity in extremely pure silicon for use in transistors has been estimated by indicator analysis, using activity measurements after labelling of the phosphorus, while arsenic or iodine have been determined by activation analysis [260].

Investigations have been carried out on the foreign atoms entering germanium during the formation of point transistors [261]. Practically carrier-free gold-199 was deposited on the pointed end of a tungsten wire and this wire was then built into the transistor. After the formation of the transistor the amount of gold introduced was determined with a counter, and the distribution of the gold by autoradiography.

Phosphors sensitive to infrared radiation usually consist of alkaline earth sulphides or selenides, and contain traces of certain rare earth elements as activators. They are prepared by crystallization from salt melts to which the activator is added. The amount of rare earths in the crystal is, however, so small that it can be determined only approximately by ordinary analytical methods. With radioactive rare earths, especially europium, accurate assay has proved possible [262–264]. Melt and crystals were separated by filtration at a high temperature, and the activity of the crystals was measured. Activation analysis may also be used to detect small amounts of activators and impurities in inorganic phosphors [265].

It has been shown with tracers that about one-third of the electrical conductivity in condenser paper is due to ionic conduction [266]. For this purpose, paper sheets were activated by dipping into solutions of radioactive rubidium carbonate, a fraction of the ions previously bound to the carboxyl groups of the cellulose being replaced by rubidium. After the excess of the uncombined rubidium had been washed out and the paper sheet had been dried, it was inserted between inactive sheets. The stack so obtained was submitted to a d.c. potential, and the current was simultaneously measured. The activity found in the initially inactive sheets, together with the known specific activity, provided an approximate value for the ionic current. A knowledge of this phenomenon also assists in understanding the electrical breakdown, and it has been found that the resistance against it is improved by acid pre-treatment of the paper [267].

Irregularities in the distribution of iron in recording tapes with a plastic (polyethylene or polyester) base can be determined after activation by autoradiography [268].

Labelled organic acids have been used to elucidate the part played by such substances in the decomposition of transformer oils. It was found that the acids enter into resinous products to a considerable extent, but that graphite powder removes much of the acids from oils by adsorption [269].

Work on electrometallurgical (p. 163) and other electrochemical production problems (p. 210), as well as studies on accumulators (p. 210) and on electroplating (p. 210), will be discussed elsewhere in this book.

References to Chapter 8

1. I.S.KULIKOV and I.A.POPOV, *Radioactive Isotopes in Metallurgy* (Russ.), Moscow 1957; German translation, Berlin 1959.
2. See M.T.SIMNAD, *Int. J. Appl. Rad. Isot.* **1**, 145 (1956); Geneva Report 803 (1958), vol 19, p. 193.
3. Russian Bibliography by H.MARTIN: *Atomkernenergie* **5**, 187 (1960).
4. N.A.BOGDANOV, V.L.REITBLAT, V.F.FUNKE and A.A.ZHUKHOVITSKII, *The Application of Radioactive Isotopes in Metallurgy* (Russ.), Moscow 1955.
5. E.W.VOICE, *Nucleonics* **9** (10), 13 (1951); *J. Iron Steel Inst.* **167**, 157 (1951).
6. A.M.SAMARIN, Geneva Report 707 (1955), vol. 15, p. 151.
7. U.A.LUOTO and E.G.ROTKIRCH, Geneva Report 1101 (1958), vol. 19, p. 28.
8. P.L.GRUZIN and S.V.ZEMSKII, *Zavod. Lab.* **22**, 169 (1959).
9. G.COURTOIS, R.HOURS, P.LECLERC and A.PONS, Copenhagen Report 88, Vol. 1, p. 405.
10. C.LEYMONIE, *Les traceurs radioactifs en métallurgie physique*, Paris 1960.
11. P.L.GRUZIN and A.A.MELIKYAN, see [6].
12. A.KOHN, Paris Report 194, vol. 1, p. 302.
13. A.V.TOPCHIEV, I.T.ALADIEV and P.S.SAVITSKY, Geneva Report 2308 (1958), vol. 19, p. 61.
14. YU.P.BELAEV, see *Nucleonics* **17** (11), 186 (1956).
15. S.E.EATON, Geneva Report 146 (1955), vol. 14, p. 61.
16. L.BOGDANDY and R.SCHMOLKE, *Stahl und Eisen* **77**, 685 (1957).
17. E.W.VOICE, *J. Iron Steel Inst.* **163**, 312 (1949); *Iron and Steel* **22**, 582 (1949).
18. E.W.VOICE, E.BELL and P.GLEDHILL, *J. Iron Steel Inst.* **177**, 423 (1954).
19. V.A.KRIVONOSOV, F.F.KOLESANOV and P.A.LUTIKOV, The Movement of Gases through Material in Lumps, in: *The Utilization of Radioactive Isotopes in Metallurgy* (Russ.), Moscow 1955.
20. T.SAITO, Geneva Report 1348 (1958), vol. 19, p. 201.
21. L.A.SCHWARZMAN, Paris Report 70, vol. 1, p. 609.
22. T.B.WINKLER and J.CHIPMAN, *Trans. Amer. Inst. Mining Metallurg. Engr.*, **167**, 111 (1946).
23. L.A.SHVARTSMAN and P.L.GRUZIN, in B.YA.LYUBOV (Ed.), *Problems of Metallurgy and Metal Physics* (Russ.), Moscow 1952.
24. I.A.TOMILIN and L.A.SHVARTSMAN, *Izvest. Akad. Nauk SSSR, Otd. Tekhn. Nauk* **1953**, 1797.
25. O.A.ESSIN and V.M.ZHIKHOV, *Doklady Akad. Nauk SSSR* **102**, 327, 583 (1955); Third Conference on the Physical Chemistry of Steel Production (Russ.), Moscow 1955.
26. V.F.SUROV, O.V.TRAVIN and L.A.SHVARTSMAN, *Ibid.*
27. A.N.MOROZOV and D.YA.POVOLOTSKII, *Ibid.*
28. L.A.SHVARTSMAN, I.A.TOMILIN, O.V.TRAVIN and I.A.POPOV, *Ibid.*
29. O.V.TRAVIN and L.A.SHVARTSMAN, *Ibid.*, and Moscow Atomic Energy Conference 1955, Session of the Technical Sciences Division, p. 48.
30. N.A.VATOLIN and E.A.VETRENKO, *Atomnaya Energiya* **4**, 603 (1958); *Kernenergie* **2**, 686 (1959).
31. S.N.STUPAR, *Stal* **17**, 707 (1957).
32. R.MAYORCAS and M.W.THRING, *Nature* **152**, 723 (1943).
33. A.I.OSIPOV, L.A.SHVARTSMAN, M.T.BULSKI and A.G.ALIMOV, *Stal* **15**, 709 (1955); see also [34].
34. A.I.OSIPOV, Conference on the Physical Chemistry of Steel Production (Russ.), Moscow 1955.
35. Report of the Ukrainian Metal Research Institute, 1954, see [6].
36. W.KOCH and K.FINK, *Arch. Eisenhüttenwesen* **22**, 371 (1951).
37. M.L.SAZONOV and L.A.SHVARTSMAN, *Int. J. Appl. Rad. Isot.* **7**, 311 (1960).
38. V.I.MALKIN and L.A.SHVARTSMAN, Third Conference on the Physical Chemistry of Steel Production (Russ.), Moscow 1955.
39. W.O.PHILBROOK, K.M.GOLDMAN and M.M.HELZEL, *J. Metals* **188**, 361 (1950).
40. H.ORNIG, *Atompraxis* **6**, 129 (1961).
41. M.M.KARNAUKHOV and S.K.CHUCHMAREV, *Izvest. Akad. Nauk SSSR, Otd. Tekhn. Nauk* **1953** (1), 82.
42. I.S.KULIKOV and A.A.ZHUKHOVITSKII, in: *The Production and Treatment of Steel* (Russ.), Moscow 1954.

43. A.I.Osipov, L.A.Shvartsman, V.E.Yudin and M.L.Sazonov, Moscow Atomic Energy Conference, 1955, Session of the Technical Sciences Division, p. 29.

44. N.G.Bogdanova, P.L.Gruzin, G.I.Yermolaev and I.D.Nikulinsky, Geneva Report 2218 (1958), vol. 19, p. 180.

45. W.Loorz and H.Weber, *Stahl und Eisen* **75**, 1241 (1955).

46. E.Eickworth, H.J.Kopineck and G.Opfer, *Stahl und Eisen* **76**, 1028 (1956).

47. M.M.Karnaukhov, A.N.Morozov and S.K.Chuchmarev, *Stal* **13**, 775 (1953).

48. A.I.Osipov et al., *Int. J. Appl. Rad. Isot.* **4**, 270 (1959).

49. A.I.Osipov, *Central Research Institute for Iron Metallurgy* (U.S.S.R.), 1952–1953.

50. V.I.Malkin and L.A.Schwarzman, Paris Report 69, vol. 1, p. 359.

51. J.Fodor and C.Varga, Geneva Report 2242 (1958), vol. 19, p. 231.

52. G.R.Church, W.C.Heselwood and G.A.Nicholson, *Nature* **179**, 1294 (1957).

53. K.G.Erwall and K.Ljunggren, Geneva Report 166 (1958), vol. 19, p. 3.

54. W.B.Frank and L.M.Foster, *J. Phys. Chem.* **61**, 1531 (1957).

55. S.I.Rempel, *Doklady Akad. Nauk SSSR* **103**, 107 (1955).

56. L.Bozoky and D.Vödrös, Geneva Report 1725 (1958), vol. 19, p. 237.

57. A.Pradzynski and Z.Orman, Copenhagen Report 118, vol. 1, p. 477.

58. J.L.Putman, *J. Inst. Met.* **82**, 414 (1953).

59. W.Gebauhr and A.Spang, *Angew. Chem.* **72**, 345 (1960).

60. P.Albert and J.Gaittet, Copenhagen Report 82, vol. 2, p. 243.

61. M.B.Neiman, *Priroda* **1954** (10).

62. W.H.T.Davison, Copenhagen Report 33, vol. 1, p. 251.

63. L.M.Jefimov, see [6].

64. C.Varga and J.Fodor, Geneva Report 2240 (1958), vol. 19, p. 235.

65. S.M.Gnuchev, Third Conference on the Physical Chemistry of Steel Production (Russ.), Moscow 1955.

66. S.M.Gnuchev and V.G.Kuklev, Moscow Atomic Energy Conference 1955, Session of the Technical Sciences Division, p. 69.

67. T.Saito et al., Paris Report 68, vol. 1, p. 362.

68. A.Kohn, *Metallurg. Rev.* **3**, 143 (1958).

69. V.A.Grigoryan and A.M.Samarin, *Izvest. Akad. Nauk SSSR, Otd. Tekhn. Nauk* **1955**, 91.

70. E.S.Kalinnikov and A.M.Samarin, Moscow Atomic Energy Conference 1955, Session of the Technical Sciences Division, p. 3.

71. Z.Bojarski, W.Orzeszko, S.Pawlowski, R.Wusatowski and Z.Ziolowski, Paris Report 71, vol. 1, p. 388.

72. C.Evans and J.Herrington, Copenhagen Report 39, vol. 2, p. 309.

73. See also S.Besnard and J.Talbot, Copenhagen Report 84, vol. 1, p. 207.

74. A.I.Chizhikov and V.K.Boyarshinov, *Zavod. Lab.* **23**, 11 (1957).

75. B.Brook, A.Zavyalov and G.Kapirin, Geneva Report 2236 (1958), vol. 19, p. 219.

76. W.Seith and A.Kottmann, *Angew. Chem.* **64**, 379 (1952).

77. R.Lindner and G.Johansson, *Acta Chem. Scand.* **4**, 307 (1950).

78. J.C.Hutter, *Bull. Soc. Chim. France* **1951**, D 45.

79. E.Broda and T.Schönfeld, see Chapter 6, ref. [1].

80. G.V.Kurdiumov, Geneva Report 702 (1955), vol. 15, p. 81.

81. A.A.Lbov, *Usp. Fiz. Nauk* **42**, 400 (1950).

82. P.L.Gruzin in: B.Ya.Lyubov (Ed.), *Problems of Metallurgy and Metal Physics* (Russ.), Moscow 1952, vol. 3, p. 201.

83. W.Seith, *Diffusion in Metallen*, Berlin 1955.

84. K.Hauffe, *Reaktionen in und an festen Stoffen*, Berlin 1955, pp. 346–350, 383–401.

85. L.Slifkin, D.Lazarus and C.Tomizuka, *J. Appl. Phys.* **23**, 1032 (1952).

86. D.Lazarus, Geneva Report 834 (1958), vol. 20, p. 108.

87. M.T.Simnad, *Ind. Eng. Chem.* **48**, 586 (1956); **49**, 617 (1957).

88. S.S.Gertsriken and I.Ya.Dekhtyar, *Diffusion in Metals and Alloys* (Russ.), Moscow 1959.

89. C.Leymonie and P.Lacombe, *Int. J. Appl. Rad. Isot.* **5**, 175 (1959).

90. A.A.Zhoukhovitzky, *Int. J. Appl. Rad. Isot.* **5**, 159 (1959).

91. A.A.JUKHOVITZKY, M.E.YANITZKAYA and A.D.SOTZKOV, Paris Report 30, vol. 1, p. 279.
92. T.PYLE and R.SHUTTLEWORTH, Paris Report 31, vol. 1, p. 598.
93. C.T.TOMIZUKA in: K.LARK-HOROVITZ and V.A.JOHNSON (Ed.), *Methods in Experimental Physics*, New York 1959, vol. 6A.
94. D.LAZARUS, Copenhagen Report 188, vol. 1, p. 159.
95. J.GROH and G.HEVESY, *Ann. Physik* **63**, 85 (1920).
96. J.GROH and G.HEVESY, *Ann. Physik* **65**, 216 (1921).
97. M.B.NEIMAN and A.YA.SHINYAEV, *Doklady Akad. Nauk SSSR* **96**, 315 (1954); **102**, 969 (1955); **103**, 101 (1955).
98. G.HEVESY, *Trans. Faraday Soc.* **34**, 841 (1938).
99. S.N.KRYUKOV and A.A.ZHUKHOVITSKI, *Doklady Akad. Nauk SSSR* **90**, 379 (1953).
100. P.L.GRUZIN and D.F.LITVIN, *Doklady Akad. Nauk SSSR* **94**, 41 (1954).
101. A.A.ZHUKHOVITSKI, Moscow Atomic Energy Conference 1955, Session of the Technical Sciences Division, p. 101.
102. S.T.KISHKIN and S.Z.BOKSTEIN, Geneva Report 703 (1955), vol. 15, p. 87.
103. W.POSCH, *Atompraxis* **4**, 123 (1958).
104. C.B.BIRCHENALL and R.T.MEHL, *J. Appl. Physics* **19**, 217 (1948).
105. P.L.GRUZIN, *Izvest. Akad. Nauk SSSR, Otd. Tekhn. Nauk* **1953**, 383.
106. P.L.GRUZIN, E.V.KUZNETSOV and G.V.KURDYUMOV, *Doklady Akad. Nauk SSSR* **93**, 1021 (1953).
107. P.L.GRUZIN, Y.F.BABIKOVA, Y.A.POLIKARPOV and G.B.FEDOROV, Paris Report 28, vol. 1, p. 249.
108. See also P.LACOMBE, P.GUIRALDENQ and C.LEYMONIE, Copenhagen Report 89, vol. 1, p. 179.
109. P.L.GRUZIN, ZH.V.KORNEV and G.V.KURDYUMOV, *Doklady Akad. Nauk SSSR* **80**, 49 (1951); see also B.YA.LYUBOV (Ed.), *Problems of Metallurgy and Metal Physics* (Russ.), Moscow 1952, vol. 3, p. 225.
110. P.L.GRUZIN and E.V.KUZNETSOV, *Doklady Akad. Nauk SSSR* **93**, 809 (1953).
111. P.L.GRUZIN, *Doklady Akad. Nauk SSSR* **100**, 65 (1955).
112. P.L.GRUZIN, B.M.NOSKOV and V.I.SHIROKOV, *Doklady Akad. Nauk SSSR* **99**, 247 (1954).
113. P.L.GRUZIN, *Doklady Akad. Nauk SSSR* **94**, 681 (1954).
114. J.C.BOKROS and P.C.ROSENTHAL, *J. Metals* **8**, 286 (1956).
115. P.L.GRUZIN, V.G.KOSTOGONOV and P.A.PLATONOV, *Doklady Akad. Nauk SSSR* **100**, 1069 (1955).
116. P.CAMAGNI, Geneva Report 1365 (1958), vol. 20, p. 113.
117. A.A.BOCHVAR, V.G.KUZNETSOVA and V.S.SERGEEV, Geneva Report 2306 (1958), vol. 6, p. 68.
118. J.J.HARWOOD, *Nucleonics* **2** (1), 57 (1948).
119. J.C.FISCHER, *J. Appl. Physics* **22**, 74 (1951).
120. V.T.BORISOV, V.M.GOLIKOV, B.J.LJUBOV and G.V.SHTCHERBEDINSKY, Paris Report 27, vol. 1, p. 112.
121. S.Z.BOKSTEIN, S.T.KISHKIN and L.M.MOROZ, Paris Report 193, vol. 1, p. 232.
122. H.SCHREINER, *Österr. Chemiker-Ztg.* **51**, 233 (1952).
123. A.KOHN, *Rev. Metallurgie* **50**, 139 (1953).
124. See D.MCLEAN, *Grain Boundaries in Metals*, Oxford 1957.
125. K.A.MAHMOUD and R.KAMEL, Paris Report 16, vol. 1, p. 271.
126. L.W.BARR, D.A.BLACKBURN and A.F.BROWN, Copenhagen Reports 45, 46, vol. 1, p. 137, 145.
127. M.B.NEIMAN and A.YA.SHINYAEV, *Zh. Neorg. Khim.* **1**, 1257 (1956).
128. C.FISHER, *Atomwirtschaft* **6**, 210 (1961).
129. See M.T.SIMNAD, Geneva Report 803 (1958), vol. 19, p. 193.
130. S.M.MAKIN, *J. Int. Appl. Rad. Isot.* **7**, 258 (1960); Copenhagen Report 26, vol. 1, p. 217.
131. I.G.POLOVTSHENKO, *Stal* **17**, 1057 (1957).
132. A.B.MICHAEL, W.Z.LEAVITT, M.B.BEVER and H.R.SPEDDEN, *J. Appl. Phys.* **22**, 1403 (1951).
133. T.WESTERMARK and L.G.ERWALL, *Research* **4**, 290 (1951).
134. H.FRAUENFELDER, *Helv. Physica Acta* **23**, 347 (1950).
135. G.TAMMANN and G.BANDEL, *Z. Metallkunde* **25**, 154, 207 (1933).
136. R.E.CARTER, F.D.RICHARDSON and C.WAGNER, *J. Metals* **7**, 336 (1955).

137. H. KRAINER and E. KRAINER, *Atompraxis* **3**, 453 (1957).
138. C. DE BEAULIEU and A. KOHN, *Compt. rend.* **245**, 1244 (1957).
139. R. C. PLUMB and J. E. LEWIS, *J. Inst. Metals* **86**, 393 (1958).
140. A. B. MICHAEL and M. B. BEVER, *J. Metals* **5**, 679 (1953).
141. L. G. ERWALL and M. HILLERT, *Research* **4**, 242 (1951).
142. L. R. STANDIFER and M. G. FONTANA, *Metal Prog.* **60**, 65 (1951).
143. W. E. STEPHENS and M. N. LEWIS, *Phys. Rev.* **69**, 43 (1946).
144. W. E. JONES, *Bull. GEC* 17 March 1947; 10 September 1948.
145. A. B. MICHAEL and M. B. BEVER, *J. Metals* **6**, 47 (1954).
146. D. JAFFE and M. B. BEVER, *J. Metals* **8**, 972 (1956).
147. W. W. SCHULTZ, H. D. BRIGGS, R. A. DEWES, E. E. GOODALE, D. H. MORLEY, J. P. NEISSEL, R. S. ROCHLIN and V. V. VERBINSKI, Geneva Report 819 (1958), vol. 19, p. 112.
148. M. HILLERT, *Research* **5**, 192 (1952).
149. H. FARAGGI, A. KOHN and J. DOUMERC, *Compt. rend.* **233**, 714 (1952).
150. B. D. GROZIN, Geneva Report 713 (1955), vol. 15, p. 160.
151. E. P. NADEINSKAYA, *Investigation of the Wear of Cutting Tools using Radioactive Isotopes* (Russ.), Moscow 1955; *Vestnik mashinostroeniya* **1**, 62 (1960); see also Moscow Atomic Energy Conference 1955, Session of the Technical Sciences Division, p. 140.
152. P. E. DYACHENKO (Ed.), *Investigations of Wear Using Radioactive Isotopes* (Russ.), Moscow 1956; German translation, Berlin 1958.
153. Review of Methods for Activation of Pieces to be Machined: A. A. EMELIN, in [152].
154. B. JAOUL, *Compt. rend.* **238**, 648 (1954).
155. B. W. SAKMANN, J. T. BURWELL and J. W. IRVINE, *J. Appl. Physics* **15**, 459 (1944).
156. J. N. GREGORY, *Nature* **157**, 443 (1946).
157. M. KERRIDGE, in: *Radioisotope Techniques*, London 1952, vol. 2, p. 26.
158. J. T. BURWELL, *Nucleonics* **1** (4), 38 (1947).
159. M. KERRIDGE, *Proc. Roy. Soc.* B **68**, 400 (1955).
160. E. RABINOWICZ, *Brit. J. Appl. Phys., Suppl.* 1, 82 (1951).
161. E. RABINOWICZ, *Proc. Phys. Soc.* B **66**, 929 (1953).
162. See also V. E. VAINSHTEIN, as well as P. E. DYACHENKO, N. N. TOLKACHEVA and K. N. GORYUNOV, in [152].
163. E. RABINOWICZ and D. TABOR, *Proc. Roy. Soc.* A **208**, 455 (1951).
164. YU. S. ZASLAVSKII and G. I. SHOR, see [150].
165. D. PAVELESCO and I. ILIUC, Geneva Report 1301 (1958), vol. 19, p. 155.
166. F. P. BOWDEN and A. C. MOORE, *Trans. Faraday Soc.* **47**, 900 (1951).
167. A. C. MOORE, *Brit. J. Appl. Physics, Suppl.* 1, 54 (1951).
168. R. B. CAMPBELL, L. GRUNBERG, A. A. MILNE and K. H. R. WRIGHT, Copenhagen Report 31, vol. 1, p. 355.
169. D. E. BEISCHER, *J. Phys. Chem.* **57**, 134 (1953).
170. G. L. CLARK, S. G. GALLO and B. H. LINCOLN, *J. Appl. Phys.* **14**, 428 (1943).
171. A. I. NISNEVICH and P. E. DYACHENKO, in [152].
172. B. L. SLINKO, in [152].
173. J. H. DETERDING and J. R. B. CALOW, Geneva Report 94 (1958), vol. 19, p. 141.
174. N. K. TOLKACHEVA, in [152].
175. J. C. BUTTON, A. J. DAVIES and R. TOURRET, *Nucleonics* **9** (5), 34 (1951); *Radioisotope Techniques*, vol. 2, p. 34, London 1952.
176. B. L. SLINKO, see [150].
177. J. T. BURWELL and S. F. MURRAY, *Nucleonics* **6** (1), 34 (1950).
178. V. K. SOSNIN, in [152].
179. P. F. GRIGOREV, in [152].
180. L. M. EFIMOV, M. T. BULSKII, V. I. YAKUSHIN, A. G. ALIMOV and A. M. SKREBTSOV, *Stal* **15**, 1090 (1955).
181. *Atomics* **4**, 279 (1953).
182. P. L. PINOTTI, D. E. HULL and E. J. MCLAUGHLIN, *Petroleum Eng.* **21** (6), 5 (1949); *J. Soc. Automot. Eng.* **57** (6), 52 (1949).

183. Yu.S.ZASLAVSKII, Moscow Atomic Energy Conference 1955, Session of the Technical Sciences Division, p. 115.
184. A.J.SNOW and H.L.SKONECKE, *Atompraxis* **3**, 299 (1957).
185. J.W.T.SPINKS, Geneva Report 216 (1958), vol. 19, p. 13.
186. J.THIERY, *Int. J. Appl. Rad. Isot.* **5**, 197 (1959).
187. Yu.S.ZASLAVSKII, in [152].
188. A.A.ZBOROVSKII, L.K.STRELKOV, M.K.SKULSKI and E.I.RABINOVICH, *Stal* **17**, 24 (1957).
189. J.E.HOWES, W.J.BRAUN and D.N.SUNDERMAN, Copenhagen Report 216, vol. 1, p. 343.
190. V.P.GUINN and R.A.COIT, *Nucleonics* **17** (12), 112 (1959).
191. V.N.BORSOFF, D.L.COOK and J.W.OTVOS, *Nucleonics* **10** (10), 67 (1952).
192. Z.FRYNTA, F.KHOL and W.KOPETZKI, Copenhagen Report 162, vol. 1, p. 381.
193. U.S.LANDERGREN, *Int. J. Appl. Rad. Isot.* **2**, 86 (1957).
194. J.D.KEYS and G.G.EICHHOLZ, Copenhagen Report 27, vol. 1, p. 397.
195. P.E.DYACHENKO, A.I.NISNEVICH and V.E.VAINSHTEIN, in [152].
196. F.A.BUCK, *Ind. Eng. Chem.* **46**, 1318 (1954).
197. B.A.FRIES, J.G.MINGLE and H.W.SIGWORTH, *Int. J. Appl. Rad. Isot.* **1**, 270 (1957).
198. H.P.LANDER and B.M.STURGIS, *Ind. Eng. Chem.* **45**, 1744 (1953).
199. D.E.COOPER, *Nucleonics* **15** (6), 136 (1957).
200. M.C.SHAW and C.D.STRANG, *J. Appl. Physics* **21**, 349 (1950).
201. B.COLDING and L.G.ERWALL, *Nucleonics* **11** (2), 46 (1953).
202. L.G.ERWALL and B.COLDING, in: Radioisotope Conference 1954, London 1954, vol. 2, p. 181.
203. M.W.MERCHANT, *J. Appl. Physics* **22**, 1507 (1951).
204. M.W.MERCHANT, Conf. Atomic Energy in Industry, Nat. Ind. Conf. Board, New York 1952.
205. M.E.MERCHANT, H.ERNST and E.J.KRABACHER, *Nucleonics* **14** (5), 55 (1956).
206. E.PETROZZI, *Nucleonics* **14** (11), 121 (1956).
207. E.I.GOODMAN and I.J.GRUVERMAN, *Nucleonics* **17** (11), 190 (1959).
208. D.I.VYSOTSKI *et al.*, *Avtomobilnaya Prom.* **9**, 24 (1959).
209. J.GOLDEN and G.W.ROWE, Paris Report 67, vol. 1, p. 343.
210. T.SATA, K.ABE and K.NAKAJIMA, Copenhagen Report 142, vol. 1, p. 387.
211. K.KAINDL and A.MATHIASCHITZ, *Werkstoffe und Korrosion* **2**, 368 (1951).
212. K.KAINDL, *Mikroskopie* **7**, 244 (1952).
213. S.M.MAKIN, *Int. J. Appl. Rad. Isot.* **4**, 253 (1959).
214. B.A.THOMPSON and C.B.MURPHY, *Int. J. Appl. Rad. Isot.* **5**, 37 (1959).
215. H.BONNEMAY, H.MAKRAM, M.ROYON and M.GRANGE, Paris Report 75, vol. 1, p. 475.
216. S.F.SINGER, *Nucleonics* **15** (7), 110 (1957).
217. M.HAISSINSKY, *La chimie nucléaire et ses applications*, Paris 1957; *Nuclear Chemistry and its Applications, Reading*, Mass. 1964.
218. M.HAISSINSKY, M.COTTIN and B.VARJABEDIAN, *J. Chim. Physique* **45**, 212 (1948); **46**, 476 (1949).
219. M.HAISSINSKY, *J. Chim. Physique* **47**, 957 (1950).
220. R.T.FOLEY, B.T.STARK and C.J.GUARE, *J. Electrochem. Soc.* **103**, 534 (1956).
221. M.T.SIMNAD and R.C.RUDER, *J. Electrochem. Soc.* **98**, 301 (1954).
222. K.LÖHBERG, *Metallforschung* **2**, 230 (1947).
223. P.M.AZIZ, *J. Electrochem. Soc.* **101**, 120 (1954).
224. N.HACKERMAN and R.A.POWERS, *J. Phys. Chem.* **57**, 139 (1953).
225. R.A.POWERS and N.HACKERMAN, *J. Electrochem. Soc.* **100**, 315 (1953).
226. D.M.BRASHER, C.P.DE, A.H.KINGSBURY and A.D.MERCER, Paris Report 66, vol. 1, p. 326; *Nature* **180**, 27, 28 (1957).
227. Č.JECH, Geneva Report 2444 (1958), vol. 20, p. 183.
228. Y.S.ZASLAVSKI, G.I.SHOR and R.N.SHNEYEROVA, Geneva Report 2198 (1958), vol. 19, p. 147.
229. Yu.S.ZASLAVSKII, S.E.KREIN and R.N.SHNEEROVA, *Zh. Fiz. Khim.* **29**, 1815 (1955).
230. D.GURINSKY, *Amer. Inst. Min. Met. Eng.* **2**, 5 (1955).
231. G.H.CARTLEDGE, Copenhagen Report 183, vol. 3, p. 549.
232. G.H.CARTLEDGE, *J. Phys. Chem.* **59**, 979 (1955); **60**, 28, 32 (1956).
233. See L.H.EVERETT and W.W.SMELTZER, *Ind. Eng. Chem.* **50**, 496 (1958).
234. J.BARDEEN, W.H.BRATTAIN and W.SHOCKLEY, *J. Chem. Physics* **14**, 714 (1946).

235. W.S.EASTWOOD, M.G.MARLEY, H.M.FINNISTON and A.E.WILLIAMS, *Radioactive Tracers in Metallurgical Research*, London 1950.
236. D.M.BRASHER and A.H.KINGSBURY, *Trans. Faraday Soc.* **54**, 1214 (1958).
237. B.V.LINCHEVSKI and N.P.ZHUK, *Zh. Fiz. Khim.* **28**, 2265 (1954).
238. L.LLOPIS, J.M.GAMBOA and L.ARIZMENDI, Paris Report 40, vol. 2, p. 491.
239. J.J.POINT, Geneva Report 127 (1958), vol. 20, p. 179.
240. L.VON ERICHSEN, *Achema* 1958.
241. S.BESNARD and J.TALBOT, Copenhagen Report 84, vol. 1, p. 207.
242. J.GUÉRON, *Nucleonics* **9** (5), 53 (1951); *Radioisotope Techniques*, London 1952, vol. 2, p. 6.
243. *Engineering* **180**, 292 (1955).
244. P.F.BERRY, J.F.CAMERON and E.J.WILSON, Copenhagen Report 16, vol. 1, p. 467; *Int. J. Appl. Rad. Isot.* **12**, 69 (1961).
245. B.CASSEN and D.BURNHAM, *Int. J. Appl. Rad. Isot.* **9**, 54 (1960).
246. G.TIDAU, *Atompraxis* **5**, 26 (1959).
247. G.E.MOORE, H.W.ALLISON and J.D.STRUTHERS, *J. Chem. Physics* **18**, 1572 (1950); see also R.W.PETERSON, D.E.ANDERSON and W.G.SHEPHERD, *Phys. Rev.* **96**, 840 (1954).
248. W.F.LEVERTON and W.G.SHEPHERD, *Phys. Rev.* **85**, 389 (1952).
249. H.W.ALLISON and G.E.MOORE, *Phys. Rev.* **78**, 354 (1950).
250. C.RÖSSELER, *Isotopentechnik* **1**, 25 (1960).
251. J.DEBIESSE and G.NEYRET, *Le Vide* **6**, 1098 (1951).
252. F.DEBOER and W.F.NIKLAS, *Brit. J. Appl. Phys.* **5**, 341 (1954).
253. M.DEVIENNE, *Compt. rend.* **232**, 1088 (1951); **234**, 80 (1951).
254. J.J.ANTAL and A.H.WEBER, *Phys. Rev.* **85**, 710 (1952).
255. J.J.ANTAL and A.H.WEBER, *Rev. Sci. Instr.* **23**, 424 (1952).
256. H.Y.WATTS, C.A.STONE and C.REIFFEL, see *Nucleonics* **13** (6), 23 (1955).
257. G.L.PEARSON, J.D.STRUTHERS and H.C.THEUERER, *Phys. Rev.* **77**, 809 (1950).
258. G.H.MORRISON, *Nucleonics* **11** (1), 28 (1953).
259. J.J.DOWD and R.L.ROUSE, *Proc. Phys. Soc.* B **66**, 60 (1953).
260. T.ICHIMAYA, H.BABA and T.NOZAKI, Copenhagen Report 143, vol. 1, p. 583.
261. M.W.AARONS, M.POBERESKIN, J.E.GATES and E.B.DALE, *Phys. Rev.* **95**, 1345 (1954).
262. R.W.MASON, C.F.HISKEY and R.WARD, *J. Amer. Chem. Soc.* **71**, 509 (1949).
263. J.PRENER, R.W.MASON and R.WARD, *J. Amer. Chem. Soc.* **71**, 1803 (1949).
264. A.DREEKEN and R.WARD, *J. Amer. Chem. Soc.* **73**, 4679 (1951).
265. E.GRILLOT and M.BANCIE-GRILLOT, *Brit. J. Appl. Physics, Suppl.* **4**, 95 (1955).
266. T.SCHÖNFELD and M.REINHARZ, *Mh. Chem.* **84**, 392 (1953).
267. T.SCHÖNFELD and M.REINHARZ, *Mh. Chem.* **83**, 753 (1952).
268. S.M.MAKIN and A.NUNLEY, *Int. J. Appl. Rad. Isot.* **7**, 123 (1959).
269. A.GEMANT, *Electr. Wld.* **133** (15), 93 (1950).
270. J.GOLDEN, P.R.LANCASTER and G.R.ROWE, *Int. J. Appl. Rad. Isot.* **4**, 301 (1958).
271. R.B.CAMPBELL and L.GRUNBERG, Copenhagen Report 32, vol. 1, p. 235.
272. A.H.W.ATEN and F.A.HEYN, *Philips Techn. Rdsch.* **8**, 289 (1946).
273. E.R.RATHBUN, *Nucleonics* **19** (2), 100 (1961).
274. M.E.DRITS, S.A.SVIDERSKAYA and E.S.KADANER, *Autoradiography in Metallurgy* (Russ.), Moscow 1961.
275. C.RÖSSELER, *Isotopentechnik* **1**, 179 (1961).
276. C.FISCHER-BARTELK, *Isotopentechnik* **1**, 171 (1961).
277. K.SCHWABE, *Chem. Technik* **13**, 275 (1962).
278. C.WEISSMANTEL, K.SCHWABE and G.HECHT, *Werkstoffe und Korrosion* **12**, 353 (1961).
279. K.SCHWABE, *Isotopentechnik* **1**, 175 (1961).
280. A.BRÜCKMAN, S.MROWEC, T.WERBER and T.GILEWICZ, *Bull. Acad. Pol. Sci., Chemical Science Series* **8**, 489 (1960).
281. A.BRÜCKMAN, S.MROWEC and T.WERBER, *Nukleonika* **6**, 17 (1961).
282. G.CARERI, A.PAOLETTI and F.SALVETTI, *Nuovo Cimento* **11**, 399 (1954).
283. N.H.NACHTRIEB and Z.PETIT, *J. Chem. Phys.* **24**, 746 (1955).
284. R.E.ECKERT and H.G.DRICKAMER, *J. Chem. Phys.* **20**, 18 (1952).

285. H. JEDRZEJOWSKI, *Compt. rend.* **194,** 1340 (1932); *Acta Phys. Pol.* **2,** 137 (1933).
286. K. SCHWARZ, *Z. Phys. Chem.* **168 A,** 241 (1934).
287. W. C. WINEGARD and B. CHALMERS, *Can. J. Phys.* **30,** 422 (1952).
288. N. HACKERMAN and H. N. SIMPSON, *Trans. Faraday Soc.* **52,** 628 (1956).
289. I. B. BOROVSKI, K. P. GUROV and I. G. MILLER, *Doklady Akad. Nauk SSSR* **118,** 280 (1958).
290. A. D. KURTZ, B. L. AVERBACH and M. COHEN, *Acta Met.* **3,** 442 (1955).
291. A. A. ZHUKHOVITSKII and V. A. GEODAKYAN, *Doklady Akad. Nauk SSSR* **102,** 301 (1955).
292. T. LIU and H. G. DRICKAMER, *J. Chem. Phys.* **22,** 312 (1954).
293. J. C. FISHER, *J. Appl. Phys.* **22,** 74 (1951).
294. P. L. GRUZIN, *Doklady Akad. Nauk SSSR* **86,** 289 (1952).
295. F. HÄSSNER and D. BERGNER, *Isotopentechnik* **1,** 193 (1961).
296. J. STEIGMAN, W. SHOCKLEY and F. C. NIX, *Phys. Rev.* **56,** 13 (1939).
297. S. WADEWITZ and A. MÜLLER, *Isotopentechnik* **2,** 81 (1962).
298. E. RABINOWICZ, *J. Appl. Phys.* **32,** 1440 (1961).
299. W. LANGE, W. PIPPEL and H. OPPERMANN, *Isotopentechnik* **2,** 133 (1962).
300. J. HOLZHEY, *Isotopentechnik* **2,** 165 (1962).
301. G. OSWALD, *Isotopentechnik* **2,** 7 (1962).
302. J. T. BURWELL, *Wear* **1,** 119 (1957).
303. S. N. SECHRIST and H. H. HAMMEN, *Ind. Eng. Chem.* **50,** 341 (1958).
304. S. MROWEC and H. RICKERT, *Z. Phys. Chemie, Neue Folge* **32,** 212 (1962).
305. S. JEFFERSON, *Radioisotopes, A New Tool for Industry,* London 1957.
306. A. KOHN, in [335].
307. W. KASPAR–SICKERMANN, *Kerntechnik,* **3,** 301 (1961).
308. G. RAMDOHR, *Kerntechnik* **3,** 19 (1961).
309. W. LANGE, A. HÄSSNER and K. SIEBER, *Isotopentechnik* **2,** 42 (1962).
310. F. GIRARDI and R. PIETRA, *Anal. Chem.* **35,** 173 (1963).
311. M. RADWAN, *Isotopentechnik* **2,** 270 (1962).
312. J. KIESZNIEWSKI, L. KUS, J. SIEWIERSKI and R. WUSATOWSKI, *Isotopentechnik* **2,** 11 (1962).
313. G. D. FATZER, J. M. SCHROER and B. E. BLAKE, *Int. J. Appl. Rad. Isot.* **10,** 167 (1961).
314. A. YA. SHINYAYEV, *Zavod. Lab.* **24,** 979 (1958).
315. R. NEIDER, *Kerntechnik* **3,** 15 (1961).
316. R. MAYORCAS and K. P. PERRY, *Some Aspects of Fluid Flow,* London 1951.
317. M. OKADA, *Nature* **196,** 1088 (1962).
318. K. SCHMEISER, *Atompraxis* **6,** 133 (1960).
319. F. P. BOWDEN and D. TABOR, *The Friction and Lubrication of Solids,* vols. 1 and 2, Oxford 1954, 1964.
320. W. LANGE and R. KISCHE, *Isotopentechnik* **2,** 2 (1962).
321. G. OSWALD, *Isotopentechnik* **2,** 7 (1962).
322. J. KIESZNIEWSKI *et al., Wire Industry (London)* **28,** 1111, 1116 (1961).
323. J. SKALA and M. MANDL, *Isotopentechnik* **2,** 246 (1962).
324. W. KÜHN, *Kerntechnik* **5,** 207 (1963).
325. W. BIERMANN and D. HEITKAMP. *Z. phys. Chem., Neue Folge,* **37,** 137 (1963).
326. B. W. SCHUMACHER, W. WOJCIK and R. C. ZAVITZ, *Int. J. Appl. Rad. Isot.* **13,** 123 (1962).
327. G. H. PRÖPSTL, *Stahl und Eisen* **80,** 863 (1960).
328. L. G. ERWALL, H. G. FORSBERG and K. LJUNGGREN, in: *Production and Use of Short-lived Radio-isotopes from Reactors,* Symposium, I.A.E.A., Vienna 1963.
329. K. KOLLMANN and D. STEGEMANN, *Kerntechnik* **4,** 41 (1962).
330. F. HARTMANN and W. SCHURICHT, *Isotopentechnik* **1,** 225 (1961).
331. L. M. FOSTER, A. S. GILLESPIE, T. H. JACK and W. W. HILL, *Nucleonics* **21** (4), 53 (1963).
332. A. M. SKREBTSOV, *Radioactive Isotopes in the Investigation of the Open Hearth (Martin) Process* (Russ.), Moscow 1962; *Radioisotope Study of the Open-hearth Process,* London 1965.
333. J. THIERY, in [335].
334. L. G. ERWALL, *Jernkont. Ann.* **143,** 646 (1959).
335. P. LÉVÊQUE (Ed.), *Les applications industrielles des radioéléments,* Paris 1962.
336. P. I. GRUZIN, V. N. AFANASIEV and S. V. ZEMSKII, *Stal* **19,** 291 (1959).

337. I.P.BARDIN, P.L.GRUZIN and S.V.ZEMSKII, *Doklady Akad. Nauk SSSR* **114**, 1220 (1957).
338. G.G.LUKACHEV, Y.G.GORBANEV, L.D.PRIKHODKO and D.V.GULYGA *Stal* **8**, 682 (1958).
339. V.F.KNIAZEV and O.V.TRAVIN, *Zavod. Lab.* **22**, 1071 (1956).
340. J.HOLZHEY, *Neue Hütte* **2**, 665 (1957).
341. A.SCHEPERS and F.R.LICHT, *Stahl und Eisen* **79**, 669 (1959).
342. B.N.KATOMIN, *Izvest. Akad. Nauk SSSR, Otd. Tekh. Nauk* **1957**, 123.
343. V.F.SMOLIAKOV, E.S.KALINNIKOV and V.D.POTAPOV, *Stal* **17**, 893 (1957).
344. E.I.MALINOVSKI and A.N.MOROZOV, *Izvest. Akad. Nauk SSSR, Otd. Tekh. Nauk* **1957**, 102.
345. E.V.LEVINTOVICH, A.N.LYULICHEV, O.M.MARGULIS and D.M.SHAKHTIN, *Ogneupory* **21**, 73 (1956).
346. D.M.MARGULIS and A.G.KARAULOV, *Determination of the Influence of Refractories on the Contamination of Steel by Tracer Methods* (Russ.), Moscow 1958.
347. H.TREPPSCHUH, E.PACHALY, K.SAUERWEIN and R.SCHRÖTER, *Stahl und Eisen* **80**, 878 (1960).
348. T.W.JOHNSON, *J. Iron Steel Inst.* **184**, 18 (1956).
349. E.B.BELL and D.THOMAS, *J. Iron Steel Inst.* **178**, 122 (1954).
350. M.J.PRYOR, F.BROWN and F.COHEN, *J. Electrochem. Soc.* **99**, 542 (1952).
351. S.L.EISLER and J.DOSS, *Metal Finishing* **52** (3), 60 (1954).
352. K.KIMURA, Geneva Report 1061 (1955), vol. 15, p. 220.
353. J.S.ELLIOT, N.E.F.HITCHCOCK and E.D.EDWARDS, *J. Inst. Petr.* **45**, 219 (1959).
354. K.KOLLMANN, W.KASPAR–SICKERMANN and D.STEGEMANN, *MTZ* **24**, 33 (1963).
355. J.J.GUMBLETON, *General Motors Engineering Journal*, July 1961, p. 7.
356. E.H.LOESER and S.B.TWISS, *Lubr. Engnr.* **14**, 343 (1958).
357. B.LE BOUCHER, C.LIBANATI and P.LACOMBE, *Compt. rend.* **248**, 2579 (1959).
358. W.SEITH and A.H.W.ATEN, *Z. phys. Chem.* B **10**, 296 (1930).
359. D.E.BEISCHER, *Science* **115**, 682 (1952).
360. G.DERGE and C.E.BIRCHENALL, *J. Metals* **5**, *Trans. A.I.M.E.* **197**, 1648 (1953).
361. K.SCHWABE, *Dechema-Monographie* **45**, 273 (1962); *Z. Physik. Chem.* **226**, 1 (1964).
362. W.J.ROSS, *Anal. Chem.* **36**, 1114 (1964).
363. H.TOWERS, M.PARIS and J.CHIPMAN, *Trans. A.I.M.E.* **197**, 1455 (1953).
364. V.J.LINNENBOM, M.TETENBAUM and C.CHEEK, *J. Appl. Phys.* **26**, 932 (1955).
365. A.D.KIRSHENBAUM and H.C.BOYNTON, *Iron Age* **171**, 138 (1953).
366. J.H.PETERSON, G.M.NICHOLS and W.F.McDEVIT, *Metal Finishing* **52**, 62 (1954).
367. A.DYSON and K.L.WILLIAMS, *J. Inst. Petrol.* **39**, 524 (1953).
368. J.H.DETERDING and A.DYSON, *Engr.* **198**, 442 (1954).
369. V.N.BORSOFF, *Lubr. Eng.* **12**, 24 (1956).
370. W.DAHL and W.LUEG, *Stahl und Eisen* **76**, 257 (1956).
371. L.A.SHVARTSMAN, O.A.PECHENEV and P.L.GROZIN, *Ogneupory* **17**, 465 (1952).
372. M.P.FEDOCK, *J. Metals* **6**, 125 (1954).
373. G.B.LINDERMAN, *U.S. Patent* 2 680 900.
374. P. L. GRUZIN (Ed.), *Applications of Radioactive Isotopes for the Control of the Blast Furnace Process* (Russ.), Moscow 1964.
375. A.L.GRAY, *Nucl. Engineering* **9**, 205 (1964).
376. M.B.BEVER, Radioactive Tracers in Physical Metallurgy Research, in: *Modern Research Techniques in Physical Metallurgy*, Cleveland 1953.
377. D.M.BRASHER and A.D.MERCER, *Trans. Faraday Soc.* **61**, 803 (1955).
378. J.KOHL, R.D.ZENTNER and H.R.LUKENS, *Radioisotope Applications Engineering*, Princeton 1961, Chapter 13.
379. R.MALVANO, *Atompraxis* **11**, 309 (1965).
380. L.G.ERWALL, H.G.FORSBERG and K.LJUNGGREN, *Industriell Isotop-Teknik*, Copenhagen 1962; *Industrial Isotope Techniques*, Copenhagen 1964.

9. APPLICATION OF RADIOACTIVITY
TO GENERAL PROBLEMS
OF THE CHEMICAL INDUSTRY

In the chemical industry, just as in other branches of industry already discussed, radioactivity has hitherto been mainly used in research and development. Particularly in those parts of the chemical industry which require exact scientific foundations for their further development, including accurate knowledge of physico-chemical quantities or of reaction mechanisms, radioactive tracers are employed to a steadily increasing extent. As far as applications directly to routine production are concerned, measurement techniques with closed radiation sources are predominant. Production control with tracers which undergo chemical change, or are transported through chemical plant, is comparatively rarely used as yet.

9.1. Determination of Technically Important Physico-chemical Quantities

9.1.1. *Problems of Structure and Chemical Bonding*

Only brief reference to the great importance of neutron diffraction for the investigation of chemical structure can be made here. This method has made it possible to solve problems beyond the scope of the analogous X-ray diffraction methods [1, 2, 158, 159, 316, 351, 369].

It has been possible to determine the position of light atoms in crystals which also contain heavy atoms, and so to obtain the complete structures of hydrides, carbides, and nitrides of heavy metals. Elements of closely similar atomic number can be distinguished in neutron diffraction in the case of alloys, and it has therefore been possible to extend the knowledge of ordered and disordered states. Magnetic materials show specific interaction with neutron beams.

A method for the investigation of structure which depends on isotopy is the study of the exchange of atoms bound in molecules or crystals. Such studies are carried out with labelled atoms of the same chemical species (see Chapters 4 and 5). In exchange processes, these atoms are introduced into the molecules. Generally speaking, atoms held by electrovalent bonds (ions) exchange with free ions or atoms of the same chemical species. An example is:

$$\text{NaCl (solid)} + {}^{24}\text{Na (gas)} = {}^{24}\text{NaCl (solid)} + \text{Na (gas)}.$$

In many cases, covalently bound atoms also undergo exchange. Thus

$$\text{Cl}^- \text{(dissolved)} + {}^{38}\text{Cl.Cl (dissolved)} = {}^{38}\text{Cl}^- \text{(dissolved)} + \text{Cl}_2 \text{(dissolved)},$$

where Cl (without index) denotes stable chlorine atoms, chlorine-35 or chlorine-37. It is clear that the covalent bond between the two chlorine atoms in the molecule is broken in this reaction. This bond must therefore be regarded as quite labile. In contrast, atoms which are bound firmly to other atoms by covalent or complex bonds do not show exchange. For example, hydrogen in hydrocarbons will not exchange with either tritium gas or tritium ions under ordinary conditions (see page 60), and the iron in ferrocyanides will not exchange with free iron ions.

The equivalence of the two phosphorus atoms in pyrophosphate has been demonstrated. Preparations of the labelled substance (^{32}P) were made by methods which should introduce the radiophosphorus selectively into some of the positions. The substances were subjected to controlled degradation, but it was established that the specific activity of the phosphorus in all positions was the same [360]. This is an application of the "synthesis–decomposition test" for equivalence [363].

Knowledge of the rate of heterogeneous isotope exchange, that is, exchange across phase boundaries, gives an insight into the structure of the boundary layers. An example is the transfer between a metal and the solution of its ions in a state of equilibrium (see Section 8.5). The fact of exchange of silicon between the surface of silicon carbide crystals and aqueous labelled silicic acid leads to the conclusion that the surface layer does not consist of carbide but of hydrated silica [3].

Detailed discussions of homogeneous and heterogeneous isotope exchange can be found in the literature [4–14, 362, 363, 392, 461] (see also p. 202).

9.1.2. *Solubilities*

The solubility of sparingly soluble salts may be readily determined by tracer methods [349]. The pioneer work on lead salts of small solubility has already been referred to (p. 65). Research on dissolution and precipitation processes of analytical importance has been discussed in Section 6.3. A new method for the determination of solubility products of salts, based on radiometric titration, has recently been proposed [359].

The determination of the very small solubility of water in pure hydrocarbons [13], which is difficult by other methods, has been carried out by an interesting working technique. The hydrocarbon was saturated by bubbling tritium-labelled water vapour through it. After equilibration, the water was removed from the hydrocarbon by treatment with calcium oxide. The radioactive hydrogen in the calcium hydroxide so formed was transferred into alcohol molecules, the hydroxyl groups of alcohol readily exchanging hydrogen. The alcohol vapour was then used to fill a gas counter, and its activity determined. As little as 10^{-12} mole of water was detectable at the specific activity employed. For example, the solubility in benzene (at 20 °C) was found to be 0·38, and in butane (at 5 °C) 0·024 g of water per litre. (In view of the great difference in mass between tritium and protium, the possibility of isotope effects should be borne in mind.) From such results relationships for the dependence of solubility on the chain length of the hydrocarbon molecule and on the number of double bonds in it were derived. For measurement, later authors dissolved the samples of water-saturated hydrocarbon in a liquid scintillator [14, 345]. The very low solubility of mercury in water and organic solvents has also been determined by a tracer method (radiomercury) [15], or by activation analysis [347].

Data on the solubility of inorganic substances in high pressure steam are important, both for the elucidation of the origin of rocks in geology, and for the practical operation of steam power stations. Values down to 10^{-5} mg/kg steam have been obtained by labelling the salts, acids or bases. The partition coefficients were found to be constant within a wide concentration range. Such experiments were, for example, carried out with silicic and boric acids, both of which are fairly volatile, as well as with the chlorides and sulphates of the alkali and alkaline earth elements, and phase diagrams have been drawn up. At temperatures above 550 °C, the decomposition of sodium chloride begins, and the hydrogen chloride so produced goes preferentially into the vapour phase [16, 202].

The crystallization of mixtures has been investigated by isotope dilution (see p. 162): a radionuclide, which is only soluble in the liquid phase, such as cobalt-60 or caesium-134 for the study of the system sodium chloride–calcium chloride, is added in known quantity. The concentration of the radionuclide in the liquid then gives immediately the volume of that phase [17].

9.1.3. *Formation of Complexes*

Radionuclides are increasingly used to find complex formation constants. In such determinations the distribution of an element between two phases is measured. When the labelled element is used, the measurement of distribution coefficients can be carried out in a simple way and over a range of many orders of magnitude. Usually different ionic and molecular species containing a certain radionuclide, such as the metal ion itself and charged and uncharged complexes of that metal, differ greatly in their distribution between an aqueous phase and an ion exchange resin, or between an aqueous phase and an organic solvent. In such two-phase systems, the distribution is thus strongly affected by complex formation, and important information about the complex formation equilibrium may be obtained by measuring the distribution as a function of the concentration of the complexing agent, the pH value, and other factors. When materials of fairly high specific activity are used, only very small amounts of an element are needed; the formation of polynuclear complexes can thus be regarded as negligible; in addition, the determination of the concentration of the free ligand is greatly simplified when only very small quantities of the element in question are used. The application of radionuclides to measurements of complex formation has been reviewed by Rydberg [18].

The study of the distribution of a radionuclide between an aqueous solution and a cation exchange resin was first applied in investigating complex formation between strontium and citrate ions [19, 20], for determining the formation constant of the ion $[SrC_6H_5O_7]^-$. In this case, the metallic ion is adsorbed by the ion exchanger, but the complex is not. Similar work was later done with several alkaline earth cations and various organic acids [21, 22]. Further examples of investigations with cation exchangers are the copper acetate system, where CH_3COOCu^+, $(CH_3COO)_2Cu$, and $(CH_3COO)_3Cu^-$ [23] are formed; the cerium (Ce^{3+} and Ce^{4+}) sulphate system, where such species as $CeSO_4^+$ [24, 25] appear; and the beryllium citrate system, where the complexes formed include $BeH_2(C_6H_5O_7)^+$, $BeH(C_6H_5O_7)$ and $Be(C_5H_5O_7)^-$ [26]. Details of the working techniques and of data evaluation are given in the papers.

Metallic elements, i.e., elements usually present in aqueous solution as cations, may be taken up by anion exchange resins in the presence of complex forming anions. This type of uptake has been investigated in numerous systems, especially in the presence of chloride as complexing anion [27]. However, the estimation of the complex formation constant is often difficult, especially when solutions of high and variable ionic strength are employed. The methods for evaluating the results of the measurements have been discussed in a number of publications [28–30]. A number of systems have been throughly investigated and the complex formation constants have been obtained. These include: silver and chloride ions, where the complexes $AgCl_2^-$, $AgCl_3^{2-}$, and $AgCl_4^{3-}$ [31] are formed; cadmium and chloride ions, involving the formation of $CdCl^+$, $CdCl_2$, $CdCl_3^-$, $CdCl_4^{2-}$ [32]; ferric and chloride ions, with the formation of $FeCl_2^+$, $FeCl_3$, $FeCl_4^-$ [33]; and thorium and nitrate ions, with that of $Th(NO_3)_4$, $Th(NO_3)_5^-$, $Th(NO_3)_6^{2-}$ [34].

In the distribution of an element between an aqueous phase and an organic solvent, usually only uncharged species are taken up into the organic phase. Consequently the measured distribution indicates the relative concentration of uncharged complexes in the aqueous phase. The method was first used to determine the complex formation constants in the systems Zr^{4+}–thenoyltrifluoroacetone (TTA) [35, 36], and Th^{4+}–acetylacetone [37]. In the latter case the uptake of thorium labelled with ^{234}Th (UX_1) by benzene was measured as a function of the concentration of the acetylacetone, and the complex formation constants of the complexes $ThAa^{3+}$, $ThAa_2^{2+}$, $ThAa_3^+$ and $ThAa_4$ (where Aa denotes acetylacetone) have been calculated.

Extraction procedures may also be used when the ligand present does not form an extractable uncharged complex with the metal ion. In this case, the distribution in a system containing extractable complexes is measured as a function of the added amount of the ligand in question. The zirconium–TTA system referred to was used in this way for the investigation of complex formation between the Zr^{4+} and the fluoride or hydrogen sulphate ions [36]. The distribution of zirconium-95 between the aqueous solution and benzene in the presence of TTA was measured in the presence of varying amounts of these ligands. The complex formation of neptunium in its quadrivalent state and the bisulphate ion has also been studied [38]. Similar procedures are suitable for the investigation of hydrolysis and polymerization processes in aqueous solution [39].

Measurement of extraction into an organic solvent has also been used to study the formation of polynuclear complexes, protonized complexes, complex compounds with the organic solvent or with materials which dissolve only in the organic phase, and mixed complexes with more than one kind of ligand (see [40–42]).

9.1.4. *Vapour Pressures*

Sensitive and often quite simple tracer methods for the determination of vapour pressures have been developed [43, 44, 318, 461]. Usually, labelled substances are used from the start, but alternatively substances may be determined by activation analysis. Thus, vapour pressure measurements for uranium were carried out by comparing the number of nuclear fissions caused by neutrons in a condensed sample of the vapour with the corresponding number for a calibration sample [315] (see p. 94).

Static methods are suitable for relatively high vapour pressures. The amount of a labelled substance in the vapour phase is estimated by its activity. The radiation emitted by the gas is measured either directly, or after condensation of the vapour (see [45]). Static methods were used for phosphorus pentafluoride [46], zinc [45], and for polonium [44], the determination in the last case being carried out by counting the α-ray tracks in a nuclear emulsion (p. 46).

The variants of the dynamic methods are capable of more general application. Thus, the vapour from the substance may be carried along by an inert gas, and the vapour is then condensed and measured [47]. Provided the gas is saturated with the vapour, the vapour pressure can be obtained directly from the volume of the gas and the amount of vapour carried over.

The boiling point method (also a type of dynamic method) does not require saturation. The pressure exerted on the test sample is varied, and the dependence of the rate of evaporation on the pressure is determined. A discontinuity in evaporation rate is observed as soon as the vapour pressure of the test sample is reached [44].

In the effusion method due to Knudsen [43, 44] the velocity with which saturated vapour emerges from a small aperture is measured. This method may be made very sensitive by employing radioactive substances. The method has been used for metals [48, 49, 315] and their halides [48], and also for organo-metallic compounds [50–52].

The method of Langmuir is based on the measurement of the rate of free evaporation from a surface. Such rates can be measured with great sensitivity with tracers [44, 47]. Another method depends on the rate of isotope exchange between a labelled and an unlabelled solid sample under high vacuum [43, 44, 53, 54, 324].

Some of these methods have been used for small vapour pressures, such as are found with pure metals (silver [47, 49], gold [56], iron [57], cobalt [58], calcium [59], strontium [59], antimony [60] and zinc [45, 61]) and with alloy components (including non-metals, such as phosphorus and sulphur in iron [49, 56]). Investigations at quite low temperatures are possible. For the determination of the vapour pressure of strontium oxide see p. 180.

Partial pressures measured with tracers may be used for the determination of the free energy of formation of solids. For example, the position of the equilibrium

$$FeS + H_2 \rightleftharpoons Fe + H_2S$$

at high temperatures has been obtained by continuously measuring the radiosulphur in a current of gas circulating through the reaction vessel [62].

The likelihood that an atom of a vapour will be retained on impact with a cooled surface depends greatly on the nature of the surface and other experimental conditions.

In the case of metal atoms this probability is usually much less than 100 per cent. Atoms which have been captured may later evaporate again. This phenomenon has been investigated with tracers (antimony [304], cadmium [304], and silver [305]). The high sensitivity of the method makes it possible to determine the capture probability over a wide range of temperatures and vapour concentrations. The sticking probability on surfaces of foreign materials can often be regarded as an adsorption probability, though in other instances [66] compounds are formed.

9.1.5. *Adsorption*

The adsorption of labelled gases on solids may be measured with high sensitivity. Thus, the adsorption of carbon dioxide has been measured on single crystal faces of copper, silver and nickel; a surface area of the order of 1 cm^2 was sufficient [63]. It was found that the amount of carbon dioxide adsorbed on nickel depends on the nature of other gases previously adsorbed there [64]. In this work a window counter built into the adsorption chamber was employed [65]. The surface diffusion of adsorbed foreign atoms has been referred to on p. 167. The adsorption of carbon monoxide will be dealt with in connection with the Fischer–Tropsch process on p. 207.

The adsorption of substances from solutions on the surface of solids can be measured by analysing either the adsorbent or the solution in equilibrium with it. Generally it is simpler to analyse the solution since the necessary phase separation is easier to carry out. The analysis can be conducted on an aliquot part of the solution, and quantitative separation of the two phases is not necessary. Unless the solid phase is too finely divided, measurements of the concentration in the solution may be performed continuously during the adsorption process. But measurements on the solution are not satisfactory when only small concentration changes take place on adsorption.

In such cases special procedures with tracers are available, which allow the amount of substance adsorbed to be determined directly, and also permit the continuous observation of the adsorption process. The adsorbent is in the form of a thin foil which constitutes the base of a cell containing the radioactive solution. The measuring instrument (usually a window counter) is placed beneath the foil. The rays from the adsorbed substance penetrate directly into the radiation detector and are counted. If the radiation is soft, only a small part of the radiation emitted in the interior of the solution can reach the measuring instrument. The intensity of this radiation can be determined by control measurements carried out under conditions in which adsorption is negligible. This is true after addition of a large excess of an inactive substance that displaces the labelled substance from the surface ("hold-back carrier", p. 55) [68, 71, 82, 306, 309] (see also Section 10.7).

Soft β-radiation suitable for such studies is emitted by sulphur-35 or carbon-14 (see also p. 255). The β-radiation of tritium is, however, so soft that it does not penetrate any foil. For harder β-radiation or for γ-radiation a modified method is employed. The foil is then left in contact with only a thin layer of the solution, but the solution is circulated through the adsorption cell and through a larger reservoir [310].

These methods have been used to determine the adsorption of cations and anions on metal surfaces, in some cases after mechanical or chemical pretreatment [73–77,

113, 289, 306, 437]. By such techniques the deposition of traces of electropositive metals (radioyttrium, radiostrontium and radiocerium) has been observed on surfaces of aluminium, lead, copper, zinc and stainless steel [77], and the uptake of caesium and the rare earths by surfaces of gold and platinum has been followed [78, 323]. The relationship between the extent of adsorption, on the one hand, and the charge of the ions, the pH value of the solution, and the nature of the counter ions, on the other hand, has been examined [323]. The nature of the anion has a strong influence on the adsorption of cations; it is assumed that different anions are attached with different strength to the surface, and that the anions thus adsorbed hold the labelled cations in the electrical double layer.

The adsorption of labelled anions has also been measured [68, 323, 346]. Adsorption of labelled anions on platinum and nickel requires the displacement of chemisorbed oxygen, and is therefore in general slow, while on surfaces free from oxygen it is rapid [68, 81, 82].

In general, the dependence of the amount of adsorption on the potential and on the charge corresponds to the usual views on the structure of the electrical double layer. The adsorption of ions is highest on a surface of opposite charge, although adsorption is also observed on uncharged surfaces and even on surfaces having like charge [79]. The effect of adsorbed ions on the potential may also be determined [80].

Ions may penetrate into microscopic cracks and may then be irreversibly attached [79]. Investigations of adsorption on metal surfaces carried out in connection with corrosion research have been referred to already (p. 177).

The adsorption of a quaternary ammonium salt containing radiocarbon from solution on the surface of the organic explosive "HMX" has been measured radiochemically. It has been suggested that changes in surface development, important for the behaviour of such explosives, can be followed by this method. Because of the small amount adsorbed, the use of tracers is essential [438].

A comprehensive review of the adsorption of radionuclides has been given by Starik [232]. This review deals with adsorption from solutions on polar crystals, glass, ion exchange resins, carbon, paper, colloids and amorphous precipitates, and also with the adsorption of radioactive gases on the solids.

According to Drude, the ellipticity of light reflected from a metal surface is a sensitive measure of the thickness of a surface layer of foreign atoms. It has been shown with tracers that the linear relationship between the ellipticity and the amount of substance in the layer on the metal (chromium) is still valid when the layer is not even unimolecular. This result was obtained with labelled octadecylamine and labelled stearic acid, which could be detected in very small quantities by their radiations [83].

Labelled stearic acid and barium stearate were also used to investigate regular surface layers of the type first studied by Langmuir and Blodgett [84]. The loss through sublimation from such surface layers was determined by activity measurement, after labelled substances had been used to build up the layers. Information about the diffusion of molecules in multimolecular surface layers has been obtained in the following way: A unimolecular labelled layer was deposited on a surface, either as the uppermost layer or as a lower layer in a multimolecular surface deposit. After removal of the uppermost layer by means of a suitable chemical reaction, the amount of labelled substance present in this layer could be determined separately, and the extent of the diffusion estimated.

The adsorption of dissolved substances at the liquid–gas interface will be dealt with on p. 255.

9.1.6. *Diffusion, Heat Conduction and Viscosity*

The methods for determining diffusion in metals have already been described (p. 165) Using related methods (sectioning or radiation adsorption) diffusion may be followed in other solids as well, and in certain cases a further method may be applied. In the exchange of a labelled gas (such as carbon dioxide) with an unlabelled solid (such as calcium carbonate), a fast reduction of the isotope concentration in the gas takes place, until a unimolecular surface is in equilibrium with the gas. Further reduction is then slower. The rate of the latter process is determined by the speed of diffusion, which may therefore be determined from the rate of isotope exchange [85–87].

The various methods referred to have in particular been used to investigate halides, oxides, silicates [88–93], calcium carbonate [85, 94], and sulphur [95]. Diffusion in glasses will be discussed on p. 244. A knowledge of the diffusion coefficients and the proportions of grain-boundary and of lattice diffusion is essential in the study of solid-state reactions. Diffusion measurements at high temperature help our understanding of the sintering process and the formation of new compounds, such as spinels [89]. Information may also be gathered about the condition of the lattice at high temperatures, the energy of formation and the movement of holes, and also the effects of ionizing radiations on these quantities and processes. A very important group of solid-state reactions, the reactions of silicates and related materials, forms the basis of important branches of industry, the ceramic industry, the production of refractories, and the cement industry (see Chapter 10).

Self-diffusion in liquids (metallic indium [96]), in solutions (uranyl nitrate [356] or alkali chlorides [97]), and in gases (xenon [98]) can, of course, also be measured with tracers (see [107] and Section 8.2). Tracer methods for transference numbers are derived from the methods for diffusion coefficients in solution [357, 358, 439, 440].

Measurements of thermal conductivity at low temperatures were used in studies of the effect of local defects in nearly perfect non-metallic crystals. By adding calcium-45 of known specific activity to a melt from which potassium chloride crystals were obtained, and subsequent radiation measurement on the crystals, crystals with small but precisely known calcium contents were produced. It has been established that each calcium ion occupies the place of a potassium ion in the lattice, with simultaneous formation of a vacancy at the position formerly occupied by a second potassium ion. In the crystals so obtained, the concentration of the foreign ion–vacancy pairs is therefore accurately known. Consequently, from the reduction in the thermal conductivity the probability of the scattering of a quantum of lattice vibration energy by a foreign ion–vacancy pair may be calculated [99].

The viscosity of opaque liquids has been determining with a falling γ-active sphere [100, 101]. This sphere is made to pass two horizontal slits arranged a fixed distance from each other. Through these slits the γ-rays pass into separate counters. The time interval required to pass from one slit to the other is automatically recorded. The shielding around the slits is arranged in such a manner that the intensity of the scattered radiation is below the limit at which the radiation detector has been set to give a signal.

9.1.7. *Surface Areas*

Absolute surface areas of finely divided salts have been determined with tracers [102–107, 350, 352]. The principle of the method developed by Paneth consists in bringing the salt into contact with a labelled solution of known specific activity of one of its ions, so that exchange occurs between the dissolved ions and the ions present in a monoatomic surface layer. The activity of the solution or the solid is measured after equilibrium has been attained. In a number of systems, satisfactory results were obtained.

As an example, the surface area of lead sulphate was determined with a lead solution labelled with thorium B [102, 352]. From the ratio between the amount of thorium B in solution and that in the solid, and from the total amount of lead in the solution, the amount of lead in the surface layer could be computed. If the area occupied by one ion in the surface is known, the area of the surface may be calculated. In the case of lead, an area of 18×10^{-16} cm^2 per ion was used for this calculation.

Attempts have been made to extend the method to non-isotopic tracers [352, 353]. For instance thorium B (lead) was used for surfaces of strontium salts. However, these methods are now obsolete.

Objections against the Paneth method have been raised [103, 107, 353]. Control experiments are needed to ensure that it is really a monoatomic layer which undergoes exchange [108–111]. Deviations in both directions have actually been observed. On the one hand, too much of the radioelement may be taken up: although true diffusion of the ions into the crystal does not play a significant part at low temperatures, recrystallization during contact with the solution may cause increased exchange, and may thus lead to exaggerated surface area values. On the other hand, especially for well-formed crystals with few defects it has been observed that by no means all the surface ions undergo exchange during a normal experiment [103]. Naturally grown lead sulphide (galena) is a case in point [352].

Similar procedures were used by Erbacher to determine the surface areas of metals, though here again the possibility of penetration of labelled atoms to deeper layers, in particular through recrystallization, must be considered [75, 112]. The increase in the surface area of metals by polishing was studied by such techniques. Thus in a certain case the true surface of a metal after polishing was 1·7 times, and after cleaning with emery paper 2·4 times, the size of the geometrical surface. These procedures have been criticized by Haissinsky. The criticism is based upon the fact that metal surfaces have a heterogeneous microstructure. In some regions, deposits several atoms deep may be formed, while in other places there may have been no uptake of atoms from the solution [7, 68, 113, 289, 322]. The non-uniform distribution of deposited radioelements has been shown clearly by autoradiography [68, 71, 114] (see Section 8.5).

It has been reported that the measurement of the adsorption of stearic acid (^{14}C) by many kinds of fine powder (nickel, zinc oxide, alumina, titanium dioxide, manganese dioxide, ferric oxide, calcium sulphate, zinc sulphide, manganous chloride, glass and clay) leads to good values of the surface area if a unimolecular layer is assumed. This is deduced from the agreement with the Brunauer–Emmett–Teller (B.E.T.) method [326].

Krypton-85 has been used to obtain the surfaces of powders by the B.E.T. method. Either the β-activity of the gas which remains unadsorbed [435], or the γ-activity of the adsorbed gas [436] is measured.

The packing density, or specific gravity, of porous solids can be obtained from the space accessible to a suitable radioactive gas (often an inert gas) in a pyknometer. When appreciable adsorption of the gas is suspected, the test may be done at elevated temperature [367, 368].

For the possibility of determining grain sizes, and consequently absolute surface areas, by emanation methods reference must be made to the literature [354, 355, 361, 364].

9.1.8. *Application of the Emanation Method*

Phase transition points, such as melting points or transition points between crystal forms, may be determined by measuring the emanating power (p. 68). The detailed shape of the curve giving emanating power as a function of temperature depends on various factors such as crystal size, rate of heating, etc. [355].

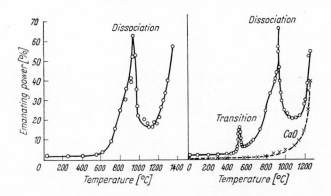

Fig. 35. Emanating power curve for calcium carbonate (calcite and aragonite) [115]

A well-investigated case is that of calcium carbonate [115] (Fig. 35). Radium is first introduced into calcium carbonate in the form of aragonite, so that radon is constantly produced in the crystals. An increase in temperature causes the lattice to be loosened, and the emanating power increases. As soon as the transition temperature from rhombic aragonite to hexagonal calcite (ca. 500°C) is reached, a sudden reduction of the emanating power occurs. A peak is also observed in the transition of calcite into calcium oxide with evolution of carbon dioxide at 920°C. Slow cooling of the calcium oxide (above 920°C) gives at first the same curve in reverse, but further cooling leads to a smooth curve from which both peaks seen on heating are absent. When calcite is cooled, no peak indicating transition to aragonite is obtained, since aragonite is only metastable.

Similar observations have been made for the emanating power of barium carbonate [115] (Fig. 36). However, here the relation between the rhombic and the hexagonal forms is enantiotropic, so that the curve for this process is to some extent reversible. The cooling of the high temperature form therefore gives a maximum in the emanating power indicating a transition point (810 °C), though this peak 'is less distinct than that observed on heating.

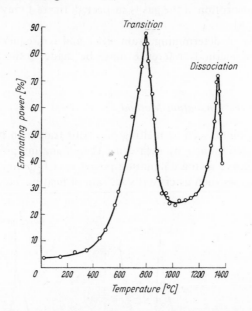

FIG. 36. Emanating power curve for barium carbonate [115]

Stepwise loss of water from crystal hydrates is revealed by several discontinuities in the curve for the emanating power. For example, in the dehydration of barium oxalate and its eventual decomposition to the carbonate five changes are observed [116]. Characteristic discontinuities in the emanating power curves have also been used to study the formation of spinels (see p. 197), e.g., by the process: $Fe_2O_3 + FeO = Fe_3O_4$ [117]. Moreover, the high temperature reactions of alumina and beryllia [321], the reactions $BaO_2 + 6 Fe_2O_3 = BaO \cdot 6 Fe_2O_3 + \frac{1}{2}O_2$ [118], and the systems TiO_2 [348], $BaTiO_3$ [348] and $U_3O_8 + TiO_2$ [119] have been investigated.

The emanation method has proved satisfactory in determinations of the relative specific surfaces of catalysts and their change on heating (see also p. 199). Such work was carried out with carbonates and hydroxides of magnesium and zinc, into which radiothorium had been incorporated [327, 331].

The ageing of precipitates, with the gradual increase in particle size with time which reduces reactivity, is accompanied by a steady decrease in emanating power. Strong effects of this kind have been noted with crystalline and amorphous precipitates, and with colloidal solutions [120, 344, 364–366].

The emanating power may show pronounced dependence on chemical constitution. This is clearly shown by the barium salts of fatty acids, the acetate having an emanating power of 3 per cent, and the palmitate of 100 per cent. This trend goes parallel to a decrease in density (looseness of lattice packing) [122, 123], but other factors also enter, as is strikingly shown by the fact that the barium salts of the three isomeric xylenesulphonic acids have emanating powers varying from 4 to 96 per cent [122].

Radioactive inert gases, such as radon or krypton-85, may be forced into thin surface layers by means of a high frequency discharge (p. 68). The area weight of the layer containing the gas atoms is of the order of $1 \ \mu g/cm^2$. The release of the radioactive gas introduced in this way may then be measured by dynamic methods under various conditions. A current of inert gas is passed over the sample, and then to a measuring instrument, such as a scintillation counter or a thin-window counter. It has been found that many materials, including silicates, alumina, platinum and germanium will release inert gas when exposed to water vapour, and the speed of release depends on the properties of a surface layer. The effect with graphite was relatively the smallest. In further experiments, radioactive gas was introduced into a hydrated salt such as calcium sulphate, and the evolution of gas during thermal dehydration was observed. Discontinuities were found at those temperatures at which the dihydrate is converted into the semihydrate, and the semihydrate into the anhydrous salt. It should be noted that results obtained by this technique apply to very much thinner surface layers than those from the classical emanation method [72, 121].

9.2. Elucidation of Reaction Mechanisms

9.2.1. *General Kinetic Problems*

Often a number of routes appear possible by which certain given reactants may be converted to the reaction products. The rates of the various processes leading to intermediates and to final products will then determine which reaction path predominates. The elucidation of such problems is the aim of kinetic research.

Kinetic problems may often be investigated in a simple and sensitive manner with radioactive tracers [4, 124, 461]. As an example we consider the measurement of the rates at which methyl radicals react with iodine, on the one hand, and with methane, on the other hand, the investigation being carried out over a wide temperature range. The labelled methyl radicals were formed by irradiation of labelled iodide with ultraviolet light, and these could then react with added iodine or methane according to:

$$^{14}CH_3 \cdot + I_2 = {}^{14}CH_3I + I$$

or

$$^{14}CH_3 \cdot + CH_4 = {}^{14}CH_4 + CH_3 \cdot$$

The activity of the products, in particular of methane, was determined. An important advantage was that very small quantities of methane could be detected in this way [126].

Investigation of the rate of exchange reactions is often very informative (see p. 191), since results from such studies are relatively simple to evaluate. Thus the homogeneous exchange of halogen atoms between halogen molecules and organic halogen compounds may be measured by mixing labelled halogen with an unlabelled compound, removing samples after certain time intervals, and determining the activity of the compound [125].

Free halogen atoms, which are naturally very reactive, may be produced within a system by means of photolysis as has been mentioned before. Photolysis has been employed in investigations of the rate of reaction chain termination in the exchange reaction between halogens and alkyl halides. The termination is due to recombination of two halogen atoms. The experiments were carried out by the method of "intermittent light" [127].

Radioactive halogen atoms, without dilution by inactive isotopes, may be produced by special radiochemical techniques, utilizing recoil effects. The rate constant and activation energy of the gas reaction

$$CH_3I + {}^{128}I = CH_3{}^{128}I + I$$

have been determined by producing the radioactive iodine atoms by the Szilard effect (p. 53) by irradiation of organic iodine compounds with neutrons [128]. Reactions of "hot" radioiodine atoms, still possessing some of the excess kinetic energy imparted to them in formation, did not interfere, since it was shown that the addition of an inert gas, which would remove the excess kinetic energy by collision, leads to no change in the reaction rate. It was also shown that γ-radiation did not influence the reaction appreciably. For this purpose, the γ-radiation field was varied by means of external radiation sources; but no change in the reaction rate occurred in these control experiments. For evaluation of the data, in a series of experiments a substance was added which competed with the methyl iodide for the iodine atoms, with a known rate constant, namely molecular iodine. This gives the reaction $I_2 + {}^{128}I = {}^{128}I \cdot I + I$.

To elucidate the nature of organic radicals which take part in reaction chains, such as pyrolytic processes, radioiodine can be introduced to capture the radicals. The reaction products are then separated chemically. These procedures with radioactive reagents have already been discussed in Section 6.4.

Excitation and ionization are primary processes in the interaction of ionizing radiations with matter, and the chemical reactions resulting from these processes are the object of radiation chemistry (see p. 24). The isotope method has become one of the most important research tools of radiation chemistry, one of its important advantages being the possibility of determining the origin of the atoms in the various positions of the reaction products [129].

An example is provided by the investigation of the γ-radiolysis products of toluene, labelled in the methyl group with tritium. The products, which include hydrogen, methane, ethane, acetylene, benzene and some benzene derivatives, were separated by various methods, including gas chromatography, and then tested for activity. The distribution of the tritium is in agreement with the view that an intermediate product arises which has symmetrical structure and in which the seven carbon atoms originally present in the toluene are equivalent [130].

In thermodynamic equilibrium, the rates of the forward and backward reactions are equal. Traditional methods of reaction kinetics do not measure such reaction rates directly. Determinations are, however, possible by labelling one constituent of the equilibrium mixture. This can, for example, be done by adding a very small quantity of the substance in labelled form, isolating the reaction products after a certain period of time, and measuring their activity. The reaction rates in esterification equilibrium can be taken as an example:

$$CH_3COOH + C_2H_5OH \rightleftharpoons CH_3COOC_2H_5 + H_2O.$$

After the addition of labelled acetic acid, radiocarbon gradually appears in the ester.

In a tracer investigation of the reaction

$$H_3AsO_3 + I_3^- + H_2O = H_3AsO_4 + 3\,I^- + 2\,H^+$$

at equilibrium, rate constants were obtained which agreed with those found previously by different methods without tracers for the same system in non-equilibrium conditions [372].

In equilibria, uniform distribution of the radioisotope over the various chemical forms must ultimately be reached, in whatever chemical form the isotope is introduced. If this is not found with a particular system, it must be concluded that no equilibrium is reached or that the reaction is not reversible in the given conditions. This test for reversibility is very sensitive.

The study of kinetic isotope effects, that is, the differences in reaction rates between molecules differing only in containing different isotopes of the same element in one or more positions, offers interesting possibilities for the elucidation of reaction mechanisms. Reviews have been published [287–290]. Data on isotope effects are often obtained with radioactive tracers. The specific activity of the reactant is compared with that of the products obtained after incomplete reaction. In most cases, heavy isotopes react more slowly than light isotopes, but inverse isotope effects also occur.

By looking for a kinetic isotope effect, it is sometimes possible to decide in favour of one out of two suggested reaction mechanisms. The existence of such an effect indicates that the breaking of a labelled bond — a bond joining two atoms, one or both of which are labelled — is a rate-determining step. Thus, tritium-labelled trialkylsilanes or triarylsilanes (R_3SiT) are hydrolysed more slowly than the non-labelled form (R_3SiH). In neutral solution, tritium-labelled solvents (alcohol or piperidine) react more slowly than the non-labelled (protium) forms. From these facts it was concluded that the breaking of the $Si-H$ bond in the silanes is a rate-determining step, and that in the transition state the hydrogen atom of the silane is comparatively strongly bonded to that of the solvent [291].

Another example is an investigation of aromatic substitution conducted with tritiated benzene. In nitration no kinetic isotope effect occurs, but in sulphonation such an effect is observed. Starting from the usual assumption that the substituent enters the molecule in the form of the corresponding cation, it was possible to decide between different reaction mechanisms:

1. Bimolecular electrophilic substitution (S_E2), in which an activated complex forms the transition state without π-electrons being shifted.

2. Formation of a quinoid intermediate state

with subsequent splitting off of the hydrogen. For the first mechanism a kinetic isotope effect is to be expected, while for the second mechanism such an effect should occur only if the splitting off of the hydrogen is the rate-determining step. It appears, therefore, that nitration occurs by the second mechanism, while it is uncertain whether sulphonation follows the first or the second mechanism, in the latter case with the decomposition of the quinoid intermediate as the rate-determining step [292, 293].

The study of kinetic isotope effects, especially with deuterated compounds, has found wide application in the elucidation of acid- and base-catalysed processes.

From the magnitude of the isotope effect, or simply from its sign, it is possible to obtain information on the bonding in the transition state of a chemical reaction. In these determinations the theory of absolute reaction rates serves as the basis [294]. It is assumed that the reaction proceeds through an activated transition state, and that the reaction velocity is proportional to the concentration of the substance in this state. Kinetic isotope effects can then be treated in a similar way as equilibrium isotope effects [295–298].

The decisive quantity in this type of treatment is the energy of activation. If the atoms for which the data are obtained are less firmly bound in the transition state than in the ground state, the heavier isotope will show a larger energy of activation than the lighter isotope, so that the molecule containing the heavier isotope will react more slowly. On the other hand, the lighter isotope will react more slowly if the bonding in the transition state is stronger than in the initial state. This type of inverse kinetic isotope effect was observed for the conversion of *o*-benzoylbenzoic acid into anthraquinone by intramolecular condensation, when the carbon atom in the carboxyl groups was labelled with ^{14}C. The reaction is induced by concentrated sulphuric acid. It was concluded that the reaction proceeds through a transition state in which a $C-C$ bond has already been formed [299].

9.2.2. *Reaction Mechanisms in Organic Chemistry*

Many organic reactions have been investigated by tracer methods. Reviews of such studies have been written [4, 67, 124, 133–137, 461]. A general principle in such work is that a definite carbon atom within the organic molecule undergoing the reaction is labelled, and the radiocarbon in the various reaction products is then determined. In many cases the position of radiocarbon within the molecule of one of the reaction products must also be determined. This is done by selective degradation procedures which permit separate determination of the radiocarbon in different positions within a molecule.

As a simple example for the elucidation of reaction mechanisms with tracers we refer to an investigation of the liberation of carbon monoxide on heating α-keto acid esters. In this reaction the ester of the acid that contains one carbon atom less than the original acid is formed. Since it was uncertain whether the carbon of the carbon monoxide is derived from the carboxyl group, from the α-carbonyl group, or from both these groups, the ethyl ester of α-^{14}C-pyruvic acid, that is, the ester of the radioisomer $CH_3 \cdot {}^*CO \cdot COOH$, was heated to 120°C, and the activity of the reaction products was determined [139]. The carbon monoxide produced proved inactive, while the ethyl acetate formed had the same specific activity per mole as the initial material. It was therefore clear that the carbon monoxide originated exclusively in the carboxyl group of the esterified ketoacid:

$$CH_3{}^*COCOOC_2H_5 \rightarrow CH_3{}^*COOC_2H_5 + CO.$$

Even in the case of quite simple reactions, where the mechanism was formerly thought to be well known, tracer investigations have led to new information. For example, the reaction of amines with nitrous acid produces alcohols. It was formerly not known that carbon atoms could be interchanged in the course of this reaction. Yet it was found after reaction of α-^{14}C-ethyl amine that a small part of the radiocarbon had migrated to the β-position of the alcohol. This can be shown by decomposing the alcohol and measuring the activity of the two carbon atoms separately:

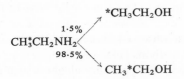

Therefore even in such an apparently simple reaction fundamental changes in the molecules are not ruled out [132, 138].

It may be important to know whether a reaction proceeds by way of a particular intermediate. To determine this, the reactant may be labelled, and the suspected intermediate may be isolated and measured for activity. When advisable, the isolation may be carried out after the addition of the non-radioactive substance as a carrier. Alternatively, it is possible to add the suspected intermediate in a labelled form to a non-radioactive reaction system, and then to test the end product for activity. In this way the formation of carbon monoxide by the combustion of methane was shown to proceed through formaldehyde as an intermediate (see p. 209).

The use of tracers in the study of polymerization reactions will be discussed in Section 10.6.2.

9.2.3. *Catalysis in Gas Reactions*

The elucidation of catalytic reactions with tracers has been discussed by Brodskii [4, 131], Roginskii [124, 144], and other authors [240, 336, 461].

We shall first consider, as an example, the transformation of α-bromonaphthalene into β-bromonaphthalene in the presence of aluminium bromide. It was supposed that bromine from the catalyst is introduced into the bromonaphthalene molecule, giving an intermediate in which the different bromine atoms exchange with each other. But experiments with labelled bromonaphthalene and labelled catalyst showed no such introduction of bromine from the catalyst into the organic molecule [140] (see also [371]). With radiofluorine it has been shown that those alkali fluorides which exchange fluorine with fluorohydrocarbons most readily are also the best catalysts for the oxidation of these substances. The order of diminishing effectiveness of the fluorides is: caesium, rubidium, potassium, sodium. The high exchange rate has been attributed to a mechanism involving lattice defects [141].

An enquiry into the synthesis of hydrocarbons from carbon monoxide and hydrogen by the Fischer–Tropsch method is of great interest [396]. The catalysts used in this process are iron and cobalt salts, and the temperatures are between $200°$ and $300°C$. Originally carbides had been regarded as the effective intermediate. It was believed that unstable methylene radicals are first formed from the carbide, and that these radicals subsequently polymerize. The synthesis was carried out in the laboratory with the addition of carbon monoxide containing radiocarbon, but no activity was observed in the catalyst, showing that no radioactive carbide had been formed. In other experiments, radioactive cobalt carbide was added to the catalyst, but after the synthesis very little activity was observed in the hydrocarbon. The earlier hypothesis of the formation of cobalt carbide as intermediate was thus shown to be incorrect, or to account at most for an insignificant fraction of the observed process [142]. This result is in agreement with results obtained by other methods [143, 144, 240].

The same group showed that radiocarbon from primary alcohols such as ethanol and propanol added to the gases used for the Fischer–Tropsch process is transferred to the hydrocarbon molecules [145–148]. Isopropyl alcohol, a secondary alcohol, gives only small quantities of higher hydrocarbons, while tertiary butyl alcohol gives none at all. Isopropyl alcohol does, however, produce isobutane. It has been concluded that carbon monoxide and hydrogen form transient complexes on the catalyst which are similar to the adsorbed primary alcohols, and that these complexes act as intermediates in the formation of higher hydrocarbons. Similar results were obtained with ethyl alcohol, whether the molecule was labelled on the methyl group or on the methylene group. This result indicates that the $C-C$ bond is either not broken during the transformation, or that it is not broken in such a way that unequal fragments are formed which would then react in different ways.

With a reaction mixture consisting of a radioactive primary alcohol (such as ethanol) and inactive synthesis gas (carbon monoxide and hydrogen) it was found that, at least within the range from C_2 to C_{10}, the molar specific radioactivity of the products was practically constant. It was concluded that the hydrocarbon molecules grow by a chain mechanism from the original oxygen-containing complex formed by adsorption of the alcohol [149, 396]. After addition of labelled ketene to the synthesis gas, it was found that the complex formed by adsorption of the ketene must resemble the C_2-complex arising as an intermediate in the hydrocarbon synthesis [150].

In further work the formation of hydrocarbons from hydrogen, ethylene and labelled carbon monoxide was studied. A linear increase of the molar radioactivity with chain length was observed, but only a small part of the carbon in the hydrocarbons was derived from the carbon monoxide. The meaning of this result is still uncertain [151].

In connection with the Fischer–Tropsch synthesis, an investigation [152] has been undertaken to find out whether the reduction in adsorption affinity with increasing surface area of the catalyst covered is due to differences in the affinity for the gas at different adsorption sites, or to a repulsion by the gas molecules already adsorbed. Using earlier studies [153–155] as a starting point, carbon monoxide was applied in two batches, only one of them labelled. Partial desorption was then carried out to see whether the batch adsorbed last was the first to be desorbed. This behaviour is to be expected if heterogeneity of the catalyst surface is the decisive factor.

With a catalyst containing iron, aluminium, zirconium and silicon, of the type used for ammonia synthesis, it was found that about half of the gas batch adsorbed first remained on the adsorbent after partial desorption, while the other half was desorbed together with the gas adsorbed in the second batch. The significance of these results is not clear, as the authors themselves admit. In particular it is not known to what extent an exchange of carbon monoxide molecules occurs between different adsorption sites on the catalyst.

It had been found by other workers [340] that after xenon samples of different isotopic compositions had been adsorbed one after another on silica gel, subsequent removal of the xenon gave samples of identical isotopic composition. This was interpreted as being due to interchange on the surface of the adsorbent. Adsorption on animal charcoal gave the opposite result.

Such "differential isotope methods", with adsorption and desorption carried out batchwise, have been used for the examination of other catalysts as well [124, 240, 333, 334, 339]. The heterogeneity of nickel surfaces has been clearly shown by successive adsorption of batches of labelled and unlabelled acetylene. The batches desorbed in succession showed different specific activities. Moreover it was found that the probability of conversion into ethylene, ethane, hydrogen and other products was different for the various batches [341]. The heterogeneity of nickel surfaces has also been demonstrated with carbon monoxide, labelled with stable isotopes; however, even at temperatures as low as room temperature rapid exchange of gas molecules between the sites was observed [374].

It is also possible to detect the heterogeneity of adsorbent surfaces by a method depending upon isotope exchange. Exchange equilibrium between gaseous acetylene and acetylene adsorbed on clay is not approached according to a simple exponential law, but with gradually decreasing relative velocity, so that the last portions of the adsorbed substance are most firmly attached [339]. In a study of the exchange between free radioactive carbon monoxide and carbon monoxide chemisorbed on iron, followed by fractional desorption, it was found that those regions of the surface where exchange was most rapid also showed most rapid desorption [342].

The poisoning of catalysts used in ammonia synthesis by oxygen-containing molecules is attributed to preferential adsorption of the poisons on the surface. With labelled carbon dioxide or carbon monoxide the amount retained has been determined. It has also been shown that the major part of the radiocarbon leaves the catalyst in the form of hydrocarbons. This is in agreement with the fact that the same catalyst is effective in respect to the Fischer–Tropsch reaction. The water produced in this process is presumably partly responsible for the poisoning [156].

The exchange of tritium between phosphoric acid and butane was measured in order to elucidate the mechanism of catalysed reactions of hydrocarbons, including isomerization [157]. The suggestion was made that the catalyst forms a complex with the substrate, within which hydrogen atoms are transferred between the hydrocarbon and the catalyst, and therefore also between different positions in the hydrocarbon molecule. Generally, the study of hydrogen exchange has often been exploited to throw light on the mechanism of gas reactions [124, 392, 397].

In cracking processes, carbon is deposited on the aluminium silicate catalyst. When pure hydrocarbons (such as n-heptane, n-octane and 1-octene) were employed that were labelled at definite positions of the molecules, the specific activity of the carbon deposited was found to be equal to that of the hydrocarbon in every case. Apparently the carbon is derived equally from all carbon atoms in the gas. It was concluded that the hydrocarbons are first adsorbed and then completely decomposed [160]. Again with radiocarbon the formation of coke during catalytic cracking was shown to increase with increasing chain length of the hydrocarbon. Particularly large quantities of coke are produced from unsaturated and hydroaromatic hydrocarbons in the mixtures [161, 337].

The catalytic conversion of cycloalkanes into aromatic hydrocarbons was studied with methyl group-labelled methylcyclohexane. Radiocarbon appeared, among other products, in benzene and in the ring of toluene, so that isomerization must have occurred [162] (see also [163]). During the dehydrocyclization of hydrocarbons, it was found that, in agreement with the theory of Rideal, ring closure is accompanied by isomerization [164].

9.2.4. Combustion Reactions

In the gasification of coal, reactions with oxidizing agents such as water vapour and carbon dioxide play an important role. Using labelled carbon dioxide, the view has been confirmed that this substance first releases an oxygen atom to the solid carbon; the oxygen forms a kind of surface layer, while the dioxide is reduced to the monoxide. It is only in a second stage of the reaction that the second carbon monoxide molecule is produced according to the overall reaction (Boudouard reaction):

$$CO_2 + C = 2\,CO.$$

This was inferred from the observation that at temperatures between 500° and 850°C neither the pressure nor the specific activity of the gas changes in the initial phase of an experimental run, although carbon monoxide is formed and appears in the gas [165] (see also [373, 430–433]). The rate of the reaction depends greatly on the pretreatment of the carbon and the presence of catalysts such as potash and iron [166]. In an investigation of this reaction in the absence of catalysts stable oxygen-18 was employed to test whether the postulated stage mechanism actually occurs [167].

The combustion of hydrocarbons occurs in stages. Intermediate products include peroxides and aldehydes. It has been shown with tracers that aldehyde groups may be formed from any carbon atom in the hydrocarbon chain [168–174, 375]. Radiocarbon has also been used to study the conversion of butane by catalytic dehydrogenation into butadiene via butene [175], as well as the accompanying decomposition of butadiene into coke and other substances [338]. These reactions are of importance in connection with the manufacture of synthetic rubber.

The part played by various intermediates in the combustion of hydrocarbons has been examined by the "kinetic tracer method". The amount of an intermediate that is present in a stationary state depends on the rate of its formation and of its consumption. In the stationary state these two processes cannot be determined separately by older methods (see p. 203), but this is possible by introducing the intermediate in a labelled form and then measuring the rate of disappearance of the labelled substance. Such measurements give the rate of conversion of the substance considered, and it may then be discovered to what extent the reaction proceeds by way of this intermediate [171, 375]. Modifications of this kinetic tracer method may also be used to investigate the sequence of intermediates, branching of reaction chains, sorption on catalysts, and the order of reactions.

With labelled carbon monoxide it has been shown that at relatively low temperatures combustion of butane to carbon dioxide takes place only to a very small extent by way of carbon monoxide as an intermediate. The major part of the process involves free radicals as intermediates. These radicals were detected by allowing them to take up tritium from labelled hydrogen gas [168, 176]. In the catalytic oxidation of ethylene at 220 °C, valuable ethylene oxide is formed in addition to carbon dioxide. It has been demonstrated that ethylene oxide is not an intermediate in the main process by which carbon dioxide is formed [177]. On the other hand, the combustion of methane at 670 °C, which was also investigated with radiocarbon [172, 174, 178], follows strictly the reaction sequence:

$$CH_4 \rightarrow CH_2O \rightarrow CO.$$

A small part of the formaldehyde is produced through methanol as an intermediate. The carbon monoxide is not further oxidized to the dioxide.

Studies of this kind provide the foundations for industrial processes for the production and isolation of valuable intermediates. For example, it follows from the results just discussed that in the preparation of ethylene oxide the important thing is not to prevent further reactions of this substance, but rather to increase the rate of its formation; on the other hand, the yield of formaldehyde from the oxidation of methane is improved by slowing down its further oxidation to carbon monoxide [179].

Experiments with stable oxygen-18 have led to the conclusion that oxidation catalysts such as manganese dioxide do not transfer their oxygen to the substrate (carbon monoxide) [180, 240, 335]. However, the behaviour of the manganese dioxide is strongly affected by its moisture content [343] (see also [4]).

9.2.5. *Inorganic Chemical Reactions*

Tracers have been applied to inorganic reactions, particularly electrochemical reactions. For example, various aspects of the electrolysis of aqueous sodium chloride have been examined, including the movement of cathodic mercury and the flow of electrolyte in the preparation of chlorate [181].

In work on the electrolytic deposition of copper from sulphate solution (using sulphur-35), it was found that both electrodes are quickly coated with a unimolecular layer of sulphate, so that the copper deposited at the cathode also contains sulphur. Its amount may vary, depending on conditions, from 10^{-5} to 10^{-8} parts of the copper deposited [183]. Other research concerned with electrometallurgy is discussed in Section 8.1.3.

Electroplating of chromium is conducted in baths containing chromic acid, i.e., hexavalent chromium. It was formerly doubtful whether the deposition of chromium occurred by way of the tervalent form, or directly from the hexavalent form. In a preliminary experiment with radioactive ions no exchange between the two forms of chromium was found. Labelled chromic salt was then added in a main experiment to the electrolytic bath, but no activity was found in the chromium layer. It was concluded that no reduction of the dissolved chromic ions to the metal occurs, and the dissolved chromic ion is no intermediate in the reduction of the chromate [182].

Silver is electroplated from baths containing very small quantities of ammonium thiosulphate. It is assumed that codeposition of minute quantities of this salt prevents the formation of large crystals. This is desirable since finely crystalline silver takes a high polish more readily. The codeposition has been confirmed and measured with radiosulphur [184]. The favourable effect of other sulphur-containing additives (brighteners) in making electrolytic deposits more uniform has been examined by similar techniques (^{35}S-sodium allyl sulphonates with nickel [185], ^{35}S-thiourea with nickel and copper [399]). The inhibition of the deposition of cobalt by organic sulphur compounds has been studied with radiosulphur [370]. The occlusion of phosphorus in nickel coatings made by reduction with hypophosphite has been demonstrated [376]. For tracer tests of the efficiency of cleaning and degreasing in electroplating, see p. 256.

The fundamental reaction in the lead accumulator is usually considered to be described by the equation:

$$Pb + PbO_2 + 2 H_2SO_4 \rightleftharpoons 2 PbSO_4 + 2 H_2O.$$

It was uncertain, however, whether the reaction proceeds by way of the solution phase, perhaps through the intermediate formation of plumbic (Pb^{4+}) ions. By adding radiolead to one electrode it has been shown that neither the opposite electrode nor an initially inactive part of the same electrode becomes active when the battery is put through a charge–discharge cycle. The accumulator acid also remains inactive. Consequently, the electrochemical process responsible for energy storage and release does not involve appreciable transfer of lead through the solution [186]. Another group of workers used radioantimony to examine the effect on the operation of the accumulator of the antimony present in the hard-lead framework of accumulator plates [187, 188].

The life of silver–zinc accumulators is increased if the battery is kept in a discharged condition when out of use. Tracer work with silver and zinc has shown that a certain amount of each metal dissolves and reaches the electrode of opposite polarity during resting periods, and more so in the charged than in the uncharged state [190].

Fused uranium tetrafluoride is considered as a nuclear fuel for a certain type of power reactor. Processes for removing fission products, in particular rare earths with high capture cross-sections for neutrons, were studied with suitable radionuclides. It was found that an exchange process can be employed for the removal of a number of fission products. The fused uranium tetrafluoride is passed over solid cerium fluoride, which is only slightly soluble in the melt. Rare earths are taken up by the solid through exchange. The cerium released absorbs slow neutrons only to a small extent [189].

Catalysts may often be made more efficient by minute additions which are difficult to determine analytically. Thus the activity of palladium catalysts acquires a maximum value when small but well-defined amounts of phosphate ions are introduced during the precipitation of the metal from solution by reduction with formate. It has been shown with radiophosphate that maximum efficiency for hydrogen peroxide decomposition is obtained with 0·005 per cent, and for the hydrogenation of ethylene with 0·2 per cent phosphorus [154, 240].

During flocculation of lyophobic colloids, small amounts of the flocculant (such as phosphate or sulphate ions) may be coprecipitated. These quantities were determined with tracers, in particular for the coagulation of silver iodide, mercuric sulphide and arsenious sulphide [191].

The relative importance of SO_2 and SO_3 in the formation of sulphatic boiler deposits with volatilized sodium chloride from coal has been estimated by passing flue gases containing SO_2 and $^{35}SO_3$ over sodium chloride at controlled temperatures and measuring the specific activity of the sulphate [151].

9.3. Chemical Process Technology

Radioactivity is often useful for the investigation and control of chemical processes. Now the investigation of typical unit processes and the determination of typical parameters will be discussed. It should be mentioned that the methods of chemical analysis based on radioactivity (Chapter 6) find application in process research and development as well as in routine process control. From the latter point of view great interest attaches to analytical procedures not needing special sampling. Methods employing the absorption or scattering of radiation are particularly appropriate in this respect. In some circumstances activation analysis and radioactive reagent methods may also be used.

9.3.1. *Mixing and Separation*

The completeness of mixing in a technical plant is easily checked by the addition of a radioelement [172, 193, 409, 452, 453]. Short-lived sodium-24 in the form of common salt is used fairly often. The method was, for example, employed for determining the effectiveness of a mixer used for mixing carbon and pitch at high temperature in the production of industrial carbon electrodes. After the charge had been mixed for a few minutes, a small amount of sodium benzoate (containing 10 mc of sodium-24) was introduced at one point, and mixing was then resumed. At various intervals the mixer was stopped and samples were taken for activity measurement from several places in the mixture. The decrease in the fluctuation of the activities indicated the progress of mixing [194] (see also [197, 434]). Other work on mixing of solids has been concerned with solid propellants [393], cattle feed [394, 409], and cement [441].

In the evaluation of the data statistical considerations must be applied. Even with samples from uniform materials the counts are subject to fluctuation. Elementary statistical analysis is needed to distinguish true differences from the random fluctuations, and so judge the significance of the experimental data collected during mixing [391].

Effectiveness of mixing was also tested in a large tank used in a petroleum refinery [162, 195]. The contents of the tank were constantly circulated by means of a pump to obtain uniform distribution of various additives. A radioactive substance was added in a single amount and the activity was then determined in the exit pipe from the tank and also in the pipe leading to the circulating pump (see also [200]). Appreciable fluctuations were observed showing that the mixing was not as efficient as expected. For following the mixing of greases in steam-heated, paddle-stirred kettles, short-lived iodine-132 has been used [395].

The continuous mixing (as distinct from batch mixing) may also be checked with radionuclides. In a simple case, one of two liquids coming together from separate pipes is radioactive [196] (see also Section 9.3.4). On the basis of observations, with radionuclides, of continuous mixing in an alkylating plant, improved jet trays could be designed [398].

Important separation procedures include fractional distillation, extraction, crystallization, precipitation and chromatography. The principles used in checking the degree of separation in such procedures with tracers are the same as those in the control of analytical separations (Section 6.3).

Boiling-point diagrams of binary and ternary systems containing methyl alcohol have been determined simply by using labelled alcohol (^{14}C). The distribution of methyl alcohol during extraction separations [198], and the removal of petroleum sulphonates from an oil by extraction with alcohol [199] were also measured in this way.

The carry-over of tar in evaporators was observed by adding non-volatile cobalt naphthenate (containing ^{60}Co) to the product mixture before distillation. In the case of the evaporator of a thermal cracking unit plant, the carry-over could amount to several per cent [162, 200, 201]. The carry-over of bitumen in the distillation of residual oils has also been observed with cobalt naphthenate. In order to reduce the amount of radioactive material, neither the entire charge, nor an appreciable part of it, was labelled. Instead, a small amount of radioactive substance was introduced into the distillation apparatus at a particular time. The distribution of the tracer over the residue and the distillate was then determined by means of a large number of activity measurements on both fractions, these measurements being carried out over a period of several hours after the addition of the tracer [300].

In a similar way the carry-over of salts was determined during evaporation in large power-station boilers. This is of great interest because of the corrosive effects of the salts. Salts containing radioactive phosphate, sulphate, calcium or sodium were added to the feed-water. Samples of condensed water (0·1–0·2 l.) were evaporated, and the activity of the residue measured [202]. The fraction of the salt carried over (ca. 0·001 per cent) depended only slightly on the operating conditions of the boiler and on the salt concentration (see also [301]). In the interpretation of the data the true solubility of the salts in the steam has to be taken into account (p. 192).

Tracers are particularly useful in checking the separation of closely similar substances, or when very small amounts must be detected. Thus, the separation of hydrocarbons boiling in a given temperature range may be determined with tracers, and the same applies to the separation of inert gases. The removal of traces of sodium, sulphur, phosphorus and strontium from potassium nitrate by a zone-melting procedure was followed after addition of suitable isotopes [204]. The removal of impurities from aluminium by zone-melting was determined by activation analysis [55, 205]. Tracers were also employed to follow the purification of $SiHCl_3$ and $SiCl_4$ for the production of high-purity silicon and silica [442].

Further examples of the investigation of separation processes are found in the preparation of extremely pure chemical reagents. Zinc impurity in manganous sulphate comes down with freshly precipitated manganous hydroxide. The zinc was labelled with zinc-65, and the coprecipitation could then be followed easily. The method was found suitable for the purification of manganese [203]. Similarly, the coprecipitation of zinc with freshly precipitated iron sulphide for removal from ferrous sulphate solutions, and the coprecipitation of cobalt on manganese dioxide for its removal from zinc sulphate solutions were studied [203]. The extent to which liquids are retained during filtration or centrifugation by solids may be estimated with tracers.

The removal of moisture, specifically the drying of polymerized trifluorovinyl chloride ("fluorolube"), under factory conditions, was followed in a sensitive and simple manner by activity measurement. The water was labelled with tritium and estimated by liquid scintillation counting [314].

A remarkable procedure has been used to determine the time average of the interface area between two liquids in a two-phase reaction mixture, which was being shaken. Polonium was added to the aqueous phase. The range of the α-rays is small compared with the dimensions of the homogeneous zones of liquid (about drop size) but may induce a radiation-chemical or nuclear reaction with a constituent of the other phase. For example, when the other phase consists of fluorinated hydrocarbons, neutrons are produced at the interface (and only there) through the (α, n)-reaction. The neutron flux, which may be measured with a boron chamber, is then a measure of the area of the interface. Through such measurements it may be decided to what extent slowness of a reaction between two phases is due to too small an interface, or, alternatively, to too slow transport within the phases [206].

9.3.2. *Detection of Losses*

Losses from a platinum–iridium catalyst used for the oxidation of ammonia in the manufacture of nitric acid were traced after activation in a reactor, the activity being mainly due to iridium-192. The amount of the catalyst deposited in various parts of the plant could then be estimated. It was also possible to follow the fate of the catalyst after its deposition [194]. Platinum losses during the catalytic oxidation of methane were determined in a similar manner [207]. Losses, through the flues of the plants, of various kinds of catalysts used in cracking could be measured in one and the same experimental run — and thus under identical operating conditions — by labelling the various substances with different isotopes [208, 424]. o-Bromophenol (^{82}Br) was used to label phenol in the investigation of losses of phenol in an extraction plant, and much of the loss was attributed to reaction with extraneous materials [390].

Losses of liquids due to spraying may be found sensitively with tracers. In the investigation of the crashes suffered by the British Comet jet aircraft a method of this kind was used to discover whether fuel could possibly have penetrated by spraying into the wrong parts of the aircraft, and could then have produced an explosion. The fuel was labelled with palladium-119 in the form of palladium acetylacetonate or palladium diethyldithiocarbamate. A flight was then carried out, and various parts of the aircraft were checked for activity. It was demonstrated beyond doubt that the disasters were not due to the spraying of fuel [209, 210].

9.3.3. *Level Gauging and Checking of Equipment Assembly*

The level of liquids, including melts, within inaccessible containers may be determined by radiation methods. These techniques may be employed at high pressures and temperatures, and also for corrosive (such as chlorine [385]), explosive or highly viscous liquids. The various types of level-gauging equipment may be used for the direct control of inflow and outflow and for automatic warning in case of overfilling. Reviews have been published on such problems [192, 211–220, 379, 388, 443, 444, 452, 455, 457], and in particular on instrumentation [387, 450, 457]. Reference should be made to these for fuller information.

In level gauges, γ-ray sources are mostly used, often cobalt-60 or caesium-137. The radiation measurements may be carried out with Geiger counters, but the efficiency of scintillation counters is superior, and for a given radiation intensity a quicker response is therefore obtained with the latter. The activity of the source is usually kept as low as possible, so that elaborate radiation protection is avoided. Reliable and rugged electronic units are now available. Instead of amplifying valves, transistors are often used. They can be enclosed in shock-proof and corrosion-resistant shells.

For continuous indication of liquid levels it is possible to use a radioactive float whose γ-radiation is measured outside the container [192, 221–223] (Fig. 37a). In another technique the source is placed at the bottom of the vessel while the measuring instrument is placed in the ceiling, so that the absorption of the rays on the way from the source to the detector depends on the amount of liquid in the vessel [192, 224, 225] (Fig. 37b). In most cases, however, a radioactive source is placed on one side of the container, and a measuring instrument on the opposite side at the same height. The intensity of the radiation falling on the measuring instrument then changes abruptly when the liquid level reaches the height of source and measuring instrument. With several radiation sources located one above the other, or with a rod-shaped source (see Fig. 37 c), accurate gauging can be carried out over a wide range of levels. In such units it may be an advantage to vary the activity from source to source, or within the rod-shaped radiator.

Two γ-ray sources may be placed one above the other on one side of the container, while on the other side a single measuring instrument is fixed at the same height as the upper source. A rise in the level of the liquid causes the intensity at the detector to decrease at first slowly, and then, as soon as the level reaches the height of the upper source, suddenly to a very small value. Level gauges containing several measuring instruments have been recommended for special purposes [332].

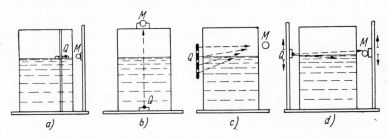

FIG. 37. Some methods for determining the level of liquids or loose materials in storage tanks. (Q) γ-ray source; (M) Radiation detector (e.g. counter)

Sensitive level detection at any point in a vessel is possible with equipment where radiation source and measuring instrument are located at the same height but on opposite sides of the vessel, and can jointly be moved up and down along the entire height of the container (Fig. 37 d). Servo-mechanisms may be used to follow the level and to register its position continuously [386].

A kind of level gauge is suitable for finding the distribution of gas and liquid, i.e., the local overall density, in a reaction vessel into which a gas is blown from below through the liquid. By this means information on the liquid content of foams, such as liquid paraffin with suspended Fischer–Tropsch catalyst plus water gas at 260 °C and 20 atm, could be obtained [317]. Similarly, the specific gravity of the water–steam emulsion in an industrial boiler can be measured, but this may also be done by dissolving sodium-24 in the water and comparing the counting rates at different levels [408]. Furthermore, the density of fluidized beds at various levels may be found by γ-ray absorption [377].

Portable level gauges ("density feelers") have been described. The source and the measuring instrument are attached to opposite prongs of a kind of fork with which the container is scanned. This type of instrument can be used, for example, with steel cylinders containing gases, or with fire-extinguishers [226, 380].

Special types of level gauges are applicable to the location of the boundary between two media of different densities [192, 227], or the measurement of liquid metals [228].

With powders (coal dust) in large containers, unevenness of the surface may cause problems. It is then possible to use several sources and measuring instruments arranged in various directions, and to obtain a combined indication, i.e., an average value [216] (see p. 122).

The back-scattering of γ-radiation may also be applied to level gauging. The measuring instrument and source are placed on the same side of the container or in the ceiling, and the direct action of the radiation from the source on the instrument is prevented by a shield. When the liquid in the container rises, back-scattering is increased and the radiation intensity recorded by the instrument therefore also rises. Discrimination between the primary and the scattered radiation is possible through the decreased energy of the latter [229, 230, 389]. A movable γ-probe has been used to find the propane–brine interface in a storage reservoir. The probe contains a caesium-137 source and a scintillation counter, which is separated from the source by lead. The intensity of the back-scattered radiation depends on the nature of medium (hydrocarbon or brine) [383].

Level gauging by γ-ray absorption has been developed into a routine method for the study of malfunction in distillation columns [389]. The method can be applied to on-line columns to indicate overloading, frothing and flooded sections. Typically, several millicuries of cobalt-60 are used, and this source may be moved up and down together with the measuring instrument. The method is also useful for checking working columns against design data. The γ-ray absorption patterns may be converted to approximate density profiles.

For special purposes neutrons may be used instead of γ-rays for level gauging. Thus, in high γ-ray fields, such as those in atomic energy plants, levels may be detected by the attenuation of a beam of fast neutrons. A hydrogen containing scintillator, in which the neutrons produce relatively strong light flashes by way of recoil protons, is a suitable detector. A discriminating unit in the instrument provides for selective registration of neutrons [231].

If the liquid in the vessel contains hydrogen or other elements which are efficient moderators, the slowing-down of neutrons may be used for level gauging. The equipment may consist of a neutron source that is permanently attached to a boron fluoride counter or to a scintillation counter sensitive to slow neutrons. As long as no moderator is present in the neighbourhood of the instrument, the recorded slow neutron flux is low. In one study, different arrangements of source and counter, some inside and others outside the container, were investigated [196, 217]. Instruments working with slow neutrons have been recommended in particular for mobile containers, such as fuel tanks in aircraft [378]. It is also possible to base level detection on the reflection of the fast neutrons by liquids containing light atoms; the instrument must then be shielded by lead against the direct beam [379].

It has been pointed out that less radiation protection is needed with neutron level gauges than with γ-ray gauges [379]. From this point of view, neutron sources which emit practically no γ-radiation are preferred, such as polonium–beryllium or plutonium–beryllium sources.

The absorption of γ-radiation can be used for a check whether packages are correctly filled, that is, whether the contents reach the prescribed level. A mechanism which rejects faulty packages can be operated by such a measuring instrument [233]. Equipment suitable for controlling the correct filling of containers of detergents, anti-freeze liquids or powders has been built. It utilizes X-rays excited by β-rays from strontium-90 (see p. 107) and a Geiger counter. In intervals when no package is in the radiation path the detector is automatically switched off by means of a photoelectric device [234]. The filling of aluminium tubes with toothpaste or of paper bags with washing powder may also be controlled automatically, preferably by β-ray absorption [235, 382]. Finally, radiation methods may be used to register the number of units passing along a production line, such as bottles in breweries, or animal carcasses in a slaughter house [236].

The absorption and scattering of radiation may also be used for measuring the density of liquids in a container, for checking the weight of such products as cigarettes, etc. (see Volume 2).

Checking the assembly of parts in a device or a machine is an application for which rather crude radiation measurements are sufficient. In the correctly assembled unit there must be a critical radiation path, i.e., a line along which a minimum or maximum of metal is found. If necessary, such a path may be provided by special slots or borings. For the test the assembled unit is placed in a well-collimated γ-ray beam in such a manner that the beam would coincide with the critical radiation path. The absorption of the radiation is then measured. If the assembly is correct, this absorption will be a maximum or a minimum. Such methods make it possible to check assemblies in a few seconds [237]. The possibilities for gauging by γ-radiation the opening between moving machine parts (distance between turbine blades and casing) have been discussed [384].

For checking the correct insertion of small parts into an assembled unit, a somewhat different procedure is suitable. The appropriate part of the equipment is made radioactive. By radiation measurement from outside, one can then determine whether the part has actually been inserted and is correctly placed. This principle has been used to check the introduction of a small copper sphere which forms part of a valve in projectiles. The sphere was made radioactive by electrolytic deposition of 0·25 μc of silver-110. Automatic equipment for radiation measurement controlling a mechanism which rejects imperfect units was specially developed for the purpose [238].

When assembling units, such as cement blocks, in house construction it may be necessary to find that point on one side of a plate which corresponds exactly to a given point on the opposite side. This can be done with a sharply collimated beam of γ-rays and a scintillation counter to locate the beam as it penetrates through the unit [239].

Increasing use is being made of limiting switches operated by radiation. A moving part or vehicle is stopped or blocked as soon as it crosses a beam of radiation (usually γ-radiation) and thereby interrupts its action on an instrument. Another principle is to mount the detection unit and the source in such a manner that the radiation intensity falling on the detector increases as the moving unit approaches the intended limit of its path. When the radiation intensity reaches a critical value a signal to a control circuit is triggered. With this type of arrangement the collision of two units, such as cranes moving on the same track may be prevented. In this case the source is mounted on one unit, the detector on the other [445]. Obviously limiting switches operated by radiation can be applied in many ways to improve safety in industry and transport [446, 447, 455].

9.3.4. *Flow Velocities*

Various procedures may be used for the determination of flow rates with radio-active tracers [330, 422, 452, 453]. These methods have several important advantages: in evaluating the experimental measurement data, no hydrodynamic calculations and no assumptions in respect to flow mechanism are involved; no flow impeding obstacles are introduced and the system is therefore not disturbed; suspended material and dirt do not interfere; no lengthy preparations are required and the measurements usually do not take much time; and, finally, the measurements may often be carried out from outside. Generally, γ-emitting nuclides have to be employed to make measurement from outside possible. In some cases, however, it has been found preferable to insert radiation detectors directly into the streaming liquid (see pp. 220 and 304).

Geiger counters or scintillation counters may serve for the measurements. For a given detector volume, scintillators are more efficient for γ-rays than counting tubes, but the measurement of the activity of dissolved materials in large volumes of water may be carried out quite efficiently with large counting tubes or groups of counting tubes. The sensitivities obtained in this way approach those with scintillation counters. Scintillation counters have the advantage of shorter dead times, but Geiger counters will withstand higher temperatures (100 °C instead of 35 °C) and may be replaced one by one, as required, without appreciable alteration in yield [328].

Methods of flow measurement using radioactive tracers are of importance for various types of industrial installations as well as for natural water courses (hydrology). The latter applications will be discussed in Chapter 12.

These methods may be used for both liquids and gases, but in our discussion we shall mainly deal with liquids. With gases special problems arise, because the linear velocities are usually much greater than with liquids, because the compressibility of the gases makes it necessary to use special devices for the injection of the radioactive gas, and because not many suitable nuclides are available [330].

The "two-point method" or "velocity method" uses two measuring instruments placed at a definite distance from each other. A small amount of a radioactive tracer is introduced, and the time is recorded when each of the two measuring instruments indicates maximum activity. Thus the time needed for passage from one detection point to the other is obtained, and the velocity is derived from this time. If the throughput (in l./sec, for example) is needed, the volume of liquid between the two instruments must obviously be known. Therefore, the method is most suitable for tubes, etc. [162, 200, 330].

An application of the two-point method to gas flow has already been given in Section 8.1.1., for the measurement of the gas flow in a blast furnace with radon liberated by the detonation of a capsule. The flow of natural gas in a pipe line was measured with argon-41 (half-life 1·82 hr) [319], but the advantages of long-lived krypton-85 (half-life 10·3 years) for such purposes have been pointed out [330].

For liquids to which the radioelements may only be added with difficulty, such as hot or corrosive liquids, activation with neutrons has been suggested. A portable accelerator could be used to provide fast neutrons capable of inducing the nuclear reactions $^{16}O(n, p)$ ^{16}N in oxygen-containing liquids. The activity of short-lived nitrogen-16 (half-life 7·5 sec) may then be determined. If the liquid contains elements that are easily activated the neutron flux from a natural neutron source, such as a polonium–beryllium source, may be sufficient for activation [241].

A second method for flow rates uses only one measuring instrument [162, 200, 242, 243, 320]. A radioactive tracer is introduced at a certain time into the pipe, and the integral count registered by the instrument is measured as the tracer passes. It is readily seen that the measured total count is proportional to the total activity of radioelement added, and inversely proportional to the velocity of the liquid. Calculation of the through-put of liquid is best based on a simple calibration, which may either be carried out on the pipe itself, or on a separate piece of pipe having the same dimensions. The section of pipe is then filled with a solution of known specific activity, and the count per unit time is determined with the measuring instrument. As we have already indicated, the following relation applies for the total count in the streaming liquid:

$$Z = k \text{ (activity of injected radioelement)/(through-put)}, \qquad (30)$$

or, written in terms of units,

$$\text{counts} = k \frac{\text{curie}}{\text{litre} \cdot \text{sec}^{-1}} \qquad (31)$$

A simple rearrangement gives

$$\text{counts} \cdot \text{sec}^{-1} = k \frac{\text{curie}}{\text{litre}} \qquad (32)$$

In this way, the measurement on the section of pipe filled with the radioactive solution gives the constant k which may then be used to evaluate the measurements on the flowing liquid. In practice this "total count method" is carried out with γ-emitting nuclides, such as caesium-134.

The distance between the point of addition of the radioactive substance and the measuring point must be so long that transverse mixing is complete. On the other hand, this distance must not be so large that, because of the spreading out of the substance in the direction of flow, the required measuring times become excessive. Complete mixing may be facilitated in the case of large volume transport by multiple injection, i.e., at several laterally spread points [403]. In practice the distance may usually be selected within rather wide limits. On certain assumptions the least distance L may be estimated by the empirical equation

$$L = aQ^{1/3} \qquad (33)$$

where L is measured in m and Q represents the water flow in m³/sec. In the case of natural waters with turbulent flow, the constant a may be taken as 200 or 50, according to whether the tracer is introduced at the edge or in the centre [302].

The total count method just described has been extended to the case in which the flowing liquid divides and a radiation measurement is carried out only on one branch. If a fraction p of the total flow passes through the branch on which the measurement is performed, numerator and denominator of the right-hand side of equation (30) are reduced by this factor (p). The quotient Z thus maintains the same value, and the equation therefore applies equally well to the branch or to the main stream of liquid. This result permits of numerous applications [242, 244].

Thus, flow in an inaccessible tube, or in a tube which cannot be calibrated easily, may be determined by measurements on a suitable side-tube, which may be specially devised for these measurements. The calibration (that is, the determination of the constant k) is then carried out on this tube, or another with identical dimensions, with stationary liquid. In the simplest form, the auxiliary branch may consist only of a bucket with inflow and outflow tubes, in which the measuring instrument is immersed. A particular advantage of this arrangement lies in the fact that the immersed counter gives a much greater measuring yield than an instrument placed outside the tube.

The total count method may be applied to many special cases [242, 244], including the determination of a continuous or occasional water flow in natural water courses or canals (see p. 304). As with the two-point method, measurements by the total count method can only be carried out intermittently so that no continuous control of flow is possible.

The total sampling method is a variant of the total count method. Instead of measuring radioactive radiations directly on the stream, a sample is taken covering the whole period of time needed for the injected tracer to pass the sampling point. Afterwards, the average tracer concentration in the sample is determined. For instance, the total sampling method may be used for flow rates in pipes. Sampling is possible by means of a tap on the pipe, which is open during the period in which the tracer passes the tap. The outflowing liquid is collected and constitutes the measuring sample [69, 70] (see also p. 304). Steam flow measurements have been carried out by the total sample method with tritium as tracer [448].

The total count method has been extended to gases for a range from a few hundred cubic feet per minute (motor car engines) to hundreds of thousands of cubic feet per minute (large industrial plants). Krypton-85, being cheap, inert and long-lived, is a suitable tracer. Its β-radiation is used for routine measurement; the sample stream taken from the gas line is passed through a β-ray chamber at atmospheric pressure. For the calibration of strong sources, however, the weak γ-radiation is preferred. For the introduction into high pressure gas, a carefully designed injector is needed. The method has been applied, for instance, to the calibration of an orifice flow-meter in an ammonia synthesis plant, and also to the estimation of a leak in a heat exchanger in the same plant [405].

A third method for determining flow rates, particularly suitable for water courses of unknown and variable cross-section, or for ill-defined flow processes in industry, uses a dilution principle. A small and constant stream of tagged material of known flow rate and activity per unit volume is injected into the fluid current to be measured. At some point, for which complete mixing of the two streams can be assumed with certainty, the specific activity of the mixture is determined, either on a sample taken from the stream, or by direct measurement on the flowing fluid. The observed dilution of the radioelement, given by the ratio of the activities per unit volume of the added current and the mixture, gives the ratio of the two flow rates, and so permits the calculation of the required flow rate [69, 162, 245, 330]. This principle has been used for the measurement of condenser water through-put in a steam power station. Salt solution (containing ^{24}Na) was injected, and a through-put of 125,000 l./min was determined [246].

The dilution principle (using radon) has also been applied to the flow of gases in wind tunnels and glass furnaces [329, 427] (see also Section 8.1.1 and [330]). More recently, xenon-133 has been used to find gas flow rates in process lines containing corrosive material and entrained particulate matter. The injection was carried out, in mixture with a large excess of nitrogen, by means of a capillary. For assay, scintillation counters or ionization chambers may be used. The method has proved valuable for flow rates between 50 and 500,000 l./min [400].

All the procedures so far described for the measurement of flow rates assume rapid mixing after the addition of the radioelement, due to lateral diffusion and convection occurring rapidly. Since the labelled fluid may then be considered to move as a piston or plug (gradually spreading out longitudinally in the direction of flow), the period during which the labelled liquid remains in a system is simply given by the ratio of the volume of the system to the flow rate [247].

The following kind of system is of a different nature. The added radioelement is rapidly mixed with the contents of a container (such as a reaction vessel or a storage tank). Inflow and outflow of inactive material occur at the same rate and are slow. The added radioelement then leaves such a system according to an exponential law, so that the amount flowing out per unit time is proportional to the amount still present at that time [389].

In many systems found in industrial practice neither of these two extreme cases actually applies [428]. The outflow of the added radioelement, or of any other dissolved or suspended material, may then be described only by some empirical function. The nature of this function, and the extent of any blocked volume, are often of great technological importance, since the residence time gives the time available for a chemical reaction within the system [69]. Such functions have therefore been determined with tracers in many studies in process technology [452, 453]. We may mention measurements of the movement of ore particles and reagents, which pass through a series of vessels during the wet processing of ores [181, 248, 249], and investigations on the behaviour of solutions and suspended particles in the Bayer process for alumina production (181, 459] (see p. 163). Retention periods in vessels connected in series in peat refining have also been measured [425]. A radioactive gas (argon-41) was used in tests of a ventilation unit for hay [428, 460].

The numerous possibilities of obtaining flow data by observing the transport and distribution of injected radioactive tracers in plants of the chemical and petrochemical industries are well illustrated by a study performed in a hydrocarbon alkylation unit [456]. It was desired to measure the flow of the sulphuric acid through various reactors and circulation loops of the plant. Radiogold in a form soluble in the acid was rapidly injected at a suitable point, and the distribution of the tracer was then followed both by measurements from the outside of pipes and on acid samples withdrawn from the vessels. The circulation rate was measured by timing the passage of tracer through a pipe of known volume. The total volume of acid was obtained by isotope dilution. The replacement rate of acid in the vessels was calculated from the observed disappearance of the tracer. The entrainment of acid in a hydrocarbon stream was measured by registering the tracer concentration arising in a second reactor.

The flow of liquids in a large distillation column used in the oil industry has been determined during routine operation. An oil-soluble radioactive antimony compound was introduced at the uppermost plate. By using counters which could be held against the outside of the column, the appearance of activity at various plates was determined. It was found that the current in the column, whose plates were provided with several down-flow tubes because of the large cross-section, was not uniform. This was indicated by the fact that the activity appeared first in one down-flow tube of a given plate, and only subsequently in others [162, 200, 250, 251]. Activity measurements on the bottom product (residue) leaving the column provided a means of determining the mixing in a column when moving over to a new (labelled) charge [195].

It has been pointed out that alkyl and aryl halides containing radioisotopes of the halogens, in particular bromine-82, and tetraalkyl germanium compounds containing germanium-75 or germanium-77 may also be suitable tracer compounds for flow studies in the petroleum and petrochemical industries [454].

A technique of activation analysis for plant stream monitoring [407] was developed first for the determination of dissolved elements. The stream is exposed to slow neutrons, and the short-lived activity induced, in such elements as fluorine or selenium, is monitored some distance away. The vessels, which serve for irradiation and counting, are equipped with baffles or stream guides to prevent channeling. When two counters are used with a suitable interval between them, a two-point neutron activation flow-rate meter is obtained [407]. A flowmeter for reactor coolants is based on the fact that, other things being equal, the activity induced by the thermal neutrons in the water depends on exposure time [406].

Rotameters may be labelled with cobalt-60, and located in a liquid by radiation measurement [252, 313]. The rotation frequency of a paddle wheel may also be found by radiation detection if one of the paddles carries a radioactive source [220, 413]. Another method provides for a fixed source and a lead covered absorbing wheel [414].

A method of this type was used for the measurement of water circulation in a high-pressure, natural-circulation boiler to check the heat transfer. A propeller was built into the downcomer tube. Two cobalt-60 sources (10 and 3 mc) were attached to propeller blades and displaced 120° relative to each other. The rotation of the propeller moved first one and then the other source into the sensitive field of the detector, thereby giving rise to two sets of output signals of different strength. The impulses were registered by a fast ink-jet recorder. Knowing the paper speed, the speed of the propeller could be determined by measuring the distance between two successive impulse maxima. Alternatively, a two-point method using radioactive ammonium bromide was used for the same boiler [402] (see also [457]).

Gas flow rates may also be measured by means of a hinged gate, to which a small radiation source is attached. With increasing gas velocity, the gate is more and more deflected from the vertical position, so that the radiation source approaches a detector outside the pipe, and the count rate increases [253].

To determine the through-put of dissolved substances, it is possible to combine in an integrator the signals obtained by γ-absorptiometry, in which a density measurement indicates the concentration, with those from a continuous flow-rate measurement on the solution using some other procedure. In the case of conducting liquids, the flow rate may, for example, be obtained by measuring the potential difference arising when a magnetic field is imposed on the flowing liquid [234].

In a fertilizer plant using recirculation, sodium-24 has been employed to find transit times. Successive peaks showed the time of arrival and the distribution in time of the repeatedly recirculated material [426].

Various tracer procedures to determine the rate of movement of suspended solid materials, such as peat particles in a processing machine or ore and coal particles in settling beds, have also been described [220]. Hydraulic transport through tubes is used for lumps of salt in potassium mines. After activating lumps of a given size range with sodium-24, their speed could be compared with that of the solution or with lumps of other sizes [416]. The relative velocities of water and of sand transported by the water in pipes under actual conditions in the industry was determined by the two-point method after tagging water and sand [458].

Measurement of the flow of catalyst in catalytic cracking plants, operating on the fluidized bed principle, has been carried out by marking single catalyst beads, with such sources as with zirconium-95. The speed of movement of single beads through a pipe may then be determined by radiation measurement at two points along the pipe. Groups of counting tubes have been used in such methods, which are analogous to the two-point method described for liquids. The variation of the velocity of the catalyst within a tube, depending on the position, has been studied. On this basis devices designed to assure uniform catalyst velocity at all positions within the tube may be improved. The same kind of equipment has also been used for continuous operational control of cracking plants. About five labelled particles were added to 10 million inactive particles [162, 195, 200, 256, 257]. The mixing of the catalyst in cracking plants has also been followed with tracers, and at the same time residence times in vessels and the total inventory were obtained [258, 259].

The flow of powdered materials of various kinds in rotary kilns will be discussed in Section 10.5 in connection with the industry of building materials.

9.3.5. *Mechanisms of Flow*

Radioactive tracers have found application for elucidating flow mechanisms and obtaining velocity profiles. A comparatively simple set-up has been used to find out how close to the wall of a tube the laws of laminar flow still hold. A vertical tube was half filled with solution containing a γ-emitter, while the other half was filled with an inactive but otherwise identical solution. Further inactive liquid was then forced into the tube, and the active solution expelled in the course of a few minutes. The radiation from the originally active half of the tube was continuously measured from outside the tube with a scintillation counter provided with entrance slits giving good collimation. The measurements, taken as the conical interface passed the counter, indicated laminar flow up to about 0·25 mm from the wall. Closer to the wall, the displacement of the liquid was more rapid than accounted for by laminar flow. This deviation was probably due to the diffusion of the labelled substance from the region nearest to the wall into more remote, and therefore more rapidly moving layers [260, 261].

Turbulent flow in wider pipes (up to 1·5 m diameter) has been investigated by injection of a liquid labelled with radiosodium at various positions in the pipe. Activity measurements carried out along the pipe indicated that the rate of movement of the injected labelled substance showed substantial variation with time [246]. Further important tracer investigations with the object of establishing to what extent the assumption of turbulent flow is justified in various conditions can only be mentioned here [312, 420, 421].

The determination of the minimum temperature gradient required to produce a convection current in a liquid enclosed in a porous medium has been carried out in a laboratory investigation [262]. For this purpose, a radiation measuring instrument was embedded into the porous medium, a small amount of radioactive phosphate was introduced near the instrument, and the temperature gradient was then increased by heating at one side. The onset of convection was revealed by a short increase in the measured radiation intensity, followed by a rapid decrease.

Tracer methods may also be used in connection with the complex phenomena arising during the transport of heat and materials through capillary porous bodies. Such phenomena are important in the combustion of solid fuels and the drying or moistening of materials. The movement of the liquid in such bodies may be followed in a stationary or non-stationary state by labelling the liquid, e.g., by dissolving radioiodine in it. The investigation is naturally easiest if only one-dimensional movement is to be studied. In one of the experiments, the samples were dried with hot air, and the temperature and flow rate were controlled. The evaporation was measured and its spatial distribution was determined by making use of the fact that the precipitation of labelled salts from their saturated solution takes place at the site of evaporation [263].

Suspensions of insoluble spherical particles, made of radioactive clay [254] or plastic substance [255], may also be used to study flow processes.

Investigation of large scale flow processes, such as in sewage disposal plants and reservoirs, and the silting of estuaries, as well as experiments on models for elucidating the movement of underground water courses will be discussed in Chapter 12.

9.3.6. *Leak Detection*

Methods for checking containers for absence of leaks are of great importance. Thus, welded containers have been tested by filling them with methyl bromide (radiobromine). The outside of the containers was covered with adhesive strips, which were then tested for activity [100]. The leakproof behaviour of heat exchangers was investigated in a simple manner by filling one side of the exchanger with the radioactive solution and carrying out measurements on the other side [69, 162, 242]. More recently, water containing tritium has been used for the purpose [401].

Hermetically sealed containers may be tested by exposing them to krypton-85 under high pressure, and measuring the amount absorbed. (Contamination of the outer surface is a serious problem here.) The high pressure may be generated by transferring the gas from a larger vessel into a small vessel by freezing out, and letting it evaporate subsequently [404, 417]. This method has been recommended for semiconductor encapsulations. Alternatively, the radiokrypton may be introduced into an object such as a clad fuel element for a reactor, and its release, if any, may be observed [404].

Leaks in oil, water and steam pipes may be detected by forcing radioactive liquids into the pipes, then flushing with inactive liquids, and finally scanning the pipe with a measuring instrument to determine the points where liquid has been forced out of the pipe (see p. 180). Sodium chloride (^{24}Na) is a convenient tracer for water; its short half-life and the high energy of the γ-radiation are advantages [246, 264, 266, 325, 409, 423]. The half-life of chlorine-38 is even shorter [425]. On the other hand, bromine-82 ($\tau = 36$ hr) is used for investigations taking more time [69].

Often, scanning may be carried out by walking along a buried pipe with a scintillation counter. However, if the earth layer above the pipe is so thick that the radiation does not penetrate well, a detector that is connected by means of a cable with the counting unit may be forced through the pipe by means of compressed air. In another procedure the entire measuring instrument is sent through the pipe line. The instrument is provided with a suitable recorder, such as a wire recorder. In order to facilitate the interpretation of such records, γ-emitting sources (e.g., cobalt-60) are arranged along the pipe at definite positions. These places are also recorded by the measuring instrument, and then serve as reference points for locating the leaks [246, 264, 265, 303, 409].

Leak detection may also be based on measurement of flow rates. Radiation detectors are placed along the pipe at accurately known distances. A radioactive liquid is then forced through the pipe at constant pressure and the intervals of time between the signals are determined. If a loss of liquid occurs between two detection instruments, the radioactive substance reaches the second of these instruments later than would have been expected [246, 264].

A method for the detection of small leaks is particularly applicable to pipe lines with numerous branches, such as those supplying hydrants. The section of pipe to be investigated is closed at both ends, and water is forced in through one of the side branches. When the water is already under pressure, a small amount of tracer solution is injected. Activity measurements carried out along the pipe line show in which direction the tracer is forced, that is to say, in which direction the leak occurs. When this procedure is then repeated by injection through other side branches, the two branches between which the leak occurs can be determined [69, 246].

Methods for detecting leaks in the inner of the two concentric tubes have also been worked out [264].

Instead of radioactive liquids, gases can be used for leak detection, especially in gas mains and gas pipe lines. For example, radioactive methyl bromide vapour, carbon dioxide or radon may be used. The speed of leak detection depends greatly on the gas pressure and also on the nature of the ground in which the pipe is buried [267, 409, 429].

Leak testing is of great importance in the electrical industries (p. 179). The procedures discussed there, for instance methods for checking the tightness of sealed electronic units, such as transistors, may also be adapted for use in other branches of industry, such as testing for leaks in the cladding of fuel elements for nuclear reactors.

9.3.7. *Determination of the Volume of Vessels and of Phases*

The determination of the volume of vessels or of phases in a chemical plant may be conducted with radionuclides. In one method the isotope dilution principle (p. 162) is used. A radioactive substance is introduced in known quantity and activity into the system. After complete mixing, the concentration of the radioactive substance is determined by activity measurement. On this basis, the volume of the system or of the phase over which the radioelement is distributed is then computed [162, 200, 456]. In this way, the amount of iron oxide sludge formed daily in a plant was determined. The measurements of activity were conducted, after thorough mixing, either on the suspension itself, or on the separated oxide [196].

A further method is suitable for the volume of vessels through which a liquid flows, and in which thorough mixing takes place. After a single injection of a tracer into such a vessel, the activity in the vessel, and therefore also the activity in the outflow, decreases exponentially with time. The rate of decrease in activity depends on the ratio of the through-put to the volume of the vessel. Hence, from the rate of activity decrease and the through-put the volume of the vessel can be calculated [162, 200, 456] (see p. 221).

For checking and controlling chemical processes increasing use is made of the determination of density and of chemical composition by radiation absorption and radiation scattering. These methods, which are described in Section 6.7 and in Volume 2, are particularly important for plants operated automatically. In addition to the applications discussed elsewhere, we may mention the possibility of using radiation absorption to determine the ratio of the volume of phases in industrial multi-phase systems. The distribution of vapour and liquid in an evaporator or condenser (p. 215) as well as the distribution of solid materials in a "fluidized bed" reactor (p. 215) or in the pneumatic and hydraulic transport of pulverized materials (see also p. 223) can be determined in this manner.

9.3.8. *Testing of Filters and Measurement of Particle Size*

Radioactive substances may be used for testing the quality of filters. Air filters of internal combustion engines have been tested with radioactive dust, the time taken being not more than 15 min. The radioactive substance was introduced as a rod which was pressed against a rotating abrasive disc. The active dust so produced was then carried away by a turbulent air current, and was forced against the filter [268]. In another procedure, developed for compressors of diesel engines, fine drops of labelled triphenylstibine were used [269]. Filters may also be tested with the decay products of radon, adsorbed on to dust [270].

Bacteriological filters have been tested using microscopic plastic spheres. These were covered with a layer of gold and then activated in a reactor. It was then found by activity measurement whether the particles penetrated the filter or were retained. The method has been used for daily checks on filters for the removal of bacteria in industry [271].

Unicellular algae (*Chlorella* or *Scenedesmus*) have also been employed for tests on filters. These cells can be considered as small spheres, easily and cheaply prepared, and are of fairly uniform size. They can be made radioactive, for example, by cultivation in a medium containing caesium-137. Experiments have shown that the radiocaesium, when once taken up by the algae, is not released again to the water. The γ-radiation of the caesium can be measured through thick layers of filters, such as sand filters, with scintillation counters [272]. Investigations on the passage of true solutions of radioactive substances through porous materials, including filter beds, will be discussed in Section 12.2.

In suitable cases particle size determinations may be carried out by a radiochemical modification of sedimentation analysis. Thus, irradiated uranium dioxide at temperatures up to 800°C was stirred into liquid sodium–potassium alloy, and then allowed to settle for a suitable period, e.g., 40 min. During settling, the activity was measured by means of a scintillation counter receiving radiation from the sedimentation tank through a narrow, highly collimating, horizontal slit [273]. A similar technique has been applied to thorium oxide powders. The irradiated powder contained thorium-233, which emits β-radiation of 1·23 MeV. This radiation was measured through a plexiglass window in the bottom of the settling cell, and the amount of deposited material determined in this way [418]. A special centrifuge permitting continuous observation of the sedimentation of labelled particles by radiation measurement has been designed [419].

Settling of particles has also been followed by scanning the settling vessels with a γ-absorptiometric technique. The sedimentation of uranium dioxide in water was determined by scanning with an americium-241 source and a scintillation counter placed on the opposite side. A particle size distribution was derived on the basis of Stokes' law [411]. The settling of suspended pigments (TiO_2) in paints contained in tins was followed by absorption of strontium-90 bremsstrahlung [410]. A review of the application of radionuclides to determinations of particle size distributions by observation of sedimentation has been given [412] (see also [451]).

9.4. Industrial Hygiene

The effectiveness of factory ventilation may be correctly determined with radioactive gases [100, 274, 311]. In the examination of a laboratory room, it was found that the amount of radioxenon (measured with an ionization chamber) in the space investigated decreased with a definite half-life. It was concluded from the exponential decline of activity that the old air continually mixed with fresh air, and that no important dead spaces were present. The half-life was about half an hour, but was much less when a fan was used.

Inert gases are suitable for such studies as they are not easily retained by surfaces and are quickly removed from the human body, thus constituting no great health hazard (see p. 321). Because of its small half-life (109 min), argon-41 is safest but this gas is only available in the neighbourhood of reactors. Other suitable nuclides are krypton-85 and xenon-133.

Radioactive noble gases have also been employed to measure the penetration of air into railway coaches under simulated operating conditions in a large test chamber [449].

Air flow in an asbestos factory has been investigated with organic vapours containing radiobromine to detect the undesirable spreading of minute asbestos particles [250]. To check ventilation in a bacteriological research establishment, a radioactive potassium compound was dispersed as dust into the atmosphere by means of a special device [250]. Another kind of device for the preparation of solid radioactive aerosols consists of an atomizer, a quartz combustion tube, a dilution chamber and an outlet [275].

The concentration of mercury vapour in air, near the places of individual workmen, can easily be measured with radiomercury. A known quantity of air is sucked through a cooled trap, where the vapour condenses. The deposited mercury may then be placed under a counter, and its activity measured. As little as 10^{-5} g of mercury per cubic metre has been estimated without difficulty [276, 277]. This quantity corresponds to one tenth of the listed tolerance concentration.

Exhaust gases from aluminium factories contain the poisonous fluorine in the form of salts. The distribution of such salts has been determined with sodium fluoride containing ^{24}Na, the finely divided state of the compound in the exhaust gas being obtained by spraying into the flue [194]. In other work, ^{64}CuO was injected into the gas released from a stack, and the dust was collected at various distances by filtration through paper. Gamma-gamma coincidence due to the radiation emitted in the annihilation of the positrons was used to discriminate against radiation from natural radioelements [415].

Radioactivity has also been employed to determine the uptake of the extremely poisonous gas arsine by charcoal filters [278]. Labelled tricresyl phophate in the form of a mist was used for testing gas masks [279].

The metabolic behaviour of many elements, including those acting as industrial poisons, has been thoroughly investigated with radionuclides. Reviews of such investigations are presented in books by Hevesy [280] and Comar [281, 282], and also in a monograph by one of the present authors [283].

An example of such investigations with significance for industrial hygiene concerns poisoning by breathing certain materials used in industry. The vapour of tetraethyl lead (an antiknock agent) was found to be absorbed by rats to the extent of 23 per cent through the lungs. The simultaneous presence of hydrocarbon vapour had no effect on the absorption. The compound was rapidly decomposed in the body of the animals. About 11 mg per kilogram of body weight were found to be fatal [284]. Carbon tetrachloride containing ^{14}C was used to follow the distribution and elimination of this compound in monkeys. The results provided information of value for human hygiene [285].

The absorption of the labelled plasticizer tricresyl phosphate by the skin has been tested by rubbing a small quantity (100–200 mg) on the palm of the human hand, and allowing it to remain there for a few hours [286]. A surprisingly large quantity of radiophosphorus was thereafter found in the blood, and was only slowly eliminated by way of the urine. In experiments on animals the specific activity of various organs after absorption could also be investigated.

References to Chapter 9

1. G.E.BACON, *Neutron Diffraction*, Oxford 1962.
2. M.K.WILKINSON, E.O.WOLLAN and W.C.KOEHLER, *Ann. Rev. Nucl. Sci.* **11**, 303 (1961).
3. S.G.CLARK and F.P.HOLT, *J. Chem. Soc.* **1957**, 5007.
4. A.E.BRODSKII, *Isotope Chemistry* (Russ.), Moscow 1957; German translation, Berlin 1961.
5. Colloque International, *J. Chim. Physique* **45**, 141 (1948).
6. R.R.EDWARDS, *Ann. Rev. Nucl. Sci.* **1**, 301 (1952).
7. M.HAISSINSKY, *J. Chim. Physique* **47**, 957 (1950).
8. M.HAISSINSKY and R.DAUDEL, *Bull. Soc. Chim. France* **14**, 552 (1947).
9. O.E.MYERS and R.J.PRESTWOOD, in [350].
10. A.A.GRINBERG, Moscow Atomic Energy Conference 1955, Div. Chem. Sciences, p. 238.
11. C.B.AMPHLETT, *Quart. Rev.* **8**, 219 (1954).
12. V.I.SPITSYN, *Acta Chim. Hung.* **12**, 119 (1957).
13. C.BLACK, G.G.JORIS and H.S.TAYLOR, *J. Chem. Physics* **16**, 45, 537 (1948).
14. B.D.CADDOCK and P.L.DAVIES, *Nature* **184**, 2011 (1959).
15. E.H.KLEHR and A.F.VOIGT, Copenhagen Report 187, vol. 3, p. 517.
16. M.A.STYRIKOVITCH, Paris Report 411, vol. 1, p. 411.
17. A.SELTVEIT and H.FLOOD, *Acta Chem. Scand.* **12**, 1030 (1958).
18. J.RYDBERG, Copenhagen Report 81, vol. 3, p. 427.
19. J.SCHUBERT, *J. Phys. Coll. Chem.* **52**, 340 (1948).
20. J.SCHUBERT and J.W.RICHTER, *J. Phys. Coll. Chem.* **52**, 350 (1948).
21. J.SCHUBERT and J.W.RICHTER, *J. Amer. Chem. Soc.* **70**, 4259 (1948).
22. J.SCHUBERT and A.LINDENBAUM, *Nature* **166**, 913 (1950).
23. S.FRONAEUS, *Acta Chem. Scand.* **5**, 859 (1950).
24. R.E.CONNICK and S.W.MAYER, *J. Amer. Chem. Soc.* **73**, 1176 (1951).
25. S.FRONAEUS, *Svensk Kemisk Tidskr.* **64**, 317 (1952).
26. J.FELDMAN, T.Y.TORIBARA, J.R.HAVILL and W.F.NEUMAN, *J. Amer. Chem. Soc.* **77**, 878 (1953).
27. K.A.KRAUS and F.NELSON, Geneva Report 837 (1955), vol. 7, p. 113.
28. S.FRONAEUS, *Svensk Kemisk Tidskr.* **65**, 1 (1953).
29. K.A.KRAUS and F.NELSON, in: W.J.HAMER (Ed.), *The Structure of Electrolytic Solutions*, New York 1959.
30. Y.MARCUS and C.D.CORYELL, *Bull. Res. Council Israel* A **8**, 1 (1959).
31. Y.MARCUS, *Bull. Res. Council Israel* A **8**, 17 (1959).
32. Y.MARCUS, *J. Phys. Chem.* **63**, 1000 (1959).
33. Y.MARCUS, *J. Inorg. Nucl. Chem.* **12**, 287 (1960).
34. J.DANON, *J. Inorg. Nucl. Chem.* **13**, 112 (1960).
35. R.E.CONNICK and W.H.McVEY, U.S. Atomic Energy Commission Report, UCRL-101 (1948).
36. R.E.CONNICK and W.H.McVEY, *J. Amer. Chem. Soc.* **71**, 3182 (1949).
37. J.RYDBERG, *Acta Chem. Scand.* **4**, 1503 (1950).
38. J.C.SULLIVAN and J.C.HINDMAN, *J. Amer. Chem. Soc.* **76**, 5931 (1954).
39. R.E.CONNICK and W.H.REAS, *J. Amer. Chem. Soc.* **73**, 1171 (1951).

40. T.V.Healy and H.A.C.McKay, *Rec. Trav. Chim. Pays-Bas* **75**, 730 (1956).
41. J.Rydberg, *Rec. Trav. Chim. Pays-Bas* **75**, 737 (1956).
42. D.Dyrssen and F.Krašovec, *Acta Chem. Scand.* **13**, 561 (1959).
43. I.S.Kulikov and I.A.Popov, *Radioactive Isotopes in Metallurgy* (Russ.), Moscow 1956; German translation, Berlin 1959.
44. A.N.Nesmeyanov, *Int. J. Appl. Rad. Isot.* **4**, 16 (1958); *Atomnaya Energiya* **3**, 227 (1957).
45. U.Croatto and L.Riccoboni, *Chim. e Industria* (Milano) **27**, 538 (1955).
46. F.D.Rosen and W.Davis, *Rev. Sci. Instr.* **24**, 349 (1953).
47. H.H.Schadel and C.E.Birchenall, *J. Metals* **188**, 1134 (1950).
48. Yu.V.Kornev and S.L.Zubkovskii, *Atomnaya Energiya* **2**, 352 (1957).
49. A.P.Lyubimov and A.A.Granovskaya, *Zh. Fiz. Khim.* **27**, 473, 1437 (1953).
50. A.S.Carson, D.R.Stranks and B.Wilmshurst, *Proc. Roy. Soc.* A **244**, 72 (1958).
51. A.S.Carson, D.R.Stranks and B.Wilmshurst, Paris Report 215, vol. 2, p. 447.
52. A.S.Carson, R.Cooper and D.R.Stranks, Copenhagen Report 41, vol. 3, p. 495.
53. A.N.Nesmeyanov, V.L.Losgachev and N.F.Lebedev, *Doklady Akad. Nauk SSSR* **102**, 307 (1955).
54. A.A.Zhukhovitskii, Moscow Atomic Energy Conference, 1955, Div. Tech. Sciences, p. 101.
55. P.Albert, F.Montariol, R.Reich and G.Chaudron, *Radioisotopes Conference*, vol. 2, London 1954, p. 75; *Compt. rend.* **238**, 815 (1954); **240**, 1087 (1955).
56. L.D.Hall, *J. Amer. Chem. Soc.* **73**, 757 (1951).
57. Yu.V.Kornev, *Doklady Akad. Nauk SSSR* **93**, 467 (1953).
58. Yu.V.Kornev and V.N.Golubkin, *Doklady Akad. Nauk SSSR* **99**, 565 (1954).
59. Yu.A.Priselkov and A.N.Nesmeyanov, *Doklady Akad. Nauk SSSR* **95**, 1207 (1954).
60. B.S.Iofa and A.N.Nesmeyanov, *Doklady Akad. Nauk SSSR* **98**, 993 (1954).
61. J.D.McKinley and J.E.Vance, *J. Chem. Phys.* **22**, 1120 (1954).
62. C.B.Alcock, *Int. J. Appl. Rad. Isot.* **3**, 135 (1958).
63. A.D.Crowell and H.E.Farnsworth, *J. Chem. Phys.* **19**, 1206 (1951).
64. J.A.Dillon and H.E.Farnsworth, *J. Chem. Phys.* **22**, 160 (1954).
65. J.A.Dillon and H.E.Farnsworth, *Rev. Sci. Instruments* **25**, 96 (1954).
66. See J.E.Willard, *J. Phys. Chem.* **57**, 129 (1953).
67. G.P.Miklukhin, *Isotopes in Organic Chemistry* (Russ.), Kiev 1961.
68. K.Schwabe, *Electrochim. Acta* **6**, 223 (1962).
69. L.G.Erwall, H.G.Forsberg and K.Ljunggren, in: *Production and Use of Short-lived Radioisotopes from Reactors*, vol. 1, I.A.E.A., Vienna 1963.
70. D.E.Hull, *Trans. Amer. Nucl. Soc.* **3**, 453 (1960).
71. K.Schwabe, *Isotopentechnik* **1**, 175 (1962).
72. Č.Jech, *Paris Report* 35, vol. 2, p. 491.
73. O.Erbacher, *Chemiker-Ztg.* **62**, 601 (1938).
74. O.Erbacher, *Z. Elektrochem.* **44**, 594 (1938).
75. W.Herr, *Angew. Chem.* **159**, 155 (1947).
76. C.Haenny and P.Mivelaz, *Helv. Chim. Acta* **31**, 633 (1948).
77. J.Siejka and I.G.Campbell, Geneva Report 1589 (1958), vol. 20, p. 148.
78. E.Herczynska and I.G.Campbell, *Z. Phys. Chem.* **215**, 248 (1960).
79. N.A.Balaschova, *Z. Phys. Chem.* **207**, 340 (1957).
80. J.Palacios and A.Baptista, *Nature* **170**, 665 (1952).
81. K.Schwabe, C.Weissmantel and W.Nowak, *Angew. Chem.* **72**, 632 (1960).
82. K.Schwabe and C.Weissmantel, *Z. Phys. Chem.* **215**, 48 (1960).
83. L.S.Bartell and J.F.Betts, *J. Phys. Chem.* **64**, 1075 (1960).
84. H.Sobotka, *J. Phys. Chem.* **62**, 527 (1958).
85. R.A.W.Haul, L.H.Stein and J.W.L.de Villiers, *Nature* **171**, 619 (1953).
86. R.A.W.Haul and L.H.Stein, *Trans. Faraday Soc.* **51**, 1280 (1955).
87. R.Haul and D.Just, *Naturwiss.* **45**, 435 (1958).
88. R.Lindner, *Acta Chem. Scand.* **4**, 307 (1950); **5**, 457 (1951); **6**, 468 (1952).
89. R.Lindner, *Z. Elektrochem.* **54**, 431 (1950); **59**, 967 (1955).
90. R.Lindner, Geneva Report 167 (1958), vol. 20, p. 116.

91. W.J.Moore, Paris Report 24, vol. 1, p. 528.
92. A.N.Murin, Paris Report 25, vol. 1, p. 549.
93. J.Bénard and J.F.Laurent, Paris Report 41, vol. 1, p. 577.
94. R.Lindner, *J. Chem. Soc. (London)* **1949,** (S) 395.
95. R.B.Cuddeback and H.G.Drickamer, *J. Chem. Phys.* **19,** 790 (1951).
96. G.Careri, A.Paoletti and F.L.Salvetti, *Nuovo Cimento* **11,** 399 (1954).
97. R.Millis, *J. Phys. Chem.* **61,** 1631 (1957).
98. I.Amdur and T.F.Schatzki, *J. Chem. Phys.* **27,** 1049 (1957).
99. R.L.Sproull, G.A.Slack, M.Moss, R.O.Pohl and J.A.Krumhansl, Copenhagen Report 197, vol. 1, p. 295.
100. J.Guéron, *Nucleonics* **9** (5), 53 (1951).
101. A.J.Rogers, J.W.Heyd, W.L.Hood and J.A.Williamson, *Nucleonics* **12** (6), 62 (1954).
102. F.A.Paneth and K.W.Vorwerk, *Z. Phys. Chem.* **101,** 445 (1922).
103. F.A.Paneth, *Z. Elektrochem.* **28,** 113 (1922); *J. Chim. Physique* **45,** 205 (1948).
104. M.M.Dubinin, *Methods of Investigating Catalysts* (Russ.), Moscow 1948.
105. A.V.Kiselev, *Usp. Khim.* **14,** 367 (1945).
106. S.E.Bresler, *The Radioactive Elements* (Russ.), Moscow 1952; German translation, Berlin 1957.
107. J.H.Wang in [350].
108. V.G.Khlopin and M.S.Merkulova, *Zh. Fiz. Khim.* **13,** 1282 (1939); *Izvest. Akad. Nauk SSSR, Otd. Khim. Nauk* **1949,** 460.
109. V.G.Khlopin and M.A.Tolstoi, *Zh. Fiz. Khim.* **14,** 941 (1940).
110. E.M.Ioffe and B.A.Nikitin, *Izvest. Akad. Nauk SSSR, Otd. Khim. Nauk* **1943,** 194.
111. L.Imre, *Kolloid-Z.* **99,** 147 (1942).
112. O.Erbacher, *Z. Phys. Chem.* A **163,** 196, 215, 231 (1933); **166,** 23 (1933); **178,** 15 (1937); **182,** 243 (1938).
113. M.Haissinsky, *Electrochimie des substances radioactives*, Paris 1946.
114. A.Coche, H.Faraggi, P.Avignon and M.Haissinsky, *J. Phys. Radium* **10,** 312 (1949).
115. K.E.Zimen, *Z. Phys. Chemie* B **37,** 231 (1937).
116. B.Sagortschew, *Z. Phys. Chem.* A **177,** 235 (1936).
117. W.Schröder, *Z. Elektrochem.* **46,** 680 (1940).
118. G.F.Hüttig, H.Jöbstl and G.Glawitsch, *Mh. Chem.* **85,** 976 (1954).
119. G.Wolf, L.Ochs and F.Strassmann, Paris Report 198, vol. 1, p. 516.
120. O.Hahn and G.Graue, *Z. Phys. Chem.*, Bodenstein Volume, p. 608 (1931).
121. Č.Jech, *Int. J. Appl. Rad. Isot.* **8,** 179 (1960).
122. F.Strassmann, *Z. Physik. Chem.* B **26,** 362 (1934).
123. J.N.Gregory, J.F.Hill and S.Moorbath, *Trans. Faraday Soc.* **47,** 1064 (1951); **48,** 643 (1952).
124. See S.Z.Roginskii, *Theoretical Principles of Isotope Methods for Investigating Chemical Reactions* (Russ.), Moscow 1956; English translation, New York 1957.
125. H.Behrens and A.G.Maddock, Radioisotope Conference 1954 (Oxford), vol. 2, London 1954, p. 33.
126. G.M.Harris and J.E.Willard, *J. Amer. Chem. Soc.* **76,** 4678 (1954).
127. V.B.Miller, M.B.Neiman and S.P.Solodovnikov, *Int. J. Appl. Rad. Isot.* **4,** 36 (1958).
128. G.S.Laurence and D.R.Stranks, Copenhagen Report 42, vol. 3, p. 483.
129. J.G.Burr, Geneva Report 928 (1958), vol. 20, p. 187.
130. K.E.Wilzbach, Copenhagen Report 278, vol. 3, p. 463.
131. A.I.Brodskii, Moscow Atomic Energy Conference 1955, Div. Chem. Sciences, p. 210.
132. J.D.Roberts and M.Halmann, *J. Amer. Chem. Soc.* **75,** 5759 (1953).
133. P.Bévillard, *Bull. Soc. Chim. France* **1954,** D 40, D 55.
134. H.Arnstein and R.Bentley, *Nucleonics* **6** (6), 11 (1950).
135. M.Schacht, *Angew. Chem.* **61,** 465 (1949).
136. F.Weygand and H.Grisebach, *Fortschr. chem. Forschung* **3,** 108 (1954).
137. J.G.Burr, *Tracer Applications for the Study of Organic Reactions*, New York 1957.
138. J.D.Roberts and J.A.Yancey, *J. Amer. Chem. Soc.* **74,** 5943 (1952).
139. M.Calvin and R.E.Lemmon, *J. Amer. Chem. Soc.* **69,** 1232 (1947).
140. N.E.Brezhneva and S.Z.Roginskii, *Usp. Khim.* **7,** 1503 (1938).

232   *Application of Radioactivity to General Problems of the Chemical Industry*

141. J.A.WETHINGTON, T.A.GENS, W.H.CHRISTIE and A.R.BROSI, Geneva Report 937 (1958), vol. 20, p. 132.
142. J.T.KUMMER, T.W.DE WITT and P.H.EMMETT, *J. Amer. Chem. Soc.* **70,** 3632 (1948).
143. YA.T.EIDUS and I.D.ZELINSKII, *Izvest. Akad. Nauk SSSR, Otd. Khim. Nauk,* **1940,** 283; **1942,** 190; **1944,** 254, 349.
144. S.Z.ROGINSKY, Paris Report 61, vol. 2, p. 1.
145. J.T.KUMMER and P.H.EMMETT, *J. Amer. Chem. Soc.* **75,** 5177 (1953).
146. J.T.KUMMER, P.H.EMMETT, H.H.PODGURSKY and W.B.SPENCER, *J. Amer. Chem. Soc.* **73,** 564 (1951).
147. W.K.HALL, R.J.KOKES and P.H.EMMETT, *J. Amer. Chem. Soc.* **79,** 2983 (1957).
148. R.J.KOKES, W.K.HALL and P.H.EMMETT, *J. Amer. Chem. Soc.* **79,** 2989 (1957).
149. See also R.B.ANDERSON, L.J.HOFER and H.H.STORCH, *Chem.-Ing.-Techn.* **30,** 560 (1958).
150. G.BLYHOLDER and P.H.EMMETT, *J. Phys. Chem.* **63,** 962 (1959).
151. A.W.FLETCHER and E.J.GIBSON, Radioisotope Conference 1954, vol. 2, London 1954, p. 40; D.S.I.R. Fuel Research Station, Annual Report for 1955.
152. J.T.KUMMER and P.H.EMMETT, *J. Amer. Chem. Soc.* **73,** 2886 (1951).
153. S.Z.ROGINSKII and O.TODES, *Acta Physicochim. URSS* **21,** 519 (1946).
154. S.Z.ROGINSKII, *Adsorption and Catalysis on Heterogeneous Surfaces* (Russ.), Moscow 1948; German translation, Berlin 1958.
155. M.P.KEIER and S.Z.ROGINSKII, *Doklady Akad. Nauk SSSR* **57,** 157 (1947); Zh. Fiz. Khim. **23,** 897 (1949); *Izvest. Akad. Nauk SSSR, Otd. Khim. Nauk* **1950,** 27.
156. C.BOKHOVEN, Radioisotope Conference 1954, vol. 2, London 1954, p. 53.
157. J.TURKEVICH and R.K.SMITH, *J. Chem. Phys.* **16,** 466 (1948).
158. H.STIPPEL, *Atompraxis* **3,** 126 (1957).
159. S.BALKE and G.LUTZ, *Chem.-Ing.-Techn.* **32,** 651 (1960).
160. R.E.MCMAHON, *Ind. Eng. Chem.* **47,** 844 (1955).
161. R.W.BLUE and C.J.ENGLE, *Ind. Eng. Chem.* **43,** 494 (1951).
162. D.E.HULL and B.A.FRIES, Geneva Report 166 (1955), vol. 15, p. 199.
163. A.E.KILNER, H.S.TURNER and R.J.WARNE, *Radioisotope Conference* 1954 (Oxford), vol. 2, London 1954, p. 23.
164. F.R.CANNINGS, A.FISHER, J.F.FORD, P.D.HOLMES and R.S.SMITH, Copenhagen Report 28, vol. 3, p. 205.
165. F.BONNER and J.TURKEVICH, *J. Amer. Chem. Soc.* **73,** 561 (1951).
166. A.A.ORNING and E.STERLING, *J. Phys. Chem.* **58,** 1044 (1954).
167. V.A.EVROPIN, N.V.KULKOVA and M.I.TEMKIN, *Zh. Fiz. Khim.* **30,** 348 (1956).
168. A.F.LUKOVNIKOV and M.B.NEIMAN, *Zh. Fiz. Khim.* **29,** 1410 (1955).
169. M.B.NEIMAN and G.I.FEKLISSOV, *Zh. Fiz. Khim.* **30,** 1126 (1956).
170. N.M.EMANUEL, Z.K.MAIZUS and L.G.PRIVALOVA, *Int. J. Appl. Rad. Isot.* **7,** 111 (1959).
171. M.B.NEIMAN, *Int. J. Appl. Rad. Isot.* **3,** 20 (1958).
172. N.B.NEIMAN, *Khim. Nauka Promyshl.* **1,** 61 (1957).
173. N.I.MEDVEDEVA and E.S.TORSUEVA, see N.SERDYUK, *Atomnaya Energiya* **2,** 293 (1957).
174. A.B.NALBANDYAN, M.B.NEIMAN and N.M.EMANUEL, Paris Report 57, vol. 2, p. 72.
175. A.A.BALANDIN, M.B.NEIMAN, G.V.ISAGULYANTS, O.K.BOGDANOVA and E.I.POPOV, Paris Report 56, vol. 2, p. 91.
176. M.B.NEIMAN, A.F.LUKOVNIKOV and G.I.FEKLISOV, *Zh. Obshch. Khim.* **25,** 1317 (1955).
177. L.YA.MARGOLIS and S.Z.ROGINSKII, *Doklady Akad. Nauk SSSR* **89,** 515 (1953); **96,** 311, 549 (1954); *Probl. Kinetiki i Kataliza* **9,** 107 (1956).
178. U.N.ANTONOVA, V.A.KUZMIN, R.I.MOSHKINA, A.D.NALBANDYAN, M.B.NEIMAN and G.I. FEKLISOV, *Izvest. Akad. Nauk SSSR, Otd. Khim. Nauk* **1955,** 789.
179. V.N.KONDRATYEV, Geneva Report 708 (1955), vol. 15, p. 3.
180. G.YA.TUROVSKII and F.M.VAINSHTEIN, *Doklady Akad. Nauk SSSR* **72,** 297 (1950); **78,** 1173 (1951).
181. T.SAITO, Geneva Report 1348 (1958), vol. 19, p. 201.
182. F.OGBURN and J.BRENNER, *Trans. Electrochem. Soc.* **96,** 47 (1949).
183. F.G.HOUTERMANS, D.VINCENT and G.WAGNER, *Z. Elektrochem.* **56,** 944 (1952).

184. S. A. EATON, *Atomic Energy in Industry*, Nat. Ind. Conf. Board, New York; Geneva Report 146 (1955), vol. 14, p. 61.
185. S. E. BEACOM and B. J. RILEY, *Nucleonics* **18** (5), 82 (1960); *J. Electrochem. Soc.* **107**, 785 (1960).
186. R. ROWAN and G. L. CLARK, *J. Amer. Chem. Soc.* **63**, 1299 (1941).
187. W. HERRMANN and G. PRÖPSTL, *Z. Elektrochem.* **61**, 1154 (1957).
188. W. HERRMANN, W. ILGE and G. PRÖPSTL, Geneva Report 988 (1958), vol. 19, p. 272.
189. W. R. GRIMES, J. H. SHAFFER, R. A. STREHLOW, W. T. WARD and G. M. WATSON, Copenhagen Report 176, vol. 3, p. 575.
190. T. Z. PALAGYI, Copenhagen Report 232.
191. D. M. STRAZHESKO and J. M. GLASMAN, *Doklady Akad. Nauk SSSR* **75**, 411 (1950).
192. N. N. SHUMILOVSKII and L. V. MELTSER, *Radioactive Isotopes in Automation and Control* (Russ.), Moscow 1959; English translation, Oxford 1963.
193. *Atomics* **2**, 285 (1951).
194. U. BEEN and E. SAELAND, Geneva Report 882 (1955), vol. 15, p. 170.
195. D. E. HULL, B. A. FRIES, J. G. TEWKSBURY and G. H. KEIRNS, *Nucleonics* **14** (5), 50, 51 (1956).
196. J. W. T. SPINKS, Geneva Report 216 (1958), vol. 19, p. 13.
197. J. N. GREGORY, Copenhagen Report 54, vol. 1, p. 415.
198. H. E. HUGHES and J. C. MALONEY, *Chem. Eng. Progr.* **48**, 192 (1952).
199. K. G. McNEILL, T. O. BUCHANAN and W. D. PICKARD, *Int. J. Appl. Rad. Isot.* **3**, 250 (1958).
200. D. E. HULL, *Nucleonics* **13** (4), 18 (1955).
201. C. D. WAGNER, H. R. LUKENS and R. R. HUGHES, *Nucleonics* **14** (4), 79 (1956).
202. M. A. STYRIKOVICH and YA. G. VINOKUR, *Doklady Akad. Nauk SSSR* **90**, 179 (1953); see also *Moscow Atomic Energy Conference* 1955, Div. Tech. Sciences, p. 210.
203. G. I. GORSHTEIN, *Zavod. Lab.* **20**, 775 (1954).
204. P. SUE, J. PAULY and A. NOUAILLE, *Bull. Soc. Chim. France* **1958**, 592.
205. W. D. MACKINTOSH, *Anal. Chem.* **32**, 1272 (1960).
206. J. C. BRESEE and C. V. CHESTER, Geneva Report 832 (1958), vol. 20, p. 168.
207. P. BUSSIÈRE and B. DOMANSKY, Paris Report 43, vol. 1, p. 43.
208. V. P. GUINN, H. R. LUKENS and C. D. WAGNER, *Symposium on Radioisotopes*, 1958, A.S.T.M. Publ. 215, Philadelphia.
209. H. SELIGMAN, Geneva Report 395 (1955), vol. 14, p. 93.
210. *Engineering* **180**, 292 (1955).
211. R. BERTHOLD, *Chem.-Ing.-Techn.* **23**, 33, 65 (1951).
212. R. BERTHOLD and A. TROST, *Chemiker-Ztg.* **78**, 729, 759 (1954).
213. H. FENDLER and H. G. FENDLER, *Z. Ver. dtsch. Ing.* **96**, 389 (1954).
214. G. G. JORDAN, V. B. BRODSKY and B. S. SOTSKOV, *Geneva Report* 704 (1955), vol. 15, p. 135.
215. A. TROST, *Atompraxis*, **5**, 59 (1959).
216. A. TROST, Geneva Report 982 (1958), vol. 19, p. 320.
217. S. BARNARTT and K. H. SUN, *Nucleonics* **13** (5), 47 (1955).
218. KH. E. GUNNE and M. V. SURGUCHEVA, *Priborostroenie* **1957** (9), 26.
219. *Jaderna Energie (Prague)* **5** (2), 62 (1959).
220. For Soviet Bibliography see H. MARTIN, *Atomkernenergie* **5**, 187 (1960).
221. M. BLAU and J. R. CARLIN, *Electronics* **21** (4), 78 (1948).
222. A. P. SCHREIBER, *Nucleonics* **2** (1), 33 (1948).
223. L. S. McCASLIN, *Oil Gas J.* **46** (24), 100 (1947).
224. A. P. SCHREIBER, *Electronics* **22** (1), 90 (1949).
225. P. WEINZIERL and A. MAYERHOFER, Geneva Report 1435 (1958), vol. 19, p. 315.
226. V. NETZ, *Isotopentechnik* **1**, 20 (1960).
227. G. G. IORDAN, *Priborostroenie* **1956** (1), 4.
228. L. K. TATOCHENKO and S. V. MEDVEDEV, *Zavod. Lab.* **21**, 1188 (1955).
229. G. G. G. HARE, *U.S. Patents* 2 323 128 (1943), 2 348 810 (1944).
230. J. H. KUNKEL, *Petroleum Engr.* **16** (12), 155 (1945).
231. T. W. MIX, *Nucleonics* **17** (8), 84 (1959).
232. I. E. STARIK, *Principles of Radiochemistry* (Russ.), Moscow 1959; English translation, Washington 1964.

233. K.Fearnside, *Radioisotope Techniques*, London 1952, vol. 2, p. 138.
234. P.C.Aebersold and E.E.Fowler, Geneva Report 1794 (1958), vol. 19, p. 76.
235. V.E.Banashek and V.A.Yanushkovskii, *Maslo Zhir. Prom.* **1957** (3).
236. Kh.E.Gunne, A.D.Tumulkan, I.A.Eimans and V.A.Yanushkovskii, *Tr. Inst. Fiz. Akad.Nauk Latv. SSR* **9** (1956).
237. G.Syke, *Radioisotope Techniques*, London 1952, vol. 2, p. 144.
238. G.G.Eichholz, C.H.Lapointe and G.E.Alexander, *Int. J. Appl. Rad. Isot.* **5**, 51 (1959).
239. J.F.Cameron and P.F.Berry, *Int. J. Appl. Rad. Isot.* **5**, 235 (1959).
240. L.Ya.Margolis, *Labelled Atoms in Catalysis* (Russ.), Moscow 1958; German translation, Leipzig 1961.
241. W.W.Schultz, H.D.Briggs, R.A.Dewes, E.E.Goodale, D.H.Morley, J.P.Neissel, R.S.Rochlin and V.V.Verbinski, Geneva Report 819 (1958), vol. 19, p. 112.
242. D.E.Hull, *Int. J. Appl. Rad. Isot.* **4**, 1 (1958); **7**, 156, 159 (1959).
243. D.E.Hull, *Ind. Eng. Chem.* **50**, 199 (1958).
244. D.E.Hull and M.Macomber, Geneva Report 817 (1958), vol. 19, p. 234.
245. S.Karrer, B.D.Cowis and P.L.Betz, *Power Plant Eng.* **50** (12), 118 (1946).
246. J.L.Putman and S.Jefferson, Geneva Report 462 (1955), vol. 15, p. 147.
247. G.G.Eichholz, *Nucleonics* **18** (10), 116 (1960).
248. J.C.Turgeon, *Trans. Can. Inst. Min. Met.* **59**, 14 (1956).
249. G.G.Eichholz, *Trans. Can. Inst. Min. Met.* **60**, 63 (1957).
250. J.Kohl, *Chem. Eng. Progr.* **48**, 611 (1952).
251. G.C.Gester, R.D.Lee and D.E.Hull, *Petroleum Processing* **8** (4), 550 (1953).
252. N.S.Korshunov and M.V.Khatskevich, *Int. J. Appl. Rad. Isot.* **4**, 121 (1958).
253. C.G.Clayton and J.W.Webb, Copenhagen Report 27, vol. 1, p. 499.
254. W.S.Ginell and G.P.Simon, *Nucleonics* **11** (3), 49 (1953).
255. M.Tubis and H.I.Jacobs, *Nucleonics* **10** (9), 54 (1952).
256. D.E.Hull and R.R.Bowles, *Oil Gas J.* **51** (46), 295 (1953).
257. H.Götte, Geneva Report 985 (1958), vol. 19, p. 297.
258. V.P.Guinn, *Nucleonics* **14** (5), 69 (1956).
259. E.Singer, D.B.Todd and V.P.Guinn, *Ind. Eng. Chem.* **49**, 11 (1957).
260. F.M.Richardson, J.K.Ferrell, H.A.Lamonds and K.O.Beatty, *Nucleonics* **13** (7), 21 (1955).
261. K.O.Beatty, J.K.Ferrell and F.M.Richardson, Geneva Report 148 (1955), vol. 15, p. 194.
262. F.T.Rogers and L.E.Schilberg, *Nucleonics* **9** (4), 47 (1951); *J. Appl. Physics* **22**, 233 (1951).
263. A.I.Veinik, Paris Report 196, vol. 1, p. 460.
264. C.G.Clayton, *Research* **12**, 148 (1959).
265. G.de Monye, *Erdöl-Z.* **75** (7) (1959).
266. T.Schönfeld, *Z. österr. Ing. Arch. Verein* **102**, 127 (1957).
267. N.Serdyuk, *Atomnaya Energiya* **2**, 394 (1958).
268. D.L.Visotski and I.G.Beloglasov; see B.D.Grozin, *Geneva Report* 713 (1955), vol. 15, p. 160.
269. R.L.Ely and J.R.Pier, *Nucleonics* **18** (3), 130 (1960).
270. D.Hasenclever, *Staub* **44**, 159 (1956).
271. H.Seligman, *Atomics* **5**, 299 (1954).
272. K.J.Ives, *Int. J. Appl. Rad. Isot.* **9**, 49 (1960).
273. B.M.Abraham, H.E.Flotow and R.D.Carlson, *Anal. Chem.* **29**, 1058 (1957).
274. H.Seligman, *Nucleonics* **9** (4), 13 (1951).
275. J.F.Pestaner and I.H.Gevantman, *Nucleonics* **14** (12), 38 (1956).
276. J.W.Irvine and C.Goodman, *J. Appl. Phys.* **14**, 496 (1943).
277. C.Goodman, J.W.Irvine and C.F.Horan, *J. Ind. Hyg. Toxicol.* **25**, 275 (1943).
278. J.W.Hickey and E.O.Wiig, *J. Amer. Chem. Soc.* **70**, 1574 (1948).
279. H.J.Born and K.G.Zimmer, *Naturwiss.* **28**, 447 (1940).
280. G.Hevesy, *Radioactive Indicators*, New York 1948.
281. C.L.Comar, *Radioisotopes in Biology and Agriculture*, New York 1955.
282. C.Comar and F.Bronner (Ed.), *Mineral Metabolism*, New York 1960.
283. E.Broda, *Radioaktive Isotope in der Biochemie*, Vienna 1958; *Radioactive Isotopes in Biochemistry*, Amsterdam 1960.

284. R.A.MORTENSEN, *J. Ind. Hyg. Toxicol.* **24**, 285 (1942).
285. D.D.MCCOLLISTER, W.H.BEAMER, G.J.ATCHINSON, and H.C.SPENCER, *J. Pharmacol. Exp. Therap.* **102**, 112 (1951).
286. H.C.HODGE, J.H.STERNER, *J. Pharmacol. Exp. Therap.* **79**, 225 (1943).
287. K.WIBERG, *Chem. Rev.* **55**, 713 (1955).
288. V.GOLD and D.P.N.SATCHELL, *Quart. Rev.* **9**, 51 (1955).
289. M.HAISSINSKY, *La chimie nucléaire et ses applications*, Paris 1957; *Nuclear Chemistry and its Applications*, Reading, Mass. 1964.
290. Relevant Articles in *Ann. Rev. Phys. Chem.*, particularly: H.CRAIG and G.BOATO, **6**, 403 (1955); J.SILVERMAN and K.COHEN, **7**, 335 (1956); E.L.KING, **8**, 273 (1957); A.FAVA, **9**, 221 (1958); V.GOLD, **10**, 169 (1959).
291. L.KAPLAN and K.E.WILZBACH, *J. Amer. Chem. Soc.* **77**, 1297 (1955).
292. L.MELANDER, *Acta Chem. Scand.* **3**, 95 (1949).
293. L.MELANDER, *Arkiv Kemi* **2**, 213 (1950).
294. S.GLASSTONE, K.LAIDLER and H.EYRING, *Theory of Rate Processes*, New York 1941.
295. H.EYRING, *J. Chem. Phys.* **3**, 1074 (1935).
296. H.EYRING, *J. Phys. Chem.* **56**, 889 (1952).
297. J.BIGELEISEN, *J. Chem. Phys.* **17**, 344, 425, 675 (1949).
298. J.BIGELEISEN, *J. Phys. Chem.* **56**, 823 (1952).
299. F.STACEY, J.LINDSAY and R.BURNS, *Can. J. Chem.* **30**, 135 (1952).
300. J.FODOR, K.VARGA, B.PECELI and L.VAJTA, *Isotopentechnik* **1**, 173 (1961).
301. G.HOFFMANN, *Isotopentechnik* **1**, 164 (1961).
302. D.E.HULL, *Int. J. Appl. Rad. Isotopes* **13**, 63 (1962).
303. J.KAKAS, *Isotopentechnik* **1**, 168 (1961).
304. F.M.DEVIENNE, *J. Phys. Rad.* **13**, 53 (1952); **14**, 257 (1953).
305. L.YANG, M.T.SIMNAD and G.M.POUND, *Acta Met.* **2**, 470 (1954); *J. Appl. Phys.* **25**, 268 (1954).
306. K.SCHWABE, *Chem. Technik* **10**, 469 (1958).
307. K.SCHWABE, *Isotopentechnik* **1**, 175 (1961).
308. C.WEISSMANTEL, *Kernenergie* **2**, 909 (1959).
309. E.A.BLOMGREN and J.BOCKRIS, *Nature* **186**, 305 (1960).
310. J.A.KALAFAS and H.C.GATOS, *Rev. Sci. Instr.* **29**, 47 (1958).
311. J.L.PUTMAN, *Chem. & Ind.* **1961**, 733.
312. C.G.CLAYTON, see [311].
313. J.F.CAMERON, P.F.BERRY and F.TAYLOR, see [311].
314. J.F.CAMERON, R.M.GLAISTER and I.S.BOYCE, *Brit. J. Appl. Phys.* **10**, 463 (1959).
315. E.G.RAUH and R.J.THORN, *J. Chem. Phys.* **22**, 1414 (1954).
316. G.R.RINGO, in: S.FLÜGGE (Ed.), *Handbuch der Physik*, vol. 32, p. 552, Berlin 1957.
317. E.J.GIBSON, J.RENNIE and B.A.SAY, *Int. J. Appl. Rad. Isot.* **2**, 129 (1957).
318. A.N.NESMEYANOV, *Vapor Pressure of the Chemical Elements* (Russ.), Moscow 1961; English translation, Amsterdam 1963.
319. D.V.KNIEBES, P.V.BURKET and W.R.STAATS, *Nucleonics* **18** (6), 142 (1960).
320. W.HERRMANN, H.K.BOTHE and H.OHLSEN, *Isotopentechnik* **1**, 232 (1961).
321. W.SCHRÖDER, *Z. Elektrochem.* **52**, 133, 140, 160, 166 (1948).
322. M.HAISSINSKY, *Experientia* **8**, 125 (1952).
323. J.BELLONI-COFLER, *Thèse No. 4644*, Paris 1961.
324. A.N.NESMEYANOV, B.Z.IOFA and B.V.KARASEV, *Doklady Akad. Nauk SSSR* **112**, 882 (1957).
325. C.FISHER, *Atomwirtschaft* **6**, 481 (1961).
326. M.C.KORDECKI and M.B.GAUDY, *Int. J. Appl. Rad. Isot.* **12**, 27 (1961).
327. G.M.ZHABROVA, M.D.SINITSYNA and S.Z.ROGINSKII, *Doklady Akad. Nauk SSSR* **117**, 255 (1957).
328. D.E.HULL, *Int. J. Appl. Rad. Isot.* **7**, 260 (1960).
329. R.MAYORCAS and M.W.THRING, *Nature* **152**, 723 (1943).
330. C.G.CLAYTON, *Nucleonics* **18** (7), 96 (1960).
331. M.D.SINITSYNA, G.M.ZHABROVA, S.Z.ROGINSKII and V.A.GORDEEVA, *Izvest. Akad. Nauk SSSR, Otd. Khim. Nauk* **1959**, 176.

332. H.ROTH, *Isotopentechnik* **1**, 153 (1961).
333. N.P.KEIER, *Probl. Kinetiki i Kataliza* **8**, 224 (1955).
334. N.P.KEIER, *Doklady Akad. Nauk SSSR* **111**, 1274 (1956).
335. V.N.VASILEV, S.YU.ELOVICH and L.YA.MARGOLIS, *Doklady Akad. Nauk SSSR* **101**, 703 (1955).
336. G.M.ZHABROVA, *Usp. Khim.* **24**, 598 (1955).
337. S.Z.ROGINSKII and T.I.ANDRIANOVA, *Zh. Obshch. Khim.* **26**, 2151 (1956).
338. G.M.ZHABROVA and B.M.KADENATSII, *Probl. Kinetiki i Kataliza* **9**, 187 (1956).
339. S.Z.ROGINSKII, *Zh. Fiz. Khim.* **32**, 737 (1958).
340. W.GROTH and P.HARTECK, *Naturwiss.* **29**, 535 (1941).
341. N.P.KEIER, *Izvest. Akad. Nauk SSSR, Otd. Khim. Nauk* **1952**, 616; **1953**, 48.
342. R.P.EISCHENS, *J. Amer. Chem. Soc.* **74**, 6167 (1952).
343. L.A.KASATKINA and G.K.BORESKOV, *Zh. Fiz. Khim.* **29**, 455 (1955).
344. F.BEHOUNEK and Č.JECH, *Nature* **166**, 792 (1950).
345. J.R.JONES and C.B.MONK, *J. Chem. Soc.* **1963**, 2633.
346. N.HACKERMAN and S.J.STEPHENS, *J. Phys. Chem.* **58**, 904 (1954).
347. S.S.CHOI and D.G.TUCK, *J. Chem. Soc.* **1962**, 4080.
348. H.KAISER, *Z. Elektrochem.* **58**, 601 (1954).
349. L.M.MIKHEEVA and N.B.MIKHEEV, *Radioactive Isotopes in Analytical Chemistry* (Russ.), Moscow 1961; German translation, Berlin 1962.
350. A.C.WAHL and N.A.BONNER (Ed.), *Radioactivity Applied to Chemistry*, New York 1951.
351. G.E.BACON, *Applications of Neutron Diffraction in Chemistry*, Oxford 1964.
352. F.A.PANETH and W.THIMANN, *Berichte* **57**, 1215 (1924).
353. R.H.SINGLETON and J.W.T.SPINKS, *Can. J. Res.* **27** B, 238 (1949).
354. S.FLÜGGE and K.E.ZIMENS, *Z. phys. Chem.* B **42**, 179 (1939).
355. K.E.ZIMENS, *Z. phys. Chem.* A **191**, 1, 95 (1942); **192**, 1 (1943).
356. A.GEMANT, *J. Appl. Phys.* **19**, 1160 (1948).
357. A.P.BRADY and D.J.SALLEY, *J. Amer. Chem. Soc.* **70**, 914 (1948).
358. L.FISCHER and G.MARX, *Naturwiss.* **49**, 606 (1962).
359. J.F.DUNCAN, *J. Inorg. Nucl. Chem.* **11**, 161 (1959).
360. M.PORTHAULT and J.C.MERLIN, *Bull. Soc. Chim. France* **1959**, 359.
361. F.STRASSMANN, *Z. phys. Chem.* B **26**, 353 (1934).
362. O.E.MYERS and R.J.PRESTWOOD, in [350].
363. V.J.LINNENBOM, in [350].
364. A.C.WAHL, in [350].
365. O.HAHN and G.GRAUE, *Z. physik. Chem.*, Bodenstein-Festband, p. 608 (1931).
366. O.HAHN, *Applied Radiochemistry*, Ithaca 1936.
367. G.GRAUE and N.RIEHL, *Angew. Chem.* **52**, 112 (1939).
368. G.GRAUE and H.KOCH, *Berichte* **73**, 984 (1940).
369. G.LUTZ, *Kerntechnik* **2**, 271 (1960).
370. J.FLACHOWSKY and K.H.HECKNER, *Z. physik. Chem.* **220**, 169 (1962); **221**, 379 (1962).
371. N.E.BREZHNEVA, *Zh. Fiz. Khim.* **14**, 1151 (1940).
372. J.N.WILSON and R.G.DICKINSON, *J. Amer. Chem. Soc.* **59**, 1358 (1937).
373. J.FREUNDLICH, *Z. Elektrochem.* **66**, 647 (1962).
374. R.SUHRMANN, H.HEYNE and G.WEDLER, *Z. Elektrochem.* **66**, 725 (1962); *J. Catalysis* **1**, 208 (1962).
375. M.B.NEIMAN, V.Y.EFREMOV and N.K.SERDYUK, *Int. J. Appl. Rad. Isot.* **13**, 295 (1962).
376. K.M.GORBUNOVA and A.A.NIKIFOROVA, *Zh. Fiz. Khim.* **31**, 1687 (1957).
377. E.W.GROHSE, *J. Amer. Inst. Chem. Engrs.* **1**, 358 (1955).
378. K.DIEBNER and H.VÖLCKER, *Kerntechnik* **3**, 323 (1961).
379. K.DIEBNER and H.VÖLCKER, *Kerntechnik* **3**, 379 (1961).
380. See *Atompraxis* **8**, 232 (1962).
381. B.A.FRIES, see *Nucleonics* **21** (6), 100 (1963).
382. A.TROST, *Kerntechnik* **3**, 22 (1961).
383. G.COURTOIS, M.GASNIER, C.LALLEMENT and A.SERVASIER, *Nucleonics* **21** (1), 76 (1963).
384. H.LÖFFLER and W.ALTMANN, *Isotopentechnik* **2**, 135 (1962).

385. F.S.McCarthy and G.A.Rice, *J. Electrochem. Soc.* **97,** 249 (1950).
386. P.Hudec and P.Schiller, *Isotopentechnik* **2,** 105 (1962).
387. L.I.Korotkov, *Handbook (spravochnik) on Radioisotope Instruments* (Russ.), Moscow 1963.
388. M.N.Gorbovets, *Automatic Level Gauging in Various Containers* (Russ.), Moscow 1962.
389. P.Johnson, R.M.Bullock and J.Whiston, *Chem. & Ind.* **1963,** 750.
390. R.E.Pegg, M.F.Hoare, J.L.Beton, H.E.Dobbs and G.B.Cook, *Brit. Chem. Eng.* **5,** 710 (1960).
391. I.Bjerle and H.G.Forsberg, in: *Production and Use of Short-lived Radioisotopes from Reactors,* I.A.E.A., Vienna 1963.
392. A.I.Shatenshtein, *Isotopic Exchange and the Replacement of Hydrogen in Organic Compounds* (Russ.), Moscow 1960; English translation, New York 1962.
393. A.M.Hoffman, *Ind. Eng. Chem.* **52,** 781 (1960).
394. S.Jefferson and A.M.Wildblood, *The Agricultural Merchant*, Sept. 1956.
395. A.Beerbower, E.O.Forster, J.J.Kolfenbach and H.G.Vesterdal, *Ind. Eng. Chem.* **49,** 1075 (1957).
396. P.H.Emmett, *Adv. Catalysis* **9,** 645 (1957).
397. See *Adv. Catalysis* **9** (1957).
398. W.H.King, *Ind. Eng. Chem.* **50,** 201 (1958).
399. A.A.Sutyagina, *Zavod. Lab.* **24,** 43 (1958).
400. R.H.Benson, see *Nucleonics* **21** (6), 100 (1963).
401. B.A.Fries, see *Nucleonics* **21** (6), 100 (1963).
402. R.Carlson, B.Cederberg and K.Ljunggren, *Teknisk Tidskrift* **11,** 257 (1961); *Combustion* **33,** 3 (1962).
403. D.E.Hull, *Nucleonics* **21** (1), 74 (1963).
404. P.F.Berry and J.F.Cameron, *Int. J. Appl. Rad. Isot.* **12,** 69 (1961).
405. B.A.Fries, *Int. J. Appl. Rad. Isot.* **13,** 277 (1962).
406. W.A.Jester, *Nucleonics* **20** (11), 72 (1962).
407. O.U.Anders, *Nucleonics* **20** (2), 78 (1962).
408. C.Maille, J.Moinard and D.Blanc, *Int. J. Appl. Rad. Isot.* **13,** 526 (1962).
409. S.Jefferson, *Radioisotopes, A New Tool for Industry,* London 1957.
410. G.Landon, *Chem. Rundschau,* 27th Feb., 1964.
411. C.P.Ross, *Anal. Chem.* **31,** 337 (1958).
412. H.Ramdohr, *Kerntechnik* **4,** 318 (1962).
413. N.N.Shumilovskii, Yu.V.Gushchin and M.I.Tolonnikov, *Scientific-Technical Conference for the Application of Radioactive and Stable Isotopes and Radiations in National Economy,* Moscow 1957.
414. W.Lange and S.Menzel, *Chem. Technik,* 15th April, 1960.
415. J.S.Watt, *Int. J. Appl. Rad. Isot.* **13,** 523 (1962).
416. M.Nawrod, H.K.Bothe and H.Langer, *Isotopentechnik* **2,** 290 (1962).
417. B.Cassen and D.Burnham, *Int. J. Appl. Rad. Isot.* **9,** 54 (1960).
418. P.Connor, W.H.Hardwick and B.J.Laundy, *J. Appl. Chem.* **8,** 716 (1958).
419. H.Ramdohr, USAEC Report NYO 9200 (1961).
420. C.G.Clayton, A.M.Ball and E.A.Spencer, A.E.R.E. Report R 3028 (Harwell, 1959).
421. C.G.Clayton, A.M.Ball and W.E.Clark, A.E.R.E. Report R 3090 (Harwell, 1959).
422. C.G.Clayton, Report DPR – INF 268 (Harwell, 1962).
423. E.A.Dore, C.H.Joiner, J.L.Putman, S.Jefferson and J.F.Cameron, *J. Inst. Water Engrs.* **7,** 160 (1953).
424. D.B.Todd and W.B.Wilson, *Ind. Eng. Chem.* **49,** 20 (1959).
425. L.G.Erwall and K.Ljunggren, Geneva Report 166 (1958), vol. 19, p. 3.
426. J.L.Putman, Geneva Report 283 (1958), vol. 19, p. 22.
427. R.Mayorcas and K.P.Perry, *Some Aspects of Fluid Flow,* London 1951.
428. A.Süss, F.Baumgärtner and A.Mannl, *Atompraxis* **6,** 138 (1960).
429. A.Gemant, E.Hines and E.L.Alexanderson, *J. Appl. Phys.* **22,** 460 (1951).
430. F.Brown, *Trans. Faraday Soc.* **48,** 1005 (1952).
431. I.G.Petrenko, *Izvest. Akad. Nauk SSSR, Otd. Tekhn. Nauk* **1955,** 157.
432. H.M.Frey, *Proc. Roy. Soc.* **228** A, 510 (1955).

433. A. A. ORNING and E. STERLING, *J. Phys. Chem.* **58**, 1044 (1954).
434. K. WAGNER, J. LEGLER, R. MÜLLER and W. HUTH, *Kernenergie* **8**, 185 (1965).
435. D. W. AYLMOR and W. P. JEPSON, *J. Sci. Instr.* **38**, 156 (1961).
436. J. T. CLARKE, *J. Phys. Chem.* **68**, 884 (1964).
437. E. HESFORD, J. WILLIAMS and G. N. WALTON, *Radiochim. Acta* **2**, 14 (1963).
438. J. HABERMAN and T. C. CASTORINA, *Anal. Chem.* **36**, 1917 (1964).
439. G. MARX, L. FISCHER and W. SCHULZE, *Radiochim. Acta* **2**, 9 (1963).
440. G. MARX and W. SCHULZE, *Kerntechnik* **7**, 13 (1965).
441. T. CLESS-BERNERT and K. DUFTSCHMID, *Atomwirtschaft* **9**, 226 (1964).
442. K. AKERMAN, M. BRAFMAN, O. KRUSZEWSKA and K. KRUSZEWSKI, *Nukleonika* **7**, 635 (1962).
443. K. DIEBNER and H. VÖLCKER, *Kerntechnik* **3**, 379 (1961).
444. M. GOLDIN, *Automatic Control of Levels by γ-radiation* (Russ.), MOSCOW 1963.
445. K. E. DUFTSCHMID, W. ATTWENGER and J. STEIDL, *Kerntechnik* **7**, 114 (1965).
446. W. HÄUSLER, *Isotopentechnik* **1**, 155 (1960).
447. V. NETZ, *Isotopentechnik* **1**, 157 (1960).
448. B. A. FRIES, *Int. J. Appl. Rad. Isot.* **16**, 35 (1965).
449. H. MAIRHOFER, *Atompraxis* **10**, 532 (1964).
450. B. MENGELKAMP, *Kerntechnik* **6**, 257 (1964).
451. H. RAMDOHR and W. KÜHN, *Kerntechnik* **6**, 416 (1964).
452. J. KOHL, R. D. ZENTNER and H. R. LUKENS, *Radioisotope Applications Engineering*, New York 1961.
453. L. G. ERWALL, H. G. FORSBERG and K. LJUNGGREN, *Industriell Isotop-Teknik*, Copenhagen 1962; *Industrial Isotope Techniques*, Copenhagen 1964.
454. K. AKERMAN and A. SZUCHNIK, *Int. J. Appl. Rad. Isot.* **15**, 319 (1964).
455. H. HART, *Radioaktive Isotope in der Betriebsmeßtechnik*, Berlin 1962.
456. D. E. HULL, B. A. FRIES and J. T. GILMORE, *Int. J. Appl. Rad. Isot.* **16**, 19 (1965).
457. R. V. DZAGATSPANYAN, R. F. ROMM and L. K. TATOCHENKO, *Applications of Radioactive Isotopes in the Control of Chemical Processes* (Russ.), MOSCOW 1963.
458. K. KORBEL, J. LASA and K. PRZEWLOCKI, *Nukleonika* **8**, 771 (1963)
459. E. BUJDOSÓ, W. MEDWEDEW and M. MISKEY, *Acta Chim. Hungar.* **42**, 433 (1964).
460. A. SÜSS and H. L. WENNER, *Kerntechnik* **4**, 100 (1962).
461. K. B. ZABORENKO, B. Z. IOFA, V. B. LUKYANOV and I. O. BOGATYREV, *Radioactive Indicator Methods in Chemistry* (Russ.), MOSCOW 1964.

10. APPLICATION OF RADIOACTIVITY
IN VARIOUS BRANCHES
OF THE CHEMICAL INDUSTRY

10.1. The Cellulose and Paper Industry

The mechanism of the biosynthesis of cellulose in plants has been largely explained in the course of biochemical investigations with radiocarbon [1]. The same is true of the biosynthesis of lignin [2].

Problems of process technology arising in the production of cellulose have frequently been tackled with isotopes. Reports refer to the experience of Scandinavian factories using the methods described in Chapter 9 to follow the circulation of liquids, such as the sulphite solution used in the boilers, and to determine blocked volumes [3, 73, 289]. The movement of bleaching agents has also been investigated [73].

The rate of movement of wood chips during the boiling process was examined after labelling individual chips by insertion of pieces of activated copper wire [73].

Work with radiosulphur has provided information about the exchange of this element between sulphonated lignin and bisulphite, and also about the rate of dissolution of the lignin [5].

The movement of the cellulose from the fibre-pulp stage up to the production of finished paper has been followed with a tracer. Several tons of fibre were labelled by treatment first with silver nitrate, then with sodium chloride, and finally with radioactive iodide. Before the exposure to the iodide, the fibre was vigorously washed to get rid of loosely adhering silver chloride. It was found that the silver iodide so obtained was not removed by washing, and was not transferred from one fibre to another. The distribution of the active fibres over the paper was determined by autoradiography or by means of a Geiger counter; in the latter case, the paper was rolled around the counter tube [6, 7].

Tagged chips of wood have been followed during their passage through the digester by means of a portable scintillation counter measuring the radiation at various points outside the digester [231, 233]. Alternatively, the movement of the chips in the production process may be followed by introducing labelled glass fibres of the same dimensions as the cellulose fibres; the two kinds of fibres moved in the same manner except in very dilute suspensions [3, 231].

Ion exchange processes on cellulose or paper, which are due to the carboxyl groups present in the cellulose (one such group to about 100 glucose units) have been studied with radionuclides [8, 61, 198, 211]. These processes can play an important part in chemical analysis (p. 75) and in the electrical industry (p. 181).

Thickness gauging of paper will be discussed in Volume 2.

10.2. The Textile Industry

Radioactive tracers have been applied to many problems in the textile industry [9, 10, 287, 294, 295].

Tests for the uptake of labelled compounds by fibres are convenient, sensitive and non-destructive, and find application in all processes in which fibres are treated with solutions. The exchange capacity of cellulose fibres for radioactive cations [16] (see also previous section) has been shown to increase during oxidation (bleaching) [211, 240]. Protein fibres exchange cations and anions [9, 12, 17, 241, 242, 251], while cellulose does not take up significant quantities of anions [16]. The hydration of cotton linters has been estimated by a blocked-volume method with radioactive complex cobalt cyanide on the assumption that the dissolved salt is excluded from the water of hydration. The cellulose was equilibrated with the solution, increasing amounts of supernatant liquid were removed mechanically, the activity of the remaining mixture of cellulose and solution was determined, and the activity plotted against weight. Extrapolation to zero activity indicated the amount of water that may be considered as water of hydration [250].

For uniform distribution of dyestuffs and auxiliary agents within yarns or fabrics in padding, the liquid must permeate uniformly. This may be checked by addition of a tracer to the liquid and measurement, at intervals, of the activity of the soaked material [13]. The uniformity of the distribution of the dyestuffs and auxiliary agents in yarns or fabrics may also be tested by applying them in radioactive form. Autoradiography is often convenient for this purpose [14].

The microdistribution of a resin finish in textiles such as tyre cords has been determined by tritium-labelling and autoradiography [296–298]. The tritium was introduced in the form of formaldehyde. This was used to prepare a precondensate solution with dimethylol urea. Special techniques of sample preparation (imbedding, sectioning, etc.) were developed so that a resolution of 1–2 μ was obtained in the autoradiographs. The influence of a number of factors, e.g., the chemical nature of the fibres, the solvent and the method of drying, on the resin distribution was studied.

The uniformity of lubrication of rayon yarn has been tested by addition to the oil of a small quantity of radiosodium as sodium oleate and subsequent autoradiography of the yarn. As little as 1 cm of yarn, weighing only 0·2 mg and containing 4×10^{-8} g of sodium was needed [4]. Uniformity of lubrication of nylon was tested by adding radioactive dibromoethylene to the lubricant [25], while triolein, after reaction with radioiodine, was used to study the distribution of size over the finished spool [207, 309]. To obtain a measure of the lipophilic properties of fibres, which influence their washing properties, the uptake of iodo-oleic acid containing ^{131}I was determined [208].

The amount of paraffin wax transferred to yarn that runs over a roller of solid paraffin wax was determined by employing wax with added, uniformly distributed cobalt naphthenate (^{60}Co) [308]. Special equipment installed in a glove box was used. This equipment closely simulated the industrial operating conditions and also made it possible to get samples of 1 cm length from the yarn on which radiation measurements were then performed. Thus data on the uniformity of lubricant transfer to the yarn were obtained.

The use of activation analysis may be advantageous for such investigations of uptake and distribution. In a study of the distribution of wax applied to wool yarn prior to machine knitting, an inactive antimony compound (triphenyl stibine) was dissolved in the wax. After application of the wax, yarn samples were irradiated in a nuclear reactor. Preliminary experiments proved that the radioisotopes of antimony could be detected by γ-spectrometry without significant interference from other nuclides produced on irradiation. The variations in the amount of wax in successive lengths of yarn were determined by measuring suitable yarn sections [299].

A special proportional counter has been constructed to measure the distribution of a radioactive substance along a yarn with good resolution. By running the yarn through a boring along the central axis of two shielding cones, the length of yarn from which radiation could enter the sensitive volume of the counter was made very small, so that a resolution of 0·5 mm was obtained [300]. Other types of counters have been constructed for rapid scanning of thread, but with much lower resolution [301].

The diffusion of dyes within fibres or films may be measured. Initial work was carried out with horn keratin, mostly as membranes, in place of wool. Diffusion of various ions, wetting agents and dyes was compared [18, 24, 302–304]. The anionic dyestuffs were found to diffuse much less rapidly than in aqueous solution [18, 24].

It is often necessary to print fabrics successively with several dyestuffs. It is then important to prevent contamination of one colour by another. It has been suggested that an inadmissible degree of contamination could be automatically signalled after labelling one of the dyestuffs (^{32}P) [15]. If such a procedure is to be used in the actual production process, radiation protection obviously requires particular attention, as is true for all processes in which radioactive substances are to be introduced into the products.

Fibres may be labelled to follow their behaviour during mechanical treatment. The movement of single wool fibres, treated with radioactive phosphoric acid, was followed during the drawing of the web between two rollers to form yarn. In order to observe the speed of the fibres, two counters, one placed behind the other, were used. The data obtained cast new light on this complicated industrial process. It was found that the fibres move independently of each other. The probability that their velocity will increase at any point between the rollers is determined by the probability of contact between them and fibres already in direct touch with the more rapidly moving front roller. The fibres can acquire speeds intermediate between those of the front and the back rollers, and they can undergo both acceleration and retardation during their passage to the front roller [19, 24].

The crimp of wool fibres is decisive for the technical properties of the fibre. This crimp is greatly modified during spinning and weaving. The change in the configuration of the fibres may now be determined by labelling individual fibres with radioactive phosphoric acid and taking autoradiographs at certain stages during the production process [21]. Labelling of fibres for such studies can also be carried out with iodine-131 [305].

Contact between the constituents of fibre assemblies has been investigated by coating one fibre with gelatine containing radiophosphate. This fibre was later introduced into a sliver. By exposing to a warm moist atmosphere, the gelatine film was softened, and some active material was transferred to those fibres which touched the labelled one. This transfer was then detected by radiation measurements on the various fibres. The points of contact could be seen by autoradiography of the fibres [306].

Fibres labelled by drawing them through a solution containing caesium-137 were employed to study the formation of lubricant films on spinner rings [308]. It was shown that such films are formed within the first 10 to 15 minutes of operation. The distribution of fibre material forming the lubricating layer was observed by autoradiography.

The preparation of viscose solution is carried out by a batch process, while the spinning process is continuous. Batches supplied to the spinning plant will therefore be of different ages, and the quality of the finished fibres is affected by this factor. To determine the age, the relatively short-lived sodium-24 was added to the viscose during preparation, and the activity was then measured at various stages of the production process [207, 309].

The removal of sulphur in the final stages of the viscose process may be studied by applying radiosulphur, and testing the yarn with a counter. The complete removal of the sulphur is important for yarn colour and strength [22]. The removal of copper from cuprammonium rayon has been checked by labelling the copper [23]. The activity in various parts of the precipitation bath was measured from outside with a counter, or by taking samples. The upper part of the bath showed weak activity, further below the activity increased steeply in a zone of turbulence, and it continued to increase steadily beyond.

As the author points out, experiments of this kind reveal the mechanism of formation of synthetic fibres in detail. It is also possible to investigate the effect of such factors as the shape of the bath, the temperature of the spinning water, and the thickness of the fibre, on rate of production and on quality. Since the tests give information directly at the place of fibre formation, they are well suited for determining the optimum arrangements for efficient and economic fibre production [14]. Radiozinc has been used to study the formation of viscose thread of high wet strength (supercord) [239, 288].

A rapid estimate of the moisture content of wool may be based on the slowing-down of fast neutrons (see p. 103). In preliminary experiments with a polonium–beryllium neutron source and a boron trifluoride neutron counter, a precision of ± 10 per cent was attained [26].

As early as the First World War, the permeability of rubber-impregnated fabrics for use in gas-proof clothing was investigated with radon [27]. This must have been one of the earliest applications of radioactivity to a technical problem.

The possibility of employing radionuclides in the leather industry has been discussed [28, 29]. The uptake of wetting agents (such as dodecyl sulphate and alkyl benzene sulphonates, containing radiosulphur) from various liquids used in leather processing has been measured with great sensitivity [29].

Investigations related to detergents and their application will be discussed on p. 255. Methods for the gauging of textiles using radionuclide sources and for the elimination of electrical charges with ionizing radiations, as well as radiation effects on textile fibres will be dealt with in Volume 2.

10.3. The Photographic Materials and Printing Industries

Activation analysis enabled a small gold content to be discovered in photographic emulsions which had proved unsatisfactory [30]. The determination of emulsion thickness by radiation absorption has already been referred to (p. 107).

Elementary silver produced during the development of the photographic emulsions may be assayed by reaction with a suitable radioactive substance, that is, by a radio-reagent method (p. 77). The distribution of the activity over the emulsion is then determined by autoradiography or with a counter, equipped with a collimator [32]. To give satisfactory results, the reagent must undergo stoichiometric reaction with the silver and must be detectable in small quantity. A solution of potassium ferricyanide and radioactive iodide, which converts the silver quantitatively into silver iodide, meets these requirements [31]. Silver halides must not be present at the start, since they also take up iodide. Other reagents may also be employed [32].

The use of autoradiography for testing emulsions has been investigated thoroughly. The determination of silver sulphide in the emulsion is an example [33]. The sulphide is first converted by bromine into the bromide, and this is made to react with radioactive iodide. Finally, the distribution of the silver iodide is determined by autoradiography and densitometry. A factor limiting the sensitivity of detection is the reaction of the labelled reagent with the gelatine. Silver sulphide in the developed emulsion may be detected in a similar way. First free silver is removed by selective dissolution with chromic acid, while the sum of the silver sulphide and the silver, the latter being in large excess, may be determined in the same way on another part of the emulsion [33]. The ripening of emulsions in the presence of thiosulphate has been studied with radiosulphur, and the chemical fate of this sulphur has been followed [227].

In printing, a thin uniform layer of the printing ink on the paper is required. Weighing is not only troublesome, but results are doubtful because of the hygroscopicity of the paper. When radiophosphorus in the form of a suitable compound (pentachloride) was added to the ink, the relative area weight of the ink could be obtained from point to point by scanning with a counting tube [34]. A method for the measurement of the thickness of printing ink layers on the rollers of printing presses by the back-scattering of the β-radiation from sulphur-35 has been described [293].

Printed characters on paper or on another base may be traced by autoradiography if the ink or one of its components gives a precipitate on reaction with a radioactive reagent (see p. 77). Thus, labelled silver present as a soluble salt may be converted by reduction into the metal and the amount precipitated is then determined by activity measurement after the removal of the remaining salt by washing [35].

Finger prints may be revealed by autoradiography after activation by the radio-reagent method. Radioactive formaldehyde is a suitable reagent for the proteins in the finger prints [36]. Alternatively, silver-110 may be deposited selectively by suitable techniques [228].

10.4. The Glass Industry

Radionuclides are used in the glass industry for research and for the control of production processes [37, 38, 42, 249, 258, 259]. It is convenient to divide the research studies into two groups: investigations of bulk glass and of glass melts on the one hand, and studies of the glass surface on the other.

A knowledge of the mobility of the various components in the glass, in the raw materials from which glass is made (glass batch), or in intermediate products, whose formation in the glass melt can be assumed, is of interest for the elucidation of the mechanism of glass formation. Measurements of diffusion and self-diffusion, carried out by the methods outlined on p. 165, are therefore important for glass research. Radioactive tracers have, for example, been used to investigate the self-diffusion of sodium in glass [39, 40, 42, 249, 254]. Not all the sodium ions in glass show the same mobility; a small portion is very firmly held and is retained even after prolonged electrolysis [42, 248]. Investigations on crystalline lead silicates with radiolead have permitted a distinction between lattice and grain boundary diffusion [41].

The route taken by sand of a particular kind during the production process in a glass factory and the efficiency of mixing with other components of the glass batch was investigated by activating the sand with a solution of barium-140 (half-life 12 days) and heating to 500 °C. Within a few days, radioactive equilibrium is established in the sand between the radioactive barium and its γ-active daughter product, lanthanum-140 (half-life 40 hr), so that the labelled sand may then be detected by γ-scintillation counting [43, 44] (see Section 12.7).

The emanation method (p. 67) also gives information on certain processes in glass production and in the subsequent heat treatment of the glass. With the parent substance of the emanation contained in the glass batch, changes occurring on heating are revealed by changes in the emanating power [45, 246, 247].

Several authors have reported studies on the flow pattern of the glass melt in the furnace [249]. Sodium-24 [42, 234, 255], cobalt-60 [47] or zinc-65 [47] have been used as γ-active tracers. The use of phosphorus-32, which emits no γ-radiation, has the advantage that less attention need be paid to radiation protection. On the other hand, the stronger self-absorption of the β-radiation makes detection more difficult. It was found that radiophosphorus added to the furnace of a bottle-producing machine was removed according to an exponential law. It could be concluded that complete mixing occurred between the material originally present and that subsequently added [48, 49]. In other work with β-active nuclides (calcium-45 and strontium-89) no such complete mixing was observed [50, 51].

In a further investigation on the movement of glass in a furnace, no radioactive substance was introduced. Inactive tantalum oxide was added to the glass before mixing. After various intervals samples were taken and activated with neutrons in a nuclear reactor. The γ-active tantalum-182 produced was then determined with a scintillation counter [37, 44]. In this way no radiation protection against penetrating radiation was required during the actual experiment, but the measurements could be carried out using such penetrating radiation and the influence of sample geometry was eliminated.

The glass industry also employs nuclear radiation for level gauging (see p. 214) [52]. Thus, cobalt sources of 200 mc in connection with water-cooled Geiger counters have been used in bottle factories. The radiation must pass through the thick walls of the furnace with sufficient intensity. Level changes amounting to only a few millimetres may be detected. The decay of the cobalt, which has a half-life of 5·3 years, is automatically compensated by an electronic device, so that the equipment will operate over a period of years without new calibration. In some installations the supply of the glass is automatically regulated by a servo-mechanism operated by the level gauge [53, 54].

The use of radionuclides has given important information about various processes at the glass surface. Thus, glasses which are known to be easily attacked chemically showed an increase in the emanating power when the surface was exposed to moist air for a prolonged period, and the dependence of emanating power on temperature was also studied [46, 55, 249, 252]. The escape rate of radioactive inert gas, fixed in the glass surface by means of a high frequency discharge (p. 201), may be used to follow changes in the surface structure as a result of chemical reactions [226].

The removal of alkali from glass by heating with clay or chromium oxide has been followed after activation of the glass surface by deuteron bombardment, using the reaction $^{23}Na(d, p)\ ^{24}Na$. The amount of sodium removed during the process was then determined by activity measurements [56]. Activation analysis lends itself well to the investigation of the attack of glass melts on the refractory bricks of the furnaces. After attack, the wall of the furnace was sectioned, and the slices irradiated with deuterons. The sodium taken up from the melt was activated much more strongly than any other element present, so that the distribution of sodium in the bricks could easily be determined by autoradiography after the irradiation. Alternatively, radioactive glass (containing ^{24}Na) may be used for the attack [57].

The absorption of radiosodium by glass from solutions has been studied [58–60]. By labelling the sodium ions in the glass with sodium-24, and simultaneously labelling the sodium ions in an aqueous solution with sodium-22, it has been shown that exchange occurs between the ions in the two phases, but that the loss of sodium from the glass exceeds the uptake from the solution. Glass previously activated in a reactor was used to determine sodium washed out by water.

The uptake of tracers by glass surfaces is largely due to cation exchange at the silicic acid end groups on the surface, but other processes, particularly the dissolution of the glass, also play a part [58–62, 209, 210, 249, 253]. Reference has already been made to the adsorption of ions at glass surfaces as a source of error in chemical analysis (p. 75).

In order to distinguish between the ion-exchange process

$$Na^+ \text{ (dissolved)} + H^+ \text{ (glass)} \rightleftharpoons Na^+ \text{ (glass)} + H^+ \text{ (solution)}$$

and the exchange of sodium ions in the solution with sodium in the surface of a soaked glass electrode, labelled sodium was introduced alternatively into the solution or into the glass phase. It has been found that after dipping the electrode into the solution ion exchange equilibrium is attained immediately only at the interface between the hydrated layer and the solution, while penetration into the hydrated layer is slow. Radioactive potassium and caesium ions are taken up only to a small extent by the hydrated layer of soda glass. After considerable time a stationary state is reached, in which the hydrated layer is broken down on the solution side and re-formed at the interface between the glass and the hydrated layer. In the same work the water content of the hydrated layer was estimated by observing the exchange with tritium-containing water [204, 205, 220]. The hydrated layer may be explored with radioactive anions [58, 282].

Adsorption experiments with radiolead have indicated that lead adsorbed by glass surfaces is present in two states of binding, the one being very stable and similar to the binding of atoms in the glass network [8, 62]. On treating glass with labelled chromic acid cleaning mixture (chromic acid dissolved in sulphuric acid), traces of radiochromium were held back, the amount being relatively large when the cleaning was incomplete. Pyrex glass retained a larger quantity of chromium than quartz glass or soda glass [63].

The transfer of material during polishing [42] (see also [256]) was investigated with glass containing strontium-89. A glass of this kind was also used to determine the thickness of thin glass layers formed on steel rods when the glass is used as a lubricant in the drawing of these rods. Thicknesses of the order of 15 to 20 μ could be determined readily [42].

In the analysis of glasses boron may be determined rapidly by neutron absorption (p. 102). Selenium which is added to glasses as a decolorizing agent may be detected with great sensitivity by activation analysis. The results are, of course, independent of the chemical form of the selenium, an important difference from the colorimetric method. As little as 2×10^{-3} per cent was detected with an accuracy of 5 per cent [37, 64]. The potash content of glasses may be determined through the natural radioactivity of the potassium [225, 236, 243, 244]. The intensity of β-ray back-scattering is a useful measure for lead contents of glasses [245].

10.5. The Building Materials Industry

The uniformity of the wet mixture of the cement raw materials has been checked by measurement of radioactivity. The water was labelled by the addition of ammonium bromide (^{82}Br) or soda (^{24}Na), while the solid constituents were activated in a reactor, with the production mainly of manganese-56 and sodium-24 [3, 73].

The rate of movement of the charge in rotary kilns for the production of cement was measured in full scale tests on production units (see also p. 163 and [47, 218]). By this means it may be found how the rate of movement depends on the chemical composition and the grain size of the raw material. Considerable differences were observed in practice. It was also found that kilns with similar dimensions behaved differently. The measurements were conducted by activating a sample of raw material in a reactor, where mainly sodium-24 was formed, and then monitoring the activity of the charge and the cement with scintillation counters, both through the furnace wall and after leaving the kiln [74, 75]. In further investigations with similar objectives thorium B (lead-212) or lanthanum-140 was employed for labelling the charge, while the density of the charge in various parts of the kiln was determined by the attenuation of the γ-radiation from cobalt-60 [76, 214].

Measurements of the rate of movement of the charge in rotary kilns have already been carried out in many plants and have given useful information for the improvement of furnace operation. A number of these investigations have been concerned with problems of the cement industry [74–76, 214–216, 238, 286], while some others have referred to the gypsum–sulphuric acid process [217, 218], or to the production of iron by the Krupp process [218].

The emanation method lends itself to the study of the solid state reactions at high temperature between some of the more important components of building materials, like silica, limestone, iron oxide and alumina [257].

The behaviour of potassium in rotary kilns has repeatedly been studied [3, 73, 231, 235]. Activated potassium was added as the sulphate, or (in order to reproduce the normal conditions more closely) as feldspar, and its movement in the kiln followed. The volatilization of potassium in the hottest zone and its appearance in the chimney were observed [3, 73, 231]. Analysis for potassium in cement or flue dust may be based on the natural activity of the element (p. 71).

Cement clinker contains, among other substances, various silicates of calcium, and may be of different grain size. Its properties may be studied by following the exchange between clinker and dissolved radiocalcium [65, 72].

Labelled tricalcium silicate, prepared by heating together inactive dicalcium silicate and lime labelled with calcium-45, has been hydrated in saturated solutions of calcium hydroxide at room temperature. Parallel studies of the rate of liberation of lime due to hydrolysis and the coincident appearance of calcium-45 in the solution indicate that the $CaO : SiO_2$ ratio in the precipitated hydrated silicate is $3 : 2$. A similar result is obtained when inactive tricalcium silicate is hydrated in an active lime solution. Comparable studies on the hydrolysis of labelled β-dicalcium silicate indicate the formation of a product with the same $CaO : SiO_2$ ratio [77].

A rapid estimate of the specific surface of cement, quartz powder or of sand, is possible through the adsorption of radioactive ions (p. 198). Good results have been reported with calcium-45, cobalt-60, strontium-89, caesium-137 and tungsten-185 [20, 71, 72].

Isotopes have been used in investigations of the setting of gypsum [78]. By labelling the calcium and sulphate ions, it has been shown that these ions pass temporarily into solution during the setting process. This was seen from the fact that during the setting of gypsum in calcium sulphate solution the specific activity of the ions in the solution increased, while after the setting the specific activities in the solution and in the deposit were identical.

Studies of the structural changes of concrete due to freezing and thawing have been carried out by observing the uptake of strontium-89 from solution. Measurement of the activity remaining in the solution gives information about the change in volume of the pores and therefore about changes in the mechanical strength of the sample [72]. Relationships have also been found between the composition of the cement and the rate of penetration of water. For this purpose, cement samples were immersed in a solution of radioactive salt. At definite intervals samples were removed, and, after their surface had been ground off, were submitted to autoradiography.

Tracer methods have also been used for checking mixing processes in the making of concrete [79, 286] (see p. 211). The preparation of light-weight concrete is an example of an industrial process where thorough mixing of the components is essential for high quality. The main components are cement, sand, aluminium powder and water. Irradiated cement and aluminium were used for tracing. Technical aluminium contains impurities, e.g., manganese, which are easily activated. In the irradiation of cement, sodium-24 and potassium-42 together with some short-lived nuclides are formed. Samples were taken during the emptying of a mixer into open moulds every tenth second and the samples were transferred to cans where the cement solidified and the activity could then be measured [232].

Radiosulphur has been used to investigate the corrosion of concrete by sulphate [80]. The influence of the duration of immersion in the sulphate solution, the water: cement ratio, and the grain size of the cement on the corrosion has been studied [72].

Determination of moisture contents in brick, concrete, gravel, sand and other building materials may be carried out by measurement of the transmission of γ-radiation. In general, the attenuation increases with moisture content. However, reliable results are obtained only when the density of the dry material is nearly constant [67, 68, 72, 221]. The operation of the shakers used to compact freshly poured concrete may also be observed by γ-absorptiometry. This is of particular importance in the compacting of special types of concrete, such as the heavy concrete for biological shields of nuclear reactors, and the hard concrete used in hydrotechnical construction [72]. The measurement of γ-radiation back-scattering is useful for the determination of the density of building materials and of earth layers [286, 290–292]. Such techniques can be employed to observe density changes taking place during building operations.

Water contents of cement may also be determined by the slowing-down of fast neutrons from a radium–beryllium source; the slow neutrons are measured with a boron trifluoride counter [260] (see also p. 103). The count rate has been greatly improved by the use of a cast-iron reflector. To compensate for variations in the sensitivity of the equipment, the count rate is always compared with the value obtained from a sample of the same dimensions, made of paraffin wax. The equipment may be calibrated with samples made from sand and sugar. An approximately linear relationship between count rate and moisture content is obtained [69, 70]. Such determinations of moisture are useful in the routine testing of sands used for the preparation of forms in foundries [90, 230] and of sands, limestone and silicates for various purposes [221, 224].

The movement of water or aqueous solutions through refractory or other bricks may be followed with a well-collimated narrow beam of thermal neutrons; the attenuation is again measured with a boron trifluoride counter. Because of the strong scattering of slow neutrons by hydrogen, the intensity of the transmitted neutrons diminishes sharply when the water reaches the height of the beam. As an example, we may mention measurements on a brick in which the rate of water rise was found to be 1·3 mm/min [66].

10.6. The Rubber and Plastics Industry

10.6.1. *Quality Control*

The influence of the degree of dispersion of carbon black on the mechanical properties of vulcanized rubber has been studied with carbon black containing carbon-14. The distribution was determined autoradiographically. High tensile strength was found to depend on uniform distribution of the carbon black. The new technique proved much superior to the microphotographic technique previously used [82]. Uniformity of the distribution of silica as a filler in rubber was checked by activation of the silica contained in the samples by immersion in a radioactive phosphate solution. The samples so treated were then covered with a thin plastic layer to prevent chemical interaction with the emulsion, and submitted to autoradiography [83]. The distribution of radiosulphur in butyl rubber was also observed by autoradiography. It was found that the smallest sulphur particles disappeared during vulcanization [47] (see p. 254). The application of a short-lived tracer (manganese-56) to a mixing problem in the rubber industry has been described [262].

The wear of car and bicycle tyres may be determined by labelling the tyres with a suitable radionuclide, and then measuring the activity transferred to a test "road" behind the tyre with a counter [84, 85, 222, 223]. In this way, wear can be related to the tyre pressure, the temperature, the nature of the road surface and the load. In the course of one investigation, in which the tyre was labelled by the addition of radioactive triphenyl phosphate, it was found that the life time of the tyre at 100 km/hr amounted to only 57 per cent of that at 50 km/hr. The main advantage of radioactivity for this kind of investigation lies in the saving of time. Earlier methods required test runs of about 8000 km. Moreover, it was hardly possible with such methods to determine the wear involved in starting and braking. Such measurements are, however, readily accomplished by the method based on radioactivity. The various methods for labelling tyres have been compared [223].

According to another method [223], a number of sources of β-active thallium-204 are introduced at a selected depth into the tyre, and the decrease in the height of the tyre during wear is deduced from the increase in the intensity of the β-radiation which penetrates the surface of the tyre.

The wear of floor wax may be measured with great sensitivity after addition of a labelled compound, such as the high polymer formed when labelled ruthenocene (dicyclopentadienyl ruthenium) is heated with indole. The thickness of the floor wax may then be determined by radiation measurement [86] (see also [285]). Labelled ruthenocene is also suitable for testing the efficiency of siccatives in drying oils, since the rate of loss of the volatile ruthenocene diminishes in the course of drying [86].

Radionuclides have been applied to the investigation of the flow processes during the extrusion of plastics [264]. When labelled adhesive (atactic ^{14}C-polypropene) is used to join glass or metal to plastic material and the bond is later broken, the amount of adhesive retained on the inorganic substrate can be estimated by its activity [263]. Some of the products of the thermal degradation of labelled condensation resins (phenol-formaldehyde resins, epoxy resins, polyacrylate) have been identified through activity measurements on separated fractions [269].

The measurement of the permeability of rubber-impregnated fabrics for radon has been referred to (p. 242). The permeability of rubber for radioactive carbon dioxide has also been measured [265]. The penetration of water through rubber and plastic sheets was determined in the course of a few minutes by placing them on gelatine saturated with water containing tritium. A current of methane was passed over the upper surface of the sheets, and the water vapour which had penetrated was carried along and was then measured by leading the gas through a counting tube [87]. The diffusion of labelled water through membranes consisting of polyethylene, polyvinyl chloride, polytri-fluorochlorethylene and rubber was measured by a similar method [88]. The rate of diffusion of labelled carbon tetrachloride and benzene through membranes made from high polymers were estimated, and the results were related to the microscopic and submicroscopic structure of the membranes [89].

Another useful application of radioactivity in this field is the measurement of the diffusion of components in systems containing high polymers. Since the introduction of radioactive substances in very small quantity does not disturb the chemical composition of a system, the system may be studied in a stationary state, and so self-diffusion may be observed. The method has, for example, been used for the rate of the diffusion of plasticizers (^{32}P-tricresyl phosphate) in polystyrene [91]. The diffusion velocity was determined by autoradiography and was found to decrease with increasing hardness of the product [200, 201]. The rate of diffusion of antioxidants (substituted phenol and phenothiazin) in polypropylene and polyformaldehyde has been measured by an absorption method (p. 165) [229]. The washing-out of labelled tricresyl phosphate from a polyvinyl chloride sheet by water (in a non-stationary state) has been followed [92].

The penetration of water into plastics or similar materials may be determined with great precision. After the sample has been kept in tritium-labelled water, thin surface layers are ground off, and the difference in activity before and after grinding is determined. The procedure has in particular been applied to the investigation of water-repellent protective layers [93]. The shortness of the range of the β-radiation from tritium makes the determination very sensitive. In all methods of this kind, relative data on water penetration or absorption are obviously easier to obtain than absolute values.

The wear of the steel moulds used in the manufacture of plastic parts may be determined rapidly and sensitively, after activation of the mould with neutrons in a reactor, by measuring the activity transferred to the plastic. Such methods are related to those for the determination of wear in drawing dies (p. 173) [94].

10.6.2. *Study of Polymerization*

Tracers are of great importance in investigations of the polymerization processes used in the production of synthetic rubber and plastics. In earlier investigations of such reactions the "catalysts" were tagged, and their incorporation into the products was measured. Later many other questions have been approached, often with radiocarbon.

In polymerization, "catalysts" are often used which start polymerization through the production of free radicals or ions, but, unlike true catalysts, are incorporated in small quantities into the resulting polymer. Such incorporation can be observed with good sensitivity with tracers. Studies of this kind have been carried out for various catalysts, such as persulphate [99–103], alkyl mercaptans [100–104], tin bromide [105], alkyl magnesium bromide [105], benzoyl peroxide [95, 106] (see below), bromobenzoyl peroxide [107, 108], azoisobutyronitrile [97], and bisulphite [99] (see also [219]). When the short half-life of bromine-82 is an obstacle, the bromine may be activated after polymerization [107–109].

If the course of the polymerization reaction is known, the molecular weight of the polymer may be calculated from the amount of catalyst incorporated; this quantity is determined by activity measurement [99, 219]. In other cases, molecular weight determinations may be carried out through the stoichiometric reaction of the end groups of the polymer with labelled reagents, i.e., by a radioactive reagent method (see Section 6.4). This has been done, for example, with the products of polycondensation reactions. Hydroxyl groups may be esterified with ^{35}S-toluene sulphonyl chloride [81].

Chain initiation by benzoyl peroxide and its derivates has been investigated in great detail. Substituent groups on the benzene ring and the monomer subjected to polymerization were varied. Substances studied included methacrylic acid, styrene and stilbene. The radicals were obtained from the peroxide by thermal or photolytic dissociation. Using chain initiators labelled on the benzene ring, that part of the benzoyl radicals which lost carbon dioxide before chain initiation but which then started the chain as phenyl radicals could be found. The basis of this technique is the fact that the labelled benzoyl groups, in contrast to the labelled phenyl groups, may be removed from the finished polymer by treatment with alkali, and can be so estimated separately [108, 110–117, 219]. In other work, the results obtained with benzoyl peroxide derivates labelled at different positions in the molecule, on the benzene ring or on the carboxyl group, were compared [118, 119, 219].

When labelled chain initiators are used, the molar specific activity of the polymer indicates to what extent the chain is terminated through disproportionation of a polymeric radical or else through the combination of two such radicals, i.e., through one of the reactions:

$$2\,RCH_2CHX\cdot \rightarrow RCH{=}CHX + RCH_2CH_2X,$$

or

$$2\,RCH_2CHX\cdot \rightarrow RCH_2CHXCHXCH_2R.$$

In the first case, each polymeric chain will contain one labelled atom, while in the second it will contain two atoms. Obviously this method applies only to polymerization in absence of chain transfer [95, 96, 120, 121]. Complications usually arise when several kinds of radicals are present [96].

Measurement of the incorporation of a labelled initiator into the polymer in the stationary state gives the rate of chain initiation, and — provided the number of molecules (radicals) capable of chain-initiation is known — the efficiency of initiation in any given polymerizable system [95, 121, 122, 219].

Introduction of various components into copolymers may be studied in a simple way if one of the monomers is labelled and the activity of the polymers produced is measured. This method is particularly important when the polymer contains only a

small amount of the monomer in question. Thus, the extent of incorporation of iso-
prene into butyl rubber was determined with a radioactive tracer; the results were used
to check measurements of the number of double bonds which can, for example, be
carried out by reaction with ozone [123]. The copolymerization of ^{14}C-benzene with
vinyl acetate was demonstrated similarly [278].

Related methods can be applied to determine the branching of high polymers
due to a chain transfer mechanism. An inactive polymer is introduced into an active
monomer, and polymerization is allowed to proceed. If chain transfer occurs, the
added polymer, which may subsequently be isolated, by fractional precipitation or
otherwise, becomes radioactive through the formation of branches [95, 129, 277].
Polyvinyl acetate, labelled in this way in the side chains only, has been used for determining the relation between the degree of branching (of which the specific activity is
a measure) and the solubility [124].

The role of transfer agents in radical polymerization may be investigated by employing such agents in a labelled form [98, 104, 108, 219, 279–281]. The radioactive
transfer agents to be used in such work may be labelled either at the atom or group of
atoms abstracted by interaction with the polymer radical, or the labelling may be in
the remainder of the molecule so that a labelled radical is formed from the transfer
agent. The advantages and limitations of these two types of labelling have been
discussed [98, 108, 219, 279].

The part played by triphenylmethane when added to polymerizing styrene has been
investigated by means of double labelling with carbon-14 and tritium [108]. It was
thought that the triphenylmethane transferred its labile hydrogen atom to the growing
polystyrene chain, terminating its growth, but thereby itself starting a new chain. If
this were in fact the mechanism, the ratio of tritium and radiocarbon in the total
polymer should be the same as that in triphenylmethane. However, the experimental
results did not correspond to these expectations, even when the isotope effect of
hydrogen was taken into account. The discrepancy has been explained by postulating
a reaction between the triphenylmethane and the chain initiator (the benzoyl radical)
which diverts labelled hydrogen from the polymerization process:

$$RCOO\cdot + C(C_6H_5)_3H \rightarrow RCOOH + C(C_6H_5)_3\cdot$$

If the mechanisms of reaction are known, the labelled transfer agents can be used
to obtain the transfer constants. This type of determination is not influenced by retardation, which may lead to erroneous results if transfer constants are calculated
from molecular weights. In the tracer method, the relative amount of transfer agent
incorporated into the polymer is obtained by measuring the activity of the polymer.
Results by this method are usually unaffected by the simultaneous occurrence of
transfer reactions with other substances not present in the labelled form. The
method is not suitable if the substance in question is not only a transfer agent but is
also copolymerized [219, 279].

Triphenylmethane has also been investigated in some detail in this connection, in
particular as to its role in the polymerization of styrene and methyl methacrylate [279].
In a study where the benzene ring of the triphenylmethane was labelled with tritium,
transfer constants were calculated. However, it was found that small amounts of

labelled impurities, present in admixture with the labelled transfer agent, may seriously interfere with the results. Triphenylmethane was also employed in deuterated form for investigating chain transfer in the polymerization of vinyl acetate [280]. In studies of diphenylamine as the transfer agent tritiated benzene rings were used [281].

Graft polymerization (planting of side chains on polymers) may be observed in a sensitive manner by introduction of radioactive monomer. This method has been employed in the study of the grafting of gaseous ^{14}C-acrylonitrile on to polymers irradiated in a vacuum [125].

Inhibition or retardation of chain growth can also be studied by isotope techniques. The effect of a radioactive inhibitor may be found by investigating the reaction product with the initiator, sometimes by the isotope dilution method. The entry of labelled inhibitor into polymer is detected by activity measurements on the polymer [95, 126, 219].

Benzoquinone is an effective inhibitor in the polymerization of methacrylic acid. One molecule of labelled benzoquinone was found in each molecule of the polymer. But further investigations with labelled chain initiators showed that each polymer molecule contained two molecules of the initiator. It was concluded that benzoquinone is taken up by the ends of the growing chain, and that the modified polymer formed in this way then combines with the radical end of a second chain. The final effect is that further growth of both chains is prevented. This mechanism has been confirmed by suitable specific degradation reactions [96].

In the case of the inhibition of the polymerization of styrene, the situation is more complicated. The ether radicals produced when growing chains take up a molecule of benzoquinone can react with a molecule of monomeric styrene instead of a second radical, so that copolymerization of benzoquinone with styrene ensues. The benzoquinone is therefore used up rapidly, and polymerization is accelerated as soon as the inhibitor has disappeared [96, 127, 219].

Under suitable circumstances, substances capable of terminating chains may be used in labelled form to determine the rate of initiation in non-catalysed (non-sensitized) polymerization. From the amount of labelled substance built into the polymer the average chain length of the polymer can be calculated provided the mechanism of chain termination is known. The ratio of amount of polymer to the mean chain length then gives directly the frequency of chain initiation. Various inhibitors have been tested in respect to their suitability for such investigations [96, 128, 219].

The extent to which certain functional groups are split off a high polymer by acids or bases has been determined after labelling these groups with radiocarbon [130].

Finally, radioactive substances are suitable for the investigation of difficult analytical separations involving polymers. Usually trial runs are carried out with one of the components whose separation is desired in labelled form; the yield in separation is then determined by activity measurements. The labelled component may be solvent, initiator, inhibitor, monomer or a polymeric fraction of a certain molecular weight range. The results obtained in such trial runs may then be used to work out a routine separation procedure for the system. Methods of fractionating polymers have been tested in this way [95, 129]. Accurate determinations of the yields achieved in the isolation of substances can, of course, be carried out by isotope dilution, as indicated above.

The use of ionizing radiations to induce polymerization and similar reactions, such as the formation of graft-polymers, and the application of such radiations for cross-linking polymers will be discussed in Volume 2.

10.6.3. *Elucidation of Vulcanization*

Determinations of the solubility of sulphur in natural or synthetic rubbers of various kinds, in vulcanizates or in related multicomponent systems may be carried out by a radiochemical method. The bottom side of the flat test piece is brought into good contact with a layer of radiosulphur of known specific activity, and this assembly is then raised to the experimental temperature. A radiation detector is placed above the sample. Increasing absorption of sulphur by the rubber sample causes the radiation intensity to increase up to a saturation value which indicates the solubility of the sulphur. Absolute values of solubility are calculated on the basis of a calibration with rubber samples of known sulphur contents. It must, of course, be noted that under certain conditions the uptake of sulphur may be accompanied by chemical reactions, such as vulcanization, so that the values found may be too great. The same set-up may be used to measure the rate of approach to saturation, and hence the diffusion constant of sulphur in the rubber. Diffusion constants of labelled accelerators or other auxiliary agents may be determined similarly [148, 149, 161, 212, 223].

Much work with tracers has dealt with the mechanism of the uptake of sulphur by the rubber during vulcanization [132–140, 212, 266, 267]. In the earliest investigations, zinc oxide, tetramethylthiuram monosulphide and radiosulphur were added. After vulcanization the chemical form into which the sulphur had been converted during the process was studied by radiochemical methods [131]. Numerous later investigations dealt with the exchange between elementary sulphur and both inorganic and organic polysulphides. It was found that only sulphur atoms attached directly to two other sulphur atoms undergo exchange easily. Apparently carbon–sulphur bonds are not broken readily, and there is little direct exchange of sulphur between vulcanized rubber and accelerators.

Probably exchange takes place by way of intermediary formation of radicals by the breaking of the $S-S$ bond in substances of low molecular weight. In the case of accelerators, the organic radicals – resembling chain initiators in polymerization – may convert rubber molecules into radicals, which then combine with other rubber chains through sulphur bridges, or may undergo polymerization. Radicals taking part in such reactions are formed not only by heating but also in the irradiation with ultraviolet light [139–147, 213].

When ^{35}S-dibenzthiazole disulphide was added in the absence of free sulphur, the activity was equally distributed between the vulcanized product and the free mercaptan. It has been concluded that the accelerator is first split symmetrically, and that thereafter one half combines with hydrogen and the other with the rubber [144].

However, other investigators believe that homolytic fission does not occur and radicals are thus not formed. Instead, the exchange is attributed to strong polarity, that is, to asymmetrical distribution of charge along the bond between the sulphur atoms and the rest of the molecule. Cross-linking occurs through the formation of an

intermediate compound between sulphur and the accelerator, this compound subsequently being decomposed. If this mechanism applies, a direct connection between
the rate of sulphur exchange and the extent of sulphur absorption by the rubber should
exist only in special cases. In support of this view it has been pointed out that inhibitors
and chain initiators have no effect on the exchange, which is, however, accelerated by
acids and bases [138].

In some of the papers referred to, attempts to carry out a thorough kinetic analysis
of vulcanization with tracers and to find the detailed mechanism of vulcanization under particular conditions have been reported. At present, however, greatly differing
views are held in the various laboratories, even on fundamental problems of the vulcanization mechanism.

The sulphur bridges between the rubber molecules may be either monosulphide or
polysulphide bridges. The ratio between the two types depends on the nature of the
accelerator, the conditions of vulcanization, and on the subsequent treatment of the
rubber. The mean length of the bridges may be determined by exchange experiments
with radiosulphur. It has been found that short bridges give a product of better quality
[132, 133, 145, 150].

The vulcanization of rubber with ionizing radiation will be discussed in Volume 2.

10.7. **The Detergents Industry**

The concentration of surface-active substances is higher at the surface than in the
bulk of the solution. The direct measurement of this enrichment was previously a
matter of great experimental difficulty, but the use of labelled surface-active materials
has opened up new possibilities [151–160]. The radioactive substance present in the
surface layer may be determined with a window Geiger counter or, preferably, a
windowless flow-counter [159] placed immediately above the surface. Deeper layers of
the liquid contribute to the measured intensity as well, but this contribution can be
corrected for on the basis of control experiments with a solution containing the radioelement in the same total concentration, but in the form of a substance which is not
surface-active (see Section 9.1.5).

The most suitable radionuclides for such work are those which emit only soft radiation since the contribution of the radioactive substance in the bulk of the liquid to the
measured radiation intensity will then be small. Thus, the concentration of sodium
dodecyl sulphate at the surface was determined after introducing radiosulphur,
while a solution of sodium ^{35}S-sulphate was used for the control experiment. Tritium,
emitting still softer β-radiation, is even more suitable than radiocarbon or radiosulphur. Under certain conditions encountered in actual work, two-thirds of the measured radiation were found to come from the surface layer [159].

Only an extremely thin surface layer contributed when the recoil nuclei consisting
of thallium-208 (thorium C″) were used that are formed in the α-decay of bismuth-212
(thorium C). The recoil nuclei were collected on a negatively charged plate placed
above the surface, and their amount then determined through their β-activity (half-life
3·1 min). The range of the recoil nuclei in water is only about 800 Å [160].

An interesting example of the application of this principle to a problem in fundamental research is the measurement of the rate of exchange of radioiodine between iodostearic acid concentrated in the surface and potassium iodide dissolved in the bulk water. The exchange was determined by following the decrease in activity of the surface layer and was found to depend strongly on conditions, including the state (phase) of the unimolecular surface layer [162, 163].

The concentration of coadsorbed counter-ions in surface layers containing surface-active substances could also be observed. Measurement of the concentration of labelled sulphate in the presence of cation-active detergents is an example. Another example is the coadsorption of bismuth-212 by sodium dodecyl sulphate. By means of the recoil technique mentioned, the kinetics of the accumulation of the counter-ion, the extent of this concentration process under various conditions, and the transformation of surface-active substances by chemical reactions into surface-inactive substances could be studied [160].

By using extremely thin foils, for example of plastic materials, the enrichment of surface-active substances at a solid–liquid interface may be observed and information about their adsorption from solution obtained. The radiation intensity is measured above the foil that rests on the surface of the liquid. Polystyrene foils can be made so thin that even with radiations as soft as those of radiocarbon the attenuation by the foil may be neglected [157] (see also Section 9.1.5). The uptake of ^{14}C-tagged polyethylene oxide by sand has been studied in order to throw light on the mechanisms involved in the action of non-ionic detergents [275].

Experiments on the adsorption of detergents on cotton fibres have been carried out on the assumption that this adsorption is essential for good washing agents [164]. The cotton was first washed repeatedly with anion-active detergents, and was then allowed to adsorb radiocalcium ions. The amount of calcium taken up served as a measure of the amount of washing agent adsorbed, and was found to increase with the number of washings. In control experiments it was shown that the uptake of the radioactive ions by the cotton was not increased in the absence of detergent, which proves that the cotton was not damaged by the treatment.

In later investigations by other workers anion-active detergents (containing carbon-14 and sulphur-35) were employed, and the amount of the agent remaining on the fibres was determined directly by the activity [165]. These and other experiments have led to the conclusion that the detergent operates not only by dispersing the dirt, but also by displacing it by competitive adsorption from the adsorbed state on the surface. The kinetics of the adsorption of detergents have been examined from this point of view [166]. It has also been possible to follow the fate of a detergent during waste water purification by the activated sludge process (^{35}S) [167].

Radioactive "dirt" was prepared in various ways from radioactive substances [168–174, 271, 273, 274, 276, 283, 284, 307], e.g. by dissolving them in oil. Objects were then treated with this dirt, subsequently washed, and the remaining dirt detected by its radioactivity. These preparations have been used to study the effect of detergents when washing metals, textiles or parts of the human body, such as the hands. The results obtained on textiles were compared with results of measurements of light reflection on materials soiled with graphite. The action of carboxymethyl cellulose in improving detergency in respect to cotton has been studied with the labelled substance (radiocarbon) [270, 272].

10.8. The Pharmaceutical and Food Industries

Physiological and biochemical science is concerned with metabolism in healthy and sick organisms. Through the application of tracers to the study of these processes, crucial information on the absorption of biologically important substances by the organism, and on the subsequent fate of these substances within the body, is obtained [1, 175, 176]. Some tracer studies of this type will be mentioned in Chapter 11. At this point we are concerned in the main with purely technical problems arising in the production and application of pharmaceuticals.

Many applications of analytical methods based on radioactivity have been reported. Direct isotope dilution (see p. 80) has been used in a number of cases to determine the content of pharmaceutically active substances, such as penicillin [188, 189], vitamin B_{12} [186, 190] and steroids [187], in preparations. Trace elements, such as gold and rare earths, in opium may be estimated by activation analysis so that the geographical origin of the drug can be found [261].

The resorption of labelled substances from ointments and similar materials can easily be observed. It is also possible to find out whether biologically active agents in an ointment reach the place where they are intended to become effective. The absorption of minute quantities of compounds containing radioactive iodine, sulphur or phosphorus has been followed [177, 178]. Other investigations have been concerned with the absorption of components of cosmetics by the skin, and with the incorporation of fluoride ions by teeth [179]. The techniques resemble some of those applied in industrial hygiene (see p. 228).

The dissolution of tablet coatings in the body, which permits absorption of the physiologically active substances, may be followed by adding a γ-active substance (sodium-24) to the tablet. As the tablet passes through the digestive tract, this substance first remains in the tablet, but when the coating is dissolved away the radionuclide distributes itself rapidly over the entire body [180].

The destruction of biologically active substances by chemical or thermal treatment, or simply on storage, may be tested by tracer methods. After treatment or storage of the labelled substance the inactive form is added as carrier. Then the intact substance is isolated from the mixture which also contains the labelled decomposition products. If necessary, hold-back carriers are added for this separation. Finally, the activity of the isolated substance is measured [181]. Because of the similarity of the active agent and its decomposition products, such separations may require several stages, and quantitative yields are not to be expected. This is not important, however, since the ratio of the amount of substance separated to the amount of carrier added gives the separation yield. From the activity and amount of the separated substance it is then possible to calculate how much intact substance remained after treatment or storage (reverse isotope dilution method, see p. 82).

Similar analytical methods have been used to determine the fate of labelled vitamins within the animal body. Not merely the distribution of the radioelement over the various organs, but also the chemical form of the element in each organ has to be established in such investigations [176]. The method has been used, for example, to follow the fate of thiamine in rats [182].

The processes which lead to the development of resistance in bacteria against drugs such as sulphonamides have been studied after labelling either the drugs or the vitamins against which they act. The results of one group of experiments were interpreted by the assumption that the resistant strains show a change in the affinity between the enzyme and its substrate [183]. In contrast to resistant strains, in non-resistant bacteria sulphanilic acid can completely displace p-aminobenzoic acid [184, 185].

In the food industry the natural γ-activity of potassium may be used for a simple, rapid and non-destructive determination of the proportion of meat and fat in hams. It is based on the fact that the fat contains no potassium. For this purpose a special scintillation spectrometer similar to a whole body counter (p. 327) and capable of taking samples of up to 80 kg has been built. When the carcass is measured for 100 sec, and the background for 200 sec, the relative standard error is only 5 per cent [191, 192, 201–203].

Tests with radioiodine have been performed to find out whether iodine should be added to domestic salt in the form of iodide or of iodate, and at what stage it should be introduced to minimize subsequent loss. It has been found preferable to use iodate; unlike the iodide, this is stable when the salt is dried at 200°C. The iodate must be added to the dry salt and not to the brine, since in the latter case on evaporation only a small part of the iodate is mechanically retained by the deposited crystals [206].

In sugar production, the level in sugar-beet bunkers may be determined by means of γ-rays [72]. The operation of Dorr thickeners has been studied with tracers. The solution was made active with sodium-24, and the slurry with lanthanum-140, which is precipitated at the prevailing pH value. Information about the rate of mixing and the period of retention within the various parts of the thickener was obtained (see [3, 231]).

Investigations of the anaerobic metabolism in brewers' yeast led to the introduction of new fermentation conditions in breweries which have doubled the capacity of the fermentation units [72, 193, 194]. The fate of various compounds containing radiocarbon in brewing has been followed [268]. Applications of radioactivity to problems of the dairy industry have also been reported [72, 195].

Methods described in Section 9.3.1 for checking mixing processes have been used to determine the uniformity of distribution of small quantities of vitamins, antibiotics and salts in the milling and animal fodder industries [72]. γ-ray level gauges are also in use in these industries, especially in silos. In the industry of fats, levels in autoclaves for hydrogenation and in vacuum evaporators for glycerol may be observed [72]. The density of glycerol–water mixtures may be determined with a float (areometer) carrying a γ-ray source [72]. We may finally mention a method for determining the distance between rollers in mills, without direct contact, by means of the β-radiation from strontium-90. The gap between the rollers serves as a collimating slit, so that the radiation intensity registered by a detector is approximately proportional to this distance [72].

The sterilization of pharmaceuticals and foodstuffs by ionizing radiations will be discussed in Volume 2. To test the sterility of solutions, a suitable substrate labelled with carbon-14, such as lactose, may be added. After a short incubation it is determined whether radioactive carbon dioxide has been formed. The method is rapid and sensitive [196, 197].

References to Chapter 10

1. See, for example, E.Broda, *Radioaktive Isotope in der Biochemie*, Vienna 1958; *Radioactive Isotopes in Biochemistry*, Amsterdam 1960.
2. G.Billek, in [1].
3. L.G.Erwall and K.Ljunggren, Geneva Report 166 (1958), vol. 19, p. 3.
4. J.W.Irvine, *Anal. Chem.* **21,** 364 (1949).
5. A.Rezanowich, G.A.Allen and S.G.Mason, *Pulp Paper Mag. Canada* **58,** 153 (1957).
6. C.A.Sankey, S.G.Mason, G.A.Allen and W.R.Keating, *Pulp Paper Mag. Canada* **52,** 137 (1951).
7. G.A.Allen, A.Rezanowich and S.G.Mason, *Svensk Papperstid.* **61,** 475 (1958).
8. T.Schönfeld and E.Broda, *Mikrochemie* **36–37,** 537 (1951).
9. See H.J.White, *Anal. Chem.* **29,** 1744 (1959).
10. See A.G.Sevostyanov, *The Application of Radioactive Isotopes to the Spinning Industry* (Russ.), Moscow 1958.
11. S.S.Shvyrev, A.N.Slatinskii and K.D.Pismannik, in [20].
12. D.L.Underwood and H.J.White, *Disc. Faraday Soc.* **16,** 66 (1954).
13. H.B.Hampson and E.W.Jones, *J. Soc. Dyers Colourists* **69,** 620 (1953).
14. K.Sauerwein, *Atomwirtschaft* **1,** 407 (1956).
15. W.Meitner and H.B.Hampson, *J. Soc. Dyers Colourists* **69,** 283 (1953).
16. M.Moncrieff-Yeates and H.J.White, *Amer. Dyestuff Reptr.* **46,** P 87 (1957).
17. D.L.Underwood and H.J.White, see [9].
18. M.L.Wright, *Disc. Faraday Soc.* **16,** 58 (1954).
19. D.S.Taylor, Radioisotope Conference 1954, London 1954, vol. 2, p. 156; *Textile Ind.* **45,** 1310 (1954).
20. All-Union Conference on the Applications of Radioactive and Stable Isotopes and Nuclear Radiations in National Economy (Russ.), Moscow 1957.
21. M.Chaikin, K.Baird, A.G.Stutter and J.Curtis, see [9].
22. A.P.Schreiber, *Nucleonics* **2** (1), 33 (1948); *Electronics* **22** (1), 90 (1949).
23. K.Sauerwein, *Angew. Chemie* **66,** 107 (1954).
24. A.Robson, *Atomics and Atomic Technology* **4,** 320 (1953).
25. E.R.Trotman, *Textile Recorder* **69,** 93 (1951).
26. J.A.Janik, A.Szkatula, S.Wronka and E.Kunisz, Copenhagen Report 114.
27. F.A.Paneth, *Angew. Chem.* **35,** 549 (1922).
28. S.M.Smirnov, in [20].
29. R.Heyden, J.Plapper and K.Sauerwein, *Das Leder* **7,** 100 (1956).
30. J.L.Putman, Geneva Report 283 (1958), vol. 19, p. 22.
31. A.E.Ballard, G.W.Stevens and C.W.Zuehlke, *Radioisotope Techniques*, London 1952, vol. 2, p. 105.
32. H.Tellez-Plasencia, Paris Report 51, vol. 2, p. 284.
33. G.W.W.Stevens and D.M.Spracklen, Copenhagen Report 38, vol. 2, p. 211.
34. R.Buchdahl and M.F.Polglase, *Anal. Chem.* **18,** 115 (1946).
35. B.E.Gordon and W.K.Lisichenko, *Atomnaya Energiya* **7,** 384 (1959); *Kernenergie* **3,** 579 (1960); *Int. J. Appl. Rad. Isotopes* **8,** 138 (1960).
36. T.Takeuchi, M.Sakaguchi, Y.Nakamoto and S.Kadokura, Geneva Report 1342 (1958), vol. 20, p. 166.

37. J.L.PUTMAN, *Nature* **181**, 318 (1958).
38. J.L.PUTMAN, *J. Soc. Glass Technology* **42**, 55 (1958).
39. J.R.JOHNSON, *J. Appl. Physics* **20**, 129, 819 (1949).
40. J.R.JOHNSON, R.H.BRISTOW and H.H.BLAU, *J. Amer. Ceram. Soc.* **34**, 165 (1951).
41. R.LINDNER, *Acta Chem. Scand.* **5**, 735 (1951).
42. J.PEYCHÈS, *Silicates Ind.* **17**, 241 (1952).
43. R.F.BARKER, see [37].
44. R.F.BARKER, *J. Soc. Glass Technology* **42**, 101, 109 (1958).
45. S.LINDROTH, *J. Amer. Ceram. Soc.* **32**, 198 (1949).
46. O.HAHN and H.MÜLLER, *Glastechn. Ber.* **7**, 380 (1929).
47. T.SAITO, Geneva Report 1348 (1958), vol. 19, p. 201.
48. B.E.MOODY, see [37].
49. B.E.MOODY and D.G.MONK, *J. Soc. Glass Technology* **42**, 88 (1958).
50. V.A.DUBROVSKII, in [20].
51. V.A.DUBROVSKII, *Steklo i keram.* **13** (2), 8 (1956); **14** (6), 1 (1957).
52. *Atomics* **5**, 303 (1954).
53. E.W.JONES, see [37].
54. E.W.JONES, *J. Soc. Glass Technology* **42**, 62 (1958).
55. O.HAHN, *J. Chem. Soc. (London)* **1949** (S), 259.
56. J.V.FITZGERALD, *Glass Ind.* **30**, 259 (1949).
57. K.M.LAING, R.E.JONES, D.E.EMHISER, J.V.FITZGERALD and G.S.BACHMANN, *Nucleonics* **9** (4), 44 (1951); *J. Amer. Ceram. Soc.* **34**, 380 (1951).
58. J.W.HENSLEY, A.O.LONG and J.E.WILLARD, *Ind. Eng. Chem.* **41**, 1415 (1949).
59. A.O.LONG and J.E.WILLARD, *Ind. Eng. Chem.* **44**, 916 (1952).
60. J.E.WILLARD, *J. Phys. Chem.* **57**, 129 (1953).
61. F.STARIK, *Principles of Radiochemistry* (Russ.), Moscow 1959; English translation, Washington 1964.
62. T.SCHÖNFELD and S.NEUMANN, *Monatsh. Chem.* **85**, 921 (1954).
63. E.B.BUTLER and W.H.JOHNSTON, *Science* **120**, 543 (1954).
64. J.L.PUTMAN and W.H.TAYLOR, *J. Soc. Glass Technology* **42**, 84 (1958).
65. A.M.SMIRNOVA and P.A.REBINDER, *Doklady Akad. Nauk SSSR* **96**, 107 (1954).
66. P.LÉVÊQUE, R.HOURS, P.MARTINELLI, S.MAY, J.SANDIER and J.BRILLANT, Geneva Report 1231 (1958), vol. 19, p. 34.
67. L.G.POLOSOVA, in [20].
68. L.G.POLOSOVA and R.P.RITSMAN, *Izvest. Akad. Nauk Eston. SSSR, Ser. Tekhn.* **6**, 122 (1957).
69. J.W.T.SPINKS, Geneva Report 216 (1958), vol. 19, p. 13.
70. J.PAWLIW and J.W.T.SPINKS, *Can. J. Technol.* **34**, 503 (1957).
71. V.S.KUDRYAVTSEV, in [20].
72. All-Union Conference on the Introduction of Radioactive Isotopes and Nuclear Radiations into the National Economy of the U.S.S.R, Riga 1960; see *Atomnaya Energiya* **9**, 221 (1960); *Kernenergie* **4**, 158 (1961).
73. U.A.LUOTO and E.G.ROTKIRCH, Geneva Report 1101 (1958), vol. 19, p. 28.
74. U.BEEN and G.SAELAND, Geneva Report 882 (1955), vol. 15, p. 170.
75. J.RUTLE, *Pit & Quarry* **48**, 120 (1955).
76. K.HOGRABE and W.A.LEHMANN, *Zement-Kalk-Gips* **9**, 133, 210 (1956).
77. W.A.G.GRAHAM, J.W.T.SPINKS and T.THORVALDSON, *Canad. J. Chem.* **32**, 129 (1954).
78. F.W.BIRSS and T.THORVALDSON, *Can. J. Chem.* **33**, 870 (1955).
79. YA.I.NATARIUS, *Gidrotekhn. Stroit.* **1959** (3), 55.
80. V.M.MOSKVIN, in [20].
81. E.G.HOFFMANN and H.HOBERG, *Z. Elektrochem.* **58**, 646 (1954).
82. A.D.KIRSHENBAUM, C.W.HOFFMAN and A.V.GROSSE, *Anal. Chem.* **23**, 1440 (1951).
83. W.HERRMANN, G.GARTMANN, H.K.BOTHE and G.HOFFMANN, *Kernenergie* **3**, 663 (1960).
84. J.KOHL, *Chem. Eng. Progr.* **48**, 611 (1952).
85. S.E.EATON, Geneva Report 146 (1955), vol. 14, p. 61.
86. H.GÖTTE, Geneva Report 985 (1958), vol. 19, p. 297.

87. *Atomics* **2**, 245 (1951).
88. E. F. FINKEL, Paris Report 34, vol. 2, p. 463.
89. J. J. POINT, Paris Report 45, vol. 2, p. 438.
90. H. A. BURLEY and M. J. DIAMOND, *Nucleonics* **19** (8), 45 (1961).
91. G. S. PARK, Radioisotope Conference 1954, London 1954, vol. 2, p. 11.
92. R. OTTO, *Isotopentechnik* **1**, 9 (1960).
93. G. D. CALKINS, M. POBERESKIN, V. E. YOUNG and L. J. NOWACKI, *Nucleonics* **13** (2), 76 (1955).
94. A. P. LANDALL, *Modern Plastics* **32** (1), 131 (1954).
95. J. C. BEVINGTON and H. W. MELVILLE, Radioisotope Conference 1954, London 1954, vol. 2, p. 3.
96. H. W. MELVILLE, *Chem. & Ind.* **1957**, 163.
97. J. C. BEVINGTON, in: Symposium on Techniques in Polymer Chemistry, Royal Institute of Chemistry, London 1956, Report 5, p. 1.
98. J. C. BEVINGTON, *Fortschr. Hochpolymerforsch.* **2** (1), 1 (1960).
99. K. L. BERRY and J. H. PETERSON, *J. Amer. Chem. Soc.* **73**, 5195 (1951).
100. W. E. MOCHEL and J. H. PETERSON, *J. Amer. Chem. Soc.* **71**, 1426 (1949).
101. W. V. SMITH and H. N. CAMPBELL, *J. Chem. Phys.* **15**, 338 (1947).
102. W. V. SMITH, *J. Amer. Chem. Soc.* **71**, 4077 (1949).
103. I. M. KOLTHOFF, P. R. O'CONNOR and J. L. HANSEN, *J. Polymer Sci.* **15**, 459 (1955).
104. C. WALLING, *J. Amer. Chem. Soc.* **70**, 2561 (1948).
105. F. LANDLER, *Rec. Trav. Chim. Pays-Bas* **68**, 992 (1949).
106. M. M. KOTON, T. M. KISELEVA and M. I. BESONOV, *Doklady Akad. Nauk SSSR* **96**, 85 (1954).
107. H. F. PFANN, D. J. SALLEY and H. MARK, *J. Amer. Chem. Soc.* **66**, 983 (1944).
108. J. C. BEVINGTON, D. E. EAVES, J. TOOLE and L. TROSSARELLI, Geneva Report 286 (1958), vol. 20, p. 128.
109. J. C. BEVINGTON, J. TOOLE and L. TROSSARELLI, *Makromol. Chem.* **32**, 57 (1959).
110. J. C. BEVINGTON and C. S. BROOKS, *J. Polymer. Sci.* **22**, 257 (1956).
111. J. C. BEVINGTON, *Proc. Roy. Soc.* A **239**, 420 (1957).
112. J. C. BEVINGTON and J. TOOLE, *J. Polymer Sci.* **28**, 413 (1958).
113. J. C. BEVINGTON, J. TOOLE and L. TROSSARELLI, *Trans. Faraday Soc.* **54**, 863 (1958).
114. J. C. BEVINGTON and T. D. LEWIS, *Trans. Faraday Soc.* **54**, 1340 (1958).
115. C. A. BARSON, J. C. BEVINGTON and D. E. EAVES, *Trans. Faraday Soc.*, **54**, 1678 (1958).
116. J. C. BEVINGTON, J. TOOLE and L. TROSSARELLI, *Makromol. Chem.* **28**, 237 (1958).
117. J. C. BEVINGTON and C. S. BROOKS, *Makromol. Chem.* **28**, 173 (1958).
118. C. A. BARSON and J. C. BEVINGTON, *J. Polymer Sci.* **20**, 133 (1956).
119. J. C. BEVINGTON, *Trans. Faraday Soc.* **53**, 997 (1957).
120. J. C. BEVINGTON, H. W. MELVILLE and R. P. TAYLOR, *J. Polymer Sci.* **12**, 449 (1954); **14**, 463 (1954).
121. L. M. ARNETT and J. H. PETERSON, *J. Amer. Chem. Soc.* **74**, 2031 (1952).
122. J. C. BEVINGTON, J. H. BRADBURY and G. M. BURNETT, *J. Polymer. Sci.* **12**, 469 (1954).
123. L. R. MCNALL and I. T. EBY, *Anal. Chem.* **29**, 951 (1957).
124. H. W. MELVILLE, F. W. PESKER and R. L. VALE, *J. Polymer Sci.* **30**, 29 (1958).
125. J. C. BEVINGTON and D. E. EAVES, *Nature* **178**, 1112 (1956).
126. E. P. BONSALL, L. VALENTINE and H. W. MELVILLE, *Trans. Faraday Soc.* **49**, 686 (1953).
127. J. C. BEVINGTON, N. A. GHANEM and H. W. MELVILLE, *J. Chem. Soc.* **1955**, 2822.
128. J. C. BEVINGTON and N. A. GHANEM, *J. Chem. Soc.* **1958**, 2254; **1959**, 2071.
129. J. C. BEVINGTON, G. M. GUZMAN and H. W. MELVILLE, *Proc. Roy. Soc.* A **221**, 437, 453 (1954).
130. J. C. BEVINGTON, D. E. EAVES and R. L. VALE, *J. Polymer Sci.* **32**, 317 (1958).
131. I. G. GEIB, *Phys. Rev.* **74**, 117 (1948).
132. B. A. DOGADKIN and S. N. TARASOVA, *Doklady Akad. Nauk SSSR* **85**, 1069 (1952); *Kolloid. Zh.* **15**, 347 (1953).
133. S. N. TARASOVA, M. YA. KAPLUNOV and B. A. DOGADKIN, *Doklady Akad. Nauk SSSR* **99**, 819 (1954).
134. E. N. GURYANOVA, *Zh. Fiz. Khim.* **28**, 67 (1954).
135. N. I. GRISHKO and E. N. GURYANOVA, *Zh. Obshch. Khim.* **28**, 1287 (1958).
136. E. N. GURYANOVA and L. A. YEGOROVA, *Zh. Obshch. Khim.* **28**, 1745 (1958).

137. R. Otto, *Kernenergie* **3**, 321 (1960).
138. G. P. Miklukhin, Moscow Atomic Energy Conference 1955, Div. Chem. Sciences, p. 251.
139. E. N. Guryanova, V. N. Vasileva and L. S. Kuzina, Moscow Atomic Energy Conference 1955, Div. Chem. Sciences, p. 270.
140. E. N. Guryanova and L. S. Kuzina, *Zh. Fiz. Khim.* **32**, 2301 (1958).
141. E. N. Guryanova and V. N. Vasileva, *Zh. Fiz. Khim.* **28**, 60 (1954).
142. B. A. Dogadkin and E. N. Belyaeva, *Vysokomolek. Soyedin.* **1**, 315 (1959).
143. D. Craig, A. E. Juve, W. L. Davidson, W. L. Semon and D. C. Hay, *J. Polymer Sci.* **8**, 321 (1952).
144. B. Dogadkin, M. Feldshtein, A. Dobromyslova, V. Shkurina and M. Kaplunov, *Doklady Akad. Nauk SSSR* **92**, 61 (1953).
145. V. N. Kondratyev, Geneva Report 708 (1955), vol. 15, p. 3.
146. D. Craig, W. L. Davidson, A. E. Juve and I. G. Geib, *J. Polymer. Sci.* **6**, 1, 7, 13, 177 (1951); *Rubber Chem. Technol.* **24**, 254, 262, 266, 269, 275 (1951).
147. B. A. Dogadkin, I. A. Tutorskii and D. M. Pevsner, *Doklady Akad. Nauk SSSR* **112**, 449 (1957).
148. S. E. Bresler, V. I. Pryadilova and V. Ya. Khainman, *Zh. Tekhn. Fiz.* **24**, 577 (1954).
149. S. E. Bresler, V. P. Kushner and M. E. Saminskii, *Zh. Tekhn. Fiz.* **24**, 2150 (1954).
150. B. A. Dogadkin, S. N. Tarasova, M. A. Vaskovskaya and M. Ya. Kaplunov, in [20].
151. K. J. Dixon, A. J. Weith, A. A. Argyle and D. J. Salley, *Nature* **163**, 845 (1949); *Proc. Roy. Soc.* A **203**, 42 (1950).
152. C. M. Judson, A. A. Argyle, K. J. Dixon and D. J. Salley, *J. Chem. Phys.* **18**, 1302 (1950); **19**, 378 (1951); **20**, 519 (1952); *J. Phys. Chem.* **57**, 916 (1953).
153. O. Lamm and G. Aniansson, *Nature* **165**, 357 (1950).
154. G. Aniansson, *J. Phys. Colloid Chem.* **55**, 1286 (1951).
155. G. Aniansson and N. Steiger, *J. Chem. Phys.* **21**, 1299 (1953); *J. Phys. Chem.* **58**, 228 (1954).
156. H. Sobotka, *Monomolecular Layers*, Washington 1954.
157. C. P. Roe and P. D. Brass, *J. Amer. Chem. Soc.* **76**, 4703 (1954).
158. R. Matsuura, H. Kimizuka, S. Miyamoto and R. Shimozawa, *Bull. Chem. Soc. Japan* **31**, 532 (1958).
159. G. Nilsson, *J. Phys. Chem.* **61**, 1135 (1957).
160. M. Avrahami and N. H. Steiger, Copenhagen Report 291, vol. 3, p. 449; *J. Coll. Sci.* **18**, 863 (1963).
161. I. Auerbach and S. D. Gehman, *Anal. Chem.* **26**, 685 (1954).
162. R. F. Robertson, C. A. Winkler and S. G. Mason, *Can. J. Chem.* **34**, 716 (1956).
163. S. G. Mason and W. Rabinovitch, *Proc. Roy. Soc.* A **249**, 90 (1959).
164. J. M. Lambert, *Ind. Eng. Chem.* **42**, 1394 (1950).
165. A. L. Meader and B. A. Fries, *Ind. Eng. Chem.* **44**, 1636 (1952).
166. A. Fava and H. Eyring, *J. Phys. Chem.* **60**, 890 (1956).
167. R. House and B. A. Fries, *Sewage and Ind. Wastes* **28**, 492 (1956).
168. J. C. Harris, R. E. Kamp and W. H. Yanko, *J. Electrochem. Soc.* **97**, 340 (1950).
169. L. Osipow, G. Segura, C. T. Snell and F. D. Snell, *Ind. Eng. Chem.* **45**, 2779 (1953).
170. J. M. Lambert, J. H. Röcker, J. J. Pescatore, C. Segura and S. Stigman, *Nucleonics* **12** (2), 40 (1954).
171. A. K. Phansalkar and R. D. Vold, *J. Phys. Chem.* **59**, 885 (1955).
172. F. E. Ehrenkranz and E. H. Jebe, *Nucleonics* **14** (3), 96 (1956).
173. R. E. Wagg and C. J. Britt, *Nature* **180**, 48 (1957).
174. G. Erdelen, *Atompraxis* **3**, 97 (1957).
175. See C. L. Comar and F. Bronner (Ed.), *Mineral Metabolism*, New York 1960.
176. See D. E. Duggan and E. O. Titus in: H. Schwiegk and F. Turba (Ed.), *Künstliche radioaktive Isotope in Physiologie, Diagnostik und Therapie*, Berlin 1961.
177. G. N. Cyr, D. M. Skanen, J. E. Christian and C. O. Lee, *J. Amer. Pharmac. Assoc. Sci. Edit.* **38**, 615, 618 (1949).
178. R. K. Thoms, L. D. Edwards and J. E. Christian, *J. Amer. Pharmac. Assoc. Sci. Edit.* **37**, 329 (1948).
179. M. F. Nelson, *Nucleonics* **14** (5), 43 (1956).
180. K. Lark-Horovitz and H. R. Lang, *Nature* **147**, 580 (1941).

181. L.Chaiet, C.Rosenblum and D.T.Woodbury, *Science* **111**, 601 (1950); **113**, 215 (1951).
182. J.M.Iacono and B.C.Johnson, *J. Amer. Chem. Soc.* **79**, 6321 (1957).
183. A.Wacker, Paris Report 152, vol. 3, p. 24.
184. A.Wacker, A.Trebst and H.Simon, *Z. Naturforsch.* **12**b, 315 (1957).
185. A.Wacker, *Klin. Wochenschr.* **37**, 1 (1959).
186. C.Rosenblum, *Anal. Chem.* **29**, 1740 (1957).
187. R.A.Donia, A.C.Ott and N.Drake, *Anal. Chem.* **29**, 464 (1957).
188. G.C.Ashton and M.C.Foster, *Analyst* **80**, 123 (1955).
189. M.Gordon, A.J.Virgona and P.Numerof, *Anal. Chem.* **26**, 1208 (1954).
190. F.A.Backer, A.E.Boley and C.E.Shonk, *Anal. Chem.* **26**, 1146 (1954).
191. R.Kulvich, L.Feinstein and E.C.Anderson, *Science* **127**, 338 (1958).
192. D.H.Pringle and R.Kulvich, *Nucleonics* **19** (2), 74 (1961).
193. A.V.Topchiev, I.T.Aladiev and P.S.Savitsky, Geneva Report 2308 (1958), vol. 19, p. 61.
194. I.Ya.Veselov, N.V.Pokrovskaya and S.S.Rylkin, *Trudy Vsesoyuz. Nauchno-Isled. Inst. Pivovar. Prom.* **1957** (7), 141.
195. A.J.Vainberg, see [20].
196. G.V.Levin, V.R.Harrison, W.C.Hess, A.H.Heim and V.L.Strauss, Geneva Report 820 (1958), vol. 19, p. 291.
197. G.V.Levin, V.R.Harrison, W.C.Hess and H.C.Gurney, *Amer. J. Public Health* **46**, 1405 (1956).
198. P.Bussière, I.Gavet and P.Rochas, *Int. J. Appl. Rad. Isot.* **8**, 168 (1960).
199. J.A.Ketelaar and D.Heijmann, *Rec. Trav. Chim. Pays-Bas* **73**, 279 (1954).
200. G.Hartmann, *Isotopentechnik* **1**, 182 (1961).
201. G.Hartmann and G.Schlesier, *Isotopentechnik* **1**, 229 (1961).
202. E.C.Anderson, *Food Research* **24**, 605 (1959).
203. A.Pfau, G.Kallistratos and J.Schröder, *Atompraxis* **7**, 279 (1961).
204. K.Schwabe and H.Dahms, *Isotopentechnik* **1**, 34 (1960).
205. K.Schwabe and H.Dahms, *Naturwiss.* **47**, 351 (1960).
206. K.Akerman, P.M.Hoffmann, E.Lelental and A.Poczynajlo, *Isotopentechnik* **2**, 73 (1962).
207. C.L.Fisher, *Atomwirtschaft* **6**, 481 (1961).
208. M.Rösseler, *Isotopentechnik* **1**, 178 (1961).
209. N.A.Ismailov and A.G.Vasilev, *Zh. Fiz. Khim.* **30**, 1500 (1956).
210. V.V.Moiseev and B.P.Nikolskii, *Vestn. Leningr. Univ., Ser. Fiz. i Khim.* **12**, 69 (1957).
211. P.Valls, A.M.Venet and J.Pouradier, *Bull. soc. chim. France* **1953**, C 106.
212. A.E.Brodskii, *Isotope Chemistry* (Russ.), Moscow 1957; German translation, Berlin 1961.
213. I.Auerbach, *Ind. Eng. Chem.* **45**, 1526 (1953).
214. H.Costa and K.Petermann, *Silikattechnik* **10**, 209, 253, 345 (1959).
215. H.Costa, *Isotopentechnik* **1**, 167 (1961).
216. H.Costa, *Wissensch. Z. Hochsch. Bauwesen* **3**, 65 (1961).
217. K.Akerman, P.M.Hoffmann, A.Poczynajlo, J.Majchrowski, J.Glondalski and J.Oglaza, *Isotopentechnik* **1**, 165 (1961).
218. K.Akerman, P.Hoffmann and W.Zablotny, Brit. Chem. Engng. **11**, (1), 26 (1966).
219. J.C.Bevington, *Radical Polymerization*, London 1961.
220. K.Schwabe and H.Dahms, *Z. Elektrochem.* **65**, 518 (1961).
221. H.Cermak, *Isotopentechnik* **1**, 140 (1961); *Kernenergie* **7**, 557 (1964).
222. T.Westermark, *Teknisk Tidskrift* **8**, 595 (1953).
223. M.Mozišek, *Isotopentechnik* **2**, 174, 205 (1962).
224. V.Schuricht, *Isotopentechnik* **2**, 101 (1962).
225. H.W.Thümmel, *Isotopentechnik* **2**, 140 (1962).
226. Č.Jech, Paris Report 35, vol. 2, p. 491.
227. H.Frieser and E.Ranz, *Z. Elektrochem.* **67**, 833 (1963).
228. E.Lelental and A.Szuchnik, *Int. J. Appl. Rad. Isot.* **15**, 373 (1964).
229. B.A.Gromov, V.B.Miller, M.B.Neiman and Yu.A.Shlyapnikov, *Int. J. Appl. Rad. Isot.* **13**, 281 (1962).
230. R.Schroller and H.Stiede, *Kernenergie* **6**, 279 (1963).

231. L.G.Erwall, H.G.Forsberg and K.Ljunggren, in: *Production and Use of Short-Lived Isotopes from Reactors*, Symposium in Vienna, I.A.E.A., Vienna 1963.
232. I.Bjerle and H.G.Forsberg, in: *Production and Use of Short-Lived Isotopes from Reactors*, Symposium in Vienna, I.A.E.A., Vienna 1963.
233. R.P.Hamilton, *Tappi* **44**, 647 (1961).
234. R.Fischer, *Silikattechnik* **11**, 559 (1960).
235. W.S.Lehmann and E.Plassmann, *Zement-Kalk-Gips* **10**, 89 (1957).
236. K.Barth, *Silikattechnik* **11**, 559 (1960).
237. P.Lévêque (Ed.), *Les applications industrielles des radioéléments*, Paris 1962.
238. P.Rabot, in [237].
239. A.Gröbe, H.Jost, G.Hartmann and G.Pfrepper, *Monatsber. Dtsch. Akad. Wiss. Berlin* **5**, 1 (1963).
240. P.Rochas, P.Bussière and L.Gavet, *Compt. rend.* **248**, 3436 (1959); *Bull. Inst. Text. France* **87**, 19 (1960); *Int. J. Appl. Rad. Isot.* **8**, 168 (1960).
241. W.S.Barnard, A.Palm, P.B.Stam, D.L.Underwood and H.J.White. *Textile Research J.* **24**, 863 (1954).
242. P.B.Stam and H.J.White, *Textile Research J.* **24**, 785 (1954).
243. S.Eklund, *Arkiv f. Matematik, Astronomi og Fysik* **32** B (1945).
244. V. L. Indenbom, Ts.A.Karchmar, L.F.Yurkov and B.M.Glukhovskoi, *Zavod. Lab.* **22**, 1293 (1956).
245. V. B. Gaidadymov and L.I.Il'ina, *Zavod. Lab.* **24**, 431 (1958).
246. R.Jagitsch, *Z. Phys. Chem.* B **36**, 339 (1937).
247. F.Strassmann, *Naturwiss.* **19**, 502 (1931).
248. P.LeClerc, *Compt. rend.* **240** 306 (1955); *Int. Glass Congress*, Paris 1956.
249. P.LeClerc, in [237].
250. B.Bloch, *Compt. rend.* **247**, 1601 (1958).
251. H.J.White, Geneva Report 160 (1955), vol. 15, p. 39.
252. H.Müller, *Z. phys. Chem.* **149**, 257 (1930).
253. W.Hinz, *Silikattechnik* **4**, 136 (1957).
254. H.H.Blau, *Int. Glass Congress*, Paris 1956.
255. P.LeClerc, *Génie civil* **8**, 182 (1958).
256. S.F.Cox and K.M.Laing, *Glass Ind.* **35**, 183, 222 (1954).
257. R.Jagitsch, *Mh. Chem.* **68**, 1 (1936).
258. H.Muth, *Glastechn. Ber.* **27**, 248 (1954).
259. A.Petzold, *Silikattechnik* **6**, 321 (1955).
260. R.Schroller and H.Stiede, *Kernenergie* **6**, 643 (1963).
261. A.C.Pappas, J.Alstad and G.Lunde, *Radiochim. Acta* **1**, 109 (1963).
262. O.U.Anders, *Nucleonics* **18** (12), 77 (1960).
263. V.K.Gromov, M.B.Neiman, V.L.Vakula and S.S.Voyutskii, *Int. J. Appl. Rad. Isot.* **14**, 351 (1963).
264. H.K.Bothe, H.Hilbig, L.Fischer and I.Legler, *Isotopentechnik* **2**, 262 (1962).
265. A.D.Kirshenbaum, A.G.Streng and W.B.Dunlap, *Rubber Age* **72**, 625 (1953).
266. G.A.Bloch, L.F.Chuprina, E.A.Golubkova and G.P.Miklukhin, *Rubber Chem. Technol.* **27**, 974 (1954); **29**, 63, 67, 1369 (1956).
267. P.Krumbiegel, *Isotopentechnik* **2**, 282 (1962).
268. W.L.Holmes and J.C.Colla, *Proc. Amer. Soc. Brewing Chemists* **1957**, 26.
269. B.M.Kovarskaya, V.D.Moiseev and M.B.Neiman, *Int. J. Appl. Rad. Isot.* **14**, 251 (1963).
270. J.W.Hensley and C.J.Inks, *Textile Research J.* **29**, 505 (1959).
271. G.Segura, C.T.Snell, S.Stigman and F.D.Snell, *Chem. & Ind.* **1953**, 1270.
272. J.Stawitz, W.Klaus and H.Krämer, *Kolloid-Z.* **150**, 39 (1957); **155**, 131 (1957).
273. J.W.Hensley, M.G.Kramer, R.D.Ring and H.R.Suter, *J. Amer. Oil Chemists Soc.* **32**, 138 (1955).
274. E.H.Armbruster and G.M.Ridenour, *Soap Chem. Spec.* **31** (7), 47 (1955).
275. Lun Hsiao and H.N.Dunning, *J. Phys. Chem.* **59**, 362 (1955).
276. W.Strauss, *Kolloid-Z.* **150**, 135 (1957).

277. M.H.Jones, H.W.Melville and W.C.P.Robertson, *Nature* **174**, 78 (1954).
278. W.H.Stockmayer and L.H.Peebles, *J. Amer. Chem. Soc.* **75**, 2278 (1953).
279. J.C.Bevington and H.G.Troth, *Trans. Faraday Soc.* **58**, 2005 (1962).
280. J.C.Bevington and H.G.Troth, *Trans. Faraday Soc.* **59**, 127 (1963).
281. J.C.Bevington and H.G.Troth, *Trans. Faraday Soc.* **59**, 1348 (1963).
282. K.Schwabe, H.Dahms, G.Nguyen and G.Hoffmann, *Z. Elektrochem.* **66**, 304 (1962).
283. J.W.Hensley, *Iron Age* **170**, 151 (1952).
284. J.W.Hensley and R.D.Ring, *Plating* **42**, 1137 (1955).
285. D.N.Sunderman, R.Lieberman and R.C.Newton, *Int. J. Appl. Rad. Isot.* **15**, 269 (1964).
286. E.Pohl, *Isotopentechnik* **1**, 138 (1960); *Kerntechnik* **3**, 59, 77 (1961).
287. W.J.Schmidt-Küster and H.Mohrhauer, *Atomwirtschaft* **9**, 611 (1964).
288. H.Klare and A.Gröbe, *Österr. Chem.-Ztg.* **65**, 218 (1964).
289. L.G.Erwall, H.G.Forsberg and K.Ljunggren, *Industriell Isotop-Teknik*, Copenhagen 1962; *Industrial Isotope Techniques*, Copenhagen 1964.
290. *Nucleonics* **8** (4), 78 (1951).
291. F.Hawliczek and F.Hernegger, *Atompraxis* **2**, 116 (1956).
292. D.J.Belcher, T.R.Crykendill and H.S.Sachs, *Tech. Development Report* **127**, Civil Aeronautics Board, Indianapolis 1950.
293. H.W.Thümmel, *Isotopentechnik* **1**, 133 (1960).
294. W.J.Schmidt-Küster and L.Wiesner (Ed.), *Anwendung radioaktiver Isotope in der Textilforschung und -technik* (Report on Symposium), Munich 1964.
295. H.E.Knobil, *J. Textile Inst. Proc.* **52**, 653 (1961).
296. G.S.Park, *J. Soc. Dyers Colourists* **76**, 624 (1960); **78**, 451 (1962).
297. G.S.Park, *Text. Inst. Ind.* **1** (8), 8 (1963).
298. R.K.Barnes in [294].
299. S.C.Ellis and D.B.Rees-Evans, *J. Textile Inst. Trans.* **53**, 340 (1962).
300. S.C.Ellis and J.H.Barnett, *J. Sci. Instruments* **40**, 35 (1963).
301. F.J.Hybart, P.F.Clemo, *et al.*, *J. Textile Inst.* **52** (3), T 122 (1961).
302. M.L.Wright, *Trans. Faraday Soc.* **49**, 95 (1953); **50**, 89 (1954).
303. J.A.Medley, *Trans. Faraday Soc.* **53**, 1380 (1957).
304. J.A.Medley and D.K.Ramsden, *J. Textile Inst. Trans.* **51**, T 1311 (1960).
305. H.E.Dobbs, *Int. J. Appl. Rad. Isot.* **14**, 238 (1963).
306. D.S Taylor, *J. Textile Inst. Trans.* **47**, T 141 (1956).
307. R.E.Wagg and C.F.Britt, *J. Textile Inst. Trans.* **53**, T 205 (1962).
308. W.Kühn in [294].
309. G.Grandclément and A.Bonnet in [294].

11. APPLICATION OF RADIOACTIVITY
IN AGRICULTURE AND FORESTRY

Agriculture and forestry may be regarded as branches of applied biochemistry and physiology. Already many fundamental questions of biochemistry and of plant and animal physiology have been clarified by the use of the isotope methods. In particular, the application of radiocarbon has marked a great step forward. In this book we shall limit ourselves to examples related to practical problems of agriculture and forestry. The use of radionuclides in general biochemistry and physiology has been discussed elsewhere [1–6, 362].

11.1. Photosynthesis as the Basis of Agriculture and Forestry

Photosynthesis is the basis of nearly all life processes in our world. It consists in the assimilation of atmospheric carbon dioxide by green plants with the aid of sunlight. The overall process involved in photosynthesis has for a long time been known to be represented by the equation for the biosynthesis of hexoses:

$$6 CO_2 + 6 H_2O = C_6H_{12}O_6 + 6 O_2.$$

Experiments with heavy oxygen have shown that the free oxygen is liberated not from carbon dioxide, but from water [8, 9, 405]. The equation would, therefore, be more suitably written by adding $6 H_2O$ to each side.

$$6 CO_2 + 12 H_2O = C_6H_{12}O_6 + 6 O_2 + 6 H_2O.$$

On the other hand, the isotopic composition of the oxygen present in leaf sugar corresponds to that of the carbon dioxide [10]. The oxygen of the carbon dioxide formed during the respiration of plants comes directly from the water, and not from the organic substance of the plants or from the air [11].

Complicated plant substances, including the higher carbohydrates, lignin, amino acids, proteins, plant pigments and alkaloids, are formed in the transformation of sugars and related substances. But it can hardly be supposed that a molecule as complicated as that of a hexose is built up from carbon dioxide and water without the formation of stable intermediates.

Information about the primary products of photosynthesis has been obtained by tracer methods. Kamen, Calvin and their colleagues [3–5, 7, 12–14, 333] exposed plants or their surviving organs to light for short periods in the presence of radioactive carbon dioxide. The plants were killed, and the substances contained in them were tested for radioactivity. In such experiments obviously only those substances can be active which have taken up carbon dioxide during the short period of illumination. The shorter this period of "radiophotosynthesis", the more strictly radioactivity is limited to the first products.

The use of radiophotosynthesis for the preparation of radioactive compounds has already been mentioned on p. 60, but for such purposes as large an absorption of active carbon dioxide as possible is needed, so that longer periods of illumination are used. Large chambers for the long-term growth of plants in an atmosphere containing radioactive carbon dioxide have been described [342–347].

The chemical nature of the substances formed is determined by extraction and chromatography. Because of the shortness of illumination, the activity is small, yet it can be measured. The most important results of these investigations are the following. Cane sugar (sucrose) appears as early as two minutes after the beginning of radiophotosynthesis. Glucose and fructose arise even more rapidly, though not in the free state, but as phosphoric acid esters. The synthesis of sucrose from the hexoses probably occurs by way of the esters. Other early products are malic acid and the amino acid alanine. The very first product so far identified, the only one produced in detectable quantity during an illumination period as short as half a second, is phosphoglyceric acid (PGA). According to Calvin, this substance is the product of the reaction of carbon dioxide with the phosphoric acid ester of a pentose (ribose):

$$\text{RDP} + CO_2 = 2\,\text{PGA}$$

Ribose-diphosphoric acid + Carbon dioxide = 2 Phosphoglyceric acid

This reaction is catalysed by a specific enzyme and does not require light. The phosphoglyceric acid is then reduced to phosphoglyceric aldehyde by hydrogen formed during the decomposition of water in the photochemical reaction. This hydrogen is in the form of reduced triphosphopyridine nucleotide (TPNH), which is very effective as a reducing agent. In the stationary state of the plant, five of the six available carbon atoms are on an average converted back into one molecule of RDP in subsequent stages. The sixth carbon atom is diverted to the synthesis of carbohydrates and other plant substances, so representing the net gain in the course of one photosynthetic cycle. In multicellular plants, the organic substances formed in the green leaves may then migrate to other parts. For instance, the cane sugar of sugar beet roots is formed in the leaves [16–21]. Such questions will be further discussed in Section 11.2.

Higher plants may also take up labelled carbon dioxide in the absence of light, for instance through the roots [16, 20–24, 358, 359, 366–368, 395–397]. The radiocarbon absorbed by roots is incorporated into organic substances and rises in the plant. The assimilation of carbon dioxide by parts of the plant not exposed to light can, of course, proceed only as long as TPNH is formed in other parts of the plant under the influence of light, and is available for the reduction of the PGA. Metabolic inhibitors (dinitrophenol or azide) depress the uptake of radioactive carbon dioxide [359].

It is possible that carbon dioxide produced by microorganisms in the soil, as in the formation of humus, and carbon dioxide from mineral carbonates may contribute to plant nutrition [26, 315]. Humus formation has been followed by analytical separation of plant and humus material after introduction of carbon-labelled dead plants into the soil [352, 360, 369].

In the various organs of the plant simple carbon compounds are converted into the whole range of complicated (secondary) plant substances. In that respect, different species of plant behave differently, and the physiological conditions may also affect results [15]. To elucidate such biosynthetic processes, suspected intermediates are introduced in labelled form into the organs, and after a suitable period the metabolite in question is tested for radioactivity. The technique of injection or implantation of (labelled) organic substances into higher plants has been described [2]. Thus the formation of radioactive rubber has been observed in kok-sagys from sucrose [27] or from other organic substances [28], and in *Hevea* from acetate or mevalonic acid [409]. Sugars must first be degraded to acetic acid and its derivatives, before their carbon can be used for the synthesis of rubber, terpenes and carotenoids (see [4]). The formation of lignin has been the subject of other work (p. 282). The investigation of the biosynthetic processes in plants with tracers provides a practically inexhaustible field for research.

These new results have as yet hardly found practical application in agriculture, but in due course they will undoubtedly lead to improvements in farming methods.

11.2. Absorption, Transport and Excretion of Substances by Plants

The first tracer investigation in biology (by Hevesy in 1923) consisted in a study of the absorption of thorium B (lead-212) by plants [194]. This work has been followed by much research on the absorption and transport of labelled material by plants. Information on the general distribution of a substance is easily obtained by autoradiography, but for quantitative work counting methods are preferred. Counters are always used when the activity measurement is preceded by chemical separation. Tracer work on the relations of electrolytes and plants has been summarized in monographs [126, 335] and survey papers [334, 418].

11.2.1. *Absorption through the Roots*

Under natural conditions, the mineral substances necessary for the growth of higher land plants are taken up through the roots. The substances include the so-called macroelements, such as potassium, phosphorus and nitrogen, and the microelements or trace elements. The concentrations of these elements within the plant should lie within definite ranges to provide optimal conditions for the plant, while their concentration in the soil may vary very widely indeed. So it may be suspected from the start that roots have mechanisms to control uptake. These mechanisms are generally explored with tracers.

Mainly as a result of tracer work [334, 354], it is at present believed that the ions from the soil first diffuse into a free space or outer space of the root. Within a few hours, equilibrium with the surroundings is established. No energy is required for this process [29–33, 126, 318]. The outer space includes the intercellular space, part of the volume of the root cell walls, and also part of the intracellular space. In parts of the outer space the ions will show roughly the same concentrations as in the surroundings of the roots; in other parts, the concentrations will be modified by cation exchange, for instance on the carboxyl groups of the pectin of the cell wall, and by Donnan equilibria. The outer space is believed to amount, depending on the conditions, to between 10 and 50 per cent of the root volume. The outer space is accessible not only to small ions, but also to other substances of low molecular weight, e.g., sugars or urea, and for this reason urea is useful as a fertilizer (see p. 276).

In a second stage certain substances are actively transported into the inner space [29, 32, 126, 334, 354, 399]. Active transport requires energy, which is provided by metabolic reactions, especially respiration [33, 318]. The substances are concentrated by the active transport, but not all concentration processes can be ascribed to active transport. Thus the strong accumulation of (radioactive) zinc by algae may be due to a passive process [329]. It is thought that a second actively transporting membrane, the tonoplast, connects the cytoplasm with the vacuole [332].

It is generally supposed that active transport through the membrane surrounding the inner space is mediated by a carrier. After being bound to the carrier, the substance passes through the membrane, and is subsequently set free from the carrier on the other side. Different carriers serve for the various kinds of ions. If different ions compete for a given carrier, this may be detected through their displacing action on each other. For instance, it has been shown with tracers that potassium and rubidium use the same carrier to enter plant cells, and so compete for places on the same carrier [29]. Ammonium competes less strongly with potassium, as has also been shown with tracers [330]. The chemical nature of the carriers is not yet known.

The capacity of doing osmotic work (active transport) cannot be explained through the carrier concept only, and the mechanism whereby the required free energy is supplied by metabolic processes and harnessed is at present a matter of lively speculation [34, 328, 331].

In the particular case of phosphate, the steps in respiration (oxidative phosphorylation) responsible for active transport have been explored with tracers [37]. For tomato roots the uptake of phosphate and potassium ions was found to decrease with diminishing partial pressure of oxygen within the range of 21 to 0·5 per cent oxygen [36].

It should be noted that active transport is a phenomenon occurring in all living cells, and only in these. Muscle cells of mammals provide a good example of active transport in animals. These cells contain about 50 times more potassium than the extracellular liquid. Exchange of radiopotassium across the membrane of the muscle cell has been demonstrated. Therefore, the maintenance of the concentration gradient must be due to a compensation of diffusion by active transport, sometimes described as the operation of an "ion pump" [34].

11.2.2. *Translocation*

The change with time of the distribution of elements over the organs of the plant after absorption may be readily followed with radioactive tracers [38–43, 321, 418]. Mineral substances ascend from the roots mainly with the current of the sap in the xylem [319]. The rate of transport may be of the order of 0·5 to 1 m/hr. Transported substances, including potassium, calcium, iron, phosphorus and sulphur, are carried especially to the developing parts of the plant, such as the leaf shoots. The effect of transpiration on the transport of minerals to the active sites has been found to decrease when the total amount of available minerals is small [45].

Plant species resistant to frost are distinguished by the rapidity of the absorption and transport of (radioactive) mineral substances even at low temperatures [35, 46, 47]. Translocation has been followed also in vegetative hybrids; they have been found to resemble natural plants in that the whole organism is involved [48, 315].

In irrigated wheat, ions and organic molecules migrate more rapidly than in non-irrigated wheat, as has been found under practical field conditions [16, 50, 52]. The rate of transport of radioactive phosphate ions from root to tip in the case of tobacco plants was found not to be reduced by a decrease in oxygen pressure, and it has been concluded that the absorption of water by the root is not inhibited by oxygen deficiency [36].

Transport away from the leaves towards the root, as well as to the developing buds, leaves and seeds, occurs through the vascular system of the phloem [40–44, 53, 54, 62]. In contrast to other macroelements, calcium does not take part in this basipetal translocation. The plant must therefore constantly be supplied with new calcium through the root [49, 55, 64]. The same applies to the trace elements iron, zinc and manganese [56]. Phosphorus is transported mainly as inorganic phosphate ion, but partly also in the form of organic phosphoric acid esters [44, 55]. Upward movement in the phloem and bidirectional movement through phloem bundles have also been demonstrated with tracers]58, 326].

Downward transport of photosynthetic products, including sugars, has also been followed with tracers [44, 59–62, 410]. The rate of transport is quite considerable, and may reach a value of 1 m/hr; it depends on temperature, though not directly on illumination [54].

Experiments with isolated stem sections have been carried out to avoid complications due to interaction with other organs. Thus, cylinders of stem 1 cm long were cut from sunflowers and placed on small blocks of agar, and drops of labelled sugar solution applied to the other end. The activity in the agar and the stem was measured after various times. It was found that the labelled sugar was transported as such at a rate of the order of 60 cm/hr, and no longitudinal direction was preferred [63].

The lateral transport of substances labelled with tritium, carbon-14 or phosphorus-32 from phloem into xylem has also been measured [44, 55, 58, 338]. The circulation of various labelled elements has been studied with beans [64], sugar-cane [65] and cotton [411]. It has been mentioned on p. 267 that the sugar of the roots of sugar beet has its origin in the leaf.

An important question is that of the mechanism of transport in the phloem. The dissolved materials move together with the solvent (water), but it has often been noticed that different labelled substances move downwards with different velocities in the same plant. It is as yet undecided whether these differences are only due to differences in the permeability of the cell walls of the vascular system, etc., or are in some cases due to specific active transport [21, 44, 50, 51, 58–60, 62, 66, 319, 321, 325, 326, 365, 398, 401]. The transport is slowed down by inhibitors which interfere with the energy supply to cells so that there can be no doubt about the overall control exercised by energy metabolism [54, 55, 63].

11.2.3. *Absorption through Leaves*

It is easily shown with tracers that plants absorb salts through their leaves (foliar absorption) [35, 39, 55, 67–70, 348, 407, 408]. The undersides of the leaves are particularly effective. The amounts taken up depend greatly on the species and condition of a plant, the temperature and the illumination. For a meaningful description of the process it would be necessary to distinguish clearly among the various steps concerned, such as resorption, transport, and perhaps also chemical reaction. Although this could be done with tracers, results do not seem to be available as yet.

Most of the work has been done with potassium and phosphate. The entire sulphur requirement of plants can be provided by sulphur dioxide [71]. On the other hand, as we have said, the alkaline earths (calcium and magnesium) and the main part of other polyvalent cations remain in the leaf [39, 55, 69, 70]. Many organic substances, such as urea [55, 69, 72, 73, 412] and amino acids [74], are also rapidly absorbed by foliage.

Quantitative data have led to the conclusion that soil fertilization may be supplemented, but not replaced, by leaf fertilization [39, 113, 114].

11.2.4. *Excretion Processes*

Substances are leached by rain from the parts of the plant above the ground. For instance, (radioactive) sodium and potassium are lost easily, iron, zinc and chloride with some difficulty [55, 68, 75, 76, 353]. Organic substances, such as carbohydrates or amino acids, may also be washed out [353]. Some of the pathways of loss from the leaves have been identified [353]. It is possible that this elimination plays a part in adjusting plants to the environment; leaves may then be considered as organs not merely of absorption, but also of excretion. In any case, the fact of excretion must be taken into account in analytical work on plants and soils, in studies on soil formation and the microflora of the soil, and in research into plant ecology and the transmission of plant diseases.

Mineral and other substances of low molecular weight (e.g., herbicides, see p. 286) may also be eliminated through the roots [29, 323]. Absorption through the roots is thus no more an irreversible process than that through the leaves, although under normal conditions absorption exceeds excretion [33]. Excretion can be detected with great ease when roots containing labelled substances are placed in an unlabelled solution and the increase of activity in the solution is determined. The solution can be of any desired chemical composition. In some conditions a net loss of substance from the root is observed [29].

11.3. Studies with Fertilizers

11.3.1. *General Considerations*

From a practical point of view, it is the increase of crop yield due to fertilizers which is of the greatest importance. The increase can be estimated by comparing the yield of fertilized and unfertilized fields, but some problems arise. First, the differential method is hardly applicable to cases where the fertilizer effect is small, or the absorption time short. Secondly, differences between the test fields and between their treatments are hard to eliminate. Thirdly, the fertilizer is likely to carry with it foreign materials, such as counter-ions and trace elements, which may affect the yield. It is, however, possible to overcome these difficulties in carefully planned investigations.

More fundamental obstacles are met with in determining the absorption of fertilizer elements by plants. This absorption could be regarded as the difference between the content of the element in question in fertilized and unfertilized plants only if the absorption of the element already present in the soil were unaffected by the addition of the identical element in the form of fertilizer. But such an assumption would be quite unfounded [39, 77–79, 357].

On the one hand, plants may be expected to prefer the more easily soluble fertilizer element to less soluble soil element, so that the former would be substituted for the latter. On the other hand, a well-fertilized, and therefore well-developed, plant has — qualitatively and quantitatively — a better root system than a poor plant, so that it is better able to exploit the substances present in the soil. Which of these two opposing effects is preponderant under practical conditions can only be determined by experiment.

It is at this point that the isotope method gives valuable results. By measuring the specific activity of the element under consideration within the plant, it is possible at any time to find the parts of the element taken from the soil or from the (labelled) fertilizer. The measurement is so sensitive that it can be started very soon after application of the fertilizer so that very young plants may be studied. The amount of labelled element (measured through the specific activity) found within the plant can in a somewhat simplified way be expressed as the sum [increase in total element uptake due to fertilization] + [soil element displaced from the plant]. Since the first term can be determined by chemical analysis, the second term can be evaluated.

The mechanism by which the plant prefers fertilizer element to soil element cannot be elucidated directly by this type of experiment, and it is of little importance for practical application. But it is important for a deeper understanding that the exchange between fertilizer element and soil element before absorption by the plant can be measured with tracers, and that displacement of fertilizer element or soil element previously absorbed into the plant by the competitor (soil element or fertilizer element, respectively) can be detected.

In the majority of investigations, radiophosphorus has been used, partly because phosphorus is a very important macroelement, and partly because phosphorus-32 is cheap, has a suitable half-life, and emits easily measured β-radiation [16, 39, 67, 77, 79, 80]. The methods of preparation of labelled fertilizers, such as superphosphate [81], double superphosphate [82], ammonium phosphate and Thomas phosphate (slag phosphate) have been reviewed [39, 357].

In labelling the complete fertilizer by irradiation with neutrons, it should be remembered that the chemical state of the phosphorus may be changed by the Szilard effect during activation through neutron capture according to the reaction $^{31}P(n, \gamma)$ ^{32}P. The phosphorus may undergo reduction to phosphite or hydrophosphite, or may be converted into pyrophosphate. Reduced or condensed phosphorus may greatly differ from phosphorus present as phosphate with respect to assimilation by plants. The use of fertilizers containing radiophosphorus in other forms than phosphate can therefore give misleading results. By heating irradiated crude phosphate to 500°C for 4 days, the undesirable forms of phosphorus-32 produced by irradiation are converted into orthophosphate [83].

The only useful radioisotope of potassium (potassium-42) has a half-life of only 12·5 hr, and so is unsuitable for long-term work. For this reason, the potassium is often labelled with the non-isotopic tracer rubidium-86 (half-life 18·7 days). For calcium, the isotope calcium-45 (half-life 154 days) is available. The preparation and use of radioactive calcium cyanamide has been described [84]. However, calcium-45 is expensive and emits only soft β-radiation, and so strontium-89 (half-life 51 days) is often substituted. γ-active calcium-47 (half-life 4·7 days) would be useful, but satisfactory specific activity requires expensive enrichment of the calcium-46 (the starting material) in natural calcium.

For sulphur, the isotope sulphur-35 (half-life 87 days) is available. Although the β-radiation is soft, and therefore hard to measure with good yield, this nuclide proves satisfactory in practice, since it is cheap and can therefore be introduced in high activity. Magnesium has recently been labelled with magnesium-28 (half-life 21·2 hr), but this isotope is expensive since it cannot be prepared by neutron capture. For nitrogen, the stable heavy nitrogen-15 must be used, and sensitive detection is not possible.

11.3.2. *Radiation Damage in Investigations with Fertilizers*

Plants are less sensitive to ionizing radiation than animals, and in practice the effect of doses smaller than a thousand rad can be neglected. Doses of this order are not needed in work with labelled fertilizers, and ought in any case to be avoided from the point of view of radiation protection. An estimation of the dose delivered to a homogeneous system by a β-radiating substance uniformly distributed within it − provided the dimensions of the system much exceed the range of the β-rays − can be obtained from the equation given in Section 5.2:

$$D = 55AE/3v\varrho.$$

As an example, let us consider a solution containing 1 μc of radiophosphorus per ml. We then obtain:

$$D = 55 \times 10^{-6} \times 1·7 \times 10^6/3 \times 1 \times 1 = \text{ca. 30 rad/day}.$$

Usually the radioelement will not be distributed uniformly, and it is often found concentrated at certain places in soils or plants. The effect of this local enrichment

T.A.R. 18

on dose distribution depends on the range of the radiation. The biological effect of a given total dose is therefore found to be sensitive to experimental conditions [85]. A treatment which takes account of all factors is extremely complicated and would be of little value for practical use. Some authors have found damage by phosphorus at a specific activity of the order of 100 $\mu c/g$ phosphorus [86], while others consider even higher doses as safe [80].

When in particular cases doubt exists whether radiation damage can occur, control experiments must be carried out. The radiation dose is then varied by changing the specific activity of the labelled substance in otherwise identical conditions.

Attempts to improve agricultural yields by irradiation will be discussed in Volume 2, but it might be observed here that the consumption by humans or the feeding to animals of plants produced with radioactive fertilizers is most undesirable from the point of view of health protection.

11.3.3. *Utilization of Individual Elements*

Provided the specific activity of fertilizer phosphorus is known, the measured specific activity of the phosphorus in the plant indicates the extent to which the total phosphorus is derived from fertilizer phosphorus, on the one hand, and from soil phosphorus, on the other. Various equations can be used for the calculation (see [357]), for instance

$$^{32}P_{pl}/P_{pl} = {}^{32}P_f/(P_f + P_s)$$

where $^{32}P_{pl}$ and $^{32}P_f$ are the activities of the radiophosphorus in the plant and fertilizer, respectively, while P_{pl} and P_f are the weights of the total phosphorus in the same quantities of plant or fertilizer. P_s is then the amount of soil phosphorus taken up, while the ratio of soil phosphorus to the total phosphorus taken in amounts to $P_s/(P_f + P_s)$. We rearrange this equation and introduce the specific activities ($S_{pl} = {}^{32}P_{pl}/P_{pl}$; $S_f = {}^{32}P_f/P_f$) which may be expressed in any suitable units, which must, of course, be the same for both fractions. One gets:

$$P_s/(P_s + P_f) = (S_f - S_{pl})/S_f.$$

Results on the utilization of soil phosphorus are given in different papers in terms of various values, such as the *L*-value or Larsen value and the *A*-value (availability value) [87, 116, 117, 123, 355, 357]. The results depend, of course, on conditions: species and state of the plant, kind of soil, the proportions of soil and fertilizer, time and method of fertilizer application, temperature, moisture, etc.

In some series of experiments, the intake of fertilizer phosphorus by the plant was found to increase with the amount of fertilizer used, but the fraction of fertilizer phosphorus taken up by the plant generally decreased with increasing amount of fertilizer added [88, 89]. In all cases, only part of the fertilizer phosphorus was taken in by the plant, so that the remainder did not contribute to the first harvest. Under practical conditions, fertilizer phosphorus may supply, according to circumstances, 20 to 80 per cent of the total phosphorus in the plant. The interesting question already raised whether an increase in the amount of phosphorus fertilizer applied increases or decreases the amount of soil phosphorus taken up has been explored in a number of investigations under different experimental conditions; either result may be found [67, 77, 78, 91, 92].

Uptake of phosphorus is highest in young plants, and even seeds absorb much labelled phosphorus [90]. The older the plant, the smaller in general is the contribution of the fertilizer to total phosphorus [77]. This may be due to growth of roots beyond the fertilized zone of the soil, and older plants may also be better equipped to absorb the less soluble soil phosphorus.

However, only a slight alteration – an increase – of the relative absorption of fertilizer phosphorus with time was found in a series of experiments with potatoes [89, 93]. It was concluded that the potato obtains its nutrients during the whole growth period from a shallow soil layer.

Conversely, tracer may be used to determine the spread of the root system of an individual plant under natural conditions, which would be difficult by other methods [16, 25]. The zone from which radiophosphorus is absorbed by the already developed plant is determined by placing, at various distances, strictly localized "cartridges" of radiophosphorus in the soil. It was found that the roots function in such a way that the root which locates a depot suddenly increases its contribution of nutrient to the plant [16]. The extent and distribution of cereal grain roots has also been estimated by detecting the radiation from the roots after injection of radiophosphorus into the stem [57].

The numerical results of experiments on fertilizer utilization are, of course, only valid for the particular type of plant and soil, and each set of conditions must be evaluated separately [89, 93, 94]. This has been shown, for example, in experiments on the intake of fertilizer phosphorus as a fraction of total phosphorus where various species of plant were compared. A short time after the application of fertilizer, this fraction was found to increase in the order: cotton, maize, tobacco. Nearer to harvest time, however, the order was: maize, cotton, tobacco. Special attention has been paid to fertilizer applications to rice [394].

The absorption of fertilizer phosphorus is reduced by liming, as was shown by experiments on the assimilation of various phosphorus fertilizers carried out in the dry climate of the Canadian prairies [96]. In experiments on wheat it was found that the phosphorus of the following compounds was taken up with decreasing efficiency in the order $NH_4H_2PO_4$, NaH_2PO_4, $Ca(H_2PO_4)_2$, $2\,CaHPO_4 + Ca(NO_3)_2$, $CaHPO_4$ (superphosphate), though under other conditions the superiority of ammonium phosphate over superphosphate was not confirmed [67, 77, 87, 93]. Ground apatite is much inferior to superphosphate, particularly in less acid soils [93, 97, 357].

Iron is found to depress in a different way the utilization of phosphorus by the plant. An increase in the absorption of phosphorus by the roots was found after addition of iron citrate to the soil, but the phosphorus remained in the roots to a higher extent, so that the phosphorus content of the tops was less than in control plants. The phosphate is evidently retained in the roots by the iron [98].

In certain soils, the assimilation of granulated fertilizer is better than that of the powdered or dissolved form, the optimum grain size depending on the degree of development of the plant [25, 67, 99].

The phosphorus contained in compost is assimilated to a lesser extent than phosphorus from superphosphate [100]. These experiments were carried out with wheat or soy-beans grown in fields containing radioactive fertilizer. The plants were harvested while still green, and composted. The compost was then used as fertilizer for a second field, and the activity of the phosphorus in the plants grown in this field was determined. In other work, oat and berseem tops (containing ^{32}P) were used [360]. The phosphorus of sheep manure was found to be assimilated about as well as that in superphosphate [101]. The absorption of mineral phosphate has been investigated in the presence of organic fertilizers [67].

Experiments with radioactive potassium [102] and calcium [87] have been carried out to study the absorption of cationic macroelements. The experiments with calcium referred mainly to its availability in soils, and will be dealt with in the next section, but it can be mentioned here that in acid soils calcium is better absorbed if present as oxide or carbonate than as sulphate [103]. Calcium in the form of calcium cyanamide is well absorbed by rice [84].

Groundnuts grow in the soil, although they are connected to the roots only through trailing branches of the plant. It has been found that the calcium in the nuts is obtained directly from the soil and not through the root system, while the sulphur may be obtained either through the roots or directly [104, 105]. In various plants, sulphur from inorganic sulphates or sulphites is converted into organic sulphur in a short time [71, 106, 107, 316].

Experiments on the assimilation of urea by rice and wheat were carried out with radiocarbon [108, 400]. The experiments thus give no direct information on the absorption of the nitrogen. For references to work on this problem with heavy nitrogen see [39].

In work on the absorption of microelements (trace elements) by plants, high sensitivity of detection is essential [2]. For example, the assimilation of molybdenum from solutions containing as little as 10^{-9} g/l. [109], of manganese [110], cobalt [102, 111] and zinc [112, 329] has been studied with tracers.

11.3.4. *Soil Condition*

When different soils are compared, for example, in terms of the Larsen value, it is usually found that the absorption of fertilizer phosphorus decreases with increasing content of phosphorus available for absorption in the soil itself. This kind of relation emerges most clearly when soils of similar types are compared [80, 87, 115–118, 337]. Hence the absorption of fertilizer phosphorus (determined radiochemically under standard conditions) may serve as a measure of the available phosphorus content in the soil.

Such tests require, however, rather long time, since it is necessary to wait for appreciable absorption of phosphorus by the plant. To avoid this delay, *in vitro* procedures not involving plants have been developed to determine the available soil phosphorus. A soil sample is treated with a solution containing radiophosphate, and the quantity of soil phosphorus going into solution by exchange is determined by the activity loss of the solution. Alternatively the soil itself can be prelabelled, and the increase in activity of the solution determined. These procedures may be looked at as applications of the isotope dilution method (p. 80). It is assumed that the available phosphorus is related to the exchangeable phosphorus.

It is not to be expected that the whole of the soil phosphate will be equally firmly bound, or equally accessible to the plant, so that it is necessary to work in standardized conditions. It is an advantage of the method, compared with the traditional treatment with citric acid, etc., that the soil is not attacked chemically, and thus no change in its chemical properties occurs. The results obtained are often, but not always, in agreement with those obtained by the older methods [91, 92, 103, 116, 119–124].

Often the change in activity with time has been studied for soils, and also for phosphate rocks and minerals. Information on the state of binding of the phosphate may be derived from such kinetic work [87, 91, 124, 125, 127–130, 337, 350, 351, 356].

The three main forms of phosphate in soils are probably the following:

1. Free dissolved phosphate in a diffusion layer surrounding the solid material (soil colloid). This exchanges instantaneously.
2. Phosphate in a surface layer on the solid material. Exchange will be rapid.
3. Phosphate in the interior of the solid material. This exchanges only slowly, the rate of exchange being determined by grain-boundary diffusion or lattice diffusion [91].

It must be borne in mind, however, that new surfaces may be formed in the solid material by recrystallization.

In analogous experiments with radiocalcium strong influence of the kind of soil has been observed. Of course, the absorption of fertilizer calcium depends on the amount of fertilizer applied [94, 131]. However, while under certain experimental conditions about half the calcium absorbed by clover and rye came from the soil, under the same conditions, but on other soils, the calcium was derived entirely from the fertilizer calcium carbonate [131]. In some soils the absorption of soil calcium was increased by addition of calcium fertilizer, in other cases it was reduced.

The available calcium in the soil can be determined in the same way as the available phosphate by isotope dilution. The soil is treated with a solution, in this case containing radioactive calcium or strontium, and the rest activity is measured [132, 133]. In one series of experiments good agreement was found between values for the available calcium content in the soil, determined by radiochemical and by conventional methods [103].

When the isotope dilution method is used with radiophosphate or radiocalcium, the possibility of exchange with non-isotopic inactive ions (e.g., carbonate or magnesium, respectively) must be kept in mind. To avoid errors due to this exchange with foreign ions, it is necessary to determine not only the remaining activity in the solution, but also the remaining quantity of the phosphorus or the calcium, as the case may be, so that both the total and the specific activities are known. From the loss of the element as a whole, the loss of the radioisotope due to exchange with foreign ions can be determined. These experiments also give information about the total exchange capacity of the soil under given conditions — which is of great practical importance. Thus, the loss of radiocalcium has been used to determine the exchange capacity of soils for cations; samples of soil were shaken with solutions of radioactive calcium salts, and the quantity of radiocalcium taken up was determined [122, 132, 134]. Instead of shaking, it is possible to let the radioactive solution flow through a column of soil and to determine the part of the column where radiocalcium has been taken up [135]. Other labelled cations may be used instead of calcium, including rubidium, caesium, strontium or barium.

The depth of penetration of labelled fertilizers in the soil has been determined by scanning a vertical section of the soil with a counter, or by autoradiography [124, 136, 137]. The depth of penetration depends greatly on the kind of soil, but in any case both phosphate and potassium penetrate to a depth of a few centimetres only. In the case of phosphate this is explained by exchange processes and by reaction with lime in the soil [136, 138], while in the case of potassium cation exchange is invoked [136, 139]. Sulphate penetrates to greater depth [137, 361].

It follows that top dressings do not reach deeper roots, yet they appear to be absorbed to an appreciable extent [67, 140]. A further series of experiments has shown that the zone of action of superphosphate does not reach far in a horizontal direction (less than 15 cm) [16, 88, 93, 161] (see also p. 275). Naturally, the plant takes longer to reach and utilize fertilizer deposited in more distant spots [142]. Because of the fixation of the phosphate by the soil, it is often preferable to deposit the fertilizer at some depth — in some cases as much as 30 cm — rather than on the surface of the soil [32, 143, 144].

The effective range of elements present in fertilizers may be increased by plant roots in the soil, since these are capable of transporting the element. Thus, phosphorus may be made available to grain crops through the root system of leguminous plants [78]. This mutual aid phenomenon is undoubtedly of great importance in farming.

Particular problems are presented by soils which have lost most of their mineral nutrients by leaching, as is true of the humid tropics. Plants can grow in such soils only by using mineral substances somehow brought to the surface from deeper layers. Such processes can be investigated well with tracers.

The density of soils can be determined *in situ* by γ-ray back-scattering, the movement of soil particles after suitable tagging, and the aeration of soil by tracing the diffusion of labelled gas in it [95]. The method for the determination of moisture in soils by slowing-down of neutrons will be outlined in Section 12.8.

11.4. Animal Husbandry

The experimental techniques necessary for tracer experiments on animals, including animal breeding, cage construction, injection technique, collection of urine, faeces and exhaled air, procuring of blood samples, etc., are described in a number of reviews [2, 145, 146, 324]. The information available on resorption by animals, transport within the organism and excretion has also been collected [2, 5, 39, 147, 421]. The importance of active transport has already been emphasized on p. 269. Tracer methods are well suited for the study of the influence of environmental, particularly climatic, factors on animal metabolism important in food production [421].

Much attention has naturally been given to the metabolism of phosphorus and calcium in domestic animals, especially in cows [1, 148–151]. Radiocalcium and radiophosphorus have also been applied to poultry [1, 151, 152], and radiomagnesium to sheep [420, 421] and other animals [421].

Much tracer work has been carried out on the absorption of inorganic sulphur by domestic animals. It has been found, for example, that sulphur in the form of sulphate is converted in poultry into a variety of organic compounds, but the amino acids methionine and cysteine are only formed to a limited extent [39, 421]. The situation is quite different in ruminants, where the microflora in the alimentary tract participate in synthesis [155].

The tracer method lends itself well to the exploration of the fate of trace elements in the animals, because quite minute quantities can be detected. The element already present within the organism before the start of the experiment does not interfere, since it is not radioactive [2, 147, 421].

In all experiments on mineral metabolism it must be kept in mind that the distribution of the tracer within the organism may depend very much indeed on the dose of the element supplied (see [4]). Therefore, with a given activity, the pattern of distribution may much depend on specific activity.

As an illustration, radioiodine in the form of iodide accumulates strongly in the thyroid gland only when the total amount of iodine supplied is small. Though the affinity of the organ for iodine is at first very great, its capacity for iodine is limited. Misleading results are therefore, obtained if too large a dose of iodine is given. The very poisonous element beryllium, if administered in weighable amounts instead of tracers, accumulates preferentially in the spleen and the liver rather than in the bones.

Cobalt, like iodine, is an essential trace element. It has been found that on soils poor in cobalt, such as some in Australia, ruminants suffer from deficiency diseases, showing signs of malnutrition in spite of an abundant supply of green plants. The main importance of cobalt lies in the fact that it is a component of vitamin B_{12}. It has been found with radiocobalt that traces of cobalt accumulate mainly in liver, heart and kidneys. Cobalt administered intravenously is less effective than when taken in with food. In the case of copper, which is also needed by animals, the situation is the reverse: injection is more effective than feeding. In cattle, the copper is mainly stored in the liver. The requirements for copper and molybdenum appear to be related, supply of the latter increasing the need for the former [2, 156, 421].

Tracer work allows the distinction, in faeces, between non-assimilated food constituents and eliminated body constituents. When the "endogenous" contribution to the faeces is known, the part of the mineral element in the fodder actually utilized may be estimated. It has been shown with tracers that the assimilating power of the animal body had often been underestimated. The body absorbs (and also eliminates) a greater quantity of mineral matter in the alimentary tract than had previously been supposed [39, 149, 157, 421].

The absorption of mineral substances, such as calcium, phosphorus and trace elements, by the animal organism depends on their chemical form. For example, the absorption of additives to common salt can be measured with tracers. Work of this kind has been done with radioactive copper [158] and iodine [159]. Copper carbonate and di-iodo-dithymol were found to be suitable sources for these elements.

Using radioactive phosphorus and calcium the amount of vitamin D present in fodder may be estimated. In animals deficient in this vitamin the uptake of phosphorus or calcium into the bones depends on the vitamin supply. On the basis of calibration curves, absolute values for the vitamin content of the fodder may be computed. This method may be considered as an application of the radioactive reagent method (p. 77) [160–162].

The biosynthetic pathways for organic substances may be elucidated with radioactive tracers [4, 5]. It is also possible to compare the extent to which different biosynthetic pathways are followed in various species and under various conditions.

Using radiocarbon the conversion of simple carbon compounds, sugars, amino acids and fatty acids, to milk constituents after injection into the blood has been measured. For example, most of the carbon of glucose appears in milk within two days. The ratio of the amounts of radiocarbon appearing as lactose and fat is about 15:1 with radioglucose as the source of supply, while it is only 0·3 or 0·7 after application of radioacetate, depending on which carbon atom in the acetate is labelled. Other compounds give values between these extremes [149]. These coefficients differ greatly, however, between different species (cattle, sheep and rabbits) [163–165, 170–172].

The high yield of fat derived from radioactive acetate is in agreement with the now accepted synthesis of the higher fatty acids from acetate; their production from glucose is thought to depend on the formation of acetate (in the form of acetyl coenzyme A) as an intermediate [173–175, 363, 421]. With radiocarbon as a tracer it has also been established that the synthesis of milk fat occurs predominantly, if not exclusively, in the mammary gland [173–176]. Just as plant cells absorb carbon dioxide in the dark in enzymatic processes (see p. 267), so the animal tissues also assimilate carbon dioxide. Hence after administration to cattle, some of the radioactive carbon supplied as carbon dioxide or bicarbonate appears in milk sugar and fat [149]. These results of tracer work would certainly have appeared surprising in earlier times.

Tracer work has shown that proteins are always synthesized from free amino acids, and not from any peptides which may have been present. For synthesis, the amino acids are grouped in the correct sequence on a template present in intracellular organelles, the ribosomes, and then peeled off. If essential amino acids (which the animal body cannot synthesize) are lacking, the synthetic mechanism does not function, and deficiency symptoms are observed. The majority of the proteins in the animal body are in a dynamic state, and their degradation is thus compensated by synthesis at equal rate. This rate can be determined with tracers [1, 314] (see also [4]).

The amino acids needed for the synthesis of milk proteins are obtained from the free amino acids in the blood serum, while those contained in serum proteins are not used to any extent in the synthesis of milk proteins [165, 172, 177, 421]. Radiosulphur has been supplied to sheep in inorganic or other forms, and the rate of its appearance in wool protein (keratin) has been measured. Under otherwise similar conditions, this rate rises and falls with the rate of wool growth [4, 166–169].

The determination of the fat content in pig carcasses by γ-radiation measurement has already been mentioned in Section 10.8.

The natural food of domestic animals may contain not only nutrients, but also, under unfavourable conditions, poisons. Radioactive tracers have been used to investigate the action of these. For example, it has been known for some time that in various parts of the United States and Canada cattle might suffer from severe bleeding when fed on sweet clover. This action has later been found to be due to di-coumarol present in this plant. This substance is an antivitamin K, i.e., it counteracts the blood-clotting effect of this. (Dicoumarol is actually used in medicine to prevent undesirable blood-clotting (thrombosis), and may also be used for rat control.) The chemical reactions of this substance and its antagonism to vitamin K have been studied by tracer methods [178–183]. It has been found that the substance accumulates in the liver and inhibits the formation of the blood-clotting agent prothrombin.

Tracers have also been used in the fishing industry [35, 315].

11.5. Forestry and the Timber Industry

Many of the techniques mentioned in connection with agriculture in Sections 11.1 and 11.2 may be adapted to forestry. Photosynthesis in trees, the absorption of nu-trients from the soil and the transport (translocation) of minerals and organic com-pounds may be investigated. In view of the size of trees, the transport of substances in these plants is an impressive phenomenon, and is also quite easy to measure [51, 184]. In trees, as well as in other plants, the water absorbed by the roots carries the mineral substances up in the xylem, while in general the organic assimilation products des-cend in the phloem.

In the summer climate of Canada, the rate of ascent of calcium-45, rubidium-86 and iodine-131 may be as much as 1 m/hr [80, 185, 186]. Similar results have been obtained with arsenic that is used as a silvicide to facilitate the debarking of the tree [80]. The poison ascends in the sapwood and then diffuses into the bark. At night and in winter, however, smaller velocities have been observed [185]. Other work refers to the mineral nutrition of fruit trees [364].

Minerals may be absorbed not only through roots and leaves (see p. 271), but also through the bark, as has been demonstrated for potassium and phosphorus with apple and pear trees [68]. The distribution of the radioelement within the tree is by no means uniform, and it seems as though particular roots supplied food preferentially to particular branches [80, 312, 313]. This distribution may be measured *in vivo* with γ-ray emitters [80, 185, 186].

Tritium has been used to investigate the utilization by small trees of water from various depths. Within four hours of placement at each depth, tritium was detected in the transpired water from nearby trees. The amount of tritium in the water depen-ded greatly on the depth and on other factors [414].

Many trees harbour on their roots symbiotic microorganisms. The effect of these organisms of the rhizosphere on the absorption of radioactive phosphorus and sulphur by roots has been investigated [187–189], with the following conclusions:

rapid multiplication of the microbes at first delays the absorption of phosphorus by the tree, but after a few days phosphorus from the microbes is transported into the tree. On the other hand, the microbes themselves take up phosphorus eliminated by the tree. This secretion is subject to a daily rhythm, with a minimum at night, and it stimulates the growth of the microflora [188]. It appears that mycorrhiza roots (of spruce) have not only a larger surface available for the absorption of phosphorus, but also a higher affinity for storing it than ordinary roots [187].

Not only nutrients but also parasites may be transferred from one tree to the next through linked roots, as has been shown with fungal spores containing radioactive silver iodide. Such experiments provide the basis for measures to prevent the spread of parasites [185].

Biosynthetic pathways in trees have been explored (see p. 267). The suspected intermediate is supplied to the tree in a labelled form and after a time the product in question is tested for radioactivity. The technique of introducing labelled organic substances into trees has been described [190].

Lignin, which accounts for one-third of the dry substance of timber, is obtained in large quantities in the paper pulp industry, but cannot generally be put to use. Current work with tracers on the chemistry of lignin, both *in vitro* and *in vivo*, may eventually lead to its utilization. In addition, progress in the chemistry and biochemistry of lignin may be helpful in timber processing, in the production of cellulose, and also in timber preservation (see p. 239).

Several groups have employed radioactive tracers for the purpose [191–193]. Growing plants, such as spruce and beans, were supplied with assumed precursors containing radiocarbon either by implantation into the cambium or by immersion of the roots in a solution. When the radiocarbon was shown to be preferentially incorporated into the lignin, it could be concluded that the true precursors had been used, and that the plant contained the specific enzymes necessary for the incorporation of these compounds, or their derivatives, into their lignin. As expected, the glucoside of coniferyl alcohol (3-methoxy-4-hydroxy-cinnamic alcohol) has been found to be one of the most important precursors of softwood lignin.

Questions of wood preservation may be solved [195]. The penetration of electrolytes into the wood may be followed with a counter or by autoradiography. For instance, in one type of American spruce radiostrontium was more strongly taken up by summer timber than by spring timber. The changes during the drying of timber have also been followed.

The uptake of labelled mercuric chloride by spruce and pine wood has been measured by autoradiography. The preservative was found to penetrate only to a small depth, so that after mechanical damage the wood would be exposed. In the case of pine, but not in that of spruce, the depth of penetration could be increased by addition of sodium chloride to the solution of mercuric chloride [196].

To determine the bulk density of pressed wood, the samples may be steeped in oil containing phosphorus-32 in the form of a dissolved organic compound. The porosity is determined from the measured activity, in good agreement with results by older methods [35]. The density of samples of wood may be measured by β-ray absorption [339 to 341]. The water content of timber, and of living trees, can be determined, as in inorganic building materials, through the scattering of soft γ-rays or through the slow-ing-down of fast neutrons [336] (see also Section 10.5).

The production of mutations by irradiation could be important for horticulture and foerstry. For example, rapidly growing or resistant variants, also of asexually propaga-ted trees, might be produced (see Volume 2).

11.6. Pest Control

To elucidate their effects on pests, numerous poisonous substances have been prepared in labelled form. The path taken by the radioactive substance in the soil and in the organisms may then be followed. Nowadays organic agents attract most interest.

The distribution of the radionuclide over the system examined is not necessarily identical with that of the originally employed labelled substance. This will be subject to chemical transformations, and, in the case of organic compounds, will often be completely decomposed. However, the part of the substance still present in soil, plants or animals in unchanged form may be determined by the isotope dilution method (p. 82), in which the sensitive detection of the radioelement by activity measurement is supplemented by the determination of its chemical form. The procedure has been described in detail in relation to the content of the herbicide Dalapon (dichloroprop-ionic acid) in grapes, alfalfa and cottonseed [198], but a thorough analysis of this kind has been omitted in many investigations.

In fodders, and particularly in human food, undecomposed or partly decomposed poisons represent a serious danger. In the analytical routine methods not using radio-activity it is assumed that the nature of the toxic residues is known, and that they can be extracted with known yields. Neither assumption is easily validated except by the use of radionuclides [391].

The isotope dilution method is also suitable for the determination of the effective compound in the mixtures which are often formed in the industrial production of pesticides. Examples are the analyses of Gammexane [199, 200] and of 2,4-D (see p. 286) [201].

Reviews of the applications of isotope methods [417] and of activation analysis [416, 419] to the determination of plant growth regulators, pesticides and food addi-tives have been published.

11.6.1. *Absorption and Transport of Animal Pesticides*

The earliest investigations were concerned with compounds of arsenic, and it has been found that acidic lead arsenate is absorbed better than the basic form by cater-pillars [202]. Lead arsenate is more strongly toxic than the arsenates of sodium or po-tassium, although it is absorbed to a smaller extent [203, 204].

Much work by indicator analysis and activation analysis has been done on the dis-tribution of inorganic poisons within the bodies of larger animals. (For the metabolism of the elements in animals see the references on p. 278.) For example, labelled zinc and phosphorus follow different routes in rats after administration of zinc phosphide [205, 206].

Recently attention is being paid mainly to the absorption of labelled organic insecticides and acaricides by the organs of plants and animals, their translocation within plants, their persistence in soil, and their resistance to chemical attack; in some cases the chemical changes in metabolism have also been investigated. Usually radioactive carbon, phosphorus, sulphur or halogen atoms are applied. Reviews are available [39, 197, 207, 213, 311, 374, 375, 392, 393, 404, 413, 418].

Radioactive tracer techniques have been widely applied to the study of insect biochemistry [379], in particular to that of the nervous system of insects [380]. Special attention has been paid to the metabolism of labelled insecticides in insects [378, 403]. The fate of the insecticides in the bodies of warm-blooded animals is of great interest from the point of view of toxicology [375–377, 390].

Highly sensitive methods are needed to follow the movement of insecticides, applied in particular solvents, over surfaces, especially over the surface of the insect, and its sensitivity of detection favours the tracer method [387]. Autoradiographical techniques in the study of the movement of the radioactive substances in insect control have been described in considerable detail [389].

Pyrethrin compounds (^{14}C) have been prepared by biosynthesis, and their fate within insects examined [197, 208–211]. When radioactive nicotin, also produced by biosynthesis, was fed to mice, the radiocarbon was rapidly eliminated in the urine, while the exhaled air remained inactive [197, 212].

Reference may be made to research on DDT (dichlorodiphenyltrichloroethane) [197, 214, 215], hexachlorocyclohexane (Gammexane or Lindane) [197, 207, 216, 217] and esters of phosphoric acid, such as Parathion (E 605, diethyl-4-nitrophenyl thiophosphate) [197, 205, 207, 218–221], TEPP (tetraethyl pyrophosphate) [197, 222, 223], DFP (di-isopropyl fluorophosphate) [197, 224–226], diethyl phosphate [222], Malathion (dimethyl-S-[dicarbethoxyethyl]-dithiophosphate) [197, 207, 322, 374, 375], HETP (hexaethyl tetraphosphate) [197] and Diazinone (isopropyl methyl oxypyrimidine diethyl thionophosphate) [227].

Some of the insecticides mentioned are systemic, i.e., after absorption by a single organ, such as a leaf, they spread over the entire plant. The insecticide becomes effective when the insect comes into contact with the plant. The systemic action is pronounced in the case of many esters of phosphoric acid. The absorption, transport and decomposition of octamethyl pyrophosphoramide

$$[(CH_3)_2N]_2PO-O-OP[N(CH_3)_2]_2,$$

also called OMPA and Schradan, and of related compounds (some of them containing fluorine) in plants have been investigated with tracers [197, 207, 228–240, 245, 374, 390, 392, 402]. Similar work has been done with Systox (diethylthionophosphoric ester of β-hydroxyethylthioethyl ether [197, 207, 240–245, 320, 327, 374, 388].

The accumulation of the insecticide, its persistence and its slow detoxication have been followed. It has been found that the lower side of leaves absorbs these compounds better than the upper side, and that the administration of the substances should be followed by a period of active photosynthesis at favourable temperatures. The insecticides are also taken up by roots, and treatment of the seeds produces plants containing insecticide. When labelled systemic insecticide is applied to the bark, lateral transport occurs to the centre of the tree. The insecticide is translocated mainly towards the young leaves, while movement downwards is slow. The extent of decomposition depends greatly on the kind of plant. The possibility of loss through evaporation of insecticide from leaves must be borne in mind. Radioactive phosphorus has been detected in honey produced from plants treated with insecticides [230, 239].

Methyl bromide, an enzyme inhibitor, is used for the disinfestation of grain. The fate of the methyl bromide has been investigated with radiocarbon and radiobromine [246]. To obtain information on the mechanism of action, radioactive phosphate was fed to the flies, both normal and poisoned with methyl bromide, until the phosphorus attained constant specific radioactivity in those body constituents which are rapidly metabolized, the flies were extracted and the paper chromatogram obtained from the extract scanned. This is known as the technique of "labelled pools" [378] (see also p. 286). It was found that poisoned flies contained much less adenosine triphosphate (ATP) than normal flies. With the same technique, but with carbon-labelled acetate, it was found that after poisoning with DFP a temporary increase in the acetylcholine content occurred [247, 248].

Much work has been devoted to the comparison of the metabolism of labelled insecticides by sensitive strains of insects and by strains resistant to these insecticides [39, 249, 250, 379, 381], for instance, in respect to permeability of the cuticle, chemical transformations and rate of excretion.

11.6.2. *Absorption and Transport of Fungicides and Herbicides*

The sensitivity of fungal spores to fungicides is determined by the absorption of the poison and its inherent toxicity. For distinction between these two factors, which is required for the planned development of effective fungicides, a sensitive method of measuring absorption is needed. It is best to use labelled fungicides.

The uptake of labelled fungicides by fungal spores (*Neurospora* and *Aspergillus*) from solutions of concentrations of the order of 10^{-4} to 10^{-3} per cent has been determined. The fungicides included salts of silver, mercury and cerium, as well as organic substances (2-heptadecyl-2-imidazolin [Glyodin], 2,3-dichloro-1,4-naphthoquinone, and iron dimethyldithiocarbamate [Ferbam]) [39, 251–255]. Saturation was attained within a few minutes, the metallic ions being strongly concentrated within the cell.

Silver or zinc could be removed from the spores by subsequent treatment with the inactive metal salts, but this was not possible with the naphthoquinone, which evidently undergoes chemical reaction within the spores. Experiments with spores disintegrated by ultrasonic vibrations showed that Glyodin and Dichlon are not adsorbed by the surface of inactive spores, but taken up into the interior of the spores [255]. In other experiments, it was observed whether different fungicides are taken up additively or displace one another [251]. In still other experiments, radioactive phosphate was introduced into the spores, and it was then observed whether the fungicide makes the membranes of the spore permeable, allowing radiophosphorus to escape [251–253]. It has been concluded that fungicides at present in use are fairly ineffective in relation to the amount absorbed, and that the development of more powerful agents may be expected [251].

The absorption of thiocarbamates (^{35}S) by spores has been measured [256, 257]. Elementary sulphur is used as a fungicide for citrus fruits; the conversion of this sulphur into other simple chemical compounds, and the incorporation of sulphur into organic substances has been followed by tracer methods [258].

Much work has been done with labelled herbicides, including selective weedkillers [39, 197, 207, 259, 260, 418]. The specific activity of ^{14}C-labelled herbicides can be made so high that their absorption and translocation may be measured with quantities of substance which have no physiological effect.

Dichlorophenoxyacetic acid (2,4-D) is translocated from the leaves as far as the roots [261, 262]. In some circumstances, the roots may release 2,4-D and so subject neighbouring plants to the action of the herbicide [263]. In the opinion of some workers, the absorption of the herbicide by foliage is increased by application of detergents [263], but there is no unanimity in this view [205].

In a detailed investigation of the fate of 2,4-D within the plant [265] it was found that its path from the cuticle to the phloem goes via the mesophyll cells of the leaves and the vascular system, and from the phloem with the current of organic materials to the meristem. A lipid membrane must be passed to enter the plant through the cuticle, so that the fat-soluble esters of the herbicide are at an advantage, but in the further transfer within the aqueous medium the salt or free acid show better mobility.

In experiments with beans, it has been found that 2,4-D undergoes chemical changes over a prolonged period [266]. It may even be oxidized as far as carbon dioxide, the carbon from different positions in the molecule being converted into carbon dioxide at different rates [267].

Autoradiographical work with 2,4-D has led to the opinion that the resistance of barley and oat plants in the 5–6 leaf stage is due to lack of translocation [268]. With the herbicide INBA (2-iodo-3-nitrobenzoic acid) it was found that the parts of bean plants containing the largest quantity of INBA showed the greatest depression of development [269]. On the other hand, it was found that barley with a similar content of INBA suffered less damage than the beans [269]. The question to what extent the selectivity of the hormonal herbicides depends on differences in the sensitivities of the cells of the various plants, and not only on differences in translocation, is still in need of further investigation [259].

4-Iodophenoxyacetic acid is effective in increasing the fruit yield of tomato plants. It has been found in tracer work that the "hormone" is concentrated in the blossom and young fruit, and directs a stream of nutrient to these sites [25, 270–227]. The mechanism of action and relevant chemical reactions of α-naphthylacetic acid [272, 273] and of 2,4-dichloro-5-iodophenoxyacetic acid [264] have also been studied.

Anomalies in the metabolism of plants after treatment with herbicide can be discovered by methods similar to the "labelled pools" method (p. 285). The damaged plant is submitted to radiophotosynthesis with ^{14}CO$_2$, and the distribution of the labelled substances in the radiochromatogram is compared with that produced by the normal plant [274]. It has been shown that the catabolism of exogenous ^{14}C-substrates by corn roots is increased by treatment with 2,4-D [406].

The uniformity of distribution of fungicides in fields worked with machines has been examined by autoradiography on sections to find out to what extent the fungicide reaches cotton seeds present in the field. This procedure is, of course, also suitable for other pesticides [275].

11.6.3. *Ecology of Animal Pests and of Other Animals*

Much tracer work has been devoted to the ecology of animal pests, particularly insects and worms. These may be labelled, as birds are ringed, then liberated, and traced through radiation measurements [39, 290, 291, 311, 371, 413, 418].

The advantages of using radioactivity in such work are the simple, rapid and unambiguous identification of the animal – even when hidden – and the retention of the tag in transformations, such as the metamorphosis of insects.

The activity is usually detected with counters, but is has been suggested that the animal could be pressed against a nuclear emulsion (p. 46). This method permits the use of the cheap and readily available α-active substances thorium and uranium, and the work can be carried out without qualified personnel or expensive instruments [276].

The population of animals of a given kind within a given living space may be determined by a kind of isotope dilution method, provided this living space is, to a sufficient approximation, bounded. A known number of labelled animals is released, and after a long enough time the number of labelled animals present in a sample caught is determined by activity measurement. The ratio of the number of released animals and the labelled fraction in the captured sample gives the total number of animals present in the area. When samples are taken at intervals of time, the natural mortality of the animals under given conditions can be determined [277, 373].

The insects or their larvae may be labelled by feeding. For this purpose larvae may be placed in radioactive solutions [80, 278, 373], since dissolved radioactive substances are usually strongly concentrated within the body of the insect. Grown insects may be allowed to feed on radioactive plants 279–283, [373], including trees [284], or on radioactive animals [285, 286], or else radioactive food is administered to them [287 to 289]. Reviews of work with radioactive insects have been published [39, 197, 290–292, 373].

The excrements of labelled insects may also be radioactive, and plants visited by the insecst may therefore be identified by means of the deposited activity [197, 291, 293]. However, the radioactive excrements may in certain circumstances complicate the location of the insects in soil, etc. Another method of labelling, avoiding such complications, will be described below. If the insect is a carrier of microbes, the origin of infections may be determined. Labelled bacteria are then supplied to the insect in its food or in other ways, but fairly high activity and good retention of the radionuclide by the microbe is needed [291, 373].

Literally hundreds of thousands of mosquitoes have been labelled for dispersal studies [80, 279, 294, 373]. They can be bred in stagnant water, to which radioactive phosphate has been added. The larvae become strongly β-active and retain part of their activity after metamorphosis to the adult form. It has been found that the mosquitoes can fly, or be carried by the wind, several miles.

The tropical mosquito *Aedes aegypti*, which carries the yellow fever disease, has also been labelled [285, 295]. To introduce radiophosphorus into the Canadian black fly, dangerous to animals, the larvae must, unlike the mosquito larvae, be kept in flowing water [80, 296]. Other dispersal studies have been made on the olive fruit fly [385, 386] and on *Anopheles* [384].

While in the studies mentioned so far a large number of animals were labelled at the same time, for other purposes labelling of single animals has been used [373]. Thus zirconium-95 has been injected into cockroaches so that these could be located again individually at fairly large distances by their γ-rays [290]. The behaviour of individuals is also interesting in the case of the larvae of a beetle, the wireworm, which feeds on the young roots of food crops. γ-radiation from the beetle and its larva can be measured through several centimetres of soil, so that the insect can carry on its normal life. In one investigation, the beetle was labelled by sticking to the underside of its wing radium sulphate contained in an aluminium capsule [297]. In other work with wireworms radiocobalt was used [80, 298, 299]. Cobalt wire was fastened to the insect or inserted into the body cavity. The insect could not be immersed in a radiocobalt solution (as the mosquitoes were immersed into radioactive phosphate solution), since cobalt is a poison. To prevent completely chemical attack on the wire, it may be advantageous to gold-plate it. The wire method has the additional advantage that no radioactive substance can be excreted and confuse the evidence for the animals' movement. Special tests indicate that inserted cobalt tags are not shed in the moulting of the larvae.

The horizontal movement of the wireworm in the "x-direction" and "y-direction" may be followed by searching continuously for the place of maximum radiation intensity at the soil surface. The vertical movement ("z-direction") may be determined by the actual value of the intensity, since the radiation is attenuated in passing through the soil. Work of this kind has shown what temperature and moisture conditions in the soils are preferred by the wireworms, and has given indications whether they seek out their food or come upon it accidentally. In some circumstances, the animals turned out to be cannibals. A movable probe carrying a counting rate meter with an almost instantaneous response has been used, and a device has even been built which follows the worm automatically above ground, i.e., moves to the point of maximum intensity, and registers its own movement [80, 298, 300].

In connection with plague research fleas have been labelled with cerium-144, and their change-over between various species of rodents observed under various conditions [301]. The grain weevil *Eurygaster integriceps* was labelled with cobalt, and a correlation established between its fat content (energy reserve) and the rate of its movement [95, 205] (see also [384]). After radioactive tagging, the Canadian grasshopper has been found to move in random direction, and not deliberately in the direction of food. At 15 °C a distance of about 6 m is covered per hour [289].

It has been possible using tracers to find out whether insects are carnivorous, and on which animals they prey [373, 383]. Certain beetles have been shown to feed on mosquito larvae, while mites may be parasites of cockroaches and take up radiophosphorus from their hosts [290]. It has been proved using tracers that both the male mosquito (which does not suck blood) and the female mosquito take in plant fluids [290, 302].

Ecological tracer work has also been done with useful insects, e.g., bees [373, 382]. After the application of radioactive phosphorus fertilizer to a field, the plants produce radioactive honey, so that the bees which have frequented this field may be recognized on their return to the hive, and also counted [309]. In other investigations, the bees were provided with ^{14}C-sugar to measure the transfer of honey from workers to drones [304].

Small mammals living out of sight, such as moles and voles [291, 305, 370], or bats [306], as well as toads [307], fish [308, 317] and free-living birds [309] have been tagged in ecological studies, and then individually followed with radiation detectors.

The true flying time of birds may be determined after fastening a polonium source on their bodies in such a way that the α-radiation can strike a piece of photographic plate only when the bird is in flight [310]. At the end of the observation period, the α-tracks in the emulsion are counted and the exposure time calculated. Such equipment weighs only a few milligrams. The author indicates that the method may be developed so that, for example, the time of gliding can be determined for gliding birds, or that of swimming for swimming birds.

The destruction of various pests by radiation will be discussed in Volume 2.

References to Chapter 11

1. G. HEVESY, *Radioactive Indicators*, New York 1948.
2. A. L. COMAR, *Radioisotopes in Biology and Agriculture*, New York 1955.
3. M. D. KAMEN, *Isotopic Tracers in Biology*, New York 1957.
4. E. BRODA, *Radioaktive Isotope in der Biochemie*, Vienna 1958; *Radioactive Isotopes in Biochemistry*, Amsterdam 1960.
5. H. SCHWIEGK and F. TURBA (Ed.), *Künstliche radioaktive Isotope in Physiologie, Diagnostik und Therapie*, Berlin 1961.
6. S. ARONOFF, *Techniques of Radiobiochemistry*, Ames 1956.
7. M. CALVIN and P. MASSINI, *Experientia* **8**, 445 (1952).
8. A. P. VINOGRADOV and R. V. TEIS, *Doklady Akad. Nauk SSSR* **33**, 490 (1941); **56**, 57 (1947).
9. S. RUBEN, M. RANDALL, M. KAMEN and J. L. HYDE, *J. Amer. Chem. Soc.* **63**, 877 (1941).
10. R. V. TEIS, *Doklady Akad. Nauk SSSR* **72**, 351 (1950).
11. B. B. VARTAPETYAN and A. L. KURSANOV, *Doklady Akad. Nauk SSSR* **104**, 272 (1955).
12. M. CALVIN and A. A. BENSON, *Science* **105**, 648 (1947); **107**, 476 (1948); **108**, 304 (1948); **109**, 140 (1949).
13. M. CALVIN and J. A. BASSHAM, Geneva Report 259 (1955), vol. 12, p. 347.
14. J. A. BASSHAM and M. CALVIN, *The Path of Carbon in Photosynthesis*, New York 1957.
15. A. A. NICHIPOROWITCH, T. F. ANDREYEVA and N. P. VOSKRESENSKAYA, Paris Report 123, vol. 4, p. 411.
16. A. L. KURSANOV, Geneva Report 618 (1955), vol. 12, p. 3.
17. M. V. TURKINA, *Biokhimiya* **19**, 357 (1954).
18. A. L. KURSANOV, *Botan. Zh.* **39**, 482 (1954).
19. O. A. PAVLINOVA, *Biokhimiya* **19**, 364 (1954).
20. A. L. KURSANOV, Paris Report 128, vol. 4, p. 494.
21. A. L. KURSANOV, *Ann. Rev. Plant. Physiol.* **7**, 401 (1956); *Adv. Botan. Res.*, vol. 1 (1963).
22. S. RUBEN, R. OVERSTREET, M. KAMEN and T. BROYER, *Proc. Nat. Acad. Sci.* **26**, 418, 688 (1940).
23. G. E. GRAF and S. ARONOFF, *Nature* **172**, 1043 (1953); *Science* **121**, 211 (1955).
24. A. M. KUZIN, V. I. MERENOVA and YA. V. MAMUL, *Doklady Akad. Nauk SSSR* **85**, 645 (1952); **94**, 573 (1954).

25. R.C.LIPPS, R.L.FOX and F.E.KOEHLER, *Soil Sci.* **84,** 195 (1957); *Plant and Soil* **20,** 337 (1964).
26. E.G.GRINFELD, *Doklady Akad. Nauk SSSR* **97,** 919 (1954).
27. M.B.NEIMAN, A.A.PROKOFEV and P.S.SHANTAROVICH, *Doklady Akad. Nauk SSSR* **78,** 367 (1951).
28. E.A.SHILLOV, Paris Report 130, vol. 4, p. 523.
29. E.EPSTEIN, *Ann. Rev. Plant Physiol.* **7,** 1 (1956).
30. E.EPSTEIN and S.B.HENDRICKS, Geneva Report 112 (1955), vol. 12, p. 98.
31. S.B.HENDRICKS, in: Conference on Use of Isotopes in Plant and Animal Research, Washington 1953.
32. G.E.BRIGGS and R.N.ROBERTSON, *Ann. Rev. Plant Physiol.* **8,** 11 (1957).
33. G.G.LATIES, *Ann. Rev. Plant Physiol.* **10,** 87 (1959).
34. H.H.USSING, *Ann. Rev. Physiol.* **15,** 1 (1953); Geneva Report 908 (1955), vol. 12, p. 252.
35. All-Union Conference on the Uses of Radioactive Isotopes and Nuclear Radiation in the National Economy of the USSR, Riga 1960; see *Atomnaya energiya* **9,** 221 (1960); *Kernenergie* **4,** 158 (1961).
36. H.T.HOPKINS, A.W.SPECHT and S.B.HENDRICKS, *Plant Physiol.* **25,** 193 (1950).
37. E.C.HAGEN and S.B.HENDRICKS, Geneva Report 1058 (1958), vol. 27, p. 19.
38. O.BIDDULPH· see [39].
39. H.LINSER and K.KAINDL, *Isotope in der Landwirtschaft*, Hamburg 1960.
40. O.BIDDULPH, *Botan. Rev.* **21,** 251 (1955).
41. A.A.PROKOFEV and A.M.SOBOLEV, *Fiziol. rasten.* **4,** 14 (1957).
42. O.BIDDULPH, in: Conference on Use of Isotopes in Plant and Animal Research, Washington 1953.
43. H.G.GAUCH, *Ann. Rev. Plant Physiol.* **8,** 31 (1957).
44. O.BIDDULPH and R.CORY, *Plant Physiol.* **32,** 608 (1957).
45. R.S.RUSSELL and V.M.SHORROCKS, Paris Report 178, vol. 4, p. 286.
46. Z.I.ZHURBITSKY and D.V.SHTRAUSBERG, Paris Report 120, vol. 4, p. 270.
47. V.I.RAZUMOV and N.D.FEOFANOVA, Geneva Report 2313 (1958), vol. 27, p. 93.
48. N.M.SISAKIAN and V.I.VORONKOVA, *Doklady Akad. Nauk SSSR* **70,** 275 (1950).
49. V.M.KLECHKOVSKII, V.N.STOLETOV and T.P.EVDOKIMOVA, *Izvest. Akad. Nauk SSSR, Biology Series* **1951** (3), 73.
50. A.L.KURSANOV, Geneva Report 696 (1955), vol. 12, p. 165.
51. M.H.ZIMMERMANN, *Science* **133,** 73 (1961).
52. V.N.SHOLKEVICH, *Doklady Akad. Nauk SSSR* **96,** 653 (1954).
53. U.V.MOSOLOV, A.N.LAPSHINA and A.V.PANOVA, *Doklady Akad. Nauk SSSR* **98,** 495 (1954).
54. K.ESAU, H.B.CURRIER and V.I.CHEADLE, *Ann. Rev. Plant Physiol.* **8,** 349 (1957).
55. S.H.WITTWER and F.G.TEUBNER, *Ann. Rev. Plant Physiol.* **10,** 13 (1959).
56. M.J.BUKOVAC and S.H.WITTWER, *Plant Physiol.* **13,** 428 (1957).
57. G.J.RACZ, D.A.RENNIE and W.L.HUTCHEON, *Can. J. Soil Sci.* **44,** 100 (1964).
58. S.BIDDULPH, O.BIDDULPH and R.CORY, *Amer. J. Botany* **45,** 648 (1958).
59. O.BIDDULPH, S.F.BIDDULPH and R.CORY, Paris Report 179, vol. 4, p. 340.
60. L.P.VERNON and S.ARONOFF, *Arch. Biochem. Biophys.* **36,** 383 (1952).
61. S.ARONOFF, *Plant Physiol.* **30,** 184 (1955).
62. M.H.ZIMMERMANN, *Ann. Rev. Plant Physiol.* **11,** 167 (1960).
63. D.DE ZEEUW, Paris Report 135, vol. 4, p. 401.
64. O.BIDDULPH, S.BIDDULPH, R.CORY and H.KOONTZ, *Plant Physiol.* **33,** 293 (1958).
65. G.O.BURR, C.E.HARTT, T.TANIMOTO, D.TAKAHASHI and H.W.BRODIE, Paris Report 133, vol. 4, p. 351.
66. C.A.SWANSON and J.B.WHITNEY, *Amer. J. Botany* **40,** 816 (1954).
67. V.M.KLECHKOVSKI, Geneva Report 694 (1955), vol. 12, p. 109.
68. H.B.TUKEY, S.H.WITTWER, F.G.TEUBNER and W.G.LONG, Geneva Report 106 (1955), vol. 12, p. 138.
69. S.H.WITTWER, H.B.TUKEY, F.G.TEUBNER and W.G.LONG, *Atompraxis* **2,** 243 (1957).
70. C.SOSA-BOURDOUIL and P.LECAT, *Année biologique* **32,** 341 (1957}.
71. M.FRIED, *Soil Sci. Soc. Amer. Proc.* **13,** 135 (1949).

72. O.N.HINSVARK, S.H.WITTWER and H.B.TUKEY, *Plant Physiol.* **28**, 70 (1953).
73. R.VOLK, C.MCAULIFFE, *Soil Sci. Soc. Amer. Proc.* **18**, 308 (1954).
74. K.MOTHES and L.ENGELBRECHT, *Monatsber. Dtsch. Akad. Wiss. (Berlin)* **1**, 367 (1959).
75. H.B.TUKEY, S.H.WITTWER and H.B.TUKEY, Paris Report 132, vol. 4, p. 304.
76. H.B.TUKEY and H.B.TUKEY, *Atompraxis* **5**, 213 (1959).
77. S.B.HENDRICKS and L.A.DEAN, *Ann. Rev. Nucl. Sci.* **1**, 597 (1952).
78. A.V.SOKOLOV, *Izvest. Akad. Nauk SSSR, Biology Series* **1953** (9), 28.
79. A.V.SOKOLOV, Geneva Report 695 (1955), vol. 12, p. 118.
80. J.W.T.SPINKS, Geneva Report 10 (1955), vol. 12, p. 75.
81. W.L.HILL, E.J.FOX and J.F.MULLINS, *Ind. Eng. Chem.* **41**, 1328 (1949).
82. J.M.BLUME and N.S.HALL, *Soil Sci.* **75**, 299 (1953).
83. A.J.MACKENZIE and J.W.BORLAND, *Anal. Chem.* **24**, 176 (1952).
84. S.MITSUI *et al.*, Geneva Report 1353 (1958), vol. 27, p. 160.
85. P.G.MARAIS, Geneva Report 1105 (1958), vol. 27, p. 23.
86. R.S.RUSSELL, *Radioisotope Techniques*, London 1953, vol. 1, p. 402.
87. L.A.DEAN, Geneva Report 104 (1955), vol. 12, p. 89.
88. H.G.DION, J.E.DEHM, J.W.T.SPINKS and J.MITCHELL, *Sci. Agric.* **29**, 167, 512 (1949).
89. B.A.KRANTZ, W.L.NELSON, C.D.WELCH and N.S.HALL, *Soil Sci.* **68**, 171 (1949).
90. L.A.ZUEV and P.F.GOLUBEVA, *Doklady Akad. Nauk SSSR* **96**, 387 (1954); *Vestn. Mosk. Univ.* **9** (10), *Fiz.- mat. Ser.* No. 7, 111 (1954).
91. F.SCHEFFER and B.ULRICH, *Naturwiss.* **45**, 49 (1958).
92. F.SCHEFFER and B.ULRICH, Geneva Report 989 (1958), vol. 27, p. 149.
93. F.W.PARKER, *Science* **111**, 215 (1950).
94. F.W. PARKER, in: S.C. ROTHMANN (Ed.), *Constructive Uses of Atomic Energy*, New York 1949.
95. D.KIRKHAM and R.J.KUNZE, *Adv. Agron.* **14**, 321 (1962).
96. J.W.T.SPINKS and G.DION, *J. Chem. Soc.* **1949** (S), 410.
97. M.FRIED and A.J.MCKENZIE, *Soil Sci. Soc. Amer. Proc.* **14**, 226 (1949).
98. R.S.RUSSELL, E.W.RUSSELL, P.G.MARAIS and W.N.FORSTER, Geneva Report 460 (1955), vol. 12, p. 103.
99. N.I.BORISOVA, *Izvest. Akad. Nauk SSSR, Biological Series*, **1954** (1), 110.
100. W.H.FULLER and L.DEAN, *Soil Sci.* **68**, 197 (1949).
101. C.D.MCAULIFFE, M.PEECH and R.BRADFIELD, *Soil Sci.* **68**, 179, 185 (1949).
102. K.SCHARRER and H.KÜHN, *Ber. Dtsch. Landwirtsch. Ges.* **1954**, No 42–43.
103. A.VAN DEN HENDE, A.COTTENIE and A.DE LOOSE, Geneva Report 116 (1958), vol. 27, p. 3.
104. R.W.BLEDSLOE, C.L.COMAR and H.C.HARRIS, *Science* **109**, 329 (1949).
105. H.C.HARRIS, *Plant Physiol.* **24**, 150 (1949); Geneva Report 108 (1955), vol. 12, p. 203.
106. M.D.THOMAS, R.H.HENDRICKS and G.R.HILL, *Soil Sci.* **70**, 19 (1950).
107. B.R.BERTRAMSSON, M.FRIED and S.L.TISDALE, *Soil Sci.* **70**, 27 (1950).
108. S.MITSUI, K.TENSHO and K.KURIHARA, Paris Report 119, vol. 4, p. 247.
109. P.R.STOUT and W.R.MEAGHER, *Science* **108**, 471 (1948).
110. C.R.MILLIKAN, *Nature* **166**, 187 (1950).
111. O.K.KEDROV-ZIKHMAN, Geneva Report 716 (1955), vol. 12, p. 123.
112. K.SCHARRER and W.HÖFNER, *Z. Pflanzenernähr. Düng. Bodenkunde* **81**, 213 (1958).
113. K.KAINDL, *Die Bodenkultur* **7**, 324 (1953).
114. K.KAINDL, Radioisotope Conference, Oxford 1954, vol. 1, London 1954, p. 397.
115. J.W.T.SPINKS and S.S.BARBIER, *Sci. Agr.* **27**, 145 (1949).
116. M.FRIED and L.A.DEAN, *Soil Science* **73**, 263 (1952).
117. S.LARSEN, *Plant and Soil* **4**, 1 (1952).
118. N.P.DATTA, N.R.DATTA and S.C.SRIVASTAVA, Geneva Report 1947 (1958), vol. 27, p. 186.
119. S.R.OLSEN, F.S.WATANABE, H.R.COSPER, W.E.LARDON and L.NELSON, *Soil Sci.* **78**, 141 (1954).
120. S.R.OLSEN, in: Conference on Use of Isotopes in Plant and Animal Research, Washington 1953.
121. O.TALIBUDEEN, Radioisotope Conference, Oxford 1954, vol. 1, London 1954, p. 405.

122. I. ANTIPOV-KARATAYEV, Geneva Report 698 (1955), vol. 12, p. 130.

123. O. GUNNARSSON and L. FREDRICKSSON, *Chimie et Industrie* **68**, 395 (1952); *Radioisotope Techniques*, London 1953, vol. 1, p. 427.

124. C. D. MCAULIFFE, N. S. HALL, L. A. DEAN and S. B. HENDRICKS, *Soil Sci. Soc. Amer. Proc.* **12**, 119 (1947).

125. R. S. RUSSELL, J. B. RICHSON and S. N. ADAM, *J. Soil Sci.* **5**, 85 (1954).

126. G. E. BRIGGS, A. B. HOPE and R. N. ROBERTSON, *Electrolytes and Plant Cells*, Oxford 1961.

127. J. DIGLERIA, Geneva Report 1713 (1958), vol. 27, p. 63.

128. J. GOVAERTS, *An. Real. Soc. Espan. Fisic. Quim. Ser. B* **50**, 259 (1954).

129. L. WIKLANDER, *Ann. Roy. Agric. Coll. Sweden* **17**, 407 (1950).

130. L. A. DEAN, *Adv. Agronomy* **1**, 391 (1949).

131. H. C. HARRIS, W. H. MACINTIRE, C. L. COMAR, W. M. SHAW, S. H. WINTERBERG and S. L. HOOD, *Science* **113**, 328 (1951).

132. J. M. BLUME and D. H. SMITH, *Soil Sci.* **77**, 9 (1954).

133. M. A. SALAM and S. HASHISH, Geneva Report 1497 (1958), vol. 27, p. 172.

134. I. T. ROSENQUIST, Radioisotope Conference 1954, vol. 1, London 1954, p. 412.

135. V. V. RACHINSKII, *Doklady Akad. Nauk SSSR* **95**, 849 (1954).

136. W. J. HENDERSON and U. S. JONES. *Soil Sci.* **51**, 283 (1941).

137. A. SÜSS, see [39].

138. J. B. RICKSON, *Radioisotope Techniques*, London 1953, vol. 1, p. 411.

139. C. KRISHNAMOORTHY and L. OVERSTREET, *Soil Sci.* **69**, 41 (1950).

140. G. STANFORD, C. D. MCAULIFFE and R. BRADFIELD, *Agronomy J.* **42**, 423 (1950).

141. J. GOVAERTS, A. LECRENIER, C. CORIN, E. DERMINE, J. TREZINSKY and O. LIARD, *Radioisotope Techniques*, London 1953, vol. 1, p. 395.

142. E. RATNER, see [16].

143. N. I. BORISOVA and O. A. SAGAINOVA, *Izvest. Akad. Nauk SSSR, Biological Series* **1953** (6), 111.

144. A. M. KUZIN, *Nauka i Zhizn* **1955** (4), 29.

145. S. L. HANSARD, *Nucleonics* **9** (1), 13 (1951).

146. S. L. HANSARD, C. L. COMAR and M. P. PLUMLEE, *Nucleonics* **9** (2), 38 (1951).

147. C. L. COMAR and F. BRONNER (Ed.), *Mineral Metabolism*, New York 1960.

148. A. H. W. ATEN and G. HEVESY, *Nature* **142**, 111 (1938).

149. M. KLEIBER, A. L. BLACK, G. P. LOFGREN, J. R. LUICK and A. H. SMITH, Geneva Report 93 (1955), vol. 12, p. 292.

150. M. KLEIBER, Conference on Use of Isotopes in Plant and Animal Research, Washington 1953.

151. C. L. COMAR, Geneva Report 90 (1955), vol. 12, p. 245.

152. R. E. CLEGG, in: Conference on Use of Isotopes in Plant and Animal Research, Washington 1953.

153. R. SASAKI, Geneva Report 1047 (1957), vol. 12, p. 275.

154. P. M. JOHNSTON and C. L. COMAR, *Amer. J. Physiol.* **183**, 365 (1955).

155. R. J. BLOCK, A. J. STEKOL and J. K. LOOSLI, *Arch. Biochem. Biophys.* **33**, 353 (1951).

156. C. L. COMAR, *Nucleonics* **3** (3), 32; (4), 30; (5), 34 (1948).

157. Food and Agricultural Organisation, Geneva Report 780 (1955), vol. 12, p. 10.

158. W. MAHAN, *Gen. Foods Techn. Bull.* **2**, 1 (1948).

159. R. R. BALDWIN, R. T. THIESSEN and E. E. MCILROY, *Science* **106**, 317 (1947).

160. R. H. SNYDER, H. J. EISNER and H. STEENBOCK, *J. Nutrition* **45**, 305 (1951).

161. P. NUMEROF, H. L. SASSAMAN, A. RODGERS and A. E. SCHAEFER, *J. Nutrition* **55**, 13 (1955)

162. S. A. BELLIN, D. C. HERTING, J. W. CRAMER, V. J. PILEGGI and H. STEENBOCK, *Arch. Biochem. Biophys.* **50**, 18 (1954).

163. T. A. ROGERS and M. KLEIBER, *Biochim. Biophys. Acta* **22**, 284 (1956).

164. C. F. BAXTER, M. KLEIBER and A. L. BLACK, *Biochim. Biophys. Acta* **21**, 277 (1956).

165. S. J. FOLLEY, *The Physiology and Biochemistry of Lactation*, London 1956.

166. H. A. BERN, D. R. HARKNESS and S. M. BLAIR, *Proc. Nat. Acad. Sci.* **41**, 55 (1955).

167. M. L. RYDER, *Nature* **178**, 1409 (1956).

168. I. A. TROITSKY, Geneva Report 2314 (1958), vol. 24, p. 128.

169. F. HAUROWITZ, S. FLEISCHER, H. WALTER and A. LIETZE, Geneva Report 837 (1958), vol. 25, p. 111.

170. J.H.BALMAIN, S.L.FOLLEY and R.F.GLASCOCK, *Biochem. J.* **56**, 234 (1954).
171. R.F.GLASCOCK, *Proc. Roy. Soc. London* B **149**, 402 (1958).
172. J.M.BARRY, *Endeavour* **18**, 173 (1959).
173. G.POPJAK, *Biochem. Soc. Symposia* **9**, 37 (1952); *Brit. Med. Bull.* **8**, 218 (1952).
174. G.POPJAK, R.F.GLASCOCK and S.J.FOLLEY, *Biochem. J.* **52**, 472 (1952).
175. G.POPJAK, G.D.HUNTER and T.H.FRENCH, *Biochem. J.* **54**, 238 (1953).
176. A.T.COWIE, W.G.DUNSCOMBE, S.J.FOLLEY, R.F.GLASCOCK, L.MASSART, G.J.PEETERS and G.POPJAK, *Biochem. J.* **49**, 610 (1951).
177. B.A.ASKONAS, P.N.CAMPBELL, C.GODIN and T.S.WORK, *Biochem. J.* **61**, 105 (1955).
178. P.F.SOLVONUK, L.B.JAQUES, J.E.LEDDY, L.W.TREVOY and J.W.T.SPINKS, *Proc. Soc. Exp. Biol. Med.* **79**, 597 (1952).
179. F.C.G.HOSKIN, J.W.T.SPINKS and L.B.JAQUES, *Can. J. Biochem. Physiol.* **32**, 240 (1954).
180. L.B.JAQUES, G.J.MILLAR and J.W.T.SPINKS, *Schweizer Med. Wochschr.* **84**, 792 (1954).
181. J.D.TAYLOR, G.J.MILLAR, L.B.JAQUES and J.W.T.SPINKS, *Can. J. Biochem. Physiol.* **34**, 1143 (1956).
182. J.D.TAYLOR, G.J.MILLAR and R.J.WOODS, *Can. J. Biochem. Physiol.* **35**, 691 (1957).
183. L.B.JAQUES, E.L.FROESE, R.O'TOOLE and J.W.T.SPINKS, *Arch. Internat. Pharmacodyn.* **111**, 478 (1957).
184. A.AKHROMEIKO, see [16].
185. J.E.KUNTZ and A.J.RIKER, Geneva Report 105 (1955), vol. 12, p. 144.
186. D.A.FRASER and C.A.MAWSON, *Can. J. Bot.* **31**, 324 (1953).
187. P.G.KRAMER and K.WILBUR, *Science* **110**, 8 (1949).
188. E.MELIN and H.NILSON, *Physiol. Plantarum*, Vol. 3 (1950).
189. A.I.AKHROMEIKO and V.A.SHESTAKOVA, Geneva Report 2312 (1958), vol. 27, p. 193.
190. B.F.GRAHAM, *Ecology* **35**, 415 (1954).
191. K.FREUDENBERG, *Angew. Chem.* **68**, 84, 508 (1956); *Science* **148**, 595 (1965).
192. K.KRATZL and G.BILLEK, *Monatsh. Chem.* **90**, 89, 536 (1956).
193. G.BILLEK, see [4].
194. G.HEVESY, *Biochem. J.* **17**, 439 (1923).
195. L.H.CAMPBELL, L.R.SNOKE and J.D.STRUTHERS, *Bell Lab. Rec.* **28**, 249 (1950).
196. O.PETER, *Holz, Roh- und Werkstoff* **11**, 50 (1953).
197. P.A.DAHM, *Adv. Pest Control Res.* **1**, 84 (1958).
198. C.T.REDEMANN and R.W.MEIKLE, *Adv. Pest Control Res.* **2**, 184 (1958).
199. N.R.TRENNER, R.W.WALKER, B.ARISON and R.P.BUSH, *Anal. Chem.* **21**, 285 (1949).
200. R.HILL, A.G.JONES and D.E.PALIN, *Chem. & Ind.* **1954**, 162.
201. P.SORENSEN, *Anal. Chem.* **26**, 1581 (1954).
202. F.L.CAMPBELL and C.LUKENS, *J. Econ. Entomol.* **24**, 88 (1931).
203. L.B.NORTON and R.HANSBERRY, *J. Econ. Entomol.* **34**, 431 (1941).
204. *Chem. Eng.* **55**, 126 (1948).
205. S.B.ANDREYEV, A.V.VSEVODIN, C.A.MOLCHANOVA and A.V.KHOTYANOVITCH, Geneva Report 2309 (1958), vol. 27, p. 85.
206. T.E.BANKS, R.L.F.TUPPER and A.WORMALL, *Biochem. J.* **47**, 466 (1950).
207. J.W.MITCHELL, B.C.SMALE and R.L.METCALFE, *Adv. Pest Control Res.* **3**, 359 (1960).
208. M.I.ZEID, P.A.DAHM, R.E.HEIN and R.H.MCFARLAND, *J. Econ. Entomol.* **46**, 324 (1953).
209. J.P.PELLEGRINI, A.C.MILLAR and R.V.SHARPLESS, *J. Econ. Entomol.* **45**, 532 (1952).
210. F.P.WINTERINGHAM, *Science* **116**, 452 (1952).
211. F.P.WINTERINGHAM, A.HARRISON and P.M.BRIDGES, *Biochem. J.* **61**, 359 (1955).
212. A.GANZ, F.E.KELSEY and E.M.GEILING, *J. Pharmacol. Exp. Therapeut.* **103**, 209 (1951).
213. F.DUSPIVA, *Angew. Chemie* **66**, 541 (1954).
214. F.O.MORRISON and W.F.OLIVER, *Can. J. Res.* D **27**, 265 (1949).
215. F.P.WINTERINGHAM, A.HARRISON, C.R.JONES, J.L.McGIRR and W.H.TEMPLETON, *J. Sci. Food Agric.* **7**, 214 (1950).
216. F.P.WINTERINGHAM, A.HARRISON and R.G.BRIDGES, *Nature* **166**, 999 (1950); *Analyst* **77**, 19 (1952); *Nucleonics* **10** (3), 52 (1952).
217. P.BRADBURY and W.WHITTAKER, *J. Sci. Food Agr.* **7**, 248 (1956).

218. S.LOCKAU, W.LÜDICKE and F.WEYGAND, *Naturwiss.* **15**, 350 (1951); *Z. Naturforsch.* **7b**, 389 (1952).
219. W.DAVID and W.ALDRIDGE, *Ann. Appl. Biol.* **45**, 332 (1957).
220. K.A.GAR and R.J.KIPIANI, Geneva Report 701 (1955), vol. 12, p. 185.
221. K.A.GAR, N.N.MELNIKOW, I.A.MANDELBAUM, W.I.TSCHERNEZOVA and K.D.SCHWEZOWA-SCHILOWSKAJA, *Sowjetwissenschaft (Naturwiss. Beiträge)* **1957**, 163.
222. H.E.FERNANDO, C.C.ROAN and C.W.KEARNS, *J. Econ. Entomol.* **43**, 319 (1950); **44**, 551 (1951).
223. R.W.BRAUER and R.L.PESSOTTI, *Feder. Proc.* **8**, 276 (1949); *J. Pharmacol. Exp. Therapeut.* **92**, 162 (1948); *Science* **110**, 395 (1949).
224. E.R.HART, J.H.FLEISCHER and A.S.MARRAZZI, *Feder. Proc.* **8**, 300 (1949).
225. B.J.JANDORF and P.D.MCNAMARA, *Feder. Proc.* **8**, 210 (1949); *J. Pharmacol. Exp. Therapeut.* **98**, 77 (1950).
226. H.O.MICHEL and S.KROP, *Feder. Proc.* **8**, 320 (1949).
227. J.P.VIGNE, R.L.TABAU, J.CHOUTEAU and J.FONDARAI, Paris Report 99, vol. 3, p. 45.
228. S.H.BENNETT and W.D.E.THOMAS, *Radioisotope Techniques*, London 1953, vol. 1, p. 439.
229. D.F.HEATH and M.V.LLEWELLYN, *Radioisotope Techniques*, London 1953, vol. 1, p. 445.
230. W.A.DAVID, *Nature* **166**, 72 (1950); *Ann. Appl. Biol.* **38**, 508 (1951); **39**, 203 (1952).
231. R.L.METCALF and R.B.MARCH, *J. Econ. Entomol.* **45**, 988 (1952).
232. G.S.HARTLEY and D.F.HEATH, *Nature* **167**, 816 (1951).
233. D.F.HEATH, D.W.LANE and M.LLEWELLYN, *J. Sci. Food Agric.* **3**, 60, 69 (1952).
234. G.S.HARTLEY, *Chem. & Ind.* **1954**, 529.
235. J.E.GARDINER and B.A.KILBY, *Biochem. J.* **51**, 78 (1952).
236. G.S.HARTLEY, D.F.HEATH, J.M.HULME, D.W.POUND and M.WHITTAKER, *J. Sci. Food Agric.* **2**, 303 (1951).
237. L.H.STEIN, T.ALPER and E.E.ANDERSSEN, *J. Sci. Food Agric.* **3**, 31 (1952).
238. W.THOMAS and S.H.BENNETT, *Ann. Appl. Biol.* **41**, 501 (1954).
239. G.D.JONES and W.D.THOMAS, *Ann. Appl. Biol.* **40**, 546 (1953).
240. H.TIETZ and R.MÜHLMANN, *Höfchen-Briefe* **7**, 1 (1954); **9**, 116 (1956).
241. W.DAVID and B.GARDINER, *Ann. Appl. Biol.* **43**, 594 (1955).
242. H.REYNOLDS, T.FUKUTO, R.METCALF and R.MARCH, *J. Econ. Entomol.* **50**, 527 (1957).
243. W.THOMAS, S.BENNETT and C.LLOYD JONES, *Ann. Appl. Biol.* **43**, 569 (1955).
244. R.METCALF, R.MARCH, T.FUKUTO and M.MAXON, *J. Econ. Entomol.* **47**, 1045 (1954); **48**, 364 (1955).
245. R.WEDDING, *J. Agr. Food Chem.* **1**, 832 (1953).
246. F.P.W.WINTERINGHAM, *J. Chem. Soc.* **1949** [s], 417; *Endeavour* **11**, 22 (1952).
247. F.P.W.WINTERINGHAM, *Int. J. Appl. Rad. Isot.* **1**, 57 (1956).
248. F.P.W.WINTERINGHAM, *Adv. Pest Control Res.* **2**, 57 (1960).
249. G.T.BROOKS, *Nature* **186**, 96 (1960).
250. H.H.MOOREFIELD, *Contrib. Boyce-Thompson Inst.* **19**, 403 (1958).
251. S.E.MCCALLAN and L.M.MILLER, *Adv. Pest Control Res.* **2**, 107 (1958).
252. L.P.MILLER and S.E.MCCALLAN, *J. Agr. Food Chem.* **5**, 116 (1957).
253. L.P.MILLER and S.E.MCCALLAN, Geneva Report 100 (1955), vol. 12, p. 170.
254. L.P.MILLER, S.E.MCCALLAN and R.M.WEED, *Contrib. Boyce-Thompson Inst.* **17**, 173, 299 (1953).
255. R.G.OWENS and L.P.MILLER, *Phytopathol.* **47**, 531 (1957).
256. H.C.PALMER, R.W.GREENLEE and M.M.BALDWIN, *Phytopathol.* **42**, 472 (1952).
257. G.D.MUNGER, R.W.GREENLEE and M.M.BALDWIN, *Phytopathol.* **44**, 499 (1954).
258. F.M.TURRELL and M.B.CHERVENAK, *Botan. Gaz.* **111**, 109 (1949); *Adv. in Chem. Ser.* **1**, 250 (1950).
259. H.LINSER, *Atompraxis* **3**, 169 (1957).
260. E.K.WOODFORD, K.HOLLY and C.C.MCCREADY, *Ann. Rev. Plant Physiol.* **9**, 311 (1958).
261. F.BIEBERDORF, *Chem. Eng. News.* **27**, 2858 (1949).
262. S.C.FANG and J.S.BUTTS, *Plant Physiol.* **29**, 56 (1954).
263. G.E.BLACKMAN, in: R.L.WAIN and F.WIGHTMAN (Ed.), *The Chemistry and Mode of Action of Plant Growth Substances*, London 1956.

264. J.W. MITCHELL and P.J. LINDER, *Science* **112**, 54 (1950).
265. A.S. CRAFTS, Geneva Report 111 (1955), vol. 12, p. 151.
266. R.W. HOLLEY, *Arch. Biochem. Biophys.* **35**, 171 (1952).
267. R.L. WEINTRAUB, J.W. BROWN, M. FIELDS and J. ROHAN, *Plant Physiol.* **27**, 293 (1952).
268. H.I. PETERSEN, *Nature* **182**, 1685 (1958).
269. J.W. WOOD, J.W. MITCHELL and G.W. IRVING, *Science* **105**, 337 (1947).
270. Y. RAKITIN, see [16].
271. R. CH. TURETSKAYA, *Izvest. Akad. Nauk SSSR, Biological Series*, **1954** (4), 35.
272. Y.V. RAKITIN and A.V. KRYLOV, Geneva Report 2133 (1958), vol. 27, p. 68.
273. A. KRYLOV, Y. RAKITIN and N. MELNIKOV, see [16].
274. A.M. KUZIN and V.I. TOKARSKAYA, Paris Report 126, vol. 4, p. 565.
275. J.R. LUICK, R.H. GARBER, N.B. AKESSON and L.D. LEACH, *Int. J. Appl. Rad. Isot.* **5**, 147 (1959).
276. M.B. ARAGAO, E. FROTA PESSOA and N. MARGEM, Geneva Report 140 (1955), vol. 10, p. 525.
277. L.M. COOK and H.B.D. KETTLEWELL, *Nature* **187**, 301 (1960).
278. J.A. SHEMANCHUK, J.W.T. SPINKS and F.J.H. FREDEEN, *Can. Entomol.* **85**, 269 (1953).
279. W.W. YATES, C.M. GJULLIN, A.W. LINDQUIST and J.S. BUTTS, *J. Econ. Entomol.* **44**, 34 (1951).
280. M.A. WATSON and H.L. NIXON, *Ann. Appl. Biol.* **40**, 537 (1953).
281. W.A. DAVID, *Ann. Appl. Biol.* **39**, 203 (1952).
282. H.B. KETTLEWELL, *Nature* **170**, 584 (1952).
283. F.P. WINTERINGHAM, P.M. LOVEDAY and G.C. HELLYER, *Biochem. J.* **55**, 33 (1953).
284. P.B. CORNWELL, *Nature* **175**, 85 (1955).
285. C.C. HASSETT and D.W. JENKINS, *Science* **110**, 109 (1949); *Physiol. Zool.* **24**, 257 (1951).
286. R.D. RADELEFF, R.C. BUSHLAND and D.E. HOPKINS, *J. Econ. Entomol.* **45**, 509 (1952).
287. H.B. KETTLEWELL, Geneva Report 1079 (1955), vol. 12, p. 214.
288. H.B. KETTLEWELL, *Nature* **175**, 821 (1955).
289. R.A. FULLER, P.W. RIEGERT, J.W.T. SPINKS and L.G. PUTNAM, *Can. Entomol.* **86**, 201, 223 (1954).
290. D.W. JENKINS and C.C. HASSETT, *Nucleonics* **6** (3), 5 (1950).
291. D.W. JENKINS, Geneva Report 224 (1955), vol. 10, p. 518.
292. H.E. HINTON, *Sci. Progress* **42**, 292 (1954).
293. M.A. HAMILTON, *Ann. Appl. Biol.* **22**, 243 (1935).
294. D.W. JENKINS, *J. Econ. Entomol.* **42**, 988 (1949).
295. J.C. BUGHER and M. TAYLOR, *Science* **110**, 146 (1949).
296. F.J.H. FREDEEN, J.W.T. SPINKS, J.R. ANDERSON, A.P. ARNASON and J.G. REMPEL, *Can. J. Zool.* **31**, 1 (1953).
297. G.A. TOMES and M.V. BRIAN, *Nature* **158**, 551 (1946).
298. A.P. ARNASON, R.A. FULLER and J.W.T. SPINKS, *Science* **111**, 5 (1950).
299. R.A. FULLER, J.W.T. SPINKS, A.P. ARNASON and H. McDONALD, 81st Annual Meeting Entomol. Soc. of Ontario, 1950.
300. B.C. GREEN and J.W.T. SPINKS, *Can. J. Technol.* **33**, 307 (1955).
301. W.V. HARTNELL, S.F. QUAN, K.G. SCOTT and L. KARTMAN, *Science* **127**, 814 (1958).
302. P.A. DAHM, Conference on Use of Isotopes in Plant and Animal Research, Washington 1953.
303. A.M. KUZIN, *Nauka i Zhizn* **1955** (4), 29.
304. E. OERTEL, R.B. EMERSON and H.E. WHEELER, *Ann. Entomol. Soc. Amer.* **46**, 596 (1953).
305. G.K. GODFREY, *Ecology* **35**, 5 (1954); *J. Mammal.* **34**, 504 (1954); *Nature* **174**, 951 (1954).
306. A. PUNT and P.J. VAN NIEUWENHOVEN, *Experientia* **13**, 51 (1957).
307. *Nucleonics* **18** (3), 124 (1960).
308. N.P. RUDAKOV, *Ryb. Khoz.* **1958** (9).
309. D.R. GRIFFIN, *Ecology* **33**, 329 (1952).
310. D.H. WILKINSON, *J. Exp. Biol.* **27**, 192 (1950).
311. *Radioisotopes and Ionizing Radiations in Entomology* (Bibliographies), I.A.E.A., Vienna 1963, 1965.
312. H. JONES, R.V. MARTIN and H.K. PORTER, *Ann. Bot.* **23**, 92 (1959).

313. R.W.RINNE and R.C.LANGSTON, *Plant Physiol.* **35**, 2 (1960).
314. R.SCHOENHEIMER, *The Dynamic State of Body Constituents*, Cambridge (Mass.) 1949.
315. A.M.KUZIN, *The Application of Labelled Atoms to Investigations in Agriculture* (Russ.), Moscow 1955.
316. F.C.STEWARD, J.F.THOMPSON, F.K.MILLAR, M.D.THOMAS and R.H.HENDRICKS, *Plant Physiol.* **26**, 123 (1951).
317. A.N.SVETLOVIDOV, in [315].
318. R.S.RUSSELL and D.A.BARBER, *Ann. Rev. Plant Physiol.* **11**, 127 (1960).
319. E.G.BOLLARD, *Ann. Rev. Plant Physiol.* **11**, 141 (1960).
320. W.DEDEK, *Isotopentechnik* **1**, 173 (1960).
321. W.STILES, *Science Progress* **47**, 313 (1959).
322. D.SPILLER, *Adv. Pest Control Res.*, vol. 4 (1960).
323. D.M.KHEIFETS, *Pochvovedenie* **1956** (7), 49.
324. E.SPODE and F.GENSICKE, *Isotopentechnik* **2**, 238 (1962).
325. R.S.GAGE and S.ARONOFF, *Plant Physiol.* **35**, 53 (1960).
326. O.BIDDULPH and R.CORY, *Plant Physiol.* **35**, 689 (1960).
327. W.DEDEK, F.GRIMMER and H.KOCH, *Isotopentechnik* **2**, 150 (1962).
328. W.WILBRANDT, *Int. Rev. Cytol.* **13**, 203 (1962).
329. E.BRODA, H.DESSER and G.FINDENEGG. *Naturwiss.* **51**, 361 (1964).
330. E.BRODA, G.FINDENEGG and H.DESSER, *Naturwiss.* **51**, 436 (1964); **52**, 350 (1965).
331. H.SPRINGER-LEDERER, *Österr. Chemiker-Zeitung* **65**, 1, 73 (1964).
332. J.DAINTY, *Ann. Rev. Plant Physiol.* **13**, 379 (1962).
333. M.D.KAMEN, *Primary Processes in Photosynthesis*, New York 1963.
334. See numerous progress reports in *Ann. Rev. Plant Physiol.*
335. J.F.SUTCLIFFE, *Mineral Salts Absorption in Plants*, Oxford 1962.
336. W.KÜHN, *Kerntechnik* **3**, 382 (1961).
337. E.ROUX, *Chimie et industrie* **73**, 296 (1955).
338. H.ZIEGLER, *Recent Adv. Botany* **2**, 1229 (1961).
339. H.HART, *Radioaktive Isotope in der Betriebsmeßtechnik*, Berlin 1962.
340. J.F.CAMERON, P.F.BERRY and E.W.PHILIPS, *Holzforschung* **13**, 78 (1959).
341. E.G.NIEMANN and W.SCHWEERS, *Atompraxis* **9**, 99 (1963).
342. N.J.SCULLY, W.CHORNEY, G.KOSTAL, R.WATANABE, J.SKOK and J.W.GLATTFELD, Geneva Report 274 (1955), vol. 12, p. 377.
343. J.C.BROWN, L.O.TIFFEN and R.S.HOLMES, *Plant Physiol.* **33**, 38 (1958).
344. D.S.JENKINSON, *Plant and Soil* **13**, 279 (1960).
345. A.ANDERSON, G.NIELSEN and H.SORENSEN, *Physiologia Plantarum* **14**, 378 (1961).
346. D.VON SAUERBECK, *Atompraxis* **6**, 221 (1960).
347. J.H.SMITH, F.E.ALLISON and J.F.MULLINS, *Atompraxis* **9**, 73 (1963).
348. K.KAINDL and C.CHWALA, *Atompraxis* **9**, 77 (1963).
349. *Radioisotopes in Soil-Plant Nutrition Studies*, Symposium in Bombay, I.A.E.A., Vienna 1962.
350. F.AMER, in [349].
351. B.ULRICH, H.LIN and H.KARAPARKAR, in [349].
352. H.W.SCHARPENSEEL, in [349].
353. H.B.TUKEY and H.B.TUKEY, in [349].
354. H.BROESHART, in [349].
355. D.A.RENNIE and E.D.SPRATT, in [349].
356. C.G.LAMM, in [349].
357. L.A.DEAN, in [349].
358. L.W.POEL, *Nature* **169**, 501 (1952); *J. Exptl. Bot.* **4**, 157 (1953).
359. W.HÖFNER, *Atompraxis* **9**, 82 (1964).
360. N.P.DATTA and N.N.GOSWAMI, in [349].
361. M.E.HARWARD, T.T.CHAO and S.C.FANG, in [349].
362. G.E.FRANCIS, W.MULLIGAN and A.WORMALL, *Isotopic Tracers, A Theoretical and Practical Manual for Biological Students and Research Workers*, London 1959.

363. J. F. MEAD and D. R. HOWTON, *Radioisotope Studies of Fatty Acid Metabolism*, London 1960.
364. C. CORIN, A. LECRENIER, B. KIRCHMAN, O. LIARD and M. A. PICARD, Paris Report 180, vol. 4, p. 382.
365. A. L. KURSANOV, 20th Timiryasev Lecture (Russ.), Moscow 1960; German translation, *Sowjetwissenschaft, Naturwissenschaftliche Beiträge* **1961** (9).
366. W. A. RHOADS and A. WALLACE, *Soil Science* **89**, 248 (1960).
367. A. A. BEDRI, A. WALLACE and W. A. RHOADS, *Soil Science* **89**, 257 (1960).
368. R. C. HUFFAKER, R. B. CLARK, R. T. MUELLER and A. WALLACE, *Soil Science* **89**, 264 (1960).
369. P. SIMONART and J. MAYAUDON, *Plant and Soil* **9**, 367, 376, 381 (1958).
370. R. W. BARBOUR, *Science* **141**, 41 (1963).
371. *Radioisotopes and Radiation in Entomology*, Symposium in Bombay, I.A.E.A., Vienna 1962.
372. *Radiation and Radioisotopes Applied to Insects of Agricultural Importance*, Symposium in Athens, I.A.E.A., Vienna 1963.
373. D. W. JENKINS, in [371].
374. J. E. CASIDA, in [371].
375. B. W. ARTHUR, in [371].
376. D. F. HEATH, in [371].
377. D. E. WEIDHAAS, C. H. SCHMIDT and W. F. CHAMBERLAIN, in [371].
378. T. L. HOPKINS, in [371].
379. F. P. W. WINTERINGHAM, in [371].
380. J. E. TREHERNE, in [371].
381. R. G. BRIDGES, H. D. CRONE and J. R. BEARD, in [371].
382. G. COURTOIS and J. LECOMTE, in [372].
383. K. GÖSSWALD and W. KLOFT, in [372].
384. M. S. QURAISHI, in [372].
385. P. S. ORPHANIDIS *et al.*, in [372].
386. C. E. PELEKASSIS, in [372].
387. C. T. LEWIS, in [372].
388. F. T. PHILLIPS, in [372].
389. D. L. JOFTES, in [372].
390. F. W. PLAPP and D. A. LINDQUIST, in [372].
391. D. F. HEATH, in [372].
392. T. SAITO, in [372].
393. W. DEDEK, *Atompraxis* **10**, 65 (1964).
394. See *International Atomic Energy Agency Bulletin* **5** (3), 17 (1963).
395. G. M. KUNITAKE, C. STITT and P. SALTMAN, *Plant Physiol.* **34**, 123 (1959).
396. W. A. JACKSON and N. T. COLEMAN, *Plant and Soil* **11**, 1 (1959).
397. J. S. D. GRAHAM and L. C. T. YOUNG, *Plant Physiol.* **34**, 520 (1959).
398. A. L. KURSANOV and N. I. BROVCHENKO, *Fiziol. rastenii* **8**, 270 (1961).
399. A. L. KURSANOV, *Izvest. Akad. Nauk SSSR, Ser. Biol.* **27**, 740 (1962).
400. S. MITSUI and K. KURIHARA, *Soil Sci. Plant Nutr. (Tokyo)* **8**, 219 (1962).
401. A. L. KURSANOV, *Endeavour* **20**, 19 (1961).
402. J. E. CASIDA, *Publ. Amer. Assoc. Advancement Science* **61**, 85 (1960).
403. J. E. CASIDA, *Proc. Fourth Intern. Congr. Biochem.*, Vienna 1958, vol. 12, p. 216.
404. F. P. W. WINTERINGHAM, *Proc. Fourth Intern. Congr. Biochem.*, Vienna 1958, vol. 12, p. 201.
405. A. P. VINOGRADOV, V. M. KUTYURIN, M. V. ULUBEKOVA and I. K. ZADOROZHNII, *Doklady Akad. Nauk SSSR* **125**, 1151 (1959).
406. T. E. HUMPHREYS and W. M. DUGGER, *Plant Physiol.* **34**, 112 (1959).
407. T. K. IKONENKO, *Fiziol. rastenii* **6**, 95 (1959).
408. G. V. BARINOV and E. I. RATNER, *Fiziol. rastenii* **6**, 324 (1959).
409. J. A. GASCOIGNE and P. JONES, *Nature* **183**, 819 (1959).
410. N. A. PRISTUPY, *Fiziol. rastenii* **6**, 30 (1959).
411. E. I. RATNER, T. A. AKIMOCHKINA and S. F. UKHINA, *Fiziol. rastenii* **6**, 3 (1959).
412. A. N. PAVLOV, *Fiziol. rastenii* **7**, 326 (1960).

413. R.D.O'Brien and L.S.Wolfe, *Radiation, Radioactivity and Insects*, New York 1964.
414. F.W.Woods and D.O'Neal, *Science* **147**, 148 (1965).
415. G.Zweig (Ed.), *Analytical Methods for Pesticides, Plant Growth Regulators and Food Additives*, New York 1963.
416. R.A.Schmitt, in [415].
417. G.N.Smith, in [415].
418. H.Broeshart *et al.*, Geneva Report 876 (1964).
419. V.P.Guinn and R.A.Schmitt, *Residue Reviews* **5**, 148 (1964).
420. A.C.Field, *Nature* **188**, 1205 (1960); *Brit. J. Nutr.* **15**, 349 (1961).
421. *Radioisotopes in Animal Nutrition and Physiology*, Symposium in Prague, I.A.E.A., Vienna 1965.

12. APPLICATION OF RADIOACTIVITY
IN HYDROLOGY AND WATER SUPPLY

12.1. Determination of Water Quality

In the analysis of water for industrial and domestic use, various nuclear methods (see Section 6.4) have been used [162]. The chloride content may be determined by titration with silver-110, and the sulphate content, after addition of traces of radioactive sulphate, by titration with barium [2]. Activation analysis has been carried out on drinking water by irradiation of 30 ml in a reactor for 16 hr, chemical separation into groups of elements and γ-spectrometry with a scintillation counter [3].

The removal of organic impurities from water by active charcoal has been tested with radioactive phenol as a model substance [4]. The fate of synthetic detergents (^{35}S) in the activated sludge process has been followed [5]. A technique for the rapid radiometric detection of contamination of water by microorganisms has already been referred to (p. 259).

12.2. Preparation and Measurement of Labelled Water

Numerous reviews and monographs [93, 111, 140, 157, 160, 162] on the applications of radioactive tracers to problems in hydrology as well as reports on relevant meetings [45, 91, 155, 156] are available.

Natural water courses may be traced by radiometric methods, and changes in such courses as a consequence of human intervention may be followed. The determination of underground connections between water courses, the estimate of the volume of underground reservoirs, and the measurement of the rate of water penetration from one course to another are important problems in hydrology [113]. Dyestuffs such as fluorescein have been used in such work, but radioactive substances are now increasingly employed. This work is of special importance for hot, arid countries; the problems under such conditions have been discussed in detail [6, 100]. The techniques are also important for karst regions [105].

Radioactively labelled water may be detected with great sensitivity. The measurement is simple and usually rapid. Moreover, the radioactive label is not destroyed in chemical processes. Hence radioactive tracer methods are applicable to city effluent, which is dark in colour and contains aggressive microorganisms. Yet they are not to be considered as a panacea. Recently attempts have been made to evaluate their possibilities in hydrology from a general point of view [100–102].

When radioactive substances are employed in hydrology, a number of sources of error must be taken into consideration. They include hydrolysis of the radioactive substance with subsequent precipitation, and adsorption of the substance by rock and soil. Such adsorption is particularly evident for cations, because they are taken up by exchange by many kinds of minerals in the soil, including clay (see p. 277). That dissolved materials often move much more slowly through soil than the water, or that they are irreversibly retained by soil, can be demonstrated quite simply. The solution is made to flow through a column of soil. The elution curve for any given column then depends strongly on the nature of the dissolved radioactive substance [7, 8, 61, 92]. Fluorescein also is only partially recovered during elution, and "tailing" is observed [7, 8].

In general, anions, such as bromide (^{82}Br) [8, 11, 77, 92, 95, 106] or iodide (^{131}I) [1, 8, 9, 12, 13, 61, 90, 95, 99] (see also p. 148) — but not phosphate (^{32}P) [80, 97] — are more suitable than cations. Though the half-lives happen to be rather short, such tracers are preferred.

When normally cationic radionuclides are present in the form of anionic complexes, losses due to adsorption are strongly reduced; complexes of cobalt with cyanide [9, 77], and of cobalt, chromium, scandium or antimony with ethylenediaminetetraacetic acid (EDTA) [10, 29, 61, 92] have been found suitable as tracers for water.

Being chemically identical with hydrogen (isotope effects should be insignificant in these applications), tritium is the ideal tracer for water [45, 61, 77, 92] (see also p. 303). Errors due to adsorption or ion exchange cannot occur. Moreover, tritium is cheap and relatively harmless. In connection with work on the size of ground water reservoirs and the direction and speed of ground water flow, the packaging and injection methods for large amounts of tritium have been discussed [84, 105].

However, tritium also has its difficulties. First, the β-radiation of tritium is so soft that windowless counters, gas counters or liquid-scintillation counters are needed for measurement ([45], see also p. 51). Measurement in the field is therefore hardly possible, so that in some field work tritium has been used in conjunction with a secondary tracer, namely, chromium-51 as the EDTA complex; the secondary tracer has been shown to behave like tritium at least in sand and gravel strata [92].

Secondly, tritium – unlike dissolved radioactive tracers – cannot be separated from water for measurement by chemical methods. Only gradual enrichment (involving separation of isotopes) is possible, as by electrolysis [122, 134] or gas chromatography [171], but the procedures are complicated and expensive. Furthermore, the actual degree of enrichment in each arrangement must be determined separately, since it depends on various factors.

The various methods of labelling water have been compared [15, 61, 93] (see also tests for water-proofness, Section 9.3.6). Of course, in the addition of radioactive substances to water courses serving populated areas permissible limits must not be exceeded.

For the measurement of dissolved tracers, Geiger or scintillation counters may be used. Samples may be taken from the water, but wherever possible it is more convenient to dip the detector into the water. For such direct measurements, the use of ratemeters is advisable [16].

Equations have been given for the calculation of the count rates to be expected when a detector is immersed in an infinitely large volume of liquid, containing a β- or a γ-ray emitter [17]. In practice, γ-emitters are preferred. In the first place, measuring equipment for γ-radiation is more robust than for β-radiation. Secondly, high measuring yields for γ-radiation are obtained with scintillation counters or batteries of Geiger counters, and since the γ-radiation from a large volume acts on the counters, the count rates are high [16, 18] (see Section 9.3.4).

It is noteworthy that the background count rate above water, and especially within water, is low. In a case reported in Sweden, the background with a scintillation counter amounted to 1500 counts per min on land, to 100 per min over a lake, and only to 40 per min at a depth of 1 m. In salt water the background is a little higher [16, 28]. In measurements on land, particularly close to the ground, the background count rate is strongly influenced by the content of radionuclides in the soil.

The maximum amount of radioactive substance to be used in a particular experiment will depend on the cost and on the radiation hazards involved; hazards both to the operating personnel and to the general public have to be considered. In certain cases, work with 20 c of a γ-emitting substance (bromine-82) — sufficient to label 300 million m^3 — has been possible [16]. In another investigation, 1000 c of tritium were employed [105].

For measurement of samples, the tracers may be concentrated. Thus radioactive iodide may be precipitated with silver ions; chloride is used as a carrier and then redissolved with ammonia [14]. Ion exchange resins may also be used for concentration, as in the case of sodium-24 [107].

12.3. Tracing of Water

To assist engineers in the design of a method for the extraction of drinking water from an underground pool, semi-tidal and partly saline, the volume of the pool was established by a dilution technique with iodine-131, and the fresh-water throughput also estimated [99].

The time of retention and the route of passage in settling tanks has been determined with sodium-24, bromine-82, rubidium-86 or iodine-131 [12, 19–25, 27, 28]. The danger of loss of ions through adsorption is smaller in such cases than in the tracing of streams, but may nevertheless be appreciable, especially when the water passes through filters and similar devices.

In the well-known circular settling tanks with radial flow, activity measurements at several of the exits on the outer edge have been used to check the uniformity of passage of water through the tank. A single injection of radioactive substance into the entry pipe has been followed by measurement of activity over a certain period at the exit points (Fig. 38). If only the activity in the combined outflow is measured, very uneven flow in the settling tank, which must involve fast currents in parts of the basin, is detected by rapid appearance of activity in the outflow, i.e, activity is found long before the passage of a volume of liquid corresponding to the capacity of the tank (see p. 221). A short retention time reduces the likelihood of self-purification of the water, so that suitable constructional changes must be carried out to remedy this situation [16, 21, 23, 25, 27, 28]. In laboratory investigations, the retention time of water in filter units has been measured. The units contained a coarse material, such as stones, etc., covered with a slimy layer of microorganisms. Excessive adsorption of sodium-24, potassium-42 and rubidium-86 was found, but satisfactory results were obtained with bromine-82 (bromide), cobalt-60 (cyanide complex) and tritium [77].

Work on the flow of waste water has been carried out on reservoirs and lakes [21], rivers [109] and the ocean [16, 143], into which effluent is introduced. In one instance, where the effluent passed through a reservoir, the depth to which the current reached was found to depend on the temperature [21]. In stationary waters, such as lakes and fjords [16] or pools [28], the influence of the wind is important.

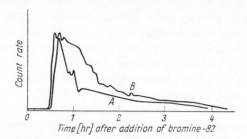

FIG. 38. Flow of a radioelement through a settling tank [21].
Bromine-82 was injected into the entry. The diagram shows the activity in the outlet of the tank.
A and *B* represent curves obtained on two different days

Momentary or continuous addition of a tracer makes it possible to map he flow and to determine the dilution of waste water in existing or planned outlets [86]. Waste water from cellulose factories has been followed with ammonium bromide (^{82}Br). Using an activity of 1 c the water flow in receivers with a volume of 100 million m^3 may be studied [16, 86]. The concentrations of the waste which would result at a steady state with a continuous discharge can be determined at various points around an outlet by integrating the measured data from a momentary activity introduction [87] or by means of a continuous addition of tracer solution during a time sufficient to reach the steady state in the zone under study. This latter method was used to measure the dilution for the wastes from a large sulphate cellulose mill [86]. The waste water was collected in a large pipe which took it to a point 5 km from the coast. The last kilometer of the pipe was perforated. 2·4 c of ammonium bromide were injected into the waste water during 2 hr, and dilutions as high as 1:10000 could be determined in the receiver. In a similar way, the steady state activity at a planned outlet for low-activity wastes from a reactor was estimated [86].

The dilution method (p. 220) is well suited for open water courses where the cross-section of flow cannot be determined easily [88]. With this method flow rates of waste water up to 4 m^3/sec have been determined from cellulose plants, and flow rates up to 100 m^3/sec for water in a hydroelectric power plant [86, 89].

In Australia, where water is scarce in many parts, mixing in open cooling ponds at power stations has been studied. Radioiodine was added to the water flowing from the plant into the pool, and its distribution was then determined as a function of time. Fluorescein was added at the same time to give a rough indication of the distribution so that samples for activity measurement could be selected most effectively. Great un-evenness of mixing ("channel formation") was observed, indicating inefficient cooling of the water. The results depended greatly on the location and depth of the pipe used to return the water to the power station, but they were also found to depend on natural conditions (air temperature and wind strength) [28].

An example of the use of a radioactive tracer (in this case iodide) for detection of a connection between two water courses is an investigation of the passage of water be-tween an alpine stream and an artificial tunnel [8]. Water seeping through reservoirs or from canals has also been detected by tracer techniques [21, 46, 104], and the ef-ficiency of a barrier of continuously injected saturated calcium hydroxide solution under a dam construction (designed to prevent leakage water containing carbon di-oxide from attacking rock containing soluble calcite) was tested [86].

The usefulness of iodine-131 as a tracer in hydrogeological research in connection with lignite mining has been discussed, and the conclusion has been reached that the radioactive tracer is to be preferred to fluorescein [90]. Iodine-131 and sulphur-35 (as sulphate) have been applied in extensive work on the structural parameters of peat and the water movements in peaty soils. A classification of peat strata has been carried out on the basis of this work, and more effective methods for draining such soils have been proposed [133]. It was found that a large part of the water in peat beds takes little part in flow processes [30–33]. Ground water aquifers were studied with iodine-131 [164, 172], the methods being similar to those described on p. 148, and also by in-troducing radioactive level gauges into wells [173].

Permeable strata or seams in a calcareous marl series, intended to support quay walls in a harbour basin, were tested with bromine-82. The tracer, after being forced into the formation by inactive water, was pumped back, and then local and overall measurements of activity permitted estimation of the recovered fraction and precise localization of the zones with appreciable backflow [106].

Studies with tritium labelling have been carried out to follow karst water in Greece [105], to detect the sources of water penetrating into a mine [141] and to observe water movement in lakes [84] (see also pp. 149 and 306).

Equipment for obtaining data on deep water currents has been constructed. A radionuclide is first ejected from the probe, and some time later the distribution of the active substance is observed with suitable radiation detectors [144]. This technique is similar to that for the measurement of horizontal ground water flow (p. 305).

So far in this section we have regarded the adsorption of dissolved radioactive sub-stances as a disturbing factor. In contrast, in tests on irrigation trenches in sugar plantations on Hawaii the adsorption of the radioelement by soil served a useful pur-pose [58]. Small quantities of radiorubidium were added to the water entering the ir-rigation trenches, giving an activity of 3 mc per 100 m of trench length. At a number of places along the trench, several layers of a coarse-meshed fabric had been laid before the beginning of the experiment. At these places, small samples of water were removed during the inflow and seeping-in of the water. The samples taken at a particular site at various times were combined to give an average sample. After the soil had taken up the water supplied, the fabric was removed and samples were taken from the soil im-mediately beneath, namely from a depth of 2·5 cm. Because of the strong adsorption of rubidium, these samples contained all the radiorubidium present in the water which had seeped into the soil. On the basis of suitable calibration measurements, the ratio of the activity of the soil sample and the water sample was calculated, and the amount of water seeping in at the site in question was obtained. The purpose of the fabric at the sampling sites was to prevent uptake of radioelement from water only flowing over the site but not seeping in. As expected, these studies showed that the water uptake varied greatly along the course of a trench. This is undesirable, since enough water (and any fertilizer dissolved in the water) should reach also places of lesser uptake. To accomplish this, the more favoured sites must receive an over-supply, which involves waste.

The evaporation of water from drops, as in spraying fields, may be estimated by dissolving a small amount of radiophosphorus in the water and comparing its concentration in the solution as prepared and in that collected after spraying [33].

12.4. Flow Velocity in Water Courses

A value for the flow rate in a pressure pipe carrying sludge has been obtained by introducing a γ-active radionuclide held by a piece of sponge rubber about the size of a cherry stone. When this passed the measuring instrument, a sharply defined activity peak was obtained [21]. However, the velocity obtained from such a measurement does not represent the average velocity of the water, since it depends on the distance from the axis of the pipe. In order to determine the velocity of the water itself, and therefore the throughput, various tracer methods have been recommended. These have already been mentioned in Section 9.3.4, and may also be used with natural water courses [97, 98].

The total count method, already described in that section, has been applied both to natural water courses and to canals (see also [83, 97, 108]). In some cases, it is an advantage to insert the radiation detector directly into the stream (*in situ* dip counting) and to calibrate by taking a single instantaneous sample from the flowing water. This sample is then compared with a suitably diluted fraction of the injected tracer solution. This is done by means of counting equipment with well-defined geometry [147].

A procedure worked out for natural water courses [1, 14] is similar to the total count method in that a single portion of radioactive substance is injected and the radioelement detected at a single location downstream. However, instead of registering a total count with a radiation detector immersed into the flowing liquid, samples are taken at regular intervals throughout the time the radioelement flows past, and the radioelement concentration in these samples is then determined. From such a series of measurements, the time integral of the radioelement concentration can then be obtained, e. g., by graphical means. This quantity has, for instance, the dimension $c \cdot l^{-1} \cdot min$. This is evaluated on the basis of the expression

$$Q = A/C,$$

where Q is the water flow per unit time (l. min^{-1}), A the total quantity of radioactive substance injected into the water (c), and C the time integral of the radioelement concentration (c · l^{-1} · min). As in the total count method, the point of sampling has to be chosen far enough downstream for transverse mixing to be complete.

For constant water throughput all along the stream, C has the same value whatever the point of measurement. However, if additional water flows into the stream, C decreases in inverse ratio to the total water flow. If water is lost, C does not change, but Q and A decrease in the same ratio. A loss of water can therefore be determined by repeating the experiment, with injection and measurement, downstream from the stretch of the original test. When the same quantity A of radioactive tracer is again introduced, and the integral value C' is obtained from the measurements, we have now for the water flow Q' at this point:

$$Q' = A/C'.$$

If the experiment is suitably arranged, inflow and loss within the same stretch may both be determined.

Radioactive iodide has generally been used as a tracer for such studies. High detection sensitivity is obtained by precipitating the iodide after sampling as the silver salt, and measuring the activity of this precipitate after filtration. A detailed description of this method of flow measurement has been given, and the advantages and drawbacks of measurement after sampling just described and of direct measurement of the activity in the flowing water (total count method) have been discussed [1]. The calculation of maximum allowable radiotracer injections for flow-rate measurements in public streams has been outlined [154].

A problem which was formerly difficult to solve is the measurement of horizontal ground water flow. The important quantities are the rate of flow and the porosity of the medium; the product of these two quantities, both of which are difficult to determine, gives the amount of water transported in unit time through unit cross-section. Recently it has become possible to determine this product relatively easily. A plastic tube several metres long with vertical slits is inserted into the ground and is filled with a solution of a suitable tracer, e.g., iodide. At intervals of time, a γ-sensitive counter is used to determine the residual activity. Experiments have shown that the water flowing into the pipe at a given height mixes uniformly with the residue of the active solution. The decrease in tracer concentration at the point of measurement will thus follow an exponential law. In the evaluation of the experiments, an extended background must be used to take care of the fact that a certain amount of the iodide is retained close to the tube, and thus contributes to the radiation intensity. It is possible to measure the fall in activity with time at various heights of the same tube in a single experiment by moving the counter up and down. Results are evaluated on the assumption that no significant vertical mixing occurs. In a field experiment, the velocity of an underground stream was determined: referred to the total cross-section of the tube, i.e., to a porosity of 100 per cent, a value of 10 m/day was found [35] (see also [90, 98, 104]). Attempts have been made to extend the method to the vertical components of ground water flow [104]. Measurements on laboratory model set-ups have been employed in the development of such methods (see, for example, [142]).

This method has also been applied to follow water movement in rock at a reactor site to test the efficiency of the drainage system. Ammonium bromide (containing ^{82}Br) was introduced into the rock at different places in a series of tests, and the activity of the drainage system determined. It was possible to find the extent of the drainage zone for the system and also the porosity of the rock in the vicinity of the injection holes [86].

A modification [96] provides for a directional measuring instrument, which can be rotated round its axis, and for a tracer which is strongly held back by the soil. The direction of flow can then be found with a single instrument from the direction of maximum radiation intensity.

The rate of movement of ice in a tunnel in Greenland was measured by inserting a rod into a vertical boring in the ice wall. At the other end of the rod, a weak radio-active source was attached. This source was pressed against a photographic film, which was fixed to the rock base of the tunnel. As the source moved with the ice, a track was produced on the photographic film [34].

The rapid changes in a river bed during a flood have been followed by the back-scattering of γ-rays from cobalt-60 or caesium-137. The counting rate increased as the probe containing a Geiger counter approached the bed, the density of the gravel being twice that of water [103].

12.5. Hydrological Methods Based on Natural Tracers

The natural tritium content of water is of significance for hydrological studies. With isotope enrichment by electrolysis and sensitive measuring methods, it is possible to detect as little as one tritium atom in 10^{19} atoms of ordinary hydrogen; the tritium content of natural water is often of the order of magnitude of $1:10^{18}$ [37, 40, 45]. The tritium is produced in nature by the action of cosmic rays on the upper atmosphere. The tritium formed in nuclear processes is converted into water vapour either immediately or with some delay, and the tritium thus comes down with the rain. It should be noted that the natural tritium content of water sets a lower limit to the concentration of tritium that may be detected in experiments with labelled water.

Interesting conclusions can be drawn from the natural tritium content of water [37–43, 47, 48, 82, 145, 146, 148]. In water which is very old compared with the half-life of tritium (12·3 years) because it has not been in contact with the atmosphere for a long period, the activity has been reduced strongly by decay. This fact has been used to date waters.

The age (storage time) of seepage water, well water, ground water, etc., has been determined by this method. No tritium could be detected in the hot steam from Lardarello (Italy), which confirmed the hypothesis that this water is juvenile. On the other hand, the water of many wells contains as much tritium as the local rain water, indicating that it is made up mainly of recent rain water. It is also possible to determine the age of agricultural products such as wines, though satisfactory results are obtained only if the age does not exceed about 50 years [40].

If the average natural tritium content of rain in a given district and also the average activity of the water in a lake located there is known, and the lake is fed only by rain and run-off, and not by old water, the mean retention time of the water in the lake may be computed on the basis of the half-life of tritium. If the amount of water flowing into the lake (from both rain and streams) is also known, the capacity of the lake can be estimated. Similar calculations are feasible for underground water deposits.

The situation for all such work has changed completely since 1954. Enormous amounts of tritium have been introduced into the atmosphere by test explosions of thermonuclear weapons [123]. Some kinds of investigations are now very complicated or quite impossible. On the other hand, observation of the activity peaks arising in water samples of various origins after the explosions has provided information on the direction and the rate of movement of water masses, and so on geophysical problems. It is possible to examine the water balance of the continents, the supplies of ground water, and the rate of mixing of bodies of water, such as the oceans, although the inter-pretation of the data may often be difficult [112, 113].

The detection of a comparatively high tritium activity in the surface layers of oceans has confirmed the view held on other grounds that layers below 50 or 100 m undergo only slow exchange with the surface layers of the oceans.

The tritium content of rain water gives information about the movement of air masses. Interpretation is based on the fact that the tritium content increases with the time of residence of the air mass, from which the rain clouds form, over land. The tritium content of sea water — even that of the relatively tritium-rich surface layers — is much smaller than that of land water. Thus the activity of rain water may serve as a criterion whether the water has entered the atmosphere through evaporation of sea water or of land water.

The exchange of tritium-containing water between air and falling drops of various size, between air and the surface of bodies of water, and between water and soil minerals, has been thoroughly investigated [41].

The radioactivity of carbon dissolved in water may also be applied to the investiga-tion of circulation. Use is made of the radiocarbon formed in the interaction of cosmic ray neutrons with nitrogen according to $^{14}N(n, p)\ ^{14}C$; much more radio-carbon than tritium is produced [44, 78, 81, 82, 163]. The time needed for radiocarbon present in the atmosphere to reach the deeper layers of the oceans has been found not to be negligible compared with the half-life of the substance (5760 years), i.e., the radiocarbon decays to an appreciable extent before it reaches the depths [36, 112, 114, 163]. In the oceans, the carbon is present mainly in the form of dissolved bicarbonate.

Age determinations by the radiocarbon method are of practical importance in the evaluation of ground water lakes in arid countries [119–121]. These water reservoirs can support extensive irrigation systems only if the water is replenished sufficiently quickly by the inflow of rain water, which may fall at a considerable distance. If re-plenishment is fairly rapid, the radiocarbon content of the dissolved bicarbonate will be considerable. Possible sources of error in such work are exchange with inactive soil carbonates or dilution by such carbonates if they are dissolved by the water. Attempts have also been made to determine ground water flow velocities from the ^{14}C activities observed at various positions within a certain ground water layer [153].

The source of saline water contaminating ground water in a coastal region has been determined on the basis of ^{14}C measurements. Since the contaminated water showed activities lower than those of related fresh water, it could be concluded that the salt is brought in by water from underlying saline ground water layers also having low ^{14}C contents, and not from the ocean, which has higher ^{14}C contents than the fresh water [152].

Investigations of some long-term processes may be carried out with beryllium-10 (half-life 2·5 million years), which is also produced by the action of cosmic radiation. After adsorption on colloidal particles, the beryllium sinks to the bottom of the sea. Thus the age of sediments may be determined through the beryllium-10 activity of drill cores taken from the ocean bottom [54, 81]. Other naturally occurring radionuclides suitable to establish time scales of natural phenomena include beryllium-7 and chlorine-36 [81].

The possibilities for tracing the movements of air masses, a central problem in meteorology and analogous to the hydrological problems discussed in this section, can only be mentioned here (see, e.g. [81, 82, 110, 115, 116, 118]). Naturally formed radioelements, including the natural radioelements as such and radioelements formed in the atmosphere by cosmic rays, as well as radioelements produced in nuclear test explosions or released from nuclear energy installations have been utilized for such studies. In a few cases elements, e.g., tungsten, were specially added to nuclear explosive devices so that the neutrons would activate these substances. Large amounts of suitable radionuclides were then produced, and their spread could be followed by activity measurements. The active substances of these various kinds may be present in molecular dispersion or as aerosols. The aerosol is gradually deposited as fall-out [110, 116, 117]. The mechanisms of dry and wet removal of fall-out from the atmosphere have been studied [110].

12.6. Productivity of Waters

Radiocarbon may be used to determine the production of phytoplankton per unit volume and unit time in fresh or salt water. The plankton suspension is exposed in presence of radioactive carbon dioxide to light of such intensity that the photosynthetic assimilation of carbon reaches its maximum value. After a time, the plankton is filtered off, and its radioactivity is measured [26, 49–55, 79, 139]. It must be noted that plankton releases inactive carbon by respiration simultaneously with the uptake of labelled carbon. The inactive carbon released is reassimilated preferentially. Thus the values for photosynthetic uptake, as obtained by activity measurements, tend to be too low. The required correction, which is obtained by special experiments, may amount to a few per cent [79].

The production of organic matter (primary plankton production) in a stationary body of water may be determined as a function of depth. Water samples from various depths are taken, and labelled bicarbonate is added. The samples are placed in glass flasks, which are then lowered to the original depth. They are kept there for a certain time, and then the activity of the plankton is measured as described. When the measurements are to be carried out on a ship, it is convenient to determine the uptake of radiocarbon by the plankton on board. In this case, temperature and illumination must be adjusted so that they correspond to the depth from which the samples came [79].

The phosphate carried into inland lakes is often available for plant growth only to a small extent, since it may form insoluble compounds and sink to lower depths where productivity is small. This process has been studied by adding radioactive phosphate to the lakes, and following its fate by measurements of activity [56]. The possibility of making such phosphate available again by stirring up the bottom layers by means of compressed air has been tested, and it has been concluded that under certain circumstances the cost might not be excessive [57].

12.7. **Movement of Sand and Gravel**

Much work on sand movement at sea coasts and in estuaries has been carried out with labelled sand. The grains carrying the radioelement should be similar to the sand in size distribution and chemical properties; for a detailed discussion of this point see [134]. The radioactive material should also be cheap and should not present a health hazard.

Thus use has been made of quartz sand, activated in a reactor. The activity was mainly due to the formation of phosphorus-32 on irradiation. As little as one active sand grain in 100,000 ordinary grains could be detected autoradiographically [72, 74]. In another case, a glass with a special composition to give suitable radionuclides and to match the sand in density was activated [134].

No reactor is required when the radionuclide is added to the glass melt. Chromium-51 [73], zinc-65 [71] and scandium-46 (see p. 310) have been used, but in the preparation of the material careful measures for radiation protection are needed.

Some other methods involve surface treatment of the sand. The density and shape of the active grains is then identical with those of the sand. For instance, sand has been stirred into barium-140 solution and subsequently baked. The daughter nuclide lanthanum-140 – which emits penetrating, and dangerous, γ-radiation – reaches saturation only after several days, provided it had been removed before the treatment of the sand [75]. Sand has also been wetted with a solution of silver-110, and then submitted to reducing treatment. The sensitivity of detection is much improved if the silver is dissolved off the sand before measurement, and then concentrated by a suitable chemical technique [76]. Gold-198 may be deposited, with a minimum of handling, on silver-coated sand [125]. Further methods for labelling sand with chromium-51 and gold-198 have been described [149–151]. A general disadvantage of labelling by adsorption or formation of surface layers consists in the fact that activity and radiation intensity are then not a direct measure of the amount (mass) of sand; the radiation emitted by unit mass is greater for the smaller grains.

Investigations on sand movements may be carried out to obtain data for the construction of harbour installations and protective walls against erosion, and also for the dredging of channels. In all this work, basically the same simple method is used. A sample of labelled sand is released near the bottom of the sea or stream, and its spread or transport is then followed by activity measurements.

On the Japanese island of Hokkaido an investigation was carried out to obtain data for planning the harbour at Tomakomei. Glass containing zinc-65 was used. The position of the sand could be determined over a period of 6 weeks with scintillation counters lowered to the sea bottom [71].

A container somewhat like a butter churn was used to release glass powder labelled with 28 c scandium-46 on the bottom of the Thames estuary. The glass powder had previously been ground to a particle size distribution approximately corresponding to that of the sludge at the river bed. The successful opening of the vessel was indicated by multi-coloured table tennis balls, which floated to the surface. Although the release took place at high tide, and the labelled sand was first moved 10 km downstream, some radioactivity was detected two weeks later 25 km upstream from the point of release. This transport was due to currents in deep water layers. In this way, the observation has been explained that in the dredging of the Thames estuary much more material must be removed than comes down the river [69, 70, 80]. Glass containing scandium-46 has also been used in the river Elbe [128], and in further studies sand labelled with scandium-46 was traced along a seashore by means of submerged detectors suspended from a helicopter [158]. Tracing of the movement of sediments may also be carried out with a limited number of radioactive grains detected singly [161].

Pebbles must be labelled in a durable way if their movement on the bottom of the sea is to be followed. Somewhat laboriously, γ-ray emitters can be introduced into holes specially drilled and then sealed with plastic material. Barium-140 is useful for the purpose. Detection of the stones is possible even when they are buried on the sea bottom by 10–15 cm of sediment [80].

12.8. Water Content of Soils

Knowledge of the moisture content of soils is important in agriculture, in the examination of soils intended to support buildings etc. [128], and can be obtained by measurement of the slowing-down of neutrons [59–66, 129, 131, 135–137, 157, 164–170] (see Sections 6.7.1, 6.7.2 and 10.5). The method has the advantage of being non-destructive, and can also be used to follow continuously changes in moisture contents. However, the slow neutron flux and therefore the counting rate depend to a considerable extent on further parameters, including density and composition of the soil. Therefore much attention has been paid to questions of calibration and to the establishment of empirical relationships between the parameters mentioned and counting rate at a given water content of the soil.

When sensitive equipment is used, a source strength of a few millicuries is sufficient, so that little shielding is needed and the weight of the equipment is not excessive. From this point of view it is best to use sources which emit only little γ-radiation. It has recently been reported that the dependence of counting rate on soil moisture, and therefore sensitivity, can be improved by surrounding the source with a thin hydrogen-containing layer [136, 137].

The flux of the slow neutrons is usually measured with boron chambers (p. 101). (For construction of instruments see [126, 132, 135, 138, 159]). Boron- or lithium-loaded scintillators have also been suggested (p. 101) [127]. Further detectors consist of Geiger counters with covers made of elements with high capture cross-sections for slow neutrons where the capture γ-radiation emitted is registered (p. 101); no complicated electronic circuits are needed, but the neutron source must be relatively strong and must not emit many γ-rays (see, for example, [67, 157]). When samples are taken from the soil, the moisture may also be estimated through the attenuation of a beam of thermal neutrons [68].

Elements strongly absorbing slow neutrons, such as boron, chlorine and the rare earth elements, interfere in all slow neutron methods (see p. 102) [134]. It should also be noted that soil may contain hydrogen not only in the form of water, but also in other forms ("structural hydrogen") [134].

The determination of the thickness of layers of snow and of the density of soils, and control of suction dredges, by γ-absorptiometry will be described in Volume 2.

References to Chapter 12

1. H. MOSER and W. RAUERT, *Atomkernenergie* **5**, 419, 462 (1960).
2. D. W. MOELLER, J. G. TERRILL and M. S. SEAL, Geneva Report 233 (1955), vol. 15, p. 49.
3. R. L. BLANCHARD, G. W. LEDDICOTTE and D. W. MOELLER, Geneva Report 796 (1958), vol. 28, p. 511; *J. Amer. Waterworks Ass.* **51**, 967 (1959).
4. A. S. GOLDIN, R. C. KRONER, A. A. ROSEN and M. B. ETTINGER, Geneva Report 232 (1955), vol. 15, p. 47.
5. R. HOUSE and B. A. FRIES, *Sewage and Industrial Wastes* **28**, 492 (1956).
6. E. HALEVY and A. NIR, Geneva Report 1614 (1958), vol. 20, p. 162.
7. J. GUÉRON, *Nucleonics* **9** (5), 53 (1951).
8. J. GUÉRON, *J. phys. radium* **15**, 65A (1954).
9. E. HALEVY, A. NIR, Y. HARPAZ and S. MANDEL, Geneva Report 1613 (1958), vol. 20, p. 158.
10. W. J. LACEY and W. DE LAGUNA, *Science* **124**, 402 (1956).
11. C. P. STRAUB and G. R. HAGEE, *J. Amer. Waterworks Ass.* **49**, 743 (1957).
12. R. S. ARCHIBALD, *J. Boston Soc. Civil Engrs.* **37**, 49 (1950).
13. E. C. TSIVOGLOU, D. A. PECSOK and R. F. VALENTINE, *Sewage and Industrial Wastes* **28**, 1211 (1956).
14. H. MOSER and F. NEUMAIER, *Atomkernenergie* **2**, 26 (1957).
15. W. J. KAUFMANN and G. T. ORLOB, *J. Amer. Waterworks Ass.* **48**, 559 (1956).
16. K. LJUNGGREN, L. G. ERWALL, J. RENNERFELT and T. WESTERMARK, *Int. J. Appl. Rad. Isot.* **5**, 204 (1959).
17. G. ANIANSSON and L. G. ERWALL, *Int. J. Appl. Rad. Isot.* **2**, 166 (1957).
18. D. E. HULL, *Int. J. Appl. Rad. Isot.* **7**, 260 (1960).
19. A. MONTENS, *Angew. Chem.* **66**, 107 (1954).
20. A. MONTENS, Radioisotope Conference 1954, London 1954, vol. 2, p. 169.
21. A. MONTENS, *Atompraxis* **1**, 2 (1955); **5**, 91, 182 (1959).
22. E. SONS, *Atompraxis* **3**, 306 (1957).
23. E. KNOP, *Wasserwirtsch.* **41**, 117 (1950).
24. G. MÜLLER-NEUHAUS, *Wasserwirtsch.* **43**, 7 (1952).
25. G. A. TRUESDALE, *Atomics* **5**, 304 (1954).
26. YU. I. SOROKIN, *Fiziol. Rastenii* **6**, 118 (1959).
27. H. A. THOMAS and R. S. ARCHIBALD, *Trans. Amer. Soc. Civil Engrs.* **117**, 839 (1952).
28. J. N. GREGORY, Copenhagen Report 54, vol. 1, p. 415.
29. E. I. GOODMAN, *Ind. Eng. Chem.* **50**, 210 (1958).
30. M. P. VOLAROVICH, N. V. CHURAEV and B. YA. MINKOV, in: All-union Conference on the Application of Radioactive Isotopes and Nuclear Radiations (Russ.), Moscow 1957.

31. M.P.VOLAROVICH, *Tekstil. Prom.* **1957** (7).
32. N.V.CHURAEV, *Nauchn. Dokl. Vysshei Shkoly, Gorn. Delo* **1959** (1), 21.
33. Scientific Conference on the Application of Radioactive Isotopes and Radiations in the Agri-culture of the USSR, Moscow 1958; *Atomnaya Energiya* **5**, 8 (1958); *Kernenergie* **2**, 406 (1959).
34. *Nucleonics* **18** (3), 125 (1960).
35. H.MOSER, F.NEUMAIER and W.RAUERT, *Atomkernenergie* **2**, 225 (1957).
36. J.C.SWALLOW, *Science Progress* **49**, 283 (1961).
37. H.v.BUTTLAR and I.WENDT, Geneva Report 1954 (1958); vol. 18, p. 591.
38. S.KAUFMANN and W.F.LIBBY, *Phys. Rev.* **93**, 1337 (1954).
39. H.v.BUTTLAR and W.F.LIBBY, *J. Inorg. Nucl. Chem.* **1**, 75 (1955).
40. W.F.LIBBY, *Z. Elektrochem.* **58**, 574 (1954).
41. B.BOLIN, Geneva Report 176 (1958), vol. 18, p. 336.
42. F.BEGEMANN and W.F.LIBBY, Paris Report 221, vol.2, p. 634; *Geochim. Cosmochim. Acta* **12**, 277 (1957).
43. F.BEGEMANN, Geneva Report 1963 (1958), vol. 18, p. 545.
44. H.CRAIG, Geneva Report 1979 (1958), vol. 18, p. 358.
45. *Tritium in the Physical and Biological Sciences*, Symposium in Vienna, I.A.E.A., Vienna 1961.
46. W.J.KAUFMANN and D.K.TODD, in [45].
47. A.E.BAINBRIDGE and B.J.O'BRIEN, in [45].
48. J.R.GAT, U.KARFUNKEL and A.NIR, in [45].
49. E.STEEMANN NIELSEN, *J. Cons. Int. Explor. Mer* **18**, 117 (1952).
50. W.RODHE, *Rappt. cons. explor. mer* **144**, 122 (1958).
51. Y.MIYAKE, Paris Report 138, vol. 4, p. 65.
52. H.JITTS and H.ROTSCHI, Paris Report 139, vol. 4, p. 607.
53. YU.I.SOROKIN, Paris Report 140, vol. 4, p. 633.
54. J.R.MERRILL, M.HONDA and J.R.ARNOLD, Geneva Report 412 (1958), vol. 2, p. 251.
55. J.H.STEELE, *J. Marine Biol. Assoc. United Kingdom* **36**, 233 (1957).
56. V.I.SHADIN, A.G.RODINA and A.S.TROSHIN, in: All-union Conference on the Application of Radioactive Isotopes and Nuclear Radiations (Russ.), Moscow 1957.
57. A.D.HESLER, Paris Report 188, vol. 4, p. 658.
58. G.O.BURR, T.TANIMOTO, C.E.HARTT, A.FORBES, G.SADAOKO, F.M.ASHTON, J.H.PAYNE, J.A.SILVA and G.E.SLOANE, Geneva Report 115 (1955), vol. 12, p. 177.
59. J.W.T.SPINKS, D.A.LANE and B.B.TORCHINSKY, *Can. J. Technol.* **29**, 371 (1951).
60. J.W.T.SPINKS, Geneva Report 10 (1955), vol. 12, p. 75.
61. R.J.HEEMSTRA, J.W.WATKINS and F.E.ARMSTRONG, *Nucleonics* **19** (1), 92 (1961).
62. W.GARDNER and D.KIRKHAM, *Soil Science* **73**, 391 (1952).
63. C.H.M.VAN BAVEL, N.UNDERWOOD and R.W.SWANSON, *Soil Sci.* **82**, 29 (1956).
64. A.H.KNIGHT and T.W.WRIGHT, Radioisotope Conference 1954, London 1954, vol. 2, p. 111.
65. L.H.STOLZY and G.A.CAHOON, *Proc. Soil Sci. Soc. Amer.* **21**, 571 (1957).
66. P.G.MARAIS, Geneva Report 1105 (1958), vol. 27, p. 23.
67. V.A.EMELYANOV and V.E.NESTEROV, *Atomnaya Energiya* **6**, 573 (1959); *Kernenergie* **3**, 198 (1960)
68. P.LÉVÊQUE, R.HOURS, P.MARTINELLI, S.MAY, J.SANDIER and J.BRILLANT, Geneva Report 1231 (1958), vol. 19, p. 34.
69. J.L.PUTMAN and S.JEFFERSON, Geneva Report 462 (1955), vol. 15, p. 147.
70. J.L.PUTMAN and D.B.SMITH, *Int. J. Appl. Rad. Isot.* **1**, 24 (1956).
71. S.INOSE, M.KATO, S.SATO and N.SHIRAISHI, Geneva Report 1053 (1955), vol. 15, p. 211.
72. E.D.GOLDBERG and D.L.INMAN, *Bull. Geol. Soc. America* **66**, 611 (1955).
73. R.HOURS, W.D.NESTEROFF and V.ROMANOVSKY, *Compt. rend.* **240**, 1798 (1955).
74. D.L.INMAN and T.K.CHAMBERLAIN, Geneva Report 2357 (1958), vol. 19, p. 349.
75. D.B.SMITH and J.D.EAKINS, Paris Report 63, vol. 2, p. 619.
76. A.GIBERT, F.ABECASIS, M.FERREIRA, J.R.DE CARVALHO and S.CORDEIRO, Geneva Report 1820 (1958), vol. 19, p. 355.
77. G.L.EDEN and K.V.MELBOURNE, *Int. J. Appl. Rad. Isot.* **8**, 172 (1960).
78. T.A.RAFTER and G.J.FERGUSSON, Geneva Report 2128 (1958), vol. 18, p. 526.
79. E.STEEMANN NIELSEN, *Ann. Rev. Plant Physiol.* **11**, 341 (1960).

80. J.L.PUTMAN, *Isotopes*, London 1960.
81. A.G.MADDOCK and E.H.WILLIS, *Adv. Inorg. Radiochem.* **3**, 287 (1961).
82. H.E.SUESS, *Ann. Rev. Nucl. Sci.* **8**, 243 (1958).
83. H. MOSER, F.NEUMAIER and W.RAUERT, *Atomkernenergie* **7**, 321 (1962).
84. B.J.FREDERICK, *Int. J. Appl. Rad. Isot.* **14**, 401 (1963).
85. *Production and Use of Short-Lived Radioisotopes from Reactors*, Symposium in Vienna, I.A.E.A., Vienna 1963.
86. L.G.ERWALL, H.G.FORSBERG and K.LJUNGGREN, in [85].
87. O.BERG and E.SOMER, in [85].
88. C.G.CLAYTON *et al.*, Proc. Symp. on Flow Measurement in Closed Conduits, Glasgow 1960, see [86].
89. O.FINEMAN, *Svensk Kem. Tidskr.* **71**, 452 (1959).
90. G. MILDE, *Isotopentechnik* **2**, 328 (1962).
91. *Radioisotopes in Hydrology*, Symposium in Tokyo, I.A.E.A., Vienna 1963.
92. G.KNUTSSON, K.LJUNGGREN and H.G.FORSBERG, in [91].
93. R.COLAS, in: P.LÉVÊQUE (Ed.), *Les applications industrielles des radioéléments*, Paris 1962.
94. E.ERIKSSON, *Tellus* **10**, 472 (1958).
95. R.HOURS, *Houille blanche*, no. special A 14 (1955).
96. H.MAIRHOFER, *Atompraxis* **9**, 2 (1963).
97. C.G.CLAYTON and D.B.SMITH, in [91].
98. J.GUIZERIX, G.GRANDCLÉMENT, B.GAILLARD and P.RUBY, in [91].
99. D.B.SMITH and W.E.CLARK, in [91].
100. Y.HARPAZ, S.MANDEL, J.R.GAT and A.NIR, in [91].
101. C.V.THEIS, in [91].
102. R.W.NELSON and A.E.REISENAUER, in [91].
103. A.ARIIZUMI and O.KONDO, in [91].
104. H.MOSER, F.NEUMAIER and W.RAUERT, in [91].
105. D.J.BURDON, E.ERIKSSON, T.PAPADIMITROPOULOS, N.PAPAKIS and B.R.PAYNE, in [91].
106. B.DEGOT, P.LÉVÊQUE, G.COURTOIS, M.GASNIER and S.GODAR, in [91].
107. M.KATO, O.SATO, Y.MORITA, M.KOHAMA and N.HAYASHI, in [91].
108. J.GUIZERIX, G.GRANDCLÉMENT, R.HOURS, H.ANDRÉ, R.WOLF and R.PEREZ, in [91].
109. M.KOBAYASHI and A.NUKAZAWA, in [91].
110. C.E.JUNGE, *Air Chemistry and Radioactivity*, New York 1963.
111. H.ISRAEL and A.KREBS (Ed.), *Nuclear Radiation in Geophysics*, Berlin 1962.
112. F.F.KOCZY and J.N.ROSHOLT, in [111].
113. E.ERIKSSON, in [111].
114. W.S.BROECKER, R.GERARD, M.EWING and B.C.HEEZEN, *J. Geophys. Res.* **65**, 2903 (1960).
115. B.BOLIN, in [111].
116. C.E.JUNGE, in [111].
117. L.FACY, in [111].
118. H.ISRAEL, in [111].
119. J.C.VOGEL and D.EHHALT, in [91].
120. J.C.VOGEL, D.EHHALT and W.ROETHES, in [91].
121. K.O.MÜNNICH and W.ROETHER, in [91].
122. H.G.ÖSTLUND and E.WERNER, in [45].
123. W.F.LIBBY, in [45].
124. C.W.CARLSTON and L.L.THATCHER, in [45].
125. B.L.CAMPBELL, *Int. J. Appl. Rad. Isot.* **14**, 286 (1963).
126. L.I.KOROTKOV, *Handbook (spravochnik) of Radioisotope Instruments* (Russ.), Moscow 1963.
127. R.SCHROLLER and H.STIEDE, *Kernenergie* **6**, 218 (1963).
128. I.WENDT, *Kerntechnik* **2**, 1 (1960).
129. G.L.STEWART and S.A.TAYLOR, *Soil Sci.* **83**, 151 (1957).
130. *Radioisotopes in Soil-Plant Nutrition Studies*, Symposium in Bombay, I.A.E.A., Vienna 1962.
131. J.DAMAGNEZ, in [130].
132. C.ANDRIEUX, L.BUSCARLET, J.GUITTON and B.MÉRITE, in [130].

133. M. P. VOLAROVICH and N. V. CHURAYEV, in [130].
134. G. H. LEAN and M. J. CRICKMORE, in [91].
135. K. UNGER, *Kernenergie* **6**, 465 (1963).
136. W. KÜHN, *Atompraxis* **5**, 133 (1959).
137. P. MORTIER, M. DE BOODT, L. DE LEENHEER, *Z. Pflanzenern. Düng. Bodenkunde* **87**, 244 (1959).
138. J. F. STONE, D. KIRKHAM and A. A. READ, *Soil Sci. Soc. Amer. Proc.* **19**, 419 (1955).
139. E. STEEMANN NIELSEN and V. K. HANSEN, *Physiol. Plant.* **12**, 353 (1959); *Deep Sea Res.* **5**, 222 (1959).
140. B. R. PAYNE, J. F. CAMERON, A. E. PECKHAM and L. L. THATCHER, Geneva Report 875 (1964).
141. C. LAPOINTE, *Dep. Mines Tech. Surv., Canada*, Ms-62-53 (1962).
142. M. BOROWCZYK, J. MAIRHOFER and A. ZUBER, *Atomkernenergie* **10**, 51 (1965).
143. J. L. PUTMAN, A. M. WILDBLOOD and J. E. ROBSON, *Water and Sanitary Eng.* **6**, 99 (1956).
144. W. H. JOHNSTON, in: U.S. Report TID-7640 (1963); JLI-2748-07 (1963).
145. H. BUTTLAR, *J. Am. Water Works Assoc.* **50**, 1533 (1958); *J. Geophys. Res.* **64**, 1031 (1959).
146. W. F. LIBBY, *J. Geophys. Res.* **66**, 3767 (1961).
147. R. P. GARDNER and J. W. DUNN, *Int. J. Appl. Rad. Isot.* **15**, 339 (1964).
148. C. W. CARLSTON, *Science* **143**, 804 (1964).
149. E. SOMER, *Ingenioeren*, Int. Ed., **4**, 88 (1960).
150. R. A. ALLINGHAM and E. SOMER, *Ingenioeren*, Int. Ed., **4**, 91 (1960).
151. B. R. PETERSEN, *Ingenioeren*, Int. Ed., **4**, 99 (1960).
152. B. B. HANSHAW, W. BACK, M. RUBIN and R. L. WAIT, *Water Resources Res.* **1**, 109 (1965).
153. B. B. HANSHAW, W. BACK and M. RUBIN, *Science* **148**, 494 (1965).
154. R. P. GARDNER, *Int. J. Appl. Rad. Isot.* **16**, 75 (1965).
155. *Application of Isotope Techniques in Hydrology*, Panel Meeting in Vienna, I.A.E.A., Vienna 1962.
156. *Isotope Techniques for Hydrology*, Panel Meeting in Vienna, I.A.E.A., Vienna 1964.
157. M. P. BELIKOV, V. A. EMELYANOV and V. E. NESTEROV, *Radioactive Isotopes in Hydroengineering* (Russ.), Moscow 1961; English translation, Jerusalem 1964.
158. M. PETERSEN, *Atomkernenergie* **10**, 285 (1965).
159. V. NETZ, in H. HART, *Radioaktive Isotope in der Betriebsmeßtechnik*, Berlin 1962.
160. L. G. ERWALL, H. G. FORSBERG and K. LJUNGGREN, *Industriell Isotop-Teknik*, Copenhagen 1962; *Industrial Isotope Techniques*, Copenhagen 1965.
161. G. COURTOIS, *Int. J. Appl. Rad. Isot.* **15**, 655 (1964).
162. H. W. FEELY, A. WALTON, C. R. BARNETT and F. BAZAN, US AEC-Report NYO-9040 (1961).
163. K. O. MÜNNICH, *Naturwiss.* **50**, 211 (1963).
164. D. KIRKHAM and R. J. KUNZE, *Adv. Agron.* **14**, 321 (1962).
165. E. R. PERRIER and W. R. JOHNSTON, *Soil Sci.* **93**, 104 (1962).
166. J. R. MCHENRY, *Soil Sci.* **95**, 294 (1963).
167. J. D. HEWLETT, J. E. DOUGLASS and J. L. CLUTTER, *Soil Sci.* **97**, 19 (1964).
168. J. LETEY, E. HSIA, R. E. PELISHEK and J. OSBORN, *Soil Sci.* **91**, 77 (1961).
169. Y. BARRADA, *Atomic Energy Review* **3** (2), 195 (1965).
170. J. F. STONE, R. H. SHAW and D. KIRKHAM, *Soil Sci. Soc. Amer. Proc.* **24**, 435 (1960).
171. M. B. A. CRESPI and H. PERSCHKE, *Int. J. Appl. Rad. Isot.* **15**, 569 (1964).
172. I. B. HAZZAA, K. F. SAAD, R. K. GIRGIS, A. A. BAKR and F. M. SWAILEM, *Int. J. Appl. Rad. Isot.* **16**, 261 (1965).
173. I. B. HAZZAA, R. K. GIRGIS and K. F. SAAD, *Int. J. Appl. Rad. Isot.* **16**, 487 (1965).

13. RADIATION PROTECTION

13.1. Preliminary Remarks

Many research workers, physicians and other personnel exposed to ionizing radiations in the days before the biological effects were known suffered injury, or even death. However, it would be wrong to conclude that to-day work with radioactive substances is more dangerous than other typical activities in modern industrial plants or laboratories. What is necessary is the careful observation of the appropriate precautions. In the case of tracer experiments in the laboratory, i.e., in work with small quantities of radioactive substances, these precautions are usually quite simple. More elaborate precautions are needed in operations with larger quantities of radioelements and with powerful radiation sources.

In the present chapter a brief review will be given which should enable the reader to decide what protective measures have to be taken in any particular situation. On the one hand, danger to personnel and to the public must be prevented. On the other hand, a correct estimate of the situation will help to avoid unnecessary alarm. A knowledge of the extent of the danger, if any, in every given case is all the more necessary, since the effect of ionizing radiations on the human organism is not accompanied by any immediate sensation.

Anyone operating with radioactive materials, or responsible for such work, should acquaint himself with the radiation protection laws and regulations valid in his country [1]. These rules deal particularly with the following problems: maximum permissible radiation doses and corresponding values for the incorporation of radioactive substances; requirements for laboratory and industrial installations; dosimetric control and compulsory medical examination of personnel; required measuring equipment; collection and disposal of radioactive wastes; transport of radioactive materials; licence for storage, use, transport, etc., of radioactive substances.

Many monographs on radiation protection have been published (in English, for example, [2 to 9, 67, 69]; in other languages [10–18]).

13.2. The Concept of Tolerance Dose

Tolerance doses, or maximum doses for exposure of human beings to ionizing radiations, have been specified. The values recommended by the International Commission on Radiological Protection (ICRP) [2, 19, 20] are in general use to-day.

The basic values given are those for persons occupationally exposed. The tolerance doses and the quantities derived from them (see Section 13.3) are so chosen that persons continually exposed during their work will not suffer any ill-effects, i.e., no so-

315

matic effects will arise, and genetic effects will be very small. The tolerance doses are regarded as maximum permissible values; the recommendation to keep the doses in actual operations as small as possible should be followed. For persons occupationally exposed, continuous dosimetric control according to a suitable scheme is assumed, meaning that occupational exposure must always occur in a controlled area.

The tolerance doses for occupational exposure cannot be applied without modification to large groups of people, or to the public as a whole. Particularly sensitive individuals, such as children, must not be allowed to receive the same dose as persons occupationally exposed; and, secondly, any significant increase in genetic damage – which must be considered as proportional to the integral dose for a population – must be prevented.

When larger groups of persons, such as the inhabitants of the neighbourhood of a controlled area, are also exposed to radiation, lower tolerance doses must be used. These may be calculated by means of certain reduction factors from the tolerance doses for occupationally exposed persons (see the following sections). In the technical applications of radioactivity discussed in this volume, radiation doses to persons other than those immediately involved in the work will in general be negligibly small, so that protective measures for such groups will normally not be required.

Tolerance doses are usually given in "rem" units (roentgen equivalent medical). This unit, which is also used in the recommendations of the International Commission on Radiological Protection, is a general measure of the biological effects of the radiations. A dose of 1 rem delivered to a tissue by any ionizing radiation was originally defined as that dose producing the same biological effect as 1 roentgen (r) of X- or γ-radiation, 1 r being equal to 98 erg g^{-1} for predominantly aqueous systems (see Section 2.18). However, since the rad is now increasingly used as a measure of physical dose, it is preferable to relate the rem to the rad. This is done by the equation

$$D_{\text{rem}} = (RBE) \cdot D_{\text{rad}},$$

where D_{rem} and D_{rad} represent the doses in rem and rad units, respectively, and (RBE) is the "relative biological effectiveness" of the radiation of the particular kind and energy.

The use of the rem to define tolerance doses has the advantage that various types of ionizing radiation can be included in a single scheme on the basis of their *RBE* values. However, the determination of *RBE* is not simple, and it must not be forgotten that the ratio between the biological effects of various types of radiations may depend on the kind of effect considered, the organ affected and its physiological condition. Difficulties are therefore experienced in establishing *RBE* values.

At the present time, the following *RBE* values are used. For X-, γ- and β-radiation: *RBE* = 1; for α-radiation: *RBE* = 10; for recoil protons (of energy less than 10 MeV): *RBE* = 10; for heavy recoil nuclei: *RBE* = 20. The large relative biological effectiveness of the heavy particles is apparently due to the high concentration of ions and excited molecules along their paths.

In considering radiation hazards and the related topics of tolerance doses and of protective measures, a distinction may be drawn between outer and inner radiation exposure. External exposure arises when human beings enter radiation fields. In industrial applications of radioactivity, γ-radiation is mainly involved here. Internal radiation exposure occurs when radiactive substances are taken into the human body. In this case, most attention has to be given to α- and β-radiation.

13.3. External Radiation Exposure

The total permissible dose for occupational exposure is laid down in relation to the age of the individual. The purpose of this regulation is the prevention of cumulative damage. Cumulative damage includes genetic radiation effects which are due to mutations in the gonads, and possibly also certain somatic effects, such as those in the blood-forming organs, which play a role in producing leukemia. Consideration of these radiation effects has led to the maximum permissible accumulated dose D, where

$$D = 5(N - 18) \text{ rem}$$

[2, 19], where N is the age in years. It follows that for persons over 18 years a dose of 5 rem/year is always permissible. Thus a general tolerance dose of 0·1 rem/week for all persons occupationally exposed is arrived at. If this value is never exceeded for any occupationally exposed person, satisfactory protection is assured. It is therefore advisable to use this dose in planning the safety measures for work with radioactive materials.

The equation which gives the permissible integral dose as a function of age involves the requirement that persons below 18 must not be allowed to work where they may be exposed to ionizing radiations. In a number of countries, this principle has been embodied in the radiation protection regulations.

The equation is satisfactory for the prevention of excessive total doses, but the period within which the permissible total dose may be received is not specified. It has been found that somatic damage arises if the dose rate exceeds certain threshold values over certain periods. Thus, the equation for total dose permits a dose of 85 rem for a person 35 years old who had never before been exposed to ionizing radiation, but such a dose given within a short period would lead to serious ill-effects. Therefore, the equation for permissible total dose must be supplemented with rules limiting the dose rate. Permissible dose rates depend on the sensitivity of the exposed organ.

For irradiation of the most sensitive organs (gonads, blood-forming organs and the lenses of the eyes) or the body as a whole, it is prescribed that the dose accumulated in any period of 13 consecutive weeks must not exceed 3 rem. Single doses up to 3 rem are therefore permitted provided that reduction in the following period ensures that the values both for integral dose and for 13 weeks dose are not exceeded. Nevertheless, large single doses should be avoided whenever possible. Because of the particular sensitivity of the blood-forming organs, changes in blood count are usually the first physiological sign of excessive radiation doses. Irradiation of the lens may lead to cataract.

For less sensitive organs, higher doses are permitted. Thus the tolerance dose for the skin is 8 rem in 13 consecutive weeks, and for the hands, forearms and feet 20 rem.

As we have already indicated, lower tolerance doses apply for persons other than those occupationally exposed. For adults in the vicinity of a controlled area, the maximum permissible dose is reduced to one-third, or about 1·5 rem/year. This reduced value is to be applied to persons who are occupied in a factory in which there is a controlled area, but themselves not employed on work involving exposure to radiation. It applies also to those who occasionally enter a controlled area. For the general population in the vicinity of a controlled radiation area (including children), a reduction of permissible doses to one-tenth, or 0·5 rem/year, is recommended. For the general population, or for large portions of it, the present recommendation is that the average integral dose due to artificial radiation sources shall not exceed 5 rem over the whole period of life.

The developing embryo is particularly sensitive to radiation; serious developmental damage or deformity may be caused by exposure. It is therefore particularly important that expectant mothers should be protected from radiation.

In order that permissible doses shall not be exceeded, the doses to be expected in intended operations with radioactive materials should be estimated. The dose delivered by any nuclide depends on the type and energy of the radiation emitted. γ-radiation doses have been calculated for a large number of nuclides [21]; some such values are given in Table 8. In using these values it must be kept in mind that the dose received decreases with the square of the distance from the radiation source.

TABLE 8. DOSE RATES FOR A NUMBER OF γ-EMITTING RADIONUCLIDES

Radionuclide	Dose rate due to γ-radiation at a distance of 10 cm (millirem hr^{-1} mc^{-1})
^{22}Na	130
^{24}Na	200
^{59}Fe	67
^{60}Co	135
^{131}I	25
^{137}Cs	31
^{192}Ir	52
^{226}Ra*	84

* In equilibrium with disintegration products and enclosed by 0·5 mm platinum.

As an example, Table 8 shows that 0·4 mc of cobalt-60, at a distance of 50 cm, gives a dose of about 2 millirem/hr. For continuous occupational exposure, of 8 hr/day, this corresponds to 5 rem/year, which is the maximum permissible dose given at the beginning of this section.

Lead or concrete walls may be used to shield against γ-radiation. Large quantities of γ-emitters should always be stored behind such walls. Table 9 gives the shield thicknesses necessary to reduce the dose by certain factors (between 2 and 10^6). The table gives data for the most important shielding materials and for various radiation energies. The values have been calculated for a broad radiation beam, so that scattering

TABLE 9. SHIELDING WALLS AGAINST γ-RADIATION
(THE TABLE GIVES THE THICKNESS OF MATERIAL WHICH IS NECESSARY TO ATTAIN
CERTAIN REDUCTIONS IN DOSE FOR A BROAD RADIATION BEAM)

Attenu-ation factor	Shielding material*	Layer thickness (cm)						
		Energy of γ- or X-radiation (MeV)						
		0·2	0·4	0·7	1·0	1·5	2·0	3·0
2	Pb	0·2	0·4	0·8	1·3	1·7	2·0	2·1
	Fe	1·3	2·3	3·0	3·4	3·8	4·0	4·4
	Concrete	7·6	11·3	12·4	12·9	13·6	14·1	15·3
	H_2O	27	28	27	28	28	30	34
5	Pb	0·4	0·9	1·9	2·8	3·8	4·3	4·6
	Fe	2·5	4·2	5·7	6·5	7·3	8·1	9·0
	Concrete	11·0	18·8	22·3	23·5	25·8	28·2	32·9
	H_2O	37	45	47	50	54	59	67
10	Pb	0·6	1·3	2·6	3·8	5·1	5·9	6·5
	Fe	3·4	5·4	7·3	8·5	10·0	11·0	12·2
	Concrete	14·6	23·7	27·6	29·9	34·0	37·6	43·4
	H_2O	45	54	58	62	70	78	88
30	Pb	0·7	1·7	3·7	5·5	7·3	8·5	9·3
	Fe	4·7	7·2	9·8	11·6	13·7	15·1	17·0
	Concrete	16·4	27·7	36·4	40·5	46·5	51·6	59·9
	H_2O	54	70	77	83	94	105	122
100	Pb	1·0	2·3	4·7	7·0	9·7	11·3	12·2
	Fe	5·9	9·0	12·2	14·7	17·6	19·7	22·3
	Concrete	21·1	35·2	45·3	50·5	58·3	65·7	77·5
	H_2O	67	86	96	105	120	134	159
10^3	Pb	1·5	3·3	7·0	10·2	14·1	16·5	18·0
	Fe	8·0	12·7	17·5	20·4	24·6	28·0	31·9
	Concrete	28·2	48·1	62·5	70·4	81·7	92·7	111
	H_2O	89	113	131	145	168	188	225
10^4	Pb	2·1	4·6	9·1	13·3	18·3	21·3	23·5
	Fe	11·1	16·6	22·2	26·2	31·4	35·8	41·0
	Concrete	35·2	60·3	79·1	89·2	104	119	143
	H_2O	109	139	162	183	213	241	290
10^5	Pb	2·4	5·4	11·1	16·5	22·7	26·2	28·9
	Fe	13·1	20·0	26·9	31·8	38·2	43·5	50·0
	Concrete	50·5	75·1	93·5	107	127	144	174
	H_2O	126	164	194	220	259	294	353
10^6	Pb	3·0	6·5	13·1	19·5	26·8	31·0	34·3
	Fe	15·4	23·6	31·5	37·1	44·6	51·0	58·8
	Concrete	66·4	89·8	109	124	150	171	205
	H_2O	146	189	224	254	302	345	417

* The following densities were assumed for the calculations: lead = 11·34; iron = 7·89; concrete = 2·3.

of radiation in the shielding wall was taken into consideration. In designing shielding walls, attention should be paid to the radiation scattered by objects in the surroundings, or by walls, floors or ceilings of the room. The subject of shielding walls has been treated in detail in a number of publications [3, 7, 12, 15, 22–24]. Because of the great weight and thickness, shielding walls make many operations cumbersome. It is therefore common practice to provide the required protection as far as possible by carrying out the operations quickly, and by maintaining the greatest possible distance between personnel and radiation source.

Because of its small range, β-radiation represents a smaller hazard than γ-radiation as far as external exposure is concerned. If the absorption of the radiation in the source itself and in the air is disregarded, the β-radiation dose delivered to the surface of the body is about 3000 millirem hr^{-1} mc^{-1} at a distance of 10 cm from a point-source. This value depends only slightly on the energy of the radiation. If desired, the attenuation of the β-radiation in the source or in an absorber can be estimated on the basis of the data of Sections 2.16 and 3.7.

In judging the protection measures needed against β-radiation, the bremsstrahlung (Section 2.16) must not be forgotten. However, this is unimportant when the β-radiation is absorbed in elements of low atomic number. Thus a small glass flask containing 10 mc of phosphorus-32, whose walls are sufficient to absorb the β-radiation completely, delivers a bremsstrahlung dose of only 1 millirem/hr at 10 cm distance.

The γ- or X-ray dose received by each individual may be measured with dosimeters. Most frequently, film badges are used for personnel dosimetry; the blackening of a photographic film by the radiation is determined. Film dosimetry may be used to obtain the dose delivered to various parts of the body, such as the hands. The photographic method suffers from the general disadvantage that the dose is obtained only after the film has been developed.

In contrast, the doses of electromagnetic radiation can be read immediately from small ionization chambers (electroscopes). These devices usually have the size and shape of a fountain pen.

Portable ionization chambers which indicate the dose rate directly are also of great practical value. For example, they are used when shipments of radioactive material are opened and handled. The dose rate meters indicate directly whether it is safe to remain indefinitely at a given point in a radiation field or whether the exposure time at such a place must be limited.

Reviews, monographs and conference proceedings on radiation protection measurements and the instruments are available [3, 7, 14, 25–37, 70–72, 78].

13.4. Internal Radiation Exposure

When the radioelements are not used in the form of sealed sources, and especially in the case of chemical operations with the radioelements, hazards from internal radiation exposure are usually greater than those from external exposure. Radioelements may be absorbed into the human body and then be deposited in organs. There they irradiate tissues over long periods, and may inflict serious damage. While α- and β-rays rarely contribute much to external exposure doses and then act only on the skin, in internal exposure these rays are of primary importance. Internal α-irradiation is all the more serious because of its high relative biological effectiveness ($RBE = 10$) compared to electromagnetic radiations. In the case of β-rays, the RBE is only unity. However, in contrast to γ-radiation, the entire energy of the β-rays is absorbed within the body, or even within the particular organ. Therefore, β-radiation is also more dangerous than γ-radiation of the same emitted energy.

The site affected by the radioelements depends on the chemical properties of the element, its chemical form, the route of entry (by respiration, by ingestion, or through the skin), the half-life of the radionuclide, and the total amount of element taken in. As would be expected, the alkaline earth elements (calcium, strontium, and radium) are deposited in the mineral substance of bone, while yttrium and zirconium (important as fission products), as well as polonium and plutonium, tend to form colloidal hydroxides and are concentrated in soft tissues, such as bone marrow and liver.

In the case of radiocarbon, the site and duration of storage depend greatly on the chemical form. When taken in as carbonate, the carbon is rapidly eliminated as carbon dioxide and is then no longer a hazard. On the other hand, radiocarbon supplied in the form of organic compounds can often be eliminated only through complicated and lengthy metabolic processes. In contrast, sodium – which is always present in the form of the simple ion – is invariably eliminated rapidly in the urine.

The very dangerous element plutonium is retained about 400 times more strongly after inhalation than after oral ingestion, while no such difference is observed in the case of radium. Radioiodine, whether supplied as iodide or free iodine, is efficiently concentrated in the thyroid, but the capacity of the gland for iodine is limited. Therefore, when the radioiodine is supplied together with a large quantity of inactive iodine, i.e., when the substance has low specific activity, only a small amount of radioiodine is retained in the thyroid gland, and the radiation dose to the thyroid is relatively small. The half-life of the radioelement affects the site of its action since the establishment of a particular distribution of the element within the body requires a finite time. Thus, radiophosphorus supplied as phosphate is first retained in soft tissues, and only after some days or weeks – when its activity has greatly diminished – it is largely concentrated in bone.

All these factors must be taken into account in setting tolerance body burdens for individual radionuclides and tolerance concentrations of such substances in air and water (maximum permissible concentrations, *MPC*). Detailed information about the behaviour of individual radioelements is therefore needed before such values can be established. Often the results from experiments with animals are used to predict the behaviour in the human body. Although much work has been carried out on such problems in recent years, the data are still far from complete, and in many cases only estimates can be given. Nevertheless, the data on permissible doses for internal exposure provided by the ICRP are of great value. These data are given for a "standard man". They make it possible to estimate when the presence of radioelements in air, drinking water or food must be regarded as hazardous.

Table 10 gives a brief excerpt from the most recent edition of the tables of the ICRP on permissible doses for internal exposure [38]. The values for a "40-hour

T.A.R. 21

TABLE 10. MAXIMUM PERMISSIBLE VALUES FOR INTERNAL RADIATION EXPOSURE

Radionuclide (S in soluble form; IS in insoluble form)	Maximum permissible body burden (μc)	Maximum permissible concentration (MPC) for intake into the body ($\mu c/cm^3$)			
		40-hr week (intake only during working hours)		168-hr week (continuous intake)	
		Water	Air	Water	Air
^3H (^3H_2O)	10^3	$0{\cdot}1$	2×10^{-5}	$0{\cdot}03$	5×10^{-6}
^{14}C ($^{14}CO_2$)	300	$0{\cdot}02$	4×10^{-6}	8×10^{-3}	10^{-6}
^{22}Na S	10	10^{-3}	2×10^{-7}	4×10^{-4}	6×10^{-8}
IS		9×10^{-4}	9×10^{-9}	3×10^{-4}	3×10^{-9}
^{24}Na S	7	6×10^{-3}	10^{-6}	2×10^{-3}	4×10^{-7}
IS		8×10^{-4}	10^{-7}	3×10^{-4}	5×10^{-8}
^{32}P S	6	5×10^{-4}	7×10^{-8}	2×10^{-4}	2×10^{-8}
IS		7×10^{-4}	8×10^{-8}	2×10^{-4}	3×10^{-8}
^{55}Fe S	10^3	$0{\cdot}02$	9×10^{-7}	8×10^{-3}	3×10^{-7}
IS		$0{\cdot}07$	10^{-6}	$0{\cdot}02$	3×10^{-7}
^{59}Fe S	20	2×10^{-3}	10^{-7}	6×10^{-4}	5×10^{-8}
IS		2×10^{-3}	5×10^{-8}	5×10^{-4}	2×10^{-8}
^{60}Co S	10	10^{-3}	3×10^{-7}	5×10^{-4}	10^{-7}
IS		10^{-3}	9×10^{-9}	3×10^{-4}	3×10^{-9}
^{89}Sr S	4	3×10^{-4}	3×10^{-8}	10^{-4}	10^{-8}
IS		8×10^{-4}	4×10^{-8}	3×10^{-4}	10^{-8}
^{90}Sr S	2	4×10^{-6}	3×10^{-10}	10^{-6}	10^{-10}
IS		1×10^{-3}	5×10^{-9}	4×10^{-4}	2×10^{-9}
^{131}I S	$0{\cdot}7$	6×10^{-5}	9×10^{-9}	2×10^{-5}	3×10^{-9}
IS		2×10^{-3}	3×10^{-7}	6×10^{-4}	10^{-7}
^{137}Cs S	30	4×10^{-4}	6×10^{-8}	2×10^{-4}	2×10^{-8}
IS		10^{-3}	10^{-8}	4×10^{-4}	5×10^{-9}
^{192}Ir S	6	10^{-3}	10^{-7}	4×10^{-4}	4×10^{-8}
IS		10^{-3}	3×10^{-8}	4×10^{-4}	9×10^{-9}
^{210}Pb S	$0{\cdot}4$	4×10^{-6}	10^{-10}	10^{-6}	4×10^{-11}
IS		5×10^{-2}	2×10^{-10}	2×10^{-3}	8×10^{-11}
^{210}Po S	$0{\cdot}03$	2×10^{-5}	5×10^{-10}	7×10^{-6}	2×10^{-10}
IS		8×10^{-4}	2×10^{-10}	3×10^{-4}	7×10^{-11}
^{226}Ra S	$0{\cdot}1$	4×10^{-7}	3×10^{-11}	10^{-7}	10^{-11}
IS		9×10^{-4}	2×10^{-7}	3×10^{-4}	6×10^{-8}
^{239}Pu S	$0{\cdot}04$	10^{-4}	2×10^{-12}	5×10^{-5}	6×10^{-13}
IS		8×10^{-4}	4×10^{-11}	3×10^{-4}	10^{-11}

week" are to be used when it can be safely assumed that the radioelement is taken in only during a working week of this length; this would be the case, for example, when the intake occurs through breathing at the place of work. The assumptions made in deriving body burdens and *MPC* values as well as calculation methods are given in the reports of the ICRP. These reports also indicate how to estimate *MPC* values when several radioelements are present simultaneously. It must be emphasized that straightforward application of the tolerance values for internal exposure is possible only when the persons involved are not exposed to appreciable external radiation. If external exposure does occur, the values must be reduced to such an extent that the combined dose from external and internal exposure for any organ is not in excess of the tolerance dose. The *MPC* values are calculated on the assumption of continuous intake. Therefore, brief periods during which intake surpasses the *MPC* values by not too large a factor need not be regarded as dangerous.

TABLE 11. MAXIMUM PERMISSIBLE CONCENTRATIONS FOR UNIDENTIFIED RADIONUCLIDES
(VALUES FOR OCCUPATIONAL EXPOSURE, CONTINUOUS INTAKE, I.E., 168 HR/WEEK)

A. MPC for water

If the following nuclides are not present:	MPC $(\mu c/cm^3)$
^{90}Sr, ^{126}I, ^{129}I, ^{131}I, ^{210}Pb, ^{210}Po, ^{211}At, ^{223}Ra, ^{224}Ra, ^{226}Ra, ^{227}Ac, ^{228}Ra, ^{230}Th, ^{231}Pa, ^{232}Th, and natural thorium	3×10^{-5}
^{90}Sr, ^{129}I, ^{210}Pb, ^{210}Po, ^{223}Ra, ^{226}Ra, ^{228}Ra, ^{231}Pa, natural thorium	2×10^{-5}
^{90}Sr, ^{129}I, ^{210}Pb, ^{226}Ra, ^{228}Ra	7×10^{-6}
^{226}Ra, ^{228}Ra	10^{-6}
in all cases	10^{-7}

B. MPC for air

If the following nuclides are not present:	MPC $(\mu c/cm^3)$
α-emitters and the β-emitters: ^{90}Sr, ^{129}I, ^{210}Pb, ^{227}Ac, ^{228}Ra, ^{230}Pa, ^{241}Pu, ^{249}Bk	10^{-9}
α-emitters and the β-emitters: ^{210}Pb, ^{227}Ac, ^{228}Ra, ^{241}Pu	10^{-10}
α-emitters and the β-emitter: ^{227}Ac	10^{-11}
^{227}Ac, ^{230}Th, ^{231}Pa, ^{232}Th, natural thorium, ^{238}Pu, ^{239}Pu, ^{240}Pu, ^{242}Pu, ^{249}Cf	10^{-12}
^{231}Pa, natural thorium, ^{239}Pu, ^{240}Pu, ^{242}Pu, ^{249}Cf	7×10^{-13}
in all cases	4×10^{-13}

For monitoring water, food and air, the *MPC* values for unidentified radionuclide mixtures (Table 11) are important [38]. They are obtained from the values for individual radionuclides, of which a few are given in Table 10. Usually only the total activity is measured, since radiochemical analysis is lengthy and tedious. The *MPC* values for unidentified radionuclide mixtures (see Table 11) then indicate in which cases the concentrations have reached levels that make a more detailed analysis necessary. To obtain the required information, it is then often sufficient to determine the content of only one radionuclide, or of a few radionuclides.

An important practical case is the measurement of the activity of fission product mixtures, as generally found in waste water from atomic energy installations. It can be seen from Table 11 that it is essential to determine the strontium-90 content as soon as the total activity exceeds 10^{-6} $\mu c/ml$. It is not necessary to determine the activity of iodine-129, as the yield of this nuclide in fission is small, and its half-life long.

Surveys of the methods for monitoring the radioactivity of water, waste water, air, etc., have been published [39, 40].

As in the case of external exposure, lower maximum permissible values for internal exposure are to be applied to persons not occupationally exposed [38]. For the population in the vicinity of a radiation area, the ICRP recommends a reduction factor of 10.

Although the applications of radioactivity referred to in this book will hardly require such precautions, it should nevertheless be mentioned that a further reduction of the maximum permissible values is recommended when the population as a whole, or a large population group, is involved. For radiation exposure of the gonads, a reduction factor of 100 is suggested, and for other organs a factor of 30. Corresponding reduction factors are applied to the *MPC* values for unidentified radionuclide mixtures.

In addition to the *MPC* values recommended for continuous intake, which have just been discussed, maximum permissible values have also been estimated for single intake of radionuclides by inhalation or through wounds [41] (see also [23]).

13.5. Some Practical Advice

The precautions to be observed in work with radioactive materials, especially materials not in the form of closed sources, have been clearly summarized by Zakovsky [42]: "It is absolutely essential that radioisotopes do not come into contact with unprotected hands ... even small amounts of radioactive material may cause burns when very close to the skin. Protection by the use of rubber gloves or paper must therefore be employed in work with such materials. In many cases, forceps or tongs must be used, and their use is advised for all handling operations. Active solutions must not be pipetted by mouth; instead, rubber balloons or injection syringes should be used. All operations involving vapours or dry materials must be carried out under a suitable hood or in an air-tight box ... For all operations desk and table surfaces must be covered with paper ... Small dishes suitably lined with blotting paper, must be available for putting down used pipettes, stirring rods, etc., since such equipment must never be placed directly on the working desks. A waste bin with a foot-operated cover should be available next to the working table."

"Great care is needed in the cleaning of glassware. All contaminated vessels must be marked immediately after use and set aside for special cleaning, since active substances are often adsorbed very strongly on glassware. Even the smallest amounts of active substances remaining in vessels must be removed ..."

"To ensure that no contamination shall be carried out of the laboratory on laboratory coats, a special supply should be provided for use only in those rooms where active material is handled. Such clothing should not be removed from the active laboratory. If it is found to be contamined, it should not be sent to a general laundry, but be washed in the laboratory itself, or safely disposed of ..."

"The storage or the preparation of food is to be prohibited in rooms used for work with active materials. Milk bottles or other containers of food must not be used for operations with, or storage of, chemicals in any such room. Similarly, smoking or the introduction of cosmetics should be forbidden in active areas, and chocolate or chewing gum should not be consumed there."

"After handling active material, the hands should be washed carefully for two to three minutes with plenty of soap and a nailbrush, also before leaving the laboratory, and especially before eating or smoking. After washing, the hands should be checked with a monitor, and, if necessary, washed again until a low enough count rate is reached. If contamination is found to persist, washing must be continued with special cleaning agents, such as titanium dioxide paste or a saturated solution of potassium permanganate, treatment with the latter to be followed by rinsing with 5 per cent sodium bisulphite ..."

"Any active material not in immediate use should be kept in a safe, where it is shielded on all sides and held under lock and key. In setting up such a safe, the possibility of radiation penetrating to neighbouring rooms above or below must not be overlooked. A thin partition wall is no adequate protection against radiation. All active solutions must be in closed vessels, while dry material must be kept in dust-proof containers. Glass vessels are to be kept in unbreakable outer containers sufficiently large to hold the entire active material if the inner vessel is broken ..."

It is advisable not to handle radioactive substances, as far as possible, in the form of dry powder – in particular when transferring from one vessel to another – so that no active dust is formed. Explosions must be prevented for the same reason.

To avoid the spread of radioactive substances in the laboratory, or at least to detect it at an early stage, routine radiation monitoring of working surfaces, floors, etc., is advisable. Usually instruments are employed which also give an audible signal. To increase the sensitivity, flat radiation detectors of relatively large surface area may be applied; suitably built scintillation detectors, bundles of several counting tubes of normal construction arranged in parallel, or special flat counters are useful. Maximum permissible activity levels for working surfaces and for the skin have been given [2, 7, 43].

Accidents involving radioactive materials, such as the spilling of highly active solutions in the laboratory or, even more seriously, upon the human body must always be regarded as very dangerous. But even in such cases, injury may be avoided or reduced by suitable counter-measures [73]. First, steps must be taken against further spread of radioelements. Then decontamination is carried out in a suitable way [44–47, 74], e.g., by washing with efficient cleaning agents or by removing solids with a vacuum cleaner. Often decontamination requires mechanical treatment of the surface, for instance, by grinding; it is then important not to breathe in radioactive dust. It is good practice to use surface coatings of special plastic materials or glass, which can, in the event of contamination, easily be removed and disposed of. Obviously, radioactive materials released in accidents should be dealt with in the same way as normal radioactive waste, so that no hazard to persons outside the radiation area arises [48–51]. In case radionuclides have been incorporated, their excretion can be hastened by suitable treatment [52, 75].

13.6. Work with High Activities

The precautions so far outlined are applicable to operations with small activities. Which activities can still be considered as "small" obviously depends on the nature of the radioelement, and in particular on its toxicity in respect to internal exposure. As a basis for the decision as to what precautionary measures have to be taken, four danger classes of radionuclides have been established [2, 7, 53]; the following list gives the assignment of the more important nuclides to these classes:

slightly dangerous: ^{3}H, ^{14}C
moderately dangerous: ^{22}Na, ^{24}Na, ^{32}P, ^{35}S, ^{42}K, ^{52}Mn, ^{56}Mn, ^{55}Fe, ^{58}Co, ^{60}Co, ^{64}Cu, ^{65}Zn, ^{76}As, ^{82}Br, ^{86}Rb, ^{95}Zr, ^{95}Nb, ^{111}Ag, ^{132}I, ^{137}Cs, ^{140}La, ^{147}Pm, ^{181}W, ^{192}Ir, ^{198}Au, ^{204}Tl
very dangerous: ^{45}Ca, ^{59}Fe, ^{89}Sr, ^{106}Ru, ^{131}I, ^{140}Ba, ^{144}Ce, ^{234}Th
extremely dangerous: ^{90}Sr, ^{210}Pb, ^{210}Po, ^{226}Ra, ^{233}U, ^{239}Pu.

A more detailed method of toxicity classification has been proposed which takes various additional factors into account, among them the specific activity of the material [76].

Obviously no special precautions are needed when the total amount of radioelement involved is smaller than the maximum permissible level for intake into the human body (see Table 10). As a rule of thumb it can be assumed that in ordinary laboratories the following amounts of radionuclides can be worked with at any one time [2, 7, 53]: up to 10 mc of slightly dangerous, 1 mc of moderately dangerous, 0·1 mc of very dangerous, and 0·01 mc of extremely dangerous radionuclides. For activities up to about 100 times these values, special laboratories with properly designed radiochemical fume cupboards and appropriately prepared surfaces (preferably with detachable plastic covers) are necessary. To prevent contamination of the rooms, gas-tight glove boxes should be used provided with a glass window. Chemical manipulations can be carried out through rubber gloves attached to the wall of the box. If the radionuclide emits electromagnetic radiation with high intensity and high energy, the wall of the glovebox facing the operator must be reinforced with lead blocks.

For particularly high activities, so-called "hot" laboratories are needed. Usually they are designed specially for the processes to be carried out. Detailed descriptions of construction and equipment of radiochemical laboratories are found in the literature [54–65].

When working with large quantities of radioactive substances, especially in hot laboratories, continuous monitoring of the working area (particularly the air) must be carried out. The results are compared with the *MPC* values given in Tables 10 and

11. It may also be necessary to determine radionuclide body burdens for the personnel. Urine analyses and, in case of γ-ray emitters, measurements with whole body counters are used for this purpose. Whole body counters are scintillation spectrometers where either liquid scintillator surrounds the body, or a large scintillator crystal is placed close to the body in a suitable position. For details of these monitoring techniques the literature must be consulted [40, 66, 77].

Finally, it should be repeated that in the great majority of the work described in the present book only small quantities of radioelements are required. The work can therefore be performed with simple precautions, such as those outlined in Section 13.5.

References to Chapter 13

1. *Great Britain:* Work with radioactive substances is regulated by a number of laws. For the applications discussed in this book, primarily the Radioactive Substances Act, 1960, and the Nuclear Installations Act, 1961, are of importance. These and other Acts are supplemented by various regulations, among which the Ionizing Radiations Sealed Sources Regulations, 1961, and the Unsealed Radioactive Substances Regulations (Draft) should be noted. Furthermore there are recommended codes of practice, in particular the Code of Practice for the Protection of Persons Exposed to Ionizing Radiations, 1957. This code is now being replaced by more specialized codes for certain activities: Code of Practice for the Protection of Persons Exposed to Ionizing Radiations in University Laboratories; Code of Practice for the Protection of Persons Exposed to Ionizing Radiations in Research and Teaching; Code of Practice for the Protection of Persons Exposed to Ionizing Radiations Arising from Medical and Dental Use.
   United States: The Atomic Energy Act, 1954, provides that radioisotopes and radioactive sources may only be used under a Federal licence. In 1959 this Act was amended making it possible to transfer jurisdiction to States having acceptable radiation control regulations and programs. The relevant Federal regulations are the Atomic Energy Commission Health and Safety Regulations, and, more recently, the guidance rules issued by the Federal Radiation Council. The Atomic Energy Commission Health and Safety Regulations are published in the Code of Federal Regulations under Title 10. Reference should be made in particular to Parts 20, 30 and 50. Corresponding State regulations are now being issued by an increasing number of States. Both Federal and State regulations make extensive use of the recommendations of the National Committee on Radiation Protection and Measurement. Regulations for transport of radioactive substances are issued as part of the Interstate Commerce Commission Regulations and the Postal Regulations. For a more detailed account of relevant U.S. regulations: see [67].
   Other countries: A survey of existing legislation covering many countries has been prepared by the World Health Organisation (WHO) [68].
2. *Safe Handling of Radioisotopes*, I.A.E.A., Vienna 1958 (Editions in English, Russian, French and Spanish).
3. *Safe Handling of Radioisotopes*. Health Physics Addendum (G.J. APPLETON and P.N. KRISHNA-MOORTHY, Ed.), I.A.E.A., Vienna 1960 (Editions in English, Russian, French and Spanish).
4. J.C. BOURSNELL, *Safety Techniques for Radioactive Tracers*, Cambridge 1958.
5. D.E. BARNES and D. TAYLOR, *Radiation Hazards and Protection*, London 1963.
6. H. BLATZ (Ed.), *Radiation Hygiene Handbook*, New York 1959.
7. R.J. SHERWOOD (Ed.), *A Short Course in Radiological Protection* (AERE L/101), Harwell, 1959.
8. R.A. FAIRES and B.H. PARKS, *Radioisotope Laboratory Techniques*, London 1958.
9. J.D. ABBATT, J.R.A. LAKEY and D.J. MATHIAS, *Protection against Radiation*, London 1961.
10. E.V. BORISOV, *Safety Techniques for Work with Radioactive Isotopes* (Russ.), Moscow 1955.
11. B. RAJEWSKY, *Strahlendosis und Strahlenwirkung*, Stuttgart 1956.
12. B. RAJEWSKY (Ed.), *Wissenschaftliche Grundlagen des Strahlenschutzes*, Karlsruhe 1957.

328   *Radiation Protection*

13. H.Beck, D.Dresel and H.J.Melching, *Leitfaden des Strahlenschutzes*, Stuttgart 1959.
14. R.G.Jaeger, *Dosimetrie und Strahlenschutz*, Stuttgart 1959.
15. Th.Jaeger, *Technischer Strahlenschutz*, Munich 1959.
16. D.Frost, *Praktischer Strahlenschutz*, Berlin 1960.
17. O.Hug, H.Muth, G.Schubert, G.Höhne and H.A.Künkel, in: H.Schwiegk and F.Turba (Ed.), *Künstlich radioaktive Isotope in Physiologie, Diagnostik und Therapie*, Berlin 1961.
18. W.Jacobi, *Strahlenschutz - Grundlagen*, Munich 1962.
19. *Radiation Protection: Recommendations of the I.C.R.P.*, London 1959; see also *Health Physics* **2**, 1 (1959).
20. K.Z.Morgan, *Science* **139**, 565 (1963).
21. L.Meyer-Schützmeister and H.Houtermans, in: *Landolt-Börnstein, Zahlenwerte und Funktionen*, 6th ed., volume I/5, Berlin 1952.
22. U.Fano, *Nucleonics* **11** (8), 9 (1953); **11** (9), 55 (1953).
23. N.G.Gusev, *Manual on Radioactivity and Radiation Protection* (Russ.), Moscow 1956; German translation, Berlin 1957.
24. K.H.Lindackers, *Praktische Durchführung von Abschirmungsberechnungen*, Munich 1961.
25. H.M.Parker, *Adv. Biol. Med. Phys.* **1**, 123 (1948).
26. D.Taylor, *J. Sci. Instruments* **29**, 315 (1952).
27. E.A.Frommhold, *Die Technik* **7**, 685 (1952).
28. E.Six, *Umschau Wiss. Technik* **52**, 139 (1952).
29. H.Fassbender and C.W.Fassbender, *Röntgenblätter* **6**, 228 (1953).
30. A.N.Krongaus, *Dosimeter for X- and γ-Rays* (Russ.), Moscow 1953.
31. G.J.Hine and G.L.Brownell (Ed.), *Radiation Dosimetry*, New York 1956.
32. K.K.Aglintsev, *Dosimetry of Ionizing Radiations* (Russ.), Moscow 1957; German translation, Berlin 1961.
33. *Use of Film Badges for Personnel Monitoring*, I.A.E.A., Vienna 1961.
34. M.I.Shalnov, *Neutron Dosimetry* (Russ.), Moscow 1960; German translation, Berlin 1962.
35. M.Oberhofer, *Strahlenschutz - Meßtechnik*, Munich 1962.
36. *Selected Topics in Radiation Dosimetry*, Symposium in Vienna, I.A.E.A., Vienna 1961.
37. *Neutron Dosimetry*, Symposium in Harwell, I.A.E.A., Vienna 1963.
38. *Health Physics* **3**, 1–380 (1960).
39. H.Kiefer and R.Maushart, *Überwachung der Radioaktivität von Wasser and Abwasser*, Stuttgart 1961.
40. *Radioactive Substances in the Biosphere*, I.A.E.A., Vienna 1961.
41. K.Z.Morgan, W.S.Snyder and M.R.Ford, Geneva Report 79 (1955), vol. 13, p. 139.
42. J.Zakovsky, *Klin. Med.* **5**, 390 (1950).
43. H.J.Dunster, *Atomics* **6** (8), 233 (1955).
44. H.A.Künkel, *Strahlentherapie* **90**, 100 (1953).
45. B.J.Barry, *Health Physics* **1**, 184 (1958).
46. H.Stephan, *Kerntechnik* **3**, 102 (1961).
47. D.G.Stevenson, *Research* **13**, 383 (1960).
48. K.Saddington and W.J.Templeton, *Disposal of Radioactive Wastes*, London 1958.
49. *Disposal of Radioactive Wastes* (Proceedings of the Conference in Monaco (November 1959)), I.A.E.A., Vienna 1960.
50. E.Glückauf (Ed.), *Atomic Energy Waste— Its Nature, Use and Disposal*, London 1961.
51. *Treatment and Storage of High-Level Radioactive Waste*, Symposium in Vienna, I.A.E.A., Vienna 1963.
52. *Diagnosis and Treatment of Radioactive Poisoning*, Symposium in Vienna, I.A.E.A., Vienna 1963.
53. H.J.Dunster, *Medicine Illustrated* **8**, 731 (1954).
54. *Nucleonics* **12** (11), 35-100 (1954).
55. H.Dreiheller and E.H.Graul, *Atompraxis* **2**, 47 (1956).
56. G.N.Yakovlev, E.P.Dergunov, I.A.Reformatsky and V.B.Dedov, Geneva Report 672 (1955), vol. 7, p. 57.
57. P.R.Fields and C.H.Youngquist, Geneva Report 725 (1955), vol. 7, p. 44.
58. U.Drehmann, *Chem. Technik* **8**, 313 (1956).

59. W.Seelmann-Eggebert and F.Wiegel, *Z. Ver. Dtsch. Ing.* **98,** 141 (1956).
60. J.R.Dunning and B.R.Prentice (Ed.), *Hot Laboratory Operation and Equipment*, London 1957.
61. G.N.Walton (Ed.), *Glove Boxes and Shielded Cells for Handling Radioactive Materials*, London 1958.
62. R.C.Goertz, Geneva Report 1796 (1958), vol. 17, p. 585.
63. J.E.Bown and E.D.Hyam, Geneva Report 1459 (1958), vol. 17, p. 597.
64. G.N.Yakovlev and V.B.Dedov, Geneva Report 2026 (1958), vol. 17, p. 652.
65. H.Götte and H.A.E.Schmidt, in: H.Schwiegk and F.Turba (Ed.), *Künstliche radioaktive Isotope in Physiologie, Diagnostik und Therapie*, Berlin 1961.
66. *Whole-body Counting*, Symposium in Vienna, I.A.E.A., Vienna 1962.
67. H.Blatz, *Introduction to Radiological Health*, New York 1964.
68. *Protection Against Ionizing Radiations, A Survey of Existing Legislation*, W.H.O., Geneva 1964.
69. G.Eaves, *Principles of Radiation Protection*, New York 1964.
70. K.K.Aglintsev, V.M.Kodyukov, A.F.Lyzkov and Yu. V.Sivintsev, *Applied Dosimetry* (Russ.), Moscow 1962; English translation, London 1965.
71. H.Kiefer and R.Maushart, *Strahlenschutzmeßtechnik*, Karlsruhe 1964.
72. *Personnel Dosimetry Techniques for External Radiation*, Symposium in Madrid, O.E.C.D., Paris 1964.
73. L.H.Lanzl, J.H.Pingel and J.H.Rust (Ed.), *Radiation Accidents and Emergencies in Medicine, Research and Industry*, Symposium in Chicago, Springfield, Ill., 1964.
74. H.Scheel, *Kernenergie* **7,** 197 (1964).
75. A.Catsch, *Radioactive Metal Mobilization in Medicine*, Springfield, Ill., 1964.
76. *A Basic Toxicity Classification of Radionuclides*, I.A.E.A., Vienna 1963.
77. *Assessment of Radioactivity in Man*, Symposium in Heidelberg, I.A.E.A., Vienna 1964.
78. *Personnel Dosimetry for Radiation Accidents*, Symposium in Vienna, I.A.E.A., Vienna 1965.

APPENDIX 1

List of Radionuclides Important for Practical Use

The following table lists the nuclides which appear most suitable for technical applications. Such nuclides must be readily available and have a half-life which is not too short. The nuclides are arranged in the table in the order of increasing atomic number. Nuclides of elements of little technical importance, such as those of the less important rare earths, are not included. In the case of elements with several suitable nuclides, only the more important ones are given.

Column 1 gives the atomic number of the element, column 2 the chemical symbol, column 3 the mass number of the isotope, column 4 the half-life, column 5 the nature of the decay (type of particle emitted), column 6 the energy of the corpuscles emitted, column 7 the energy of the emitted photons, and column 8 the principal method of making the nuclide, i.e., the nuclear reaction and the radiation source employed. Where it is possible to use a reactor to produce the radionuclide, this is the method given; production with other radiation sources is only cited when the reactor cannot be employed.

Column 9 gives the saturation activity (in mc/g) that is produced by irradiation of the element in its natural isotopic composition with a thermal neutron flux of $10^{11} cm^{-2}$ sec^{-1}. The saturation activity is, of course, obtained only after irradiation periods long in comparison with the half-life of the radionuclide produced (see p. 89). Since the induced activity is proportional to the neutron flux, the figures given can be used to calculate the activity produced by other neutron fluxes.

Column 10 gives radioisotopes of the same or of chemically similar elements, which are unavoidably formed together with the nuclide in question when the latter is prepared. Easily separated radioelements are not listed. Column 11 gives active daughter products of the radionuclide.

Complete tables of the known nuclides are available, and should be consulted where necessary. They give also information on decay schemes. See, in particular,

D. STROMINGER, J. M. HOLLANDER and G. T. SEABORG, *Rev. Mod. Phys.* 30, 585 (1958).

Nuclear Data Sheets, Washington 1958.

W. KUNZ and J. SCHINTLMEISTER, *Tabellen der Atomkerne*, Berlin 1958.

Catalogues of the available radionuclides and radioactive compounds are now issued by many atomic energy centres and firms. Part I of the *Radiochemical Manual*, published by the Radiochemical Centre, Amersham, Buckinghamshire, England, is a collection of physical data for uses of radionuclides. There is also an international catalogue where the most important data from the individual catalogues are compiled: *International Directory of Radioisotopes* (3rd edition), I.A.E.A. Vienna 1964.

RADIONUCLIDES IMPORTANT FOR TECHNICAL APPLICATIONS

Z	Symbol	A	Half-life	Type	E_p (MeV)	E_γ (MeV)	Most important method of production	Normal saturation activity (mc/g)	Important active impurities	Active daughter products
1	H	3⊙	12·3 y	β^-	0·018		R Li (n, α)			
4	Be	7⊙	53 d	K, γ		0·48	A Li (d, n)			
6	C	14⊙	5760 y	β^-	0·155		R N (n, p)			
9	F	18⊙	1·87 h	β^+, K	0·65		R Li (n, d) t; ^{16}O (t, n)			
11	Na	22⊙	2·6 y	K, β^+, γ	0·54	1·28	A Mg (d, α)	39		
11	Na	24	15·0 h	β^-, γ	1·39	2·76	R Na (n, γ)			
12	Mg	28⊙	21·2 h	β^-, γ	0·42	1·35	A Cl $(p, 6p4n)$ t; ^{6}Li (n, α) t; ^{26}Mg (t, p)			
14	Si	31	2·6 h	β^-	1·48		R Si (n, γ)			
15	P	32	14·3 d	β^-	1·70		R P (n, γ)	0·2		
15	P	32⊙	14·3 d	β^-	1·70		R S $(\bar{n}, p)$	12		
16	S	35	87 d	β^-	0·168		R S (n, γ)	0·54		
16	S	35⊙	87 d	β^-	0·168		R Cl (n, p)	ca. 2×10^5		
17	Cl	36	3×10^5 y	β^-	0·71		R Cl (n, γ)			
19	K	42	12·5 h	β^-, γ	3·56	1·53	R K (n, γ)	2·7		
20	Ca	45	154 d	β^-	0·26		R Ca (n, γ)	0·48		
20	Ca	45⊙	154 d	β^-	0·26		R Sc $(\bar{n}, p)$			
21	Sc	46	84 d	β^-, γ	0·36	1·12	R Sc (n, γ)	750		
23	V	48⊙	16 d	β^+, K, γ	0·7	1·32	A Ti (p, n)	16		
24	Cr	51	27·8 d	K, γ		0·32	A Cr (n, γ)			
24	Cr	54⊙	291 d	K, γ		0·84	A Cr (d, n)			
25	Mn	56	2·58 h	β^-, γ	2·8	2·1	R Mn (n, γ)	390		
26	Fe	55	2·6 y	K			R Fe (n, γ)	1·46	^{59}Fe	

RADIONUCLIDES IMPORTANT FOR TECHNICAL APPLICATIONS (CONTINUED)

Z	Symbol	A	Half-life	Type	E_β (MeV)	E_γ (MeV)	Most important method of production	Normal saturation activity (mc/g)	Important active impurities	Active daughter products
26	Fe	55⊙	2·6 y	K			R Fe (n, γ) Sz.E		59Fe	
26	Fe	59	45·1 d	β^-, γ	0·46	1·29	R Fe (n, γ)	0·08	55Fe	
26	Fe	59⊙	45·1 d	β^+, K, γ	0·46	1·29	R Fe (n, γ) Sz.E		55Fe	
27	Co	58⊙	71 d	β^-, γ	0·47	0·80	R Ni $(\bar{n}, p)$			
27	Co	60	5·24 y	β^-, γ	0·31	1·33	R Co (n, γ)	830		
28	Ni	63	125 y	β^-	0·067		R Ni (n, γ)	0·08 (4 weeks)		
29	Cu	64	12·8 h	β^-, β^+, K	0·66β^+ / 0·57β^-		R Cu (n, γ)	50		
30	Zn	65	245 d	β^+, K, γ	0·32	1·1	R Zn (n, γ)	6·8	69,69m Zn	
31	Ga	72	14·1 h	β^-, γ	3·1	2·5	R Ga (n, γ)	30		
32	Ge	71	11·4 d	K			R Ge (n, γ)	12	77Ge	
33	As	76	26·4 h	β^-, γ	3·0	1·21	R As (n, γ)	90		
33	As	76⊙	26·4 h	β^-, γ	3·0	1·21	R As (n, γ) Sz.E			
33	As	77⊙	38·7 h	β^-	0·7		R Ge (n, γ) 77Ge$\xrightarrow{\beta^-}$			
34	Se	75	121 d	K, γ		0·40	R Se (n, γ)	4·9		
35	Br	82	35·9 h	β^-, γ	0·46		R Br (n, γ)	35		
35	Br	82⊙	35·9 h	β^-, γ	0·46		R Br (n, γ) Sz.E			
36	Kr	85⊙	10·3 y	β^-	0·67		R U (n, f)			
37	Rb	86	18·7 d	β^-, γ	1·78	1·08	R Rb (n, γ)	10		
38	Sr	89	51 d	β^-	1·46		R Sr (n, γ)	0·078		
38	Sr	89⊙	51 d	β^-	1·46		R U (n, f)		90Sr	90Y
38	Sr	90⊙	28 y	β^-	0·54		R U (n, f)		89Sr	90Y
39	Y	90⊙	64·2 h	β^-	2·2		R U (n, f)			
39	Y	91⊙	58 d	β^-	1·54		R U (n, f)			

RADIONUCLIDES IMPORTANT FOR TECHNICAL APPLICATIONS (CONTINUED)

Z	Nuclide Symbol	Nuclide A	Half-life	Radiation Type	Radiation E_p (MeV)	Radiation E_γ (MeV)	Most important method of production	Normal saturation activity (mc/g)	Important active impurities	Active daughter products
40	Zr	95	65 d	$\beta-, \gamma$	0·40	0·74	R Zr (n,γ)	0·3		^{95}Nb
40	Zr	95⊙	65 d	$\beta-, \gamma$	0·40	0·74	R U (n,f)			^{95}Nb
41	Nb	95⊙	35 d	$\beta-, \gamma$	0·15	0·76	R U (n,f)			
42	Mo	99	66 h	$\beta-, \gamma$	1·23	0·75	R Mo (n,γ)	1·7		
44	Ru	103	40 d	$\beta-, \gamma$	0·23	0·50	R Ru (n,γ)	9	^{106}Ru	
44	Ru	103⊙	40 d	$\beta-, \gamma$	0·23	0·50	R U (n,f)			
45	Rh	105⊙	36·5 h	$\beta-, \gamma$	0·57	0·32	R Ru (n,γ) ^{105}Ru $\xrightarrow{\beta-}$			
46	Pd	103	17 d	K			R Pd (n,γ)	0·6	^{109}Pd	^{103m}Rh [$\tau = 57$ m; $E(\gamma) = 0·04$]
46	Pd	109	13·5 h	$\beta-$	1·02		R Pd (n,γ)	44	^{103}Pd	^{109}Ag [$\tau = 39·2$ s; $E(\gamma) = 0·088$]
47	Ag	110^m	253 d	$\beta-, \gamma$	0·53	0·88	R Ag (n,γ)	17		^{110}Ag [$\tau = 24$ s; $E(\beta-) = 2·8$; $E(\gamma) = 0·65$]
47	Ag	111⊙	7·5 d	$\beta-, \gamma$	1·04	0·34	R Pd$(n,\gamma)^{111}$Pd $\xrightarrow{\beta-}$	0·57	^{109,115m}Cd	
48	Cd	115^m	43 d	$\beta-, \gamma$	1·6	1·30	R Cd (n,γ)	4·3	^{109,115m}Cd	
48	Cd	115	2·3 d	$\beta-, \gamma$	1·1	0·52	R Cd (n,γ)	36	^{114}In	
49	In	114^m	50 d	γ		0·19Δ	R In (n,γ)			^{114}In [$\tau = 72$ s; $E(\beta-) = 1·98$]
50	Sn	113	119 d	K			R Sn (n,γ)	0·16	^{121,123,125}Sn	^{113}In [$\tau = 104$ m; $E(\gamma) = 0·39$]
51	Sb	122	2·8 d	$\beta-, \gamma$	1·97	0·56	R Sb (n,γ)	52	^{124}Sb	
51	Sb	124	60 d	$\beta-, \gamma$	2·3	1·7	R Sb (n,γ)	15	^{122}Sb	
51	Sb	125	2·0 y	$\beta-, \gamma$	0·62	0·60	R Sn$(n,\gamma)^{125}$Sn $\xrightarrow{\beta-}$			^{125m}Te

RADIONUCLIDES IMPORTANT FOR TECHNICAL APPLICATIONS (CONTINUED)

Z	Sym-bol	A	Half-life	Type	E_p (MeV)	E_γ (MeV)	Most important method of production	Normal saturation activity (mc/g)	Important active impurities	Active daughter products
52	Te	127^m	105 d	γ		0·084$\triangle$	R Te (n,γ)	0·18	123m,125m, 127,129,131Te	^{127}Te [$\tau = 9\cdot3$ h; $E(\beta^-) = 0\cdot7$]
53	I	131$\odot$	8·0 d	β^-,γ	0·60	0·36	R Te$(n,\gamma)^{131}$Te $\xrightarrow{\beta-}$ R U (n,f)			
55	Cs	134	2·1 y	β^-,γ	0·66	0·80	R Cs (n,γ)	290		
55	Cs	137$\odot$	30 y	β^-	0·52		R U (n,f)			^{137m}Ba [$\tau = 2\cdot6$ m; $E(\gamma) = 0\cdot66$]
56	Ba	131	12 d	K,γ		0·5	R Ba (n,γ)	0·03		^{131}Cs
56	Ba	140$\odot$	12·8 d	β^-,γ	1·02	0·5	R U (n,f)			^{140}La
57	La	140	40 h	β^-,γ	2·26	1·6	R La (n,γ)	100		
57	La	140$\odot$	40 h	β^-,γ	2·26	1·6	R U (n,f)			
58	Ce	141	33·1 d	β^-,γ	0·58	0·14	R Ce (n,γ)	3	143Ce; 143Pr	
58	Ce	144$\odot$	285 d	β^-,γ	0·30	0·13	R U (n,f)			^{144}Pr [$\tau = 17\cdot3$ m; $E(\beta^-) = 2\cdot97$]
61	Pm	147$\odot$	2.65 y	β^-	0·22		R U (n,f)	1000		
69	Tm	170	129 d	β^-,γ	0·97	0·084	R Tm (n,γ)	15		
72	Hf	175	70 d	K		0·34	R Hf (n,γ)	32		
72	Hf	181	46 d	β^-,γ	0·41	0·48	R Hf (n,γ)	150		
73	Ta	182	115 d	β^-,γ	0·51	1·2	R Ta (n,γ)	6	187W	
74	W	185	73·2 d	β^-	0·42		R W (n,γ)	90	185W	
74	W	187	24·0 h	β^-,γ	1·3	0·7	R W (n,γ)	330	188Re	
75	Re	186	89 h	β^-,K,γ	1·07	0·14	R Re (n,γ)	11		
76	Os	191	16 d	β^-,γ	0·14	0·13	R Os (n,γ)	3000		
77	Ir	192	74·4 d	K,β^-,γ	0·66	0·32	R Ir (n,γ)		193,199Pt	
78	Pt	197	18 h	β^-,γ	0·67	0·08	R Pt (n,γ)	2·5		

RADIONUCLIDES IMPORTANT FOR TECHNICAL APPLICATIONS (CONTINUED)

Z	Symbol	A	Half-life	Radiation Type	E_β (MeV)	E_γ (MeV)	Most important method of production	Normal saturation activity (mc/g)	Important active impurities	Active daughter products
79	Au	198	2·69 d	β^-, γ	0·96	0·41	R Au (n, γ)	780		
80	Hg	197	65 h	K, γ		0·08	R Hg (n, γ)	40	^{197m}Hg	
80	Hg	203	47 d	β^-, γ	0·21	0·28	R Hg (n, γ)	8	^{197}Hg	
81	Tl	204	4·0 y	β^-	0·76		R Tl (n, γ)	18		
82	Pb	210 (RaD)⊙	19·4 y	β^-, γ	0·017	0·04	N			^{210}Bi; ^{210}Po
82	Pb	212 (ThB)⊙	10·6 h	β^-, γ	0·57	0·24	N			^{212}Bi; ^{212}Po, ^{208}Tl
83	Bi	210 (RaE)⊙	5·0 d	β^-	1·17		N			^{210}Po
83	Bi	210 (RaE)	5·0 d	β^-	1·17		R Bi (n, γ)	0·15		^{210}Po
83	Bi	212 (ThC)⊙	1·0 h	α, β^-, γ	2·2(β)	0·73	N			^{212}Po, ^{208}Tl [τ = 3·1 m; $E(\gamma)$ = 2·62]
84	Po	210 (RaF)⊙	138·4 d	α	5·3		N; R Bi (n, γ) ^{210}Bi $\xrightarrow{\beta-}$			
88	Ra	226	1620 y	α, γ	4·78	0·19	N			Various daughter products
90	Th	234 (UX1)⊙	24 d	β^-, γ	0·2	0·09	N			^{234m}Pa (UX 2) [τ = 1·18 m; $E(\beta^-)$ = 2·3; $E(\gamma)$ = 1·0]
91	Pa	233⊙	27 d	β^-, γ	0·26	0·42	R Th (n, γ) ^{233}Th $\xrightarrow{\beta-}$			^{233}U

Explanation of symbols:

m = excited state; ⊙ = carrier-free or with little carrier; K = electron capture; $\varDelta$ = strongly converted; N = natural radioelement; R = reactor; A = accelerator; $\bar{n}$ = fast neutron; f = nuclear fission; Sz.E = Szilard effect; y = year; d = day; h = hour; m = minute; s = second.

APPENDIX 2

Important Units and Conversion Factors

A. *Activity and Reaction Cross-section*

1 curie = 1 c = $3 \cdot 7 \times 10^{10}$ disintegrations/sec
1 barn = 10^{-24} cm^2

B. *Radiation Dose*

1 roentgen = 1 r = $7 \cdot 09 \times 10^4$ MeV $(cm^3_{air})^{-1}$ = 88 erg $(g_{air})^{-1}$
1 rad = 100 erg g^{-1} = $6 \cdot 24 \times 10^{13}$ eV g^{-1}
1 megarad per hour = $2 \cdot 8$ watt/kg
Average energy required for the production of an ion pair in air by X- or γ-radiation = 34 eV

C. *Charge and Mass*

Unit charge (electron or proton):
    $e = 4 \cdot 802 \times 10^{-10}$ electrostatic units = $1 \cdot 602 \times 10^{-19}$ international coulombs
Mass of electron: $m_e = 9 \cdot 1066 \times 10^{-28}$ g
Mass of proton: $m_p = 1 \cdot 67247 \times 10^{-24}$ g
Mass of the (light) hydrogen atom: $m_H = 1 \cdot 67339 \times 10^{-24}$ g
Mass of neutron: $m_n = 1 \cdot 6751 \times 10^{-24}$ g
Ratio of masses of proton and electron: $m_p/m_e = 1836$
Avogadro (Loschmidt) number (number of atoms per gram-atom):
    $N = 6 \cdot 024 \times 10^{23}$ (for the new atomic weight scale: ^{12}C $= 12 \cdot 0000$)

D. *Energy and Velocity*

1 electron volt = 1 eV = $1 \cdot 602 \times 10^{-12}$ erg
1 electron volt per atom = $23 \cdot 05$ kcal/g-atom
Planck's constant: $h = 6 \cdot 624 \times 10^{-27}$ erg sec
Boltzmann's constant: $k = 1 \cdot 38047 \times 10^{-16}$ erg deg^{-1}
Velocity of light: $c = 2 \cdot 99776 \times 10^{10}$ cm sec^{-1}
Quantum energy: E (in keV) = $12 \cdot 4 \, \lambda^{-1}$ (wavelength λ in Å; 1 Å = 10^{-8} cm).

INDEX

Abrasion 170–176

Absorber (radiation energy determination or discrimination) 53, 54, 83, 92

Absorption analysis 71, 99–109, 227

Absorption coefficient 49, 104, 106

Absorption, foliar 271

Absorption (radiations)
applications 54, 71, 102–109, 122, 124, 151, 160, 165, 166, 211, 214–218, 223, 227, 248, 282, 319, 320
fundamentals 17–24, 48–50, 99–101, 104, 106, 107

Absorption (recoil nuclei) 166

Absorption (substances by plants, insects and other organisms) 268–276, 282–287

Acaricides 284

Accelerator (particle) 2, 16, 52, 86, 88, 96, 98, 106, 128, 142–147, 219; see also Bore-hole accelerators

Accelerator (rubber) 254, 255

Accident (radiation) 325

Accumulator 210

Acetate (metabolism) 268, 280

Acetic acid (labelled) 59, 280

Acid catalysis 204

Acid treatment (bore-holes) 147

Actinium 70
series 27

Actinon 68; see also Emanation

Activated complex 204

Activated sludge 256

Activation analysis 55, 71, 83–100, 120, 121, 127, 137, 164, 169, 178–181, 192, 194, 211, 213, 214, 219, 222, 241, 243–246, 251, 257, 283, 299
instrumental 87

Activation cross-section 86, 89–91

Activation energy 202, 204

Activation logging 128, 137–139, 147

Activity 25–29, 33, 64
absolute 33, 43
specific 34, 52–54, 59, 61, 65, 66, 71, 82, 274

Additives (food) 283

Additives (oil, fuel) 172, 173, 175, 176, 178

Adenosine triphosphate 285

Adhesive 249

Adsorption 55–59, 74, 75, 120, 125, 126, 168, 172, 177, 180, 195, 198, 207, 208, 245–247, 256, 300, 303, 308, 309

Aedes aegypti 288

Aeration 278

Aerosol 228, 308

Agglomeration (ore) 160, 161

Agriculture 266–289

Air (analysis for traces) 97, 110

Air (circulation) 227, 228, 308

Air (exhaled, investigation of metabolism) 278, 284

Aircraft 127, 214, 216

Alcohols 172, 206

Aldehydes 209

Alfalfa 283

Algae 60, 227, 269

Alkali elements (analysis, separation) 74, 92, 93; see also the individual elements

Alkaline earths (analysis, separation) 74; see also the individual elements

Alkylation 212, 221

Alkyl halides 60

Alloys 166–170, 191, 194

Alloys (analysis) 106; see also the individual elements

Alloy steel 94

Alpha-decay 12, 13, 15

Alpha-rays 12, 16, 18, 19, 25, 35, 50, 96

Alpha-rays (health hazard) 316, 317, 320

Alpha-rays (measurement) 36, 37, 40, 41, 44, 46, 50

Alpha-rays (sources of) 16, 97

Alumina 221

Aluminium (alloys) 168, 170

Aluminium (analysis, separation) 74, 77, 94, 95, 104, 123, 142, 247

Aluminium (corrosion) 177

Aluminium (crystallization) 163, 168

Aluminium (detection by logging) 138, 139, 147

Aluminium (production) 163, 228

Aluminium (trace analysis in) 92, 94, 103, 110, 164, 213

Aluminium chloride (radioreagent) 78

Americium-241 (radiation source) 85, 107, 108

Aminoacids 56, 76, 81, 83, 266, 267, 271, 280

Made in Great Britain